A History of
American Physical Anthropology
1930–1980

We, like dwarfs on the shoulders of giants, can see more and farther not because we are keener and taller, but because of the greatness by which we are carried and exalted.

Bernard of Chartres

A History of
American Physical Anthropology
1930–1980

EDITED BY

Frank Spencer

Department of Anthropology
Queens College of the City University of New York
Flushing, New York

1982

ACADEMIC PRESS
A Subsidiary of Harcourt Brace Jovanovich, Publishers

New York   London
Paris   San Diego   San Francisco   São Paulo   Sydney   Tokyo   Toronto

ACADEMIC PRESS, INC.
111 Fifth Avenue, New York, New York 10003

United Kingdom Edition published by
ACADEMIC PRESS, INC. (LONDON) LTD.
24/28 Oval Road, London NW1 7DX

Library of Congress Cataloging in Publication Data

Main entry under title:

A History of American physical anthropology, 1930-1980.

   Bibliography: p.
   Includes indexes.
   1. Physical anthropology--History--Congresses.
2. Anthropology--United States--History--Congresses.
I. Spencer, Frank. II. American Association of Physical
Anthropologists.
GN50.4.H57 1982   573   82-8849
ISBN 0-12-656660-7   AACR2

PRINTED IN THE UNITED STATES OF AMERICA

82 83 84 85   9 8 7 6 5 4 3 2 1

To Ariadne

Contents

Contributors   xiii
Preface   xv

Introduction   1

1 The Roots of the Race Concept in American Physical Anthropology   11

C. Loring Brace

Earnest Albert Hooton   12
Alĕs Hrdlička   15
Samuel George Morton   17
The Ethos of Broca's Société   20
The Romantic Conception of Race   21
What Now?   23
References   24

2 The Effects of Funding Patterns on the Development of Physical Anthropology   31

Thelma S. Baker and Phyllis B. Eveleth

The Early Period 1930–1949   32
The Middle Period 1950–1965   37
The Late Period 1965–1980   41
References   45

3   A Short History of Primate Field Studies: Old World Monkeys and Apes   49

Rosalind Ribnick

The Initial Period 1929–1950   50
The Formative State 1950–1959   54
The Prolific Period 1960 to ?   62
Conclusions and Summary   64
References   66

4   Primate Neuroanatomy: An Evolutionary Perspective   75

Dean Falk

The 1930s   75
The 1940s   78
The 1950s   81
The 1960s   82
The 1970s   85
Summary and Conclusions   88
References   90

5   Molecular Anthropology: Its Development and Current Directions   105

Morris Goodman and J. E. Cronin

Genealogical Description of Primate Phylogeny   107
The Tempo and Mode of Molecular Evolution   119
Future Prospects   136
Conclusion   139
References   140

6   Basic Primatology and Prosimian Evolution   147

Matt Cartmill

Le Gros Clark and the Origins of Modern Primatology   148
Simpson and the Primatological Synthesis   151
Simons and Russell: New Light on Old Bones   152
The Eviction of the Tree Shrews   154
New Definitions of Primates   154
Prosimian Field Studies and Their Evolutionary Implications   156
The Collapse of Classical Primate Systematics   158

After Phylogeny, What?   161
Prosimian Adaptations, Anthropoid Parallels,
    and Evolutionary Theory   170
References   172

7 Fifty Years of Higher Primate Phylogeny   187

John G. Fleagle and William L. Jungers

Prelude   188
1930–1950: Moderation and Parallelism   195
1950–1960: Fossils and the Evolutionary Synthesis   201
1960–1970: Fossil Phylogenies   206
1970–1980: Diversity and Debate   211
Overview   217
References   221

8 Reflections on Human Paleontology   231

Ernst Mayr

Historical Comments   231
The Hominid Series   236
References   237

**9 American Research on Australopithecines and Early *Homo*,
    1925–1980   239**

Noel T. Boaz

The Effect of Discoveries of South African Australopithecines   240
The Debunking of a Supposed Pliocene Hominid, *Eoanthropus*   243
The Input of Biological Sciences into Early Hominid Studies   244
The Effect of Discoveries of Early Hominids in Eastern Africa   245
Field Methods: Development of Theory and Method
    for Data Collection   247
Development of Hominid Paleoecology as an Outgrowth of the
    "New Physical Anthropology"   249
Importance of Functional Morphology to Early Hominid Studies   250
Interpretations of Early Hominid Phylogeny   252
Conclusions and Future Directions in Early Hominid Research   252
References   253

10   A History of *Homo erectus* and *Homo sapiens* Paleontology in America   261

Erik Trinkaus

Hrdlička, The Neandertals, "Pithecanthropus,"
   and Piltdown   261
Evolutionary Theory and the Evolution of the Genus *Homo*   266
Recent Developments   268
References   270

11   Inquiries into the Peopling of the New World: Development of Ideas and Recent Advances   281

Albert B. Harper and William S. Laughlin

Early Inquiries   281
Development of Modern Scientific Inquiry and Theory   282
Recent Advances   288
Summary   299
References   301

12   The Theoretical Foundations and Development of Skeletal Biology   305

George J. Armelagos, David S. Carlson, and Dennis P. Van Gerven

Race, Type, and Historical Reconstructions   306
Anthropometry, Statistics, and Biological Processes   313
Analysis of Form and Function   316
References   321

13   Five Decades of Skeletal Biology as Reflected in the *American Journal of Physical Anthropology*   329

C. Owen Lovejoy, Robert P. Mensforth, and George J. Armelagos

Content Analysis   330
Trends in Skeletal Biology by Decade   331
Discussion   334
References   336

14   The Development of American Paleopathology   337

Douglas H. Ubelaker

Early History of the Discipline   338
Paleopathology as a Distinct Discipline   341
Hooton: The Epidemiological Approach   342
Paleopathology Today   344
Summary and Concluding Remarks   348
References   349

15   Forensic Anthropology   357

David D. Thompson

Pre–1939   358
1939–1972   360
1972–1980   365
References   366

**16   Genes, Populations, and Disease, 1930–1980:
A Problem-Oriented Review   371**

Kenneth M. Weiss and R. Chakraborty

The Age and Origin of Racial Diversity   373
Mutations, Eugenics, and Genetic Load   375
The Population Genetics of Disease and the Maintenance
    of Polymorphism   381
Aging and Life Span: The Biology of Human Life History   392
Conclusion   393
References   394

17   The Development of Ideas about Human Ecology and Adaptation   405

Michael A. Little

Current Theory: Ecology, Evolution, and Adaptation
    to the Environment   405
History of the Concepts   408
Approaches to the Study of Human Adaptation   414
Current Trends in Human Ecology   419
References   422

18   The Development of Research Strategies for Studies of Biological Variation in Living Human Populations   435

Jere D. Haas

Introduction   435
Brief Historical Summary   436
Methodological Development as Reflected by Content Analysis
  of Two Scientific Journals   439
Studies of Migrating Populations and Natural Experiments
  in Human Variability   442
Conclusion   443
References   444

19   An Historical Perspective on Studies of Human Growth and Development in Extreme Environments   447

Cynthia M. Beall

Early Studies   449
Major Research Strategies of Historical Importance   449
Current and Future Trends   455
References   457

20   The Last Fifty Years of Human Population Biology in North America: An Outsider's View   467

G. Ainsworth Harrison

Conceptual Reorientations   468
Outside Relations   470
References   472

Author Index   473

Subject Index   487

Contributors

Numbers in parentheses indicate the pages on which the authors' contributions begin.

George J. Armelagos (305, 329), Department of Anthropology, University of Massachusetts, Amherst, Massachusetts 01003

Thelma S. Baker (31), Department of Anthropology, Pennsylvania State University, University Park, Pennsylvania 16802

Cynthia M. Beall (447), Department of Anthropology, Case Western Reserve University, Cleveland, Ohio 44106

Noel T. Boaz (239), Department of Anthropology, New York University, New York, New York 10003

C. Loring Brace (11), Museum of Anthropology, University of Michigan, Ann Arbor, Michigan 48104

David S. Carlson (305), Center for Human Growth and Development, University of Michigan, Ann Arbor, Michigan 48104

Matt Cartmill (147), Department of Anatomy, Duke University Medical Center, Durham, North Carolina 27710

R. Chakraborty (371), Center for Demographic and Population Genetics, University of Texas, Houston, Texas 77025

J. E. Cronin* (105), Department of Anthropology and Biology, Harvard University, Cambridge, Massachusetts 02138

Phyllis B. Eveleth (31), Fogarty International Center, National Institutes of Health, Bethesda, Maryland 20205

Dean Falk (75), Department of Anatomy, University of Puerto Rico, San Juan, Puerto Rico 00936

John G. Fleagle (187), Department of Anatomical Sciences, School of Medicine, State University of New York at Stony Brook, Stony Brook, New York 11794

Morris Goodman (105), Department of Anatomy, Wayne State University, College of Medicine, Detroit, Michigan 48201

*Present address: Department of Anthropology, University of California, Berkeley, California 94720.

Jere D. Haas (435), Division of Nutritional Sciences, Cornell Univeristy, Ithaca, New York 14850

Albert B. Harper (281), Department of Biobehavioral Sciences, University of Connecticut, Storrs, Connecticut 06268

G. Ainsworth Harrison (467), Department of Biological Anthropology, Oxford University, Oxford OX2 6QS, England.

William L. Jungers (187), Department of Anatomical Sciences, School of Medicine, State University of New York at Stony Brook, Stony Brook, New York 11794

William S. Laughlin (281), Department of Behaviorial Sciences, University of Connecticut, Storrs, Connecticut 06268

Michael A. Little (405), Department of Anthropology, State University of New York at Binghamton, Binghamton, New York 13901

C. Owen Lovejoy (329), Department of Anthropology, Kent State University, Kent, Ohio 44240

Ernst Mayr (231), Museum of Comparative Zoology, The Agassiz Museum, Harvard University, Cambridge, Massachusetts 02138

Robert P. Mensforth (329), Department of Anthropology, Kent State University, Kent, Ohio 44240

Rosalind Ribnick (49), Department of Sociology, Anthropology and Social Welfare, Humboldt State University, Arcata, California 95521

David D. Thompson (357), Laboratory of Biological Anthropology, Department of Behavioral Sciences, University of Connecticut, Storrs, Connecticut 06268

Erik Trinkaus (261), Department of Anthropology, Harvard University, Cambridge, Massachusetts 02138

Douglas H. Ubelaker (337), Department of Anthropology, U.S. National Museum of Natural History, Smithsonian Institution, Washington, D.C. 20560

Dennis P. Van Gerven (305), Department of Anthropology, University of Colorado, Boulder, Colorado 80309

Kenneth M. Weiss (371), Center for Demographic and Population Genetics, University of Texas, Houston, Texas 77025

Preface

From April 22 to April 25, 1981 the American Association of Physical Anthropologists held its fiftieth annual meeting in Detroit, Michigan. Included in the festivities celebrating the occasion was a symposium entitled "American Physical Anthropology, 1930–1980," which convened on Friday, April 24, to review and appraise the progress made in the discipline during the five decades that have elapsed since the association held its first meeting in Charlottesville, Virginia in April 1930. The review, it was hoped, would provide not only a clearer understanding of how we came to be where we are today, but also some insight that might guide us toward sensible conclusions about the directions of future research in the discipline.

Because the symposium was confined to one day, both the number and length of the papers presented were restricted. As a consequence, several important subjects, such as paleopathology and forensic anthropology, had to be omitted from the program. In this volume, an attempt has been made to fill these gaps with contributions from C. Loring Brace, John G. Fleagle and William L. Jungers, Ernst Mayr, David D. Thompson, and Douglas H. Ubelaker. The other chapters in this volume are all revised versions of the addresses originally delivered at the symposium in Detroit.

This volume does not pretend to give a complete or systematic account of the discipline's development during the past 50 years. Such a synthesis would require not one but several volumes. However, since no summing-up of this scope has been attempted before, it is hoped that this volume will prove to be of use to students in both anthropology and the biological sciences, as well as to those with a specific interest in the recent history of science.

As director of the symposium and editor of the volume, I wish to express my sincere gratitude to the many people who contributed to the symposium both in the planning stages and during the sessions themselves and to the preparation of this book for publication. First, I wish to thank all of the contributors for their unremitting enthusiasm and cooperation. Next, gratitude is owed to the Association's Committee on History, namely G. E. Erikson T. Dale Stewart, Mildred Trotter, and Sherwood L. Washburn, for their support and guidance as the symposium progressed from idea to reality. Special thanks are due also to William S. Pollitzer, who, as president of the association from 1979 to 1981, was largely responsible for making the symposium possible.

Others to whom I am particularly grateful for encouragement and aid of various kinds include Noel T. Boaz, who willingly served in multiple roles connected with the symposium and with this volume; Frank B. Livingstone and Barry A. Bogin, for their cheerful assistance in Detroit; and Paul E. Mahler and Sara Stinson, who graciously served as chairpersons of the symposium.

We also thank the Wenner-Gren Foundation for Anthropological Research for a grant-in-aid that helped support the Detroit celebration of which the symposium was a part.

Finally, I wish to thank the staff of Academic Press for their patient assistance in preparing the final manuscript.

Introduction

Frank Spencer

It will probably come as a surprise to many readers to learn that 50 years ago, the science of physical anthropology afforded full-time employment to only a handful of individuals in the United States. Also, whereas today the majority of the members of the American Association of Physical Anthropologists (AAPA) consciously identify themselves as "professional physical anthropologists" and function primarily in an academic milieu, in 1930, the association's membership was predominantly made up of professional anatomists who, by and large, regarded physical anthropology as an ancillary occupation. Indeed, until the beginning of the 1950s the main strength of the science resided in a community composed principally of workers who had been trained in either medicine or anatomy and who worked in either museums or academic anatomy departments.

The past 50 years have thus witnessed a fundamental change in the institutional structure of physical anthropology in North America, namely, the development of graduate instruction in the science at major universities. Because this change has clearly had a profound effect on the conceptual growth of the discipline, I will briefly review the profession's institutional history before proceeding to the essays in this volume. Since this discussion can only touch on the highlights, the reader who wishes to investigate this topic further is advised to consult Brew (1968), Darnell (1970, 1974), Erickson (1974), Haller (1971), Hinsley (1981), Hrdlička (1914, 1918), Penniman (1965), Spencer (1979, 1981), and Stocking (1969, 1974).

When the association held its inaugural meeting in Charlottesville, Virginia in April 1930, there were already several American universities with established departments of anthropology. Only one, Harvard, offered a program leading to a Ph.D. in physical anthropology. All other departments at that time were controlled by anthropologists who favored the development of an anthropology curriculum

A HISTORY OF AMERICAN
PHYSICAL ANTHROPOLOGY, 1930–1980

that emphasized cultural and historical problems. Consequently, the future of the Harvard program was not nearly as certain at that time as it is now in retrospect.

The department at Harvard was founded at the close of the nineteenth century by Frederic Ward Putnam (1839–1915) (Figure 1). In addition to having the distinction of being the oldest (continuously operating) department in the country, it was also responsible for producing, in 1898, the first Ph.D. in physical anthropology in America, which was awarded to Frank Russell (1868–1903), whose dissertation was concerned with Eskimo crania. In spite of Putnam's passion for archaeology, it was his expressed intention to develop an anthropology program with a broad scope that would embrace all three major subdisciplines: archaeology, ethnology, and physical anthropology (or *somatology* as it was then called). This ambition was clearly realized in the first batch of Ph.D.s produced by the department (Table 1). However, after 1905 there was a decided shift in the department's emphasis, to archaeology, and, as a result, a virtual neglect of the

Figure 1   Frederic Ward Putnam. Courtesy of Peabody Museum, Harvard University.

Table 1 A Comparison of the Subdisciplinary Specialization of Ph.D.s in Anthropology Produced at Harvard, Columbia, Berkeley, and Pennsylvania from the Beginning of the Respective Programs to 1925

Institution	Subdisciplinary specialization	1890	1895	1900	1905	1910	1915	1920	1925	Total
Harvard	Ethnology	—	—	2	—	—	—	2	1	5
	Archaeology	—	1	—	2	1	2	2	1	9
	Physical anthropology	—	—	1	1	—	1	—	—	3
Columbia	Ethnology				2	5	5	2	2	16
	Archaeology				—	—	—	—	—	0
	Physical anthropology				—	—	—	—	—	0
University of California, Berkeley	Ethnology				1	1	—	—	—	2
	Archaeology				—	—	—	—	—	0
	Physical anthropology				—	—	—	—	—	0
University of Pennsylvania	Ethnology				—	1	—	—	1	2
	Archaeology				—	—	—	—	—	0
	Physical anthropology				—	—	1	—	—	1

graduate program in physical anthropology (Table 1)—a development that appears to have been linked with Putnam's retirement and a resulting change in the political structure of the department.

The importance of this emphasis shift lies in the fact that the Columbia anthropology department, then the only other major source of Ph.D.s in the discipline, had also developed a bias. As indicated in Table 1, the Columbia graduate program, which had been organized under the aegis of Franz Boas (1857–1942) (Figure 2), had from its beginnings offered concentrations only in ethnology and ethnolinguistics. This is somewhat surprising when one considers Boas's active interest in problems related to human growth and development. Although there is some evidence to suggest that Boas's plans to develop a "well rounded school of anthropology" in New York City had been thwarted by his inability to develop operative links with other departments at the University, it is also apparent that his

Figure 2   Franz Boas. Courtesy of the American Museum of Natural History.

primary concerns had been, from the outset, the definition and resolution of problems that had their origin in the cultural and historical sphere. No matter what the reasons were for this bias, the fact remains that all students studying under Boas who received their doctorates prior to 1925 had little or no active interest in the development of physical anthropology.

Thus it was in this developing climate that Aleš Hrdlička (1869–1943) (Figure 3), most of whose professional career had been spent at the National Museum of Natural History (USNM) in Washington, D.C., endeavored to direct physical anthropology in America along the same path Paul Broca (1824–1880) had chosen for the discipline in France.

During the third quarter of the nineteenth century, Broca had founded first, in 1859, the Société d'Anthropologie de Paris, followed by the Laboratoire d'Anthropologie (de l'Ecole pratique des Hautes-Etudes) in 1867, and then, in

Figure 3   Aleš Hrdlička. Courtesy of National Anthropological Archives, Smithsonian Institution.

1875–1876, the internationally famed Ecole d'Anthropologie. When formed, this loose federation of society, laboratory, and school, sometimes known informally as "Broca's Institute," represented the institutional and intellectual center of late-nineteenth- and early-twentieth-century French anthropology. Mindful of this, Hrdlička, who had received his training in anthropology there in 1896, had resolved to found a similar institutional complex in America. Such an institute, he contended, would serve not only as the "home" of a future national society of physical anthroplogists but also as a "center for instruction [Hrdlička 1899, 1908, 1918, 1929]." In brief, he saw this as an attractive institutional alternative that would provide both coherence and a powerful impulse to the development of the discipline in the United States.

During the first decade of his tenure at the USNM (1903–1913), Hrdlička made several unsuccessful attempts to found such an institute. Unable to arouse interest in the scheme, he subsequently turned his attention to the task of building his division at the USNM into a major center for research and instruction in the hope that at some future date he might be able to persuade the authorities at the Smithsonian Institute to upgrade his division to the status of an "Institute."

Although this scheme was never fully realized, Hrdlička did succeed, between 1914 and 1920, in attracting a steady stream of workers to his laboratory at the USNM for instruction in anthropology and anthropometric techniques. It was also during this period that he launched the *American Journal of Physical Anthropology* (*AJPA*) (1918). This event is an important landmark in the profession's history because (*a*) it had the immediate effect of securing the discipline's identity; (*b*) it provided Hrdlička with an opportunity to codify the discipline in broader and essentially more modern terms; and (*c*) it gave him a platform from which to continue his campaign for the recognition of physical anthropology as a legitimate and independent science.

In the years immediately following World War I, Hrdlička established through the *AJPA* a small but highly active network of researchers, many of whom were professional anatomists who later formed the nucleus of the AAPA. Evidently, through this network he hoped to secure a beachhead for the science in the medical fraternity while at the same time gathering support for his plan to found an institute.

Meanwhile, at Harvard, Earnest Albert Hooton (1887–1954) (Figure 4) had been struggling since his appointment in 1913 to resuscitate the program in physical anthropology. His progress, however, had been slow, perhaps due as much to his own inexperience as to the general climate of the department. It was not until the early 1920s that he was finally able to accept his first graduate student: Harry L. Shapiro, who received his doctorate in 1926. Thereafter, at almost yearly intervals, Hooton was to see at least one, and sometimes as many as three, graduate students receive their Ph.D.s in physical anthropology, and many of these new Ph.D.s were subsequently to play an integral role in the development of academic physical anthropology after World War II.

While clearly supporting Hooton's efforts at Harvard, Hrdlička remained con-

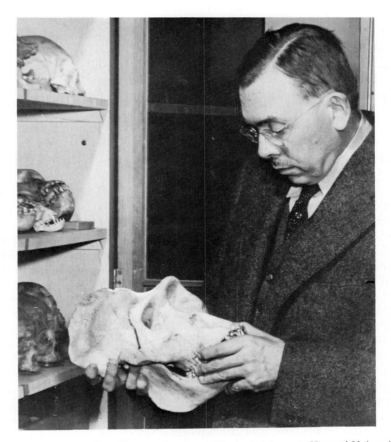

Figure 4   Earnest Albert Hooton. Courtesy of Peabody Museum, Harvard University.

vinced that until a more "regular and extended" training program could be established, there would be little prospect for the discipline's advancement and consequent attainment of its "rightful place in the American scientific community [Spencer 1979]." In his opinion, the "Institute" was the only solution, and toward this end he apparently made two unsuccessful attempts, during the first half of the 1920s, to obtain funding through the National Research Council of the National Academy of Sciences. However, on both occasions the proposal was blocked by Boas's former students, who were at that time in control of the National Research Council's anthropological committee.

Unwilling to admit defeat, Hrdlička bided his time until December 1928. Then, taking advantage of the group of sympathetic workers assembled in New York City at the Section H meeting of the American Association for the Advancement of Science in New York City, he persuaded them that the time was ripe for founding an independent body devoted exclusively to the needs of furthering physical anthropology and requested that a committee of organization be formed immediately. The proposal was unanimously endorsed, and an organizing committee was formed (see Hrdlička 1929). Not surprisingly, among the 12 objectives (formulated by Hrdlička) toward which the future association would direct its activities was "the eventual establishment, in the most favorable location, of the 'American Institute of Physical Anthropology' [Hrdlička 1929:305]."

Throughout 1929, Hrdlička, assisted by the organizing committee, worked diligently to enlist members in the new association. By March 1930, they had founded 83 charter members—49 professional anatomists, 18 anthropologists (of whom only 8 were full-time professional physical anthropologists), 8 zoologists, and 8 others whose professional affiliation is not known.

Since the majority of the association's members were anatomists, it was decided for pragmatic as well as political reasons to hold the inaugural meeting in conjunction with the annual meeting of the American Association of Anatomists, which, in 1930, was scheduled to meet in Charlottesville, Virginia. At this meeting, Hrdlička's journal was officially adopted as the association's organ, and a constitution and bylaws were also adopted. This constitution consisted of the same set of objectives Hrdlička had presented earlier in New York City; in both cases, objective 12 dealt with the question of the institute. In this respect, it is interesting to note that whereas the charter members apparently accepted the idea in principle, they were unwilling to go along with Hrdlička's proposal to sell "cheap $25 life memberships" to raise funds quickly to launch the project. Whether the incorporation of objective 12 into the constitution was simply a gesture to appease Hrdlička, or whether the membership recognized the possible future utility of the institute is no longer clear; regardless, because of subsequent developments after World War II, the association was never obliged to act on this objective.

Following the close of World War II, there was an unprecedented growth of higher education in the United States that was initially underwritten by the passage of the GI Bill and later underwritten by the so-called "postwar baby boom." In addition to transforming the American academic landscape, which hitherto had been essentially a middle-class domain, it also contributed to the apparent change in the ethos of American anthropology. This change is perhaps best characterized by an emerging diversification in research interests and the growth of what has been called "cultural materialism," with its emphasis on cultural ecology, which prompted a growing interest in the connections between the cultural and biological spheres. Thus, it was in this changing intellectual context that physical anthropology was presented with an opportunity to advance.

The early postwar period also saw a change in the pattern of anthropological research funding with the creation of two new funding organizations in the private and public sectors: namely, the Wenner-Gren Foundation and the National Science Foundation (NSF), respectively. The relative impact of these and other funding organizations, such as the National Institutes of Health (NIH), on the development of physical anthropology is discussed in this volume by Baker and Eveleth.

From all appearances, the initial development of academic programs in physical anthropology in the 1950s was confined to those universities that already had established anthropology departments (e.g., Arizona, Berkeley, Chicago, Columbia, UCLA, Michigan, Pennsylvania, and Wisconsin). And almost without exception, these graduate programs were organized by either former students of Hooton or by a student of a Hooton student.

After this initial period of expansion, there was a rapid proliferation of new programs that continued on through the 1960s and into the early 1970s. By this time, the number of graduate programs had risen to a figure just short of 50, which essentially represented most of the major universities in the country possessing graduate departments of anthropology. At the same time that this stage was reached, academia began to experience a general and rapid decline in enrollments. To make matters worse, the country entered a concomitant period of economic instability. As of this writing, we are still adjusting to these new and continuing conditions. There are many researchers who forecast a gloomy future for the field, but if we have imagination and the determination to adapt, there is every reason to expect the coming decades to exhibit "dynamic equilibrium."

The effect of this growth in academia over the past 30 years is clearly reflected in the association's membership and its journal. Prior to 1964, the *AJPA* had been limited to one volume per year (usually consisting of about 500 pages). After that date it expanded to two volumes per year and more recently has gone from being a bimonthly to a monthly publication. For a discussion of the changing content of *AJPA* during this period, see Lovejoy *et al.* and Haas, respectively, in this volume. As for the association's membership, it grew at an exponential rate after 1950 and is now clearly dominated by academically trained physical anthropologists. Today the association's membership is well in excess of 1100 and represents the largest community of its kind in the world.

References

Brew, J. O. (editor)
  1968   *One hundred years of anthropology.* Cambridge, Massachusetts: Harvard University Press.
Darnell, R.
  1970   The emergence of academic anthropology at the University of Pennsylvania. *Journal of the History of the Behavioral Sciences* 6:80–92.
  1974   *Readings in the History of Anthropology.* New York: Harper.
Erickson, P. A.
  1974   The origins of physical anthropology. Unpublished Ph.D. thesis, Department of Anthropology, University of Connecticut, Storrs.
Haller, J. S.
  1971   *Outcasts from evolution: scientific attitudes of racial inferiority, 1859–1900.* Chicago: University of Illinois Press.

Hinsley, C. M.
  1981   *Savages and scientists: the Smithsonian Institution and the development of American anthropology, 1846–1910*. Washington, D.C.: Smithsonian Institution Press.
Hrdlička, A.
  1899   The needs of American anthropologists. *American Naturalist* **33**:684–688.
  1908   Physical anthropology and its aims. *Science* **38**:33–43.
  1914   Physical anthropology in America. *American Anthropologist* **16**:508–554.
  1918   Physical anthropology: its scope and aims; its history and present status in America. *American Journal of Physical Anthropology* **1**:3–23, 133–182, 377–402.
  1929   The American Association of Physical Anthropologists. *American Journal of Physical Anthropology* **12**:519–521.
Penniman, T. K.
  1965   *A hundred years of anthropology*. London: Duckworth.
Spencer, F.
  1979   Aleš Hrdlička, M.D., 1869–1943: a chronicle of the life and work of an American physical anthropologist. Unpublished Ph.D. thesis, Department of Anthropology, University of Michigan, Ann Arbor.
  1981   The rise of academic physical anthropology in the United States, 1880–1980: an historical review. *American Journal of Physical Anthropology* **56**:353–364.
Stocking, G. W.
  1969   *Race, culture and evolution: essays in the history of anthropology*. New York: Free Press.
  1974   *The shaping of American anthropology, 1887–1911: a Franz Boas reader*. New York: Basic Books.

1

The Roots of the Race Concept
in American Physical Anthropology

C. Loring Brace

> Institutions are largely, but certainly not entirely, the shadows of their founders.
>
> E. D. Baltzell 1979

American physical anthropology, the largest such entity in the world at the moment, was mainly created by two preeminent individuals, Earnest Albert Hooton and Aleš Hrdlička, during the first half of the twentieth century. Hooton, in his four decades of teaching at Harvard, launched the careers of most of the generation of physical anthropologists who went on to establish physical anthropology curricula in the universities and colleges where the discipline presently thrives. Hrdlička was chiefly responsible for creating the *American Journal of Physical Anthropology*—the journal in which these anthropologists published their principal contributions—and the American Association of Physical Anthropologists—the society that served as the principal basis on which they could establish a professional identity and a research orientation.

Occasionally, the feeling is expressed that anything done 5 or 10 years ago is of no particular importance and what really matters is only the most recent of research publications. This viewpoint was evident 15 years ago when it was announced that "physical anthropology has now come of age [Lasker 1964:iii]." It is perfectly true that in a rapidly developing field, research methods and results are often superseded in very short order. However, there is more than a little reason to suspect the maturity of any scholarly realm that is ignorant of the work of the previous generation, or even that of more distant predecessors. Current research cannot be pursued effectively, and future efforts cannot be planned, until our present status is clear. And we cannot really know where we are unless we have some understanding of our past.

Now that the American Association of Physical Anthropologists can look back on a half century of existence, we should have obtained enough perspective on our current position to begin to exhibit some of that maturity we have so rashly claimed for ourselves in years gone by. Some effort has been made to view the practices of

A HISTORY OF AMERICAN
PHYSICAL ANTHROPOLOGY, 1930–1980

paleoanthropology from a historical perspective (Brace 1964b; Trinkaus present volume), but with occasional exceptions (e.g., Montagu 1942, 1952, 1965; Erickson 1974a, 1974b) this has not been the case for the rest of the physical anthropology our founders bequeathed us.

If paleoanthropology, the study of the fossil evidence for human evolution, is one of the two realms that physical anthropology can claim as uniquely its own province, the other is the study of contemporary human variation subsumed by convention under that single, four-letter word *race*. Although there have been many studies reflecting on the use of the concept of race in historical and sociopolitical contexts (Benedict 1945; Chase 1977; Gossett 1963; Haller 1970, 1971; Stanton 1960; Stocking 1968), they have not been the works of physical anthropologists.

Curiously, the one piece of research that attempted to put the concept of race in the perspective of intellectual history, written by a historian (Barzun 1937), appears to have had little if any impact on anthropological thinking. Hrdlička, in fact, greeted its (unspecified) "errors" and "misconceptions" with a vigorous denunciation, suggesting that Barzun had "gone astray" to the extent that "he would lead anthropology to a crucifixion [Hrdlička 1937:227]." The strength of Hrdlička's response suggests that Barzun had touched a raw nerve. It should be recalled that this took place before the "Synthetic Theory of Evolution" had its major impact on biological science in general (Huxley 1940; Olson 1960; Mayr and Provine 1980) and on anthropology in particular (for example the *Cold Spring Harbor Symposium in Quantitative Biology* in 1950). Although paleoanthropology shows signs of the systematic incorporation of evolutionary theory in its approach (Wolpoff 1980), the assumption that contemporary human variation can be understood in terms of "racial" variation, despite some pointed critiques (Brace 1964a; Livingstone 1962), sails on without any substantial change from the time when Hrdlička and Hooton were shaping the field into its subsequently recognizable form. The factors that influenced their shaping, then, stem from an earlier era. Consequently, we should take a closer look at the factors that conditioned the outlook of our "founding fathers."

Earnest Albert Hooton

Aside from the gratitude he expressed toward his teachers in England, Hooton showed little interest in examining the roots of the field that grew in America under his benevolent nurturing. Much the same can be said for the majority of the students he produced at Harvard. Most of Hooton's formal education, including his Ph.D. at Wisconsin in 1911, was in the classics. His training in anthropology at Oxford began just after the establishment of the Diploma in Anthropology, which distinction was awarded to him in 1912 (Howells 1954). That program included study both in science and the humanities, something that is still unusual in an English higher education and that was then quite a novelty (Marett 1937). At a time when C. P. Snow's "two cultures" had just about stopped communicating with each other (Snow 1963), this was a laudable effort to keep the rift from becoming a chasm. Even so, the most significant figure in his training was Robert Ranulph Marett, Reader in Social Anthropology, Rector of Exeter College, and himself a classical scholar of note.

The other major influence on Hooton was Sir Arthur Keith. Athough Keith, like Arthur Thomson, Hooton's other mentor at Oxford, was an anatomist and presumably represented the scientific training in his background, he was very far from being the cautious empirical worker that we associated with those scientific traditions stemming from the world of the Enlightenment.

Keith gained his medical training at Aberdeen in the 1880s at a time when medicine owed far more to the traditions of the healing arts than to those of science. Furthermore, in his autobiography, Keith spoke of his admiration for "the personality of Thomas Carlyle, who made so strong an appeal in my youthful years [Keith, 1943, 1950:562]." By contrast, he then mentioned "the personality of Charles Darwin, who engaged the wholehearted admiration of my later years [1950:562]." In his mid-60s, however, Keith was still quoting from Carlyle's *Sartor Resartus* (1931:27) to justify the conclusion of his rectorial address to the students of the Aberdeen University that "race prejudice . . . works for the ultimate good of mankind and must be given a recognized place in all our efforts to obtain natural justice for the world [1931:48]."

The Scottish Enlightenment, which had played such an important role in shaping the intellectual styles of Darwin and Lyell, had long since given way to the Romanticism exemplified by Carlyle (Brace 1981; Hook 1975; Olson 1975; Rosenberg 1974). In that same unfortunate rectorial address—as in his no more admirable Robert Boyle lecture given at Balliol College, Oxford, a decade earlier (Keith 1919)—Keith opined to his student audience,

If . . . universal deracialization ever comes before you . . . as the sole way of establishing peace and good will in all parts of our world, I feel certain both head and heart will rise against it. There will well up within you an overmastering antipathy against peace at such a price. This antipathy or race prejudice Nature has implanted within you for her own ends—the improvement of Mankind through race differentiation [Keith 1931:48].

In this and in other passages, Keith embodies the essence of the romantic movement as contrasted with the characteristics of the preceding Age of Reason. The distinction has been characterized as "the rebellion of feeling against reason, of instinct against intellect, of sentiment against judgment, . . . of subjectivism against objectivity, . . . of religion against science [Durant and Durant 1967:887]." Another passage from Keith's essay on prejudice displays this as clearly as possible:

The human heart, with its prejudices, its instinctive tendencies, its likes and dislikes, its passions and desires, its spiritual aspirations and its idealism, is an essential part of the great scheme of human evolution . . . . Prejudices, I believe, have their purpose. Man has become what he is, not by virtue of his head, but because of his heart [Keith 1931:26].

Keith spent the last quarter of his long and influential life in a house on the Darwin estate at Downe, considered by many to represent the continuity and embodiment of Darwinian tradition. Yet, although he was thoroughly familiar with Darwin's life and works, he rejected Darwin's basic tenet that natural selection was the principal mechanism by which evolution occurred. In reference to the resistance that Darwin encountered, he observed that "the vast majority of naturalists held (correctly, in my opinion) that natural selection did not account, as Darwin believed it did, for the wonderful contrivances which Archdeacon Paley had so extolled in his *Natural Theology* [Keith 1955:103]."

Although he stated unequivocally "I believe in Darwin and Darwinism [Keith 1955:289]," his de facto rejection of the basis of the Darwinian view preserves the essentials of Paley's position even if it is more Presbyterian than High Church Anglican: "I could as easily believe the theory of the Trinity as one which maintains that living developing protoplasm, by mere throws of chance, brought the human eye into existence [Keith 1946:217]." Keith in fact was a romantic evolutionist in the mold of Henri Bergson, Teilhard de Chardin and especially Ernst Haeckel (Brace 1981). When he declared "the essence of living protoplasm is its purposiveness," and "there are evolutionary processes in living things and therefore in Nature— trends of change which are akin to human purpose and human policy [Keith 1946:217–218]," he was declaring his faith in a Bergsonian élan vital, which in fact was no different from Haeckel's *Monism*—a manifestation of romantic mysticism that is the very antithesis of Darwinism (Gasman 1971; Brace 1981).

Now, although some of the analysts of Romanticism have championed its "flexible and humane pragmatism," as opposed to the perceived evils of "materialistic mechanism" (Barzun 1958:16), or claimed that some of its mani- festations pose no threat to the present and "are in the end quite harmless [Hook 1975:126]," one could suggest that the victims of two world wars and various manifestations of European colonialism would argue to the contrary. Carlyle himself displayed sentiments that were considerably less than enlightened in his "Discourse on the Nigger Question [1853]," and Keith added his own affirmation: "Like most of my fellows, I was a sober imperialist. . . . Rudyard Kipling sang our creed [1950:228]"; "races were assorted in my mind into superior and inferior; I of course was of the superior race [1950:119]."

There is a remarkable similarity between these views and the proto-Nazi sentiments of the German romantic evolutionist Ernst Haeckel (Gasman 1971; Brace 1981), whom Keith uncritically admired (Keith 1935). Such views also characterized the anthropology of Paul Broca in late-nineteeth-century France (Barzun 1965:125), and it may well have been the unflattering nature of the exposé that aroused the ire of the Francophile Hrdlička.

With this as his background in "science," it is no wonder that the anthropology of Earnest Albert Hooton was tinged with more than a little biological determinism ("the primary cause of crime is biological inferiority [Hooton 1939:130]") and racism ("we are fairly safe in assuming that the Australian is far less intelligent than is the Englishman [Hooten 1946:158].") Some of these "racist overtones" survived in the works of Hooton's prominent pupil, the late Carleton Coon (1962, 1965; see Trinkaus, in the present volume). Here the influences of French "polyphyletism" (Vallois 1952) and Keith's similar model are both quite clear, although Coon gratuitously attributed this to Weidenreich, to whom he dedicated his work of 1962. In his last pronouncement on the subject, Keith articulated the theme that Coon was later to elaborate, without attribution, as the controversial core of his book:

> It still seems to me a very surprising thing that the modern races of mankind which we count to be members of a single species—*Homo sapiens*—should be descendants of ancestors which are regarded as being different species. If my theory is true, then the races of mankind must have converged, not diverged as time went on [Keith 1950:631].

Aleš Hrdlička

If Hooton and his students were less than fully conscious of the strains of romantic racism that constituted a major part of their background, Hrdlička was very much aware and made a conscious effort to look at the historical antecedents of the organizational framework he sought to give to American physical anthropology, in America, which was a prominent part of three of the first four issues of the *America Journal of Physical Anthropology (AJPA)* (Hrdlička 1918, revised for separate publication in 1919). This thorough and conscientious survey provides valuable perspective and information, beginning with the development of the field and continuing through its tentative beginnings in the United States.

Although they may be of no great moment, there are some interesting aspects of emphasis that may reveal how he chose to treat his subject. This in turn may help to explain the perpetuation of certain traditions of perspective in physical anthropology that Hrdlička helped to transmit but which, curiously, were not central to his own way of thinking. For example, the conventional view for over a century has been to give credit to Johann Friedrich Blumenbach for being the "father" of physical anthropology (Bendyshe 1863–1864, 1865; Radl 1930:167; Brace and Montagu 1977:22). In his survey, Hrdlička does mention Blumenbach's name, but only as one among a group of "naturalists and anatomists" that included Daubenton, Camper, Lamarck, Soemmering, Lacépède and a number of others (Hrdlička 1918:5). In Hrdlička's view, France was identified as "the mother-country of physical anthropology [1919:5]," and its "principal founder" was Paul Broca (Hrdlička 1918:4).

This is not just a quibble over priorities and credits, for it reveals an aspect of Hrdlička's outlook that has created something of a legacy for the field as a whole, even if the result was not quite what Hrdlička may have intended. Just from the nature of Hrdlička's treatment of certain issues (the Neandertal question, for example), it is possible to suspect that he had a bias against things German (Brace 1964b:14, 1981). When his complex and interesting background is examined carefully, this supposition is easily documented (Spencer 1979:15, 18, 123, 769–770). His prejudice is understandable, given his origins in a Bohemia still under the thumb of Austrian domination, even when one considers that his maternal family was of Bavarian origin, and that German as well as Czech was spoken in his home.

This same eastern European background also evidently predisposed him to admire things French, even before he knew their substance. Paris, the "City of Light," has long held place as the symbol of enlightenment for eastern European intellectuals, and for the rest of his life, Hrdlička abstained from criticizing the products of French scholarship, even when they differed radically from the conclusions that emerged from his own work (Spencer 1979). When others, such as Barzun, pointed to the culturally ingrained bigotry so prominent in French physical anthropology—and did so with a mastery of the French context that only one who had grown up with all the dimensions of a French education could display—Hrdlička would continue to denounce the criticism, if only from a position of offended loyalty.

The intensity of Hrdlička's Francophilia, despite the brevity and occasional squalor of his crucial stay in Paris in 1896, is clearly evident in his letters to his wife-to-be in New York (Spencer 1979: Chapters 2 and 4). During Hrdlička's three months of study in Paris, his principal contact was with Leonce Manouvrier, who was to remain a friend and confidant until his death. Manouvrier, Broca's pupil and director of the Laboratoire d'Anthropologie at the Ecole pratique des Hautes-Etudes from 1903 until his death in 1927 (Vallois 1940), held views that were in marked contrast to those of his own mentor. Although his work did not completely reflect an evolutionary point of view, his perspective on functional anatomy recognized a major component of environmental influence, and he deplored the racism of the anthropology that developed under Broca and that was used to justify French colonial enterprises (Barzun 1965:125, Schiller 1979:138; Spencer 1979:116–119).

Despite the fact that the anthropology that Hrdlička subsequently put into practice took its orientation more from Manouvrier than from the predominant ethos of his French contemporaries, nonetheless, it was Hrdlička's continuing dream to found in America something equivalent to what Broca had established in France (Spencer 1979: Chapters 7, 12, and 13, 1981:358–360). Although he never did succeed in getting a laboratory of physical anthropology institutionalized as an entity on its own, he did manage to launch a journal and a society, based on the French model, at a time when France and her allies had triumphed over German attempts at military annexation. French influence rose to new heights in the English-speaking world as a partial consequence. In physical anthropology, that influence did not focus on the mechanism stressed by Manouvrier. Instead, one finds the a priori and Platonic essentialism of Paul Broca. Insofar as evolution was contemplated in this ethos, it was the romantic evolutionism of Haeckel, Keith, and Bergson, all of whom specifically rejected the basic aspects of Darwinian mechanism (Brace 1981). It is not surprising, then, that works actually attempting to deal with the processes of evolution are so notably scarce in the pages of the AJPA (see Lovejoy *et al.* in the present volume).

Samuel George Morton

Whereas French influence on American physical anthropology in the twentieth century is reasonably well recognized, the nineteenth-century background to it is not only less obvious, but indeed, has been largely overlooked. In his historical review, Hrdlička did observe with considerable insight that "Physical Anthropology is a comparatively recent branch of science" and, further, "it is interesting to know that one of its main incentives was the discovery of America with its new race of people, no mention of which occurred in any of the old accounts or traditions [1918:5]." The circumstances were even more compelling, for it was due to "the characteristic American situation of three races in uneasy conjunction [Stanton 1960:193]," that the assessment of race had immediate and major application in law, economics, politics, and all aspects of national life. The impetus for the development of physical anthropology had a drive in America, as shown for example in the career of Samuel Stanhope Smith (Jordan 1965; Brace 1974), which exceeded that present in the older intellectual European contexts, even where the latter had the stimulus of colonial involvement.

In his conscientious assessment of the individuals who responded to this impetus, Hrdlička gave full and proper recognition to the remarkable and original works of the Philadelphia physician and scientist Samuel George Morton. As Hrdlička notes, "Physical Anthropology in the United States speaking strictly, begins with Sameul G. Morton, in Philadelphia, in 1830 [1918:137]." Hrdlička went on to describe Morton's methodological innovations and their application to the comparative assessment of native American (Morton 1839) and Egyptian (Morton 1844) crania. Yet the fact that Morton's name rarely appears in English language sources after the American Civil War is not suprising, for as Hrdlička concluded

it is plain that Morton may be justly and with pride termed the father of American anthropology; yet it must be noted with regret that, like others later on, he was a father who left many friends to the science and even followers, but no real progeny, no disciples who would continue his work as their special or life vocation [1918:146].

In this assessment, however, it would seem that Hrdlička, despite his uncritical loyalty to French anthropology, seems to have missed an important aspect of the background of that phenomenon. It is true that Morton had no true American continuity. Although the failure of Philadephia to nurture leadership (Baltzell

1979) and the appendage of a phrenological essay to his principal work may have played some role, certainly a major reason for this lack of following is because those who claimed to be his disciples, after his early death in 1851, used his name and his work to try to justify the institution of slavery in the American South (Gibbes 1851; Nott and Gliddon 1854). The publication of Darwin's *Origin of Species* (1859) and Lyell's *Antiquity of Man* (1863)[1] deprived the so-called disciples' use of Morton's work of any intellectual justification, and the defeat of the South in the American Civil War removed their social base of support. The result was the effective eclipse of interest in Morton's work in America.

In continental Europe, however, where Darwin was slow in being accepted and where the American social context was so remote that it did not influence judgment, Morton's pioneering work took root and flourished. During his life, he had been lauded by Alexander von Humboldt (Meigs 1851:48). He had received similar praise from Anders Retzius (Patterson 1855:xxxiii; Retzius 1860:264). But the person who really should be regarded as the one who continued Morton's work as his own special vocation was none other than Paul Broca. Some recognition has been granted to the fact that Broca was "heir to both the French and the American traditions of Polygenism [Stocking 1968:40]," but the extent to which he literally represented the continuation of Morton's initiatory efforts has never been pointed out.

Broca's contribution, of course, involved a great deal more than simply carrying on Morton's work. His neurological research is viewed as having been original and fundamentally important (Schiller 1979), and there can be no denying the energy and leadership he displayed in institutionalizing physical anthropology in France. His actual anthropological work, although showing the same levels of energetic application, was somewhat less original. The first major anthropological work for which he is known was his essay "Des phénomènes d'hybridité dans le genre humain," which was the conclusion to his "Mémoire sur l'hybridité en général, sur la distinction des espéces animales et sur les métis obtenus par le croisement du lièrre et du lapin," which he began in 1858 (Broca, 1959–1960b). On closer inspection, it is remarkably similar to Chapter 12 of *Types of Mankind*, "Hybridity of Animals Viewed in Connection with the Natural History of Mankind," which was written by Morton's self-declared disciple Josiah Clark Nott (Nott and Gliddon 1854). The latter in turn took the more respectable parts of its orientation from the essay on hybridity by Morton himself (1847).

To be sure, these arguments over whether the production of viable fertile offspring was an adequate test of the specific identity of the parents go back to the time of John Ray in the seventeenth century and were discussed by Linnaeus and Buffon in the eighteenth century, as Broca, Morton, Nott, Prichard, and others writing on the subject were well aware. Furthermore, Morton's orientation in applying the arguments to the human condition was essentially the same as that of the French polygenist Bory de Saint-Vincent (1827 [Vol. I]:69), whose influence,

---

[1]See reference list for complete titles of these two volumes.

among others, Morton was careful to acknowledge. Broca's use of the hybridity argument, then, clearly has both French and American antecedents, but because the approach of the American Civil War was bringing such matters into the arena of public debate, the impact of its American manifestation was especially strong on like-minded readers elsewhere, as is clearly apparent in Broca's essay.

The other particular influence that Morton may have exerted on Broca has to do with the use of anthropometric techniques. Morton's remarkable volume of 1839 was the first comparative and metric treatment of prehistoric human skeletal material. As Hrdlička noted, 6 of Morton's 10 cranial measures were taken in the same way and from the same landmarks as those formalized at the Monaco agreement in 1906 "though Morton was not remembered at that convention [Hrdlička 1918:139]." Morton's pioneering efforts may have been forgotten by that time, but an earlier generation had been aware of them. When American anthropology, although then principally an exercise in applied bigotry by Nott and Gliddon, was the subject of discussion at the July meetings of the Société d'Anthropologie de Paris in 1862, the "German Francophile" (Schiller 1979:141) Franz Ignaz Pruner-Bey sought to sustain the view that polygenism was a doctrine that was "completely and eminently French, and the Americans referred to could only count as a pale copy (Pruner-Bey 1862:420–421)." He was gently put in his place by Broca himself, who noted that, "If Germany has had her Blumenbach, and England her Prichard, America has had her Morton; so far French anthropology has had no name that can be put on a level with them [Broca 1862a:423]."

Pruner-Bey went on to complain that Morton was being regarded "as if he had founded a science." He concluded that "he has founded nothing at all" and belittled what Morton had actually accomplished (Pruner-Bey 1862:431). Broca never produced a coordinated work to represent the accomplishments of his school, but his most eminent pupil and successor, Paul Topinard, did just that in his model text l'Anthropologie. In this he recognized Morton's contribution, saying "only with Morton, however, did craniometry really take off [Topinard 1876:234]." Topinard had been in school in Philadelphia when Morton was at the height of his career, but there is no record of whether there was any direct influence or, if so, whether this played any role in his outlook after he returned to France following the revolution of 1848 (Hodge 1912).

If the florescence of anthropometry was largely the result of the energy and application of Broca (see the collected papers in Broca [1871, 1875]), the foundation on which Broca built had been solidly laid by Morton, even though Morton has never been given the credit he is due. The techniques that Broca elaborated from Morton's beginnings were adopted in England following the translation of Topinard's book (Turner 1884:3), and, later, Hrdlička and Hooton saw to it that these returned to American anthropology as it grew in the twentieth century. Broca did in fact become the manifestation of what he had observed to Pruner-Bey to have been previously lacking in France, and he did so with such resounding success that the impact of the racial situation in the New World and of the work of Morton in shaping this branch of anthropology has been almost entirely forgotten.

The Ethos of Broca's Société

Broca founded the Société d'Anthropologie de Paris in 1859, the same year that Charles Darwin published the *Origin of Species*. However, the date represents the only point of similarity when the implications of the ethos created by the two are considered. Broca's Société was founded for the specific purpose of promoting the "doctrine" of polygenism, which was regarded as based in "science," as opposed to the position of monogenism, which was considered to owe its formulation to a primary loyalty to Christian orthodoxy (Broca 1860a:662; Pouchet 1864:3).

In this regard, Broca and his associates continued in the same vein as their French precursors (Bory de Saint-Vincent 1827; Desmoulins 1826; Virey 1801. Even more obviously, their defense of polygenism and their attack on monogenism used the same examples, the same analogies, and even the same rhetoric as had previously been used in America by Nott, that "prototypical Southern racist [Brace 1974:516]," in his altercation with that equally bigoted monogenist, John Bachman of Charleston, South Carolina (Bachman 1850, 1854; Nott 1849; Nott and Gliddon 1854). The main difference between Broca and the "American School" was his feeling that the polygenism to which he subscribed did not justify the institution of slavery:

> One could say that the polygenist doctrine assigns a more honorable place to the inferior races of humanity than does the opposing doctrine. To be inferior to another man, be it in intelligence, vigor or beauty, is not a humiliating condition. One might blush on the other hand to have undergone a physical or moral degradation, to have descended the scale of beings, and to have lost one's rank in creation [Broca 1860a:439, 1860b:664].

In this sense, he felt that polygenism was ethically, as well as scientifically preferable to Bachman's monogenism (Broca 1860a:438, 1960b:663).

Along with his commitment to the idea that "the great and typical differences that separate human groups are primordial [Broca 1862b:283]," Broca initially declared his faith in the fixity of species:

> To place in doubt the permanence of species would be to attack respected traditions and at the same time to undermine the foundations of natural history, that is to say in its classifications; which by consequence would be to upset the whole world [Broca 1860a:435].

No sooner had he said this, however, than he had to contend with the phenomenon of Charles Darwin.

His first reaction to Darwin was from a position of lofty, if not very well-informed sarcasm. "When Mr. Darwin speaks to me about my trilobite ancestors, I do not feel humility, but I tell him: what do you know of it? You were not there. And those who refute it know more about it than he [Broca 1862b:314]." Furthermore, he articulated a theme that has echoed through French biology right up to the present day (Ruse 1981). "Is Mr. Darwin wrong or right? I know nothing of that, I do not even want to know [Broca, 1862b:314]." The same tack was taken later by Albert Gaudry, widely credited with convincing French scientists of the value of "the evolutionist theory" (Vallois 1966:206). Gaudry recognized that evolutionary mechanics was "well worthy of the attention of naturalists. But on that subject I avow my ignorance [Gaudry 1878:257]." Perhaps the most extreme statement of such a position was by the physiologist Claude Bernard, a pre-Bergsonian champion of *force vitale*, who declared, "I support ignorance. That is my philosophy. I have the tranquility of ignorance and faith in science [Cotard 1898:53]." When Rudolf Virchow, the German physician–anthropologist and admirer of Broca and his ethos (Virchow 1880, 1882), used the same tack in a debate with Haeckel and preened himself on the knowledge of his own ignorance (Virchow 1877:14), Haeckel in some glee twitted him for not knowing how ignorant he was (Haeckel 1878:27).

In a later and much more considered treatment of Darwin, Broca was forced to admit that "it is very probable that species are variable and subject to evolution [1870:238]." He then sounded a rather typical French note, echoed by his student and follower, Topinard (1876:547), of giving Lamarck the credit for developing the theory of evolution and denying that Darwin's mechanism of natural selection was more than a "shining mirage" (Broca 1870:171, 238). He concluded with the suggestion that the concept appeared first with Buffon and that it ought to be called "transformisme polygenique" (1870:191), but that it causes "are still unknown [1870:238]." The legacy that this established has remained a guide to physical anthropology ever since, and until very recently, there was little on the course of human evolution and less on the mechanisms involved that appeared in the major journals presumably devoted to that subject on either side of the Atlantic Ocean.

The Romantic Conception of Race

More recent treatments of race in American physical anthropology have principally been the works of the students of Hooton (Coon 1962, 1965; Coon et al. 1950; Garn 1965). To an increasing extent, these have focused on the testable aspects of human biology, but in the end, they generally conclude with a named list of human "races" assigned to various geographic and local regions. The connection between the biology discussed and the races named at the end is never clearly spelled out, and in fact the attentive reader cannot discover, from the information presented, just how the racial classification was constructed—other than the fact that this just seems to be the way anthropologists have always done things.

In an earlier work, however, Coon (1939) had suggested that the work of Joseph Deniker "has had a greater influence upon subsequent classifications of race than any of his nineteenth century contemporaries [1900:280]." He then labeled Deniker "the most important classifier" (Coon 1939:280). Deniker, who became the librarian at the Museum d'Histoire Naturelle, settled into the surroundings of Parisian anthropology in the mid-1870s and faithfully reflected the ethos of Broca's Société (Deniker 1880, 1892, 1897).

The race classification that Deniker used was an elaboration of that favored by Broca and Topinard. The basis of the scheme was the recognition of five "families of races" or "souches" (stocks), labeled according to geographic rather than descriptive terms (Broca 1860a:605). This in turn was essentially the same as the approach taken by Buffon, and especially by Blumenbach, and adopted by Morton with full credits to his predecessors (Morton 1839:iv). Morton labeled his five geographic divisions "races." It is interesting to note, however, that the elaboration that he then produced by dividing these into twenty-two "families" (1839:4–95) is clearly a first version of what Deniker was to do over a generation later. Morton's list (1839:5–7) is almost exactly the same as that produced more than a century later as the accepted views of American physical anthropology (Coon *et al.* 1950:115–140). Once again, it would seem, the influence of Morton lives on, even if it is unacknowledged.

Where it is a matter of concept, however, Morton acknowledged the priority of early-nineteenth-century French authorities, such as Virey (1801) and Bory de Saint-Vincent (1827). These and their intellectual descendants in Broca's school in late-nineteenth-century Paris would all conform to the generalization offered to explain why natural selection has never been accepted in France: "The French mentality happens to be peculiarly typological [Pasteur 1971:751]." From Cuvier to Broca to Topinard (1885:189), and on into the twentieth century, the a priori nature of race was taken as a given. As noted for Cuvier, all of them exhibited "a particular kind of typological thinking, an attitude of mind that also reflected an a priori conceptualization about the natural world [Lurie 1960:61]."

Late in the nineteenth and early in the twentieth centuries, the categorical and hierarchical way of looking at the rest of the world was recast and tied to aspirations of "becoming," to produce the romantic evolutionism of Ernst Haeckel, Henri Bergson, and Sir Arthur Keith. This in turn was transmitted by Hrdlička, whatever his real intent, and Hooton to American physical anthropology and has remained a poorly acknowledged thema within the field ever since.

Coon's book of 1939 hinted at the French source of the classification used, even if it missed Morton's part in shaping that source. But what is at least as important is the fact that it assured the continuity of the romantic conception of race, even though the definition was no longer verbalized. Coon's work was commissioned by the publisher to update the very popular book of the same title written by William Z. Ripley at the turn of the century (Coon 1939; Ripley 1899).

Ripley's work, in turn, based on his Lowell Institute Lectures of 1896, was an effort to simplify the complexities of Deniker's presentation and appeal to a general readership. Indeed, it first appeared in a series of installments in Appleton's *Popular Science Magazine* (Ripley 1897a, 1897b, 1898). As Stocking has pointed out, "it was primarily through his [Ripley's] work that the residual polygenism of European physical anthropology had its American impact [Stocking 1968:61]," although, as should be obvious from the previous discussion, the polygenism mentioned was a good deal more than residual. Ripley, a lecturer in both sociology and "anthropo-geography" at Columbia and Harvard (Hrdlička 1918:274), was a protege of the immigration restriction enthusiast and president of M.I.T., General Francis Amasa Walker (Chase 1977:108). His book enjoyed considerable success and provided the basis for other more inflammatory works that led to the immigration restriction quotas being signed into law by President Calvin Coolidge in 1924 (Chase 1977:270, 274, 344; Stocking 1968:68).

Aside from the applied consequences of the genteel racism of Ripley and his followers, the most important thing about his book was the nature of the race concept articulated within it. Ripley attributed his definition to Topinard, and although the latter never put it in quite that way in all the various times he tried to express what he meant (cf. Topinard 1879), it captured the essence of Topinard's intent so well that the spokesman for French anthropology over half a century later continued to quote it as Ripley had phrased it (Vallois 1953:151):

> Race in the present state of things is an abstract conception, a notion of continuity in discontinuity, of unity in diversity. It is rehabilitation of a real but directly unattainable thing [Ripley 1899:111–112].

Surely this would qualify as an example of what the historian of ideas, A. O. Lovejoy, labeled "the pathos of the esoteric. How exciting and how welcome is the sense of initiation into hidden mysteries. [1936:11]." It could even qualify for Lovejoy's "metaphysical pathos"—"the pathos of sheer obscurity, the loveliness of the incomprehensible [1936:11]." In his assessment, Lovejoy was appraising the change in views, particularly as represented in Bergson (1907) and others, which marked the rise of romanticism at the expense of the preceding age of En-lightenment. The description fits the ethos of American physical anthropology as it grew in the first half of the twentieth century. Even that choleric anti-Darwinian and latter-day defender of romanticism, Jacques Barzun, would have to admit that his lament that "the Romantic order of diversity in unity had merely been wished for and had not come to pass [Barzun 1958:332]" would not apply to physical anthropology.

What Now?

The reader may well be driven to inquire, "Are things really all that bad?" The answer, of course, is "No, they are not." The average practicing physical anthro-pologist today is not primarily motivated by a desire to study human races. In teaching, the discussion of race is often saved until the end of the course and then mentioned with an awkward and slightly embarrassed bow to the traditions of the field. Others deal comfortably with real data from reference populations, whether these are given geographically or sociologically determined labels. Of course, those who focus on remote prehistoric populations are absolved from some of the embarrassment of the specific traditions mentioned previously, although they have been hampered by other traditions derived from the same source (Brace 1964b, 1981).

Historical assessment does no good if it simply turns into an exercise of self-flagellation. As we look down and behold our feet exposed in historical perspective, if we are concerned about the quantity of clay apparent in their composition, we can actually do something about providing a sturdier underpinning for the future yet to come. To exorcise the demons of our past, the first thing we must do is to realize that the race concept that we inherited was partially the result of Hrdlička's failure to confront the racism in the ethos of the French anthropology that he admired so uncritically. At the same time, we must recognize the "white-man's burden" strain of elitism promoted by the Harvard of Hooton's era, enhanced by a "Proper Boston, rooted in Anglophilia [Baltzell 1958:230]."

When we have confronted all this, we can abandon the race concept as a device for dealing with the biological nature of the humanity that is the object of study in our discipline. Instead, we can make an explicit virtue out of what in fact is a practical reality. Gene frequencies are figured as percentages of populations sampled, and the populations need only be identified as coming from a known area. In time, we can acquire gene frequency and trait manifestation data for the whole world. This we can do in relation to the intensity and duration of known or projected selective forces. In this way, we can take major steps toward dealing with the evolution of recent human populations.

What we have before us, then, is the prospect of applying to *Homo sapiens* the systematic perspective of Darwinian biology. It may seem curiously late in the history of science to be making a beginning at such an effort—a full century after Darwin's death—but the opportunity has yet to be exploited in systematic fashion, and it allows us the chance of dealing with major aspects of human variation with the excitement and enthusiasm that has tended to disappear from the well-ploughed fields of nonhuman zoology. The opportunity is ours, and if we don't sieze it, others will.

References

Bachman, J.
   1850   *The doctrine of the unity of the human race, examined on the principles of science.* Charleston, South Carolina: C. Canning.
   1854   Review of *Types of mankind,* edited by J. C. Nott and G. R. Gliddon. *Charleston Medical Journal* 9:627–659.
Baltzell, E. D.
   1958   *Philadelphia gentlemen.* Glencoe, Illinois: Free Press.

1979   *Puritan Boston and Quaker Philadelphia: Two Protestant ethics and the spirit of class authority and leadership.* New York: Free Press.

Barzun, J.
1937·   *Race: A study of modern superstition.* New York: Harcourt.
1958   *Darwin, Marx, Wagner: critique of a heritage* (second edition) Garden City, New York: Doubleday.
1965   *Race: a study in superstition* (second edition). New York: Harper.

Bendyshe, T.
1863–
1864   The history of anthropology. *Memoirs of the Anthropological Society of London* 1:335–458.
1865   *The Anthropological treatises of Johann Freidrich Blumenbach.* London: Longmans, Green.

Benedict, R.
1945   *Race: science and politics.* New York: Viking Press.

Bergson, H.
1907   *L'évolution créatrice.* Paris: Felix Alcan.

Bory de Saint-Vincent, J.
1827   *L'homme (Homo): essai zoologique sur le genre humain* (second edition, 2 vols.). Paris: Rey and Gravier.

Brace, C. L.
1964a   The concept of race. *Current Anthropology* 4:313–320.
1964b   The fate of the "classic" Neanderthals: a consideration of hominid catastrophism. *Current Anthropology* 5:3–43.
1974   The "ethnology" of Josiah Clark Nott. *Bulletin of the New York Academy of Medicine* 50:509–528.
1981   Tales of the phylogenetic woods: The evolution and significance of evolutionary trees. *American Journal of Physical Anthropology* 56:411–429.

Brace, C. L. and A. Montagu
1977   *Human evolution: an introduction to biological anthropology.* New York: Macmillan.

Broca, P.
1858   Mémoire sur l'hybridité en général, sur la distinctión des espéces animales et sur les métis obtenus par le croistment du lièvre et du lapin. *Journal de la Physiologie de l'Homme et des Animaux* 1:433–471, 684–729.
1859a   Mémoire sur l'hybridité en général sur a distinction des espècts animales et sur les métis obteuus par le croisement du lièvre et du lapin. *Journal de la Physiologie de l'Homme et des Animaux* 2:218–250, 345–396.
1859b   Des phénomènes d'hybridité dans le genre humain. *Journal de la Physiologie de l'Homme et des Animaux* 2:601–625.
1860a   Des phénomènes d'hybridité dans le genre humain. *Journal de la Physiologie de l'Homme et des Animaux* 3:392–439.
1860   *Recherches sur l'hybridité animal en général et sur l'hybridité humaine en particulier, considérées dans leurs rapports avec la question de la pluralité des espèces humaines.* Paris: J. Claye.
1862a   Discussion sur les Americains. *Bulletin de la Société d'Anthropologie de Paris.* 3:417–437.
1862b   La linquistique et l'anthropologie. *Bulletin de la Société d'Anthropologie de Paris* 3:243–319.
1870   Sur le transformisme. *Bulletin de la Society d'Anthropologie de Paris,* Series 2 5:168–242.
1871   *Mémoires d'anthropologie.* Paris: C. Reinwald.
1875   Instructions craniologiques et craniometriques. *Mémoires de la Societe d Anthropologie de Paris,* Series 2. 2:1–203.

Carlyle, T.
1853   *Occasional discourse on the nigger question.* London: T. Bosworth.

Chase, A.
1977   *The legacy of Malthus: the social costs of the new scientific racism.* New York: Knopf.

Coon, C. S.
1939   *The races of Europe.* New York: Macmillan.

1962   *The origin of races.* New York: Knopf.

1965   *The living races of man.* New York: Knopf.

Coon, C. S., S. M. Garn, and J. Birdsell

1950   *Races: a study of the problems of race formation in man.* Springfield, Illinois: Thomas.

Cotard, H.

1898   *La Pénsée de Claude Bernard.* Grenoble: Editions Françaises Nouvelles.

Darwin, C.

1859   *On the origin of species by means of natural selection, or the preservation of the favoured races in the struggle for life.* London: John Murray.

Deniker, J.

1880   Quelques observations et mensurations sur les Nubiens qui ont été exposés à Génève en aout 1880. *Bulletin de la Societe d'Anthropologie de Paris,* Series 3. **3**:594–603.

1892   Anthropologie et ethnologie (de l'Europe). *La Grand Encyclopedie* **16**:807–813.

1897   Les races de l'Europe. *Bulletin de la Societe d' Anthropologie de Paris,* 4 Series **8**:291–302.

1900   *Les races et les Péuples de la Térre: eléments d'anthropologie et d'ethnographie.* Paris: Schleicher frères.

Desmoulins, A. (1826) *Histoire naturelle des races humaines.* Paris: Mequignon-Marvis.

Durant, W., and A. Durant

1967   *Rousseau and revolution: the story of civilization,* Part 10. New York: Simon and Schuster.

Erickson, P. A.

1974a   The origins of physical anthropology. Unpublished Ph.D. Dissertation, Department of Anthropology, University of Connecticut, Storrs.

1974b   Racial determinism and nineteenth century anthropology. *Man* **9**:489–491.

Garn, S. M.

1965   *Human races.* (second edition). Springfield, Illinois: Thomas.

Gasman, D.

1971   *The Scientific origins of national socialism: social Darwinism in Ernst Haeckel and the German Monist League.* New York: Elsevier.

Gaudry, A.

1878   *Les enchainements du monde animal dans le temps géologiques: mammiferes tertiaires.* Paris: Masson.

Gibbes, R. W.

1851   Death of Samuel George Morton, M.D. *Charleston Medical Journal.* **6**:594–598.

Gossett, T. F.

1963   *Race, the history of an idea in America.* Dallas: Southern Methodist Press.

Haeckel, E.

1878   *Freie Wissenschaft und freie Lehre, Eine Entgegnung auf Rudolf Virchow's Munchener Rede uber Die Freiheit der Wissenschaft in modernen Staat.* Stuttgart: E. Schweizerbart'sche Verlagshandlung.

Haller, J. S. Jr.

1970   The species problem: nineteenth-century concepts of racial inferiority in the origin of man controversy. *American Anthropologist* **72**:1319–1329.

1971   *Outcasts from evolution: scientific attitudes of racial inferiority, 1859–1900.* Urbana: University of Illinois Press.

Hodge, F. W.

1912   Paul Topinard. *American Anthropologist* **14**:196–197.

Hook, A.

1975   *Scotland and America: a study of cultural relations, 1750–1835.* Glasgow: Blackie.

Hooton, E. A.

1939   *Crime and the man.* Cambridge, Massachusetts: Harvard University Press.

1946   *Up from the ape.* New York: Macmillan.

Howells, W. W.

1954   Obituary of Earnest Albert Hooton. *American Journal of Physical Anthropology* **12**:445–453.
Hrdlička, A.
    1918   Physical anthropology: its scope and aims; its history and present status in America. *American Journal of Anthropology* **1**:3–23, 133–182, 377–402.
    1919   *Physical anthropology, its scope and aims; its history and present status in the United States.* Philadelphia: Wistar Institute Press.
    1937   Review of race: a study of modern superstition by J. Barzun. *American Journal of Physical Anthropology* **23**:227.
Huxley, J. S.
    1940   *The new systematics.* Oxford: Clarendon.
Jordan, W.
    1965   *An essay on the causes of the variety of complexion and figure in the human species by S. S. Smith.* Cambridge, Massachusetts: Belknap Press.
Keith, A.
    1919   *Nationality and race from an anthropological point of view.* London: Oxford University Press.
    1931   *The place of prejudice in modern civilization (prejudice and politics).* London: Williams and Norgate.
    1935   The ordeal of Ernst Haeckel. *Rationalist Annual.* Pp. 3–12.
    1943   Carlyle and Darwin as interpreters of the truth. *Rationalist Annual.* Pp. 17–24.
    1946   *Evolution and ethics.* New York: Putnam.
    1950   *An autobiography.* London: Watts.
    1955   *Darwin revalued.* London: Watts.
Lasker, G. W.
    1964   Preface. *Yearbook of Physical Antrhopology* **9**:iii–v.
Livingstone, F. B.
    1962   On the non-existence of human races. *Current Anthropology* **3**:279–281.
Lovejoy, A. O.
    1936   *The great chain of being: a study of the history of an idea.* Cambridge, Massachusetts: Harvard University Press.
Lurie, E.
    1960   *Louis Agassiz: a life in science.* Chicago: University of Chicago Press.
Lyell, C.
    1863   *Geological evidences of the antiquity of man.* London: John Murray.
Marett, R. R.
    1937   Anthropology at Oxford. *Zeitschrift fuer Rassenkunde und die Gesamte Forschung am Menschen* **6**:243–244.
Mayr, E., and W. B. Provine
    1980   *The evolutionary synthesis: perspectives on the unification of biology.* Cambridge, Massachusetts: Harvard University Press.
Meigs, C. D.
    1851   *A memoir of S. G. Morton.* Philadelphia: Collins.
Montagu, M. F. A.
    1942   The genetical theory of race, and anthropological method. *American Anthropologist* **44**:369–375.
    1952   *Man's most dangerous myth: The fallacy of race.* New York: Harper.
    1965   *The idea of race.* Lincoln: University of Nebraska Press.
Morton, S. G.
    1839   *Crania Americana.* Philadelphia: Dobson.
    1844   *Crania Aegyptiaca.* Philadelphia: Penington.
    1847   Hybridity in animals, considered in reference to the unity of the human species. *American Journal of Science* Series 2 **3**:39–50, 203–212.

Nott, J. C.
    1849   *Two lectures on the connection between the biblical and physical history of man.* New York: Bartlett and Welford.
Nott, J. C., and G. R. Gliddon (editors)
    1854   *Types of mankind.* Philadelphia: Lippincott, Grambo.
Olson, E. C.
    1960   Morphology, paleontology and evolution. ın *The evolution of life,* edited by S. Tax. *Evolution after Darwin,* Vol. 1. Chicago: University of Chicago Press. Pp. 523–545.
Olson, R.
    1975   *Scottish philosophy and British physics, 1750–1880. A study in the foundations of Victorian scientific style.* Princeton, New Jersey: Princeton University Press.
Pasteur, G.
    1971   Evolution in France. *Science* **171**:751.
Patterson, H. S.
    1855   Memoir of the life and scientific labors of Samuel George Morton. In *Types of mankind,* edited by J. C. Nott and G. R. Gliddon. Philadelphia: Lippincott, Grambo. Pp. xvii–lvii.
Pouchet, G.
    1864   *De la pluralité des races Humaines: essai anthropologique* (second edition). Paris: Masson.
Pruner-Bey F.
    1862   Sur le rapport de M. Dally concernant les Américains. *Bulletin de la Societe d'Anthropologie de Paris* **3**:417–421, 430–433.
Radl, E.
    1930   *The history of biological theories.* London and New York: Oxford University Press.
Retzius, A. A.
    1860   Present state of ethnology in relation to the form of the human skull. Annual report of the Board of Regents of the Smithsonian Institute, 1859. Washington, D.C.: T. H. Ford. Pp. 251–270.
Ripley, W. Z.
    1897a   The racial geography of Europe. A sociological study. *Popular Science Monthly* **50**:454–468, 577–594, 757–780.
    1897b   The racial geography of Europe. A sociological study. *Popular Science Monthly* **51**:17–34, 192–209, 289–307, 433–453, 613–634, 721–739.
    1898   The racial geography of Europe. A sociological study. *Popular Science Monthly* **52**:49–68, 145–170, 304, 469–486, 591–608.
    1899   *The races of Europe: a sociological study.* New York: Appleton.
Rosenberg P.
    1974   *The seventh hero: Thomas Carlyle and the theory of radical activism.* Cambridge, Massachusetts: Harvard University Press.
Ruse, M.
    1981   Review of the evolutionary synthesis by E. Mayr and W. B. Provine. *Science* **211**:810–811.
Schiller, F.
    1979   *Paul Broca: Founder of French anthropology, explorer of the brain.* Berkeley: University of California Press.
Snow, C. P.
    1963   *The two cultures: and a second look* (second edition). New York: Mentor.
Spencer, F.
    1979   Aleš Hrdlička, M.D., 1869–1943. A chronicle of the life and work of an American physical anthropologist. Unpublished Ph.D. Dissertation, Department of Anthropology, University of Michigan, Ann Arbor.
    1981   The rise of academic physical anthropology in the United States (1850–1980): a historical review. *American Journal of Physical Anthropology* **56**:353–364.
Stanton, W.

1960   *The leopard's spots: scientific attitudes toward race in America, 1815–59.* Chicago: University of
          Chicago Press.

Stocking, G. W., Jr.
1968   *Race, culture, and evolution: essays in the history of anthropology.* New York: Free Press.

Topinard, P.
1876   *L'anthropologie.* Paris: C. Reinwald.
1879   De la notion de race en anthropologie. *Revue d'Anthropologie,* Series 2 **2**:589–660.
1885   *Elements d'anthropologie générale.* Paris: Delahaye and Lecrosnier.

Turner, W.
1884   Reports on the human crania and other bones of the skeletons collected during the voyage
          of H. M. S. Challenger. I. Crania. *Challenger Reports,* Part 19, Zoology **10**:1–130.

Vallois, H. V.
1940   Le laboratoire Broca. *Bulletin de la Société d'Anthropologie de Paris,* Series 9 **11**:1–18.
1952   Monophyletism and polyphyletism in man. *South African Journal of Science* **49**:69–79.
1953   Race. In *Anthropology today.* edited by A. L. Kroeber Chicago: University of Chicago Press.
          Pp. 145–162.
1966   More on the fate of the "classic" Neanderthals *Current Anthropology* **7**:205–208.

Virchow, R.
1877   *Die Freiheit der Wissenschaft im modernen Staat.* Berlin: Wiegandt, Hempel and Parey.
1880   Address by the President. *Verhandlungen der Deutschen Gesellschaft fuer Anthropologie,
          Ethnologie und Urgeschichte* **11**:22–24.
1882   Darwin et l'anthropologie. *Revue Scientifique de la France et de l'Etranger,* Series 3 **3**:417–421.

Virey, J. J.
1801   *Histoire naturelle genre humain.* Paris: Crochard.

Wolpoff, M. H.
1980   *Paleoanthropology.* New York: Knopf.

2

The Effects of Funding Patterns on the Development of Physical Anthropology

Thelma S. Baker and Phyllis B. Eveleth

The considerable effects of patterns of funding on the development of American science have been studied by a number of scholars. The research has included investigations of the contributions of individual patrons (Miller 1970), philanthropic institutions (Reingold 1979), private industry (Galambos 1979), and the federal government (Kidd 1959). It has been suggested in these analyses that the source and purpose of funds made available to scientists·has influenced the development and direction of scientific disciplines. In this chapter we propose to examine how funding patterns have influenced the development of physical anthropology from 1930 to the present in order to contribute to the understanding of the history of the discipline being reviewed in this volume. Our data were collected from a broad range of primary and secondary sources, including institutional histories (Brew 1966a, b, 1968), individual archives (Carpenter 1932–1972), key informant interviews, private foundation reports (Sontag 1960; Wenner–Gren Foundation 1952, 1963), and disciplinary histories (Penniman 1965; Stocking 1968; Voegelin 1953) as well as federal reports.

We have divided the past five decades into three periods: the early period, comprising the years from 1930 to 1950; the middle period, which includes the years from 1951 to 1962; and the late period from 1963 to 1980. For each period, we will review private and public major sources of support for the discipline and assess, on the basis of amount and direction of support, the influence of funding on disciplinary development. We have chosen to investigate funding for three fields of disciplinary inquiry: primatology, paleobiology, and human population biology.

A HISTORY OF AMERICAN
PHYSICAL ANTHROPOLOGY, 1930–1980

The Early Period 1930–1949

From the 1930s to the beginning of World War II, funding for scientific research in the United States continued in the tradition of the early twentieth century, with support coming from a spectrum of private donors, new research universities, community institutions, and public appropriations. During this early period, there was little assurance of continued long-term support from any single source of public or private funds (Miller 1970). In physical anthropology, however, the influence of such scholars as Franz Boas, Aleš Hrdlička, T. Wingate Todd, and Earnest A. Hooton encouraged the participation of museums and universities in the funding of the activities of the emerging discipline, whereas the concern and intellectual curiosity of philanthropists, such as Samuel Fels and Axel Wenner-Gren, initiated an ongoing commitment from private resources (Darnell 1974; Stocking 1968).

Primatology

Funding for private research studies in the 1930s was found through the entrepreneurial efforts of the great early scholars in primatology. Research expeditions to French Guinea, the Belgian Congo, Panama, the Canal Zone, and Costa Rica were organized to study the anatomy, morphology, and behavior of nonhuman primates. These expeditions were supported financially and logistically through a combination of university, foundation, private industry, and governmental sources. The studies of Yerkes (1929/1970), Nissen (1931), Bingham (1932), Schultz (1937 [see Schultz 1963:Bibliography]), and Carpenter (1932–1972) were funded by Yale University through its Laboratories of Comparative Psychobiology, The Johns Hopkins Laboratory of Physical Anthropology, the New York Zoological Society, the Carnegie Institution of Washington, the Pasteur Institute of Paris, and the United Fruit Company (see Ribnick, present volume, for further details). The federal government provided support mainly through the National Research Council Fellowships in the Biological Sciences, which provided salary support, and the Committee for Research in the Problems of Sex, which funded studies of the reproductive biology of primates (Carpenter 1934, 1935).

Harold J. Coolidge, Jr., Secretary of the American Committee for International Wild Life Protection, was primarily responsible for coordinating funding sources for the Asiatic Primate Expedition of 1937, which he organized with Adolph Schultz and C. R. Carpenter. The purpose of the expedition was to study the behavior of gibbons and orangutans in Siam, Sumatra, and Borneo and to collect anatomical and taxonomic specimens of primates (Carpenter 1939). Sherwood L. Washburn, a graduate student on the expedition, commented on Coolidge's resourcefulness in eliciting funds for the expeditions (S. L. Washburn, personal communication 1981). Carpenter's journal notes that of the $5800 that he was to expend on the expedition, $1500 of his salary came from Bard College, $1000 from the Social Science Research Council, $2300 from Columbia University's Social Science Research Council, and $1000 from Coolidge personally (Carpenter 1932–1972). Additional funds were provided by two of Harvard's museums, Comparative Zoology and the Peabody, as well as grants from the Carnegie Institution of Washington, the Netherlands Indian Society for Natural Preservation (Java), and the Netherlands Committee for International Nature Protection (Amsterdam) (Carpenter 1938).

In later years, 1947–1949, the Wenner-Gren Foundation for Anthropological Research funded four individual research projects in primatology, committing a modest 4% of its physical anthropology research expenditure by supporting the ongoing studies of Adolph Schultz and Ashley Montagu, who were also supported by their respective academic institutions (Wenner-Gren Foundation 1952).

Aside from support to individual scholars through the National Research Council, we did not find evidence of primary research support for primate studies by the federal government during this period.

Paleobiology

The Department of Anthropology of the United States National Museum (USNM) of Natural History has a long tradition of paleobiology research. Aleš Hrdlička was the first physical anthropologist in the department, arriving there in 1903. Prior to World War II, the USNM supported a number of expeditions to Alaska led by Hrdlička. One of the purposes of these was to gather skeletal material for the collections. Before his death in 1943, he finished his major reference work, *Catalog of Human Crania in the United States National Museum Collections*, representing 7500 nonwhite crania (Smithsonian Institution 1930–1979).

The USNM had been conducting research on early man in Latin America before World War II (Stewart 1952). Matthew Stirling discovered 52 skulls buried in pottery vessels during an expedition to Cerro de Las Mesas, Mexico. Marshall T. Newman worked with scientists from the Institute of Andean Research in studying the skeletons from the archaeological sites of Supé, Ancon, and Pachacamac. T. Dale Stewart also contributed to the craniology of South America with studies on cranial deformity. The help of the North Americans in research in Latin America was soon terminated by the onset of the war, and anthropologists perforce had to turn their energies to work within the United States.

Private sources of support for work in paleobiolgy in the prewar period came from private museums and university departments of anthropology (Brew 1966b; Darnell 1970; Ross 1979). The Peabody Museum at Harvard supported regional expeditions in all subdisciplines of anthropology. From the early 1930s, data were collected on prehistoric populations in the United States and Middle and South America as well as the Near East, Asia, and Oceania. In describing the expeditions and research in physical anthropology funded by the Peabody, Brew noted that the archaeological expeditions included studies of skeletal material and that the ethnological expeditions often included the anthropometry of living populations (Brew 1966a).

Among the most memorable of these expeditions was the one to Iran and Iraq, which was supported jointly by the Peabody Museum, the Field Museum in Chicago, the American Museum of Natural History (AMNH), and the University of Pennsylvania. In addition to museum support, university departments of anthropology became major contributors to the research by providing staff salaries and laboratory and library facilities as well as small grant support. Actual dollar expenditures from these sources are not available; however, the relative contribution of museums, foundations, and university departments may be estimated somewhat from the publications in the *American Journal of Physical Anthropology* (*AJPA*) (Goldstein 1940). From all appearances, three expeditions were museum- or foundation-supported (the USNM, the AMNH, and the Carnegie Institution of Washington), and seven were supported by university departments of anthropology (Washington University at St. Louis, Case Western Reserve, Columbia, Harvard, Yale, Tulane, and the Johns Hopkins University).

Immediately after the war, the Wenner-Gren Foundation (called the Viking Fund during that era) began its long-term support of research in paleobiology, and in a period of 6 years, from 1944 to 1950, funded 18 major projects, allocating 46% of its physical anthropology budget ($90,000) to this topical area (Wenner-Gren Foundation 1963).

Human Population Biology

Prior to and during World War II, the federal government supported only a minor proportion of scientific research. There were no large competitive research grant programs, and much of the federally funded research in physical anthropology was carried out under contract. To give some idea of the early activity, the first National Institutes of Health (NIH) research grants-in-aid to universities and individuals were awarded in 1937 by the National Cancer Institute for basic and clinical research (NIH–OAM 1976; Oakleaf 1961), the National Science Foundation (NSF) was not established until 1950 (NSF 1978), and the Smithsonian pre- and postdoctoral fellowship program did not begin until 1960.

During this period, the federal government did support a number of anthropological studies that were related to the war and military personnel. These were mostly involved in collecting anthropometric data (Baker 1953; Wulsin 1948).

The first sustained efforts in the United States in human engineering took place during the war, mostly by Hooton's students (or former students) at Harvard. Data were collected on body size and dimensions of the military, and the results were applied in designing military clothing, oxygen masks, and airplane cockpits (Damon *et al.* 1966). Anthropometric surveys were supported by the United States Army Quartermaster Corps, the United States Air Force, the Department of the

Navy, the Veterans Administration, and the United States Public Health Service (USPHS).

These studies were concerned with the relation of human body size to military aircraft and equipment. In the United States Air Force study, data were collected to guide the designers of aircraft and flying equipment. The concept of the functional man was developed by Albert Damon and his colleagues, which considered not only normal human variations in size and proportions but also the space requirements and working area in the aircraft and the limitations on function imposed by equipment and clothing (Randall *et al.* 1946). This approach involved the development of a new set of functional body measurements of the human body in action that found joint funding from the Harvard School of Public Health and the American Heart Association.

The USNM also conducted some research on living human populations. Hrdlička traveled to Alaska and measured Eskimos; Newman evaluated the physical status of Okinawans on Ryukya and continued his investigations on the nutrition of Native Americans; Stewart advised the Naval Medical Research Institute on cockpit design and anthropometric methods. During the war, the USNM Division of Physical Anthropology provided the Office of Strategic Services with photographs of various Asiatic physical types and data on body size for Europeans and Asiatics (Smithsonian Institution 1930–1979).

Following World War II, anthropologists used their skills to identify human skeletal remains for the military (see Thompson, present volume). This provided a unique opportunity to examine thousands of skeletons of known age, sex, race, and stature; sometimes clinical histories were available as well (Kerley 1978).

The initiative for population surveys began before World War II. The United States Department of Agriculture's (USDA) Bureau of Home Economics did an anthropometric survey of women from 1939 to 1940, to collect data for garment manufacturing and pattern makers (O'Brien and Shelton 1941). They also conducted with the Works Progress Administration (WPA) an anthropometric survey of children (White 1978). The Office of Education, Department of Health, Education and Welfare contracted with the University of Michigan to do functional body measurements of children to be used in designing school equipment (Martin 1955).

In the postwar period attention was again paid to the civilian population when reference data on body dimensions were collected to be used in the manufacture of vehicles. The studies of Damon and Stoudt were pioneering applications of anthropometry to the design of trucks and buses (Damon *et al.* 1966).

In 1946, the National Mental Health Act established a broad program of grants for research and training. Anthropological research applications were funded under this program. However, the federal government actually was supporting rather little research during this period compared to its considerable participation in the 1950s and 1960s, and research on living human populations was funded largely from the private sector. For example, Harvard's Peabody Museum sponsored 20 major anthropometric studies from 1928 to 1939 as well as 9 on population comparisons and numerous studies on the relationship of morphology and behavior, morphology and diet, race and criminal behavior, and secular trends in growth. Research was conducted in all regions of the world from Abyssinia to Tibet, and on native populations in habitats ranging from Albania to the Chicago World's Fair. The anthropological studies by Carleton S. Coon in the Near East (Coon 1963), Gordon T. Bowles in China and Tibet, and Henry Field in Iran and Iraq are examples of joint expeditions that collected archaeological, ethnological, and anthropometric data on both living and prehistoric populations. During this time, the Peabody Museum funded the initiation of W. W. Howells's long-term research in the Pacific and Joseph Birdsell's research in Australia (Brew 1966b). Comparable research was being funded by the AMNH Department of Anthropology, the Bernice P. Bishop Museum in Hawaii, and other major university departments of anthropology.

Three private funding sources are of special interest here since they provided a counterbalance to the generous resources of the USNM, of which primary research activity was paleobiology. The Carnegie Institution of Washington supported research in the Pacific and Joseph Birdsell's research in Australia (Brew 1966b). the Fels Research Institute, through its Department of Physical Growth, emphasized the study of longitudinal growth as an important research area in living human populations. The Wenner-Gren Foundation, for example, allocated almost 50% of its expenditure in physical anthropology from 1944 to 1950 to the study of living populations (Wenner-Gren Foundation 1952).

In addition to support for research, the funding of related activities was an important influence on the discipline's development. The Wenner-Gren Foundation perceived its role in supporting anthropological research as a broader one than its title would indicate. The Foundation not only supported scholarly research through its individual grants program, but also provided funds for education, communication, facilities, and travel. These other activities were especially important in the period immediately following the end of World War II since academic development of the discipline—such as the training of graduate students, the building and equipping of laboratories, and the acquisition of library holdings—had come to a standstill from 1941 to 1944. Two kinds of foundation-supported activities that had special significance for physical anthropology were inaugurated during this period: the Supper Conference and the Summer Seminars in Physical Anthropology. Each session of the Supper Conference was devoted to the discussion of a single topic in anthropology. Of the 100 conferences held from 1944 to 1951, 18 of these were concerned with physical anthropology. Representative topics and speakers were S. L. Washburn, 1946, "The Biological Basis of Measurement"; W. M. Cobb, 1946, "A Graphic Approach to Compleat Anatomy"; W. M. Krogman, 1947, "Contributions of Physical Anthropology to Pediatrics and Orthodontics"; W. C. Dupertuis, 1948, "Recent Trends in Constitutional Anthropology"; and J. S. Huxley, 1951, "Biological Evolution and Human History" (Wenner-Gren Foundation 1952).

A major influence on the future of the discipline were the Summer Seminars in Physical Anthropology, organized by Washburn, then Secretary of the American

Association of Physical Anthropologists (AAPA). The seminars were funded by the Foundation and were conducted under the auspices of the Columbia University Summer School. Each year from 1945 to 1952, leading professional physical anthropologists and graduate students met to discuss topics in the discipline for 6 weeks of the summer. The topics for the first seminar included reports of research on fossil man, living human populations, and methodology. Subsequent seminars reviewed the year's accomplishment in research in physical anthropology and provided training in new methods and techniques. It was Washburn's hope that the discipline as a whole would benefit from the seminars, and with the help of the Foundation, he inaugurated the publication of seminar results in the *Yearbook of Physical Anthropology* (Lasker 1945, 1973).

In summary, the early period was characterized by major support for research in two areas—paleobiology and living human populations. The joint anthropological expedition, funded from both private and federal resources, provided a descriptive data bank on living and extinct populations that was to be mined in future years. Since funding sources had not yet developed the clearly defined research missions of the next periods, growth in topical areas reflected the interests of individual scholars and their ingenuity in pursuing funding sources.

The Middle Period 1950–1965

The Second World War had a profound effect on scientific research in the United States. Numerous studies were carried out on military personnel and war plant employees and, as stated previously, physical anthropologists were prominent in these. The impetus in research resulted because the federal government was providing direct health services to military personnel and dependents and had to acquire relevant knowledge in order to do so (NIH–OAM 1976). The wartime health experience showed the enormous possibilities of research, and the postwar years saw a significant expansion of scientific research, with Congress playing an increasingly important role. This resulted in the most extensive support of research undertaken by any government.

In 1950, National Science Foundation (NSF) was established to promote and advance scientific progress in the United States. The NSF supports, but does not conduct, scientific research and education projects (The NIH both supports *and* conducts research). The NSF Anthropology Program, which includes physical anthropology, having originally been part of the Social Science Research Program, is now part of the Behavioral and Neural Sciences Division. Population biology and the physiological ecology program are under the Environmental Biology Program (NSF 1978).

In the 1950s, NSF supported graduate education as well as dissertation research for predoctoral students. Today, NSF supports research only; the grants last up to

24 months and are intended to improve the scientific quality of the doctoral dissertation.

Primatology

In the 1950s, several groups were concerned that the United States had no long-term primate research facilities, although private research facilities, such as Yerkes, did exist. An organizational committee was set up to plan and review the centers that had been proposed. In 1960, Congress appropriated $2 million to NIH to establish the first primate colonies in the United States. Initially they were used to study heart disease in relation to heredity during the life span of the animals. By 1962, seven centers were established as part of a long-range coordinated effort to use the primate model in studying human disease. Today they are used in research in reproductive biology, population control, mother–infant relationships, infectious disease, cardiovascular diseases, and diseases of the central nervous system (NIH–DRR 1968).

The National Science Foundation supported some primate research at this time (i.e., the 1960s), but not as much as it would later, in the 1970s. Studies that received NSF grants were those of Russell H. Tuttle on function and evolution of the hands in Anthropoidea, Melvin Moss on the morphology of the primate pelvis, and Sherwood Washburn and Irven DeVore on primate behavior. The latter's was the first award listed in the NSF grant records that dealt with primates. After that, primate research gained in importance. Both NIH and NSF supported William Montagna's studies on the structure and function of primate skin (NSF n.d.).

In the private sector, Wenner-Gren supported 10 primate studies using about 7% of its research budget.

Paleobiology

During the period from 1950 to 1965, NSF funded Edward Lanning's study of early man in South America, Alphonse Riesenfeld's research on upright posture and bone formation, Shutter's discovery of Pleistocene Man at Tule Springs, L. S. B. Leakey's work at Olduvai Gorge, Olaf Prufer s study of paleo-Indian remains, and Ralph Solecki's excavation's in Nubia and Shanidar (NSF n.d.). Support for the Shanidar expeditions in the late 1950s and the 1960s also came from the USNM, and Columbia University and NSF supported a conference with the National Academy of Sciences on the recovery of Pleistocene fossils.

Plans were underway to rehabilitate and modernize the USNM exhibition halls. In 1952, the Museum was putting together a new exhibit using the face masks Hrdlička had made depicting the races of the world. Congress appropriated money for the rehabilitation project in 1954. In 1963, J. Lawrence Angel became Curator of Physical Anthropology and continued to pursue, with Donald Ortner, his research in chronic disease, aging, and mortality among prehistoric populations, ancient Greeks, Eskimos, and whites in the United States (Smithsonian Institution 1930–1979).

During the decade, 1951–1961, the Wenner-Gren Foundation committed itself to the major support of paleoanthropology; 61% of its research budget for that period supported 47 research projects. Additional support was provided for conferences on early man and for the publication of results. The first conference, held at Burg Wartenstein, was organized by Washburn and the topic was the social life of early man. A review of the projects supported by the Wenner-Gren Foundation shows that every major scholar in paleoanthropology was either partially or totally funded by the Wenner-Gren Foundation. It should be noted that federal support was not limited in those early years to scholars of American origin. Similarly, the Wenner-Gren Foundation included in its mission the support of international scholars as well as those from the United States.

Human Population Biology

The NSF Anthropology Program expanded in the late 1950s and the 1960s, and physical anthropology research was part of this. In fiscal years 1958 and 1960, out of a total of 30 and 49 grants, respectively (mostly in archaeology), the physical anthropologists received 3 grants each year. In fiscal year 1965, they were awarded 5. The studies on human populations that were supported in these years were those of M. T. Newman, J. B. Birdsell, W. S. Laughlin, and F. S. Hulse.

In 1966, NSF and the Wenner-Gren Foundation supported the "Conference on the Biology of Human Variation," chaired by Josef Brožek. The aim of the conference was "to provide a *broad picture* of human variation [Brožek 1966:502]," including biometrics and mechanisms of variability in populations and individuals and their implications for biomedicine. The conference increased the visibility of human variation as an area for study, especially in relation to such diseases as coronary heart disease and hypertension (Brožek 1966).

The National Institutes of Health exanded greatly during these years. Funding for some physical anthropologists was provided by the National Heart Institute, the National Institute of Dental Research, the National Institute of Arthritis and Metabolic Diseases, and the National Institute of Neurological Diseases and Blindness, all established between 1948 and 1950. In 1962, both the National Institute of Child Health and Human Development and the National Institute of General Medical Sciences were established (NIH–OAM 1976). Human genetic projects and training grants for anthropologists were supported by the latter institute.

In the 10 years from 1950 to 1960, NIH extramural research funds increased sevenfold, from $6 million to $42 million. In 1957, Congress more than doubled the NIH appropriation since NIH was not able to fund all approved grant applications. At the same time, they reviewed the procedures underlying approvals to assure adherence to high standards and agreed to pay all approved grants (Oakleaf 1961). Today, NIH can no longer fund all approved grant applications. The number of applications to NIH has continued to increase as availability of resources has become better known. President Eisenhower asked for assurances that federal funds would not be substituting for funds from nonfederal sources earmarked for research and training (Oakleaf 1961). However, that apparently is what was actually occurring in anthropology as well as in biomedical research. In 1940, 7% of the medical research was supported by federal funds; in 1950, 41%; and in 1960, 53% (NIH–OPPE–DRG 1980).

Some physical anthropologists felt that they did not reap sufficient rewards from this boom (Kelso 1972). The reason given is that although physical anthropology was considered a part of the social sciences, to social scientists the physical anthropologists were biologists. Thus they felt they suffered in the review of their applications to NIH.

The National Institutes of Health began supporting pre- and postdoctoral fellowships in 1947 for training in those biological sciences basic to health research. After NSF was created in 1950, the predoctoral program was transferred to it; however, the NSF funds were more limited, and because more disciplines were competing, fewer awards were made. In 1955, Congress reacted to this unsatisfactory situation and reinstated the NIH predoctoral program in medical areas. In 1955, 437 awards were made by NIH, whereas 1021 were granted in 1960. Some physical anthropologists benefited from these fellowships.

The postwar period saw a continuation of anthropometric studies of military personnel, both in the United States and in other countries, funded by the United States Air Force, Navy, and Marine Corps (Clauser et al. 1972). In fact, there was considerable activity overseas as Americans expanded their outlook abroad. Many developing countries were surveyed in studies on body size and nutritional status under United States federal programs organized by the Interdepartmental Committee on Nutrition and National Defense (ICNND). Anthropologists were involved in some of these studies, which were located in Ecuador, Chile, Bolivia, Colombia, Lebanon, Burma, Uruguay, East Pakistan, Jordan, Malaya, and Paraguay; some Native American groups were included as well (ICNND 1964). Anthropometric surveys were carried out in Turkey, Greece, and Italy in 1960–1961 sponsored by the NATO Advisory Group for Aeronautical Research and Development (Hertzberg et al. 1963). In Central America, the Institute of Nutrition of Central America and Panama (INCAP) was established as a center of the Pan American Health Organization and received partial support from NIH (see Beall; Haas; Little; all in the present volume).

In 1959, surveys were initiated on the American population by the United States Public Health Service (USPHS) in the National Health Examination Surveys (HES). The first cycle sampled a statistical representative group of American adults and was completed in 1962 (Stoudt et al. 1965). In 1963, the HES involved a variety of somatic and physiological examinations aimed at assessing growth and developmental status among children (Hamill et al. 1970).

Studies in human adaptability (HA) during this period were supported by contract from the United States Department of Defense, for example, the work of Paul T. Baker and his associates on the biological effects of high altitude on populations in Peru (Baker 1978), T. H. Hammel's Chilean expedition, and Carleton S. Coon's trips around the world to collect material for his book *The Origin of Races* (1963). Wenner-Gren and NSF also supported Coon.

Marshall T. Newman, the Associate Curator of the National Museum at that time, was involved with biological and nutritional studies in Vicos, Peru. He collaborated with Peruvian scientists and had support from the USPHS and UNICEF. He was also involved in analyzing the relationship of body surface area to climate (Smithsonian Institution 1930–1979).

In 1965, J. Lawrence Angel of the USNM reported on body composition, serum, and anthropometric and anthroposcopic changes related to aging in a restudy of senior Jefferson Medical College students whom he had first examined as freshmen. He also collaborated with Paul T. Baker on old age changes in bone density.

The Atomic Energy Commission at this time started the support of its long-term research interest in Japan, carrying out studies in human genetics, growth, and physique and dental development (see Weiss and Chakraborty, in the present volume). The Fels Research Institute, under the leadership of Stanley M. Garn, conducted a variety of studies on growth in children (Sontag 1960). Wenner-Gren funded 37 projects, (32% of its budget) on living populations, and provided support for a range of activities connected with the Darwin centennial as well as continued support for the publication of the *Yearbook of Physical Anthropology* (Wenner-Gren Foundation 1963, 1965).

The Late Period 1965–1980

Whereas the middle period was marked by a great increase in scientific research accompanied by an equal increase in funding, the late period shows a leveling off of the funding.

Primatology

There was a surge in primate research during the 1970s (while HA projects decreased in number). Some NSF-supported projects were those of Donald S. Sade on social behavior; David Pilbeam, Charles E. Oxnard, and Sherwood L. Washburn on evolution; John Buettner-Janusch on hemoglobins; James A. Gavan, Patrick Dwyer, Jack T. Stern and Russell H. Tuttle on primate locomotion; Clifford Jolly on genetics; and Christine M. Duggleby and Donald S. Sade, using the Cayo

Santiago macaque population (NSF n.d.). The Cayo Santiago population of free-ranging *Macaca mulatta* is a valuable resource for primatologists doing observational studies on behavior (see Ribnick, in the present volume). It is administered by the Caribbean Primate Research Center in San Juan, Puerto Rico, and is supported by the NIH Division of Research Resources (NIH–DRR) (NIH–DRR 1968, 1971).

The Wenner-Gren Foundation organized the Burg Wartenstein conferences to encourage interdisciplinary communication in scientific research. From 1958 to 1980, 86 conferences in anthropology were convened, 27 of which were concerned with physical anthropology. From these conferences, 21 major books were published (Burg Wartenstein Papers 1958–1980). Seven conferences were devoted to primate studies; the first was organized in 1965 by Phyllis Jay, the topic being primate behavior. The conferences on primate studies stimulated interest in research in behavior, social organization, communication, and phylogeny. In the 1970s, Wenner-Gren funded 24 projects in primate studies, amounting to 20% of the individual grants budget.

Paleobiology

Beginning in 1963, the Bone Biology Project was initiated at the USNM under Donald Ortner (Ortner 1976). Gross, histological, and molecular anatomy of skeletal material has been examined under this project in order to learn more about the history of disease in human populations. In addition, a registry of skeletal diseases has been developed with medical documentation. In the early stages, from 1969 to 1973, this program was supported by the National Institute of Child Health and Human Development. Prior to that, the Smithsonian Research Foundation was assisting the work on bone tissue dating through nitrogen decay rates. By fiscal year 1972, the Bone Biology Project was a line item for the Smithsonian budget and still is supported as such at about $50,000 per year (D. J. Ortner, personal communication 1980).

The National Science Foundation continued to support many studies on early man during this period, such as those of Edward P. Lanning in South America, William M. Bass on the Plains Indians, Jesse D. Jennings in Utah, Glynn Isaac in Kenya, R. McNett in the Delaware Valley, Phillip Rightmire in East Africa, Stephen Molnar on dentition, Ralph Holloway on the evolution of the human brain, Jane E. Buikstra on cortical bone, Donald C. Johanson in Ethiopia, Opdyke in Pakistan, Timothy White in Tanzania, and Alan Walker in Kenya. From the 1950s to the 1970s, there was little change in the amount of research supported by NSF in paleontology (NSF n.d.; see also Boaz, in the present volume).

In the private sector, the Wenner-Gren Foundation continued its funding of individual scientists and during the 1970s funded 65 projects on early man, amounting to 54% of its research budget. The National Geographic Society undertook the financing of the Leakey investigations in East Africa.

Human Population Biology

In 1964, the International Biological Program (IBP) was formally established to encourage international scientific collaboration (see Little, in the present volume). The Burg Wartenstein Conference in 1964, organized by Joseph Weiner, summarized the state of knowledge on the biology of human adaptability and provided the organizing framework for the HA Section of the IBP (Baker and Weiner 1966). The HA Section promoted and coordinated many investigations by physical anthropologists. Paul T. Baker played both a national and international role as the United States Convenor in planning the scope of the HA program with J. S. Weiner in the United Kingdom (Baker and Weiner 1966). According to E. B. Worthington (1975), the United States entered the IBP somewhat hesitantly. There were some questions from the Americans as to the aims. Margaret Mead had tried to get the HA Section changed to a program in the social sciences but this change was not accepted because it was considered quite outside the province of the human biologists.

Both NSF and NIH supported various projects under the IBP—such as the high altitude studies of Paul T. Baker and his associates; the Harvard Solomon Islands project of W. W. Howells, S. T. Damon, J. Friedlander and E. Giles; the population genetics of South American Indians under J. V. Neel and N. Chagnon and others (Eveleth and Tanner 1971); and the analysis of variation in human growth by P. B. Eveleth and J. M. Tanner (1976). As the IBP terminated in 1974, efforts were made to transfer some of the projects to the Man and the Biosphere (MAB) Program (see Little, in the present volume). In fiscal year 1975, NSF sponsored the Workshop for Planning and Development of the Man and the Biosphere Program.

In the 1970s physical anthropology formed an increasingly important part of the NSF Anthropology Program. In fiscal year 1970, 10% of approximately 145 awards were in physical anthropology; in 1975, 23%; and in 1979, 27%. The latter comprised 35 awards out of a total of approximately 128 (NSF n.d.). This was a remarkable increase over the 5 grants out of a total of 122 given in fiscal year 1965, which reflects the increasing interest in physical anthropology. As stated previously, the 1970s generally was a period of leveling off in federal spending on research programs following the postwar boom period of the 1950s and 1960s. It is interesting to note that in spite of the overall plateau, physical anthropology at NSF was still growing. Research in human living populations became relatively less important, however, while primatological research increased.

There was new activity in human growth and physique and the health of Americans. The National Center for Health Statistics (USPHS) conducted the third cycle of the Health Examination Survey from 1963 to 1970. This was followed by the expanded Health and Nutrition Examination Surveys (HANES I and II) from 1971 to 1974 (Engel et al. 1978) and from 1977 to 1980. Several anthropologists have acted as consultants for the surveys, helping train the measuring teams in anthropometry, and participating in the analyses and publications.

The Center for Disease Control (CDC), USPHS, conducted the Ten State

Nutrition Survey in the 1970s. Once again, anthropologists were awarded contracts for analysis of the growth data. The CDC also has been carrying out growth and nutrition studies in Nepal and Vietnam.

The trend during the middle period toward ever-increasing federal support of research is evidenced by the fact that in 1960, 53% of medical research was funded by the federal government and that this had risen to 60% in 1969 and was still at that level in 1979 (NIH–OPPE–DRG 1980). In the latter year, private nonprofit foundations, voluntary health agencies, and such accounted for only 8% of the total research spending, whereas industry paid for 29%. At the same time, however, the private nonprofit agencies and the educational institutions were actually the doers, performing 49% of the research.

The federal government was doing only 18%, and industry 28% (NIH–OPPE–DRG 1980). This reflects the increased government support of research being done outside by universities, the institutions that had at one time supported much of the work with their own funds.

There was no significant increase in the amount in constant dollars that was paid for research from 1965 to 1980. In current dollars the amount increased 100% reflecting the rising inflationary trend.

The National Institutes of Health is the principal federal agency supporting health research and development, with 68% of the total federal activity in health. One of the authors (PBE) has looked at the participation of physical anthropologists in NIH grants and contracts (Eveleth 1981). In fiscal year 1975, physical anthropologists were principal investigators on 58 research projects grants, 8 contracts, and 20 projects in program project grants from NIH. They had 9 grants from other USPHS Institutes. One may assume that other physical anthropologists in addition to the principal investigators were also active on some of these grants. They may also have been active on grants to other nonanthropologist principal investigators, but this information is not archived on the NIH data file.

The institutes with the most grants to physical anthropologists were the National Institute of Child Health and Human Development, the National Institute of Dental Research, the National Heart, Lung, and Blood Institute and the National Institute of General Medical Sciences. The Division of Research Resources awards a Biomedical Research Support Grant to institutions receiving over $200,000 in NIH money. Many young anthropologists have been funded from this award, which is administered by the relevant universities. By tabulating the credits in the 1980 American Association of Physical Anthropologists (AAPA) meeting abstracts, it was found that more than half the 52 different NIH grants cited were from the Division of Research Resources and the National Institute of Dental Research.

A comparison of the NIH figures with those of NSF revealed that NIH has been funding more physical anthropologists, at least in 1975 and 1978, than NSF. In 1978, NIH made 45 awards to anthropologists, as compared to 22 from NSF. (This NIH figure does not include contracts or program projects.) In 1975, NIH funded 58 active grants to anthropologists while NSF funded 14. Moreover, the NIH awards tended to be larger and of longer duration that NSF ones (Eveleth 1981).

One of the major trends in funding throughout the past half century has been the decrease in research support by the private foundations and the universities and the unprecedented increase in funding by the federal government. Associated with this was the effort by the government to promote research in specific directions through funding and conference mechanisms. Physical anthropologists passed from what was principally a data-collection period into one oriented toward specific problems, many of which were identified by the federal government and were related to health research. Congress and nonscientists have frequently specified what those areas should be and have even made some effort to coordinate research.

We may soon see a reversal in the form of a shift to more private support of research. As a result of the restricted federal funds, efforts are beginning to be made to encourage collaborative support by the private sector.

Acknowledgments

We would like to thank the following individuals for their contributions: Lita Osmundsen and the staff of Wenner-Gren Foundation for providing information on the various aspects of funding for physical anthropology; Leon Stout, curator of the C. R. Carpenter papers, for providing access to the as yet uncataloged papers; JoAnn Martz of Pennsylvania State University for assistance in the tabulation of data; Mary Green for providing printouts from the Anthropology Program, National Science Foundation; Dr. Donald Ortner of the Smithsonian Institution; and Marie Morris for typing the final manuscript.

References

Baker, P. T.
    1953   *The effects of a hot–dry climate on gross morphology.* Lawrence, Massachusetts: Quartermaster Climate Research Laboratory.
    1978   *The Biology of high altitude peoples.* Cambridge: Cambridge University Press.
Baker, P. T., and J. S. Weiner (editors)
    1966   *The biology of human adaptability.* Oxford: Clarendon.
Bingham, H. C.
    1932   Gorillas in a native habitat. *Carnegie Institution of Washington* Publication No. 426, Washington, D.C.
Brew, J. O.
    1966a   *Early days of the Peabody Museum at Harvard University.* Cambridge, Massachusetts: Peabody Museum, Harvard University.
    1966b   *People and projects of the Peabody Museum, 1866–1966.* Cambridge, Massachusetts: Peabody Museum of Harvard University.
    1968   (editor) *One hundred years of anthropology.* Cambridge, Massachusetts: Harvard University Press.

Brožek, J. (editor)
  1966   The biology of human variation (symposium). *Annals of the New York Academy of Sciences* **134**:497–1066.
Burg Wartenstein Papers
  1958–   Unpublished data on file at the Wenner-Gren Foundation for Anthropological Research
  1980   Inc., New York.
Carpenter, C. R.
  1932–   C. R. Carpenter Papers. Unpublished manuscript on file in the Penn State Room,
  1972   Pennsylvania State University Libraries, University Park.
  1934   A field study of the behavior and social relations of howling monkeys. *Comparative Psychology Monographs* **10** (2).
  1935   Behavior of red spider monkeys in Panama. *Journal of Mammalogy* **16**:171–180.
  1938   *A survey of wild life conditions in Atjeh, North Sumatra. Communication No. 12.* Amsterdam: Netherlands Committee for International Nature Protection.
  1939   Behavior and social relations of free-ranging primates. *Scientific Monthly* **48**:319–325.
Clauser, C. E., P. E. Tucker, J. T. McConville, E. Churchill, and L. L. Laubach
  1972   *Anthropometry of Air Force women.* Aerospace Medical Research Laboratory, Wright-Patterson Air Force Base, Ohio. Washington, D.C.: U.S. Government Printing Office.
Coon, C. S.
  1963   *The origin of races.* New York: Knopf.
Damon, A., H. W. Stoudt, and R. A. McFarland
  1966   *The human body in equipment design.* Cambridge, Massachusetts: Harvard University Press.
Darnell, R.
  1970   The emergence of academic anthropology at the University of Pennsylvania. *Journal of History of the Behavioral Sciences* **6**:80–92.
  1974   *Readings in the history of anthropology.* New York: Harper.
Engel, A., R. S. Murphy, K. Maurer, and E. Collins
  1978   *Plan and operation of the HANES I augmentation survey of adults 25–74 years. Vital Health and Statistics, Series 1, No.* **14**. Washington, D.C.: U.S. Government Printing Office.
Eveleth, P. B.
  1981   Physical anthropology and research programs at the National Institutes of Health. *American Journal of Physical Anthropology* **53**:573–578.
Eveleth, P. B., and J.M. Tanner
  1971   *Progress in growth and physique studies.* London: International Biological Programme.
  1976   *Worldwide variation in human growth.* Cambridge: Cambridge University Press.
Galambos, L.
  1979   The American economy and the reorganization of the sources of knowledge. In *The organization of knowledge in modern America, 1860–1920,* edited by A. Oleson and J. Voss. Baltimore: Johns Hopkins Press. Pp. 269–282.
Goldstein, M. S.
  1940   Recent trends in physical anthropology. *American Journal of Physical Anthropology* **26**:191–209.
Hamill, P. V. V., F. E. Johnston, and W. Grams
  1970   *Height and weight of children in the United States. Vital Statistics, Series 11, No.* **104**. Washington, D.C.: U.S. Government Printing Office.
Hertzberg, H. T. E., E. Churchill, C. Dupertuis, R. M. White, and A. Damon
  1963   *Anthropometric survey of Turkey, Greece and Italy.* Oxford: Pergamon.
Interdepartmental Committee on Nutrition and National Defense (ICNND)
  1964   *Blackfeet Indian Reservation nutrition survey, August–September 1961.* Washington, D.C.: U.S. Government Printing Office.
Kelso, J.
  1972   The current status of physical anthropology. *Yearbook of Physical Anthropology* **16**:145.

Kerley, E. R.
  1978   Recent developments in forensic anthropology. *Yearbook of Physical Anthropology* **21**:160–173.
Kidd, C. V.
  1959   *American universities and federal branch.* Cambridge, Massachusetts: Harvard University Press.
Lasker, G. W.
  1945   Physical anthropology, 1953–1961. *Yearbook of Physical Anthropology* **1**:3–5.
  1973   *Yearbook of Physical Anthropology bibliographies and proceedings from Volumes 1 through 8, 1945–1952.* Ann Arbor, Michigan: University Microfilms.
Martin, W. E.
  1955   *Children's body measurements for planning and equipping schools, Special Publication No.* **4.** Department of Health, Education and Welfare. Washington, D.C.: U.S. Government Printing Office.
Miller, H. W.
  1970   *Dollars for research: science and its patrons in nineteenth century America.* Seattle: University of Washington Press.
National Institutes of Health, Division of Research Resources (NIH–DRR)
  1968   *Regional primate research centers: the creation of a program, No.* (NIH) **76–1166.** Department of Health, Education and Welfare. Washington, D.C.: National Institutes of Health.
  1971   *NIH primate research centers: a major scientific resource.* Washington, D.C.: U.S. Government Printing Office.
National Institutes of Health, Office of Administrative Management (NIH–OAM)
  1976   *History, mission and organization of the Public Health Service.* Department of Health, Education, and Welfare, Public Health Service. Washington, D.C.: U.S. Government Printing Office.
National Institutes of Health, Office of Program Planning and Evaluation, Division of Research Grants (NIH–OPPE–DRG)
  1980   *Basic data relating to the National Institutes of Health.* Washington, D.C.: U.S. Government Printing Office.
National Science Foundation (NSF)
  1978   *Guide to program, fiscal year 1979.* Washington, D.C.: U.S. Government Printing Office.
  (n.d.)   *Grants in anthropology: fiscal years 1958 to 1979.* Computer listing on file at the National Science Foundation, Washington, D.C.
Nissen, H. W.
  1931   A field study of the chimpanzee. *Comparative Psychology Monographs* **8**(1):1–122.
Oakleaf, M.
  1961   *The National Institutes of Health. A history of the extramural projects, 1930–1960.* Manuscript on file at the Office of Extramural Research and Training, Office of the Director, National Institutes of Health, Bethesda, Maryland.
O'Brien, R., and W. C. Shelton
  1941   *Women's measurements for garment and pattern construction,* Miscellaneous Publication No. 454. U.S. Department of Agriculture, Bureau of Home Economics. Washington, D.C.: U.S. Government Printing Office.
Ortner, D. J.
  1976   The paleopathology program at the Smithsonian Institution: purposes and present status. *Bulletin of the New York Academy of Medicine* **52**:1197–1206.
Penniman, T. K.
  1965   *A hundred years of anthropology.* London: Duckworth.
Randall, F. E., A. Damon, R. S. Benton, and D. I. Pratt
  1946   *Human body size in military aircraft and personal equipment.* Dayton, Ohio: Army Air Force, Wright Field.

Reingold, N.

1979   National science policy in a private foundation: The Carnegie Institution of Washington. In *The organization of knowledge in modern America, 1860–1920,* edited by A. Oleson and J. Voss. Baltimore: Johns Hopkins Press. Pp. 313–341.

Ross, D.

1979   The development of the social sciences. In *The organization of knowledge in America, 1860–1920,* edited by A. Oleson and J. Voss. Baltimore: Johns Hopkins Press. Pp. 107–138.

Schultz, A. H.

1963   Age changes, sex differences and variability as factors in the classification of primates. In *Classification and human evolution,* edited by S. L. Washburn. Chicago: Aldine. Pp. 85–115.

Smithsonian Institution

1930–   *Report of the United States National Museum.* Washington, D.C.: U.S. Government Printing
1979   Office.

Sontag, L. W.

1960   *Fels research institute for the study of human development, report for the period ended 12/31/59.* Philadelphia: Samuel S. Fels Fund.

Stewart, T. D.

1952   *A bibliography of physical anthropology in Latin America: 1937–1948.* New York: Wenner-Gren Foundation for Anthropological Research, Inc.

Stocking, G. W., Jr.

1968   *Race, culture, and evolution: essay in the history of anthropology.* New York: Free Press.

Stoudt, H. W., A. Damon, R. A. McFarland, and J. Roberts

1965   *Weight, height and selected body measurements of adults, United States, 1960–62,* Publication No. 1000, *Vital Health and Statistics, Ser. 11, no.* **8**. Washington, D.C.: U.S. Government Printing Office.

Voegelin, E. W.

1953   United States of America. In *International directory of anthropological institutions,* edited by W. L. Thomas, Jr. and A. M. Pikelis. New York: Wenner-Gren Foundation for Anthropological Research, Inc. Pp. 331–427.

Wenner-Gren Foundation

1952   *The first ten years, 1941–1951.* New York: The Viking Fund.

1963   *Report for 1952–1962.* New York: Wenner-Gren Foundation for Anthropological Research, Inc.

1965   *Report for 1963–1964.* New York: Wenner-Gren Foundation for Anthropological Research, Inc.

White, R. M.

1978   Anthropometry and human engineering. *Yearbook of Physical Anthropology* **21**:41–62.

Worthington, E. B.

1975   *The evolution of the International Biological Programme.* Cambridge: Cambridge University Press.

Wulsin, F. R.

1948   *Responses of man to heat.* Office of the Quartermaster General. Washington, D.C.: U.S. Government Printing Office.

Yerkes, R. M., and A. W. Yerkes

1970   *The great apes. Landmarks in anthropology,* edited by W. La Barre. New York: Johnson Reprint. (Originally published, 1929, New Haven: Yale University Press.)

3

A Short History
of Primate Field Studies:
Old World Monkeys and Apes

Rosalind Ribnick

Today, primate behavior is one of the subdisciplines of physical anthropology. If one examines chonicled histories of anthropology, almost no mention is made of primate behavior (Brew 1968; Penniman 1974). Initially conducted by psychologists, primate field studies are now multidisciplinary efforts, involving zoologists and anthropologists as well. The first field studies were conducted in 1929, but it was not until the latter part of the 1950s that physical anthropologists actively began to conduct research on free-ranging primates.

Because of the multidisciplinary nature of primate studies, it is not possible to discuss the role of physical anthropology without considering the contributions of other disciplines. Even though each discipline has a slightly different perspective, communication among those conducting field studies on nonhuman primates is relatively easy. Regarding this, Stuart Altmann has said "It would seem that, in studies cf animals of this group at least, the old barriers to communication between members of various scientific disciplines are, if not dead, at least moribund [1967:xii]."

In this chapter, only those events considered most important to the development of naturalistic primate behavior research are presented. Space limitations prevent a complete exposition, but this general overview will give the reader a good understanding of what took place in the early history of field studies on nonhuman primates. Since is is necessary to limit the scope of this chapter, the following discussion is confined to Old World monkeys and apes. Research on New World primates and Old World prosimians is omitted with a few exceptions, such as the early research by Clarence Ray Carpenter, whose pioneering work in South America preceded research on Old World primates.

A HISTORY OF AMERICAN
PHYSICAL ANTHROPOLOGY, 1930–1980

The Initial Period 1929–1950

Before 1929, information on the behavior of free-ranging primates came from anecdotal sources and traveler's tales; no systematically planned field research had been conducted when psychologist Robert Yerkes at Yale University sponsored the 1929 field studies of Henry Nissen on chimpanzees in West Africa (Nissen 1931) and Harold Bingham on gorillas in East Africa (Bingham 1932). An example of the kind of information known from anecdotes is the following, written by the noted naturalist, Buffon in 1775, on "orangutans" (chimpanzees): "This animal is as tall and as strong as a man, and as desirous of the female sex . . . which they keep with them for the pleasure of their company, feeding them very plentifully all the time [as quoted in Zuckerman 1932]."

By today's standards, a credible field study would generally require at least one full annual cycle in the field. Nissen's and Bingham's studies would be considered short, therefore, each lasting less than three months. Nonetheless, they are significant because they represent the first attempt at formal study of nonhuman primate behavior in the wild. Both Nissen and Bingham encountered problems in the field, such as moving through dense bush; however, the greatest problem for both men was locating and observing the animals. Neither managed to log very many hours of observation, but the precedent of conducting field research on primates had been set.

Reflecting the traditional interests of his discipline, Yerkes concentrated on learning and intelligence; it was his goal (among others) to breed apes in captivity to study these phenomena. In sending Nissen and Bingham to the field, he planned to gather data about apes in their natural environment to ensure the success of a captive colony. In 1929, Yerkes and his wife, Ada, published a compilation of all current knowledge about primates in the volume, *The Great Apes*. For obvious reasons, there is no field research reported in their work. Interestingly, *The Great Apes* was republished in *Landmarks in Anthropology*, a series of reprints in cultural anthropology edited by anthropologist Weston La Barre (Yerkes and Yerkes 1929/1970).

Another psychologist, C. R. Carpenter, conducted the most significant behavioral research on free-ranging primates during this early period. Also sponsored by Yerkes, Carpenter carried out his pioneering research on Barro Colorado Island in the Panama Canal where he observed the howling monkey (*Alouatta palliata*) (1934) and the red spider monkey (*Ateles geoffroyi* Kuhl) (1935). In 1937, Carpenter was part of the Asiatic Expedition (see the following section). It was during this expedition that he observed and filmed gibbon behavior (*Hylobates lar*) (1940); the original film is housed at the Harvard Museum of Comparative Zoology. Carpenter systematically gathered information on ecology, reproduction, and population dynamics, developing a methodology that set a standard of excellence for later generations. In spite of the brevity of his time in the field, 6 months at longest, it is to his credit that when subsequent studies were conducted by anthropologists Lewis Klein on New World monkeys (Klein and Klein 1973) and John Ellefson on gibbons (1968), some two-and-a-half decades later, the results of Carpenter's 1930s research were corroborated.

The research of Sir Solly Zuckerman during this period is also significant. A British medical doctor and endocrinologist born in South Africa, Zuckerman published *The Social Life of Monkeys and Apes* in 1932, which contained his behavioral observations on chacma baboons (*Papio ursinus*) in the field. Despite its title, almost no data on apes appear in this publication. For many years, Zuckerman's field research was considered an objective study and was frequently cited as such; actually, only 9 days were spent in the field of South Africa. These shortcomings aside, Zuckerman had an impact on the development of primate studies, particularly among British researchers (Haraway 1978). Prior to 1929, a major focus of primate studies had been on anatomy, particularly the comparison of human and nonhuman primates to assess degrees of evolutionary affinity (e.g., Gregory 1922), and on intelligence (e.g., Thorndike 1901). Zuckerman emphasized the importance of understanding social behavior, and even though some of his conclusions concerning social organization have been proved invalid (Lancaster and Lee 1965), many of the problems he formulated are current, such as the relationship between physiology and behavior.

Drawing conclusions based largely on the behavior of a group of hamadryas baboons (*P. hamadryas*) at the London Zoological Gardens, Zuckerman theorized sexual behavior was the determining factor in primate social group organization. When data was obtained on free-ranging social groups in the late 1950s and 1960s, it was shown that many primates have one or two breeding seasons per year. This discovery left sociality during most of the year unexplained by Zuckerman's theory of sociality (Lancaster and Lee 1965).

No other fieldwork was conducted until the 1950s. The intitial development of primate field research, therefore, consisted of the Bingham and Nissen studies, about 2½ months each; Zuckerman's brief field research; and the studies by Carpenter. Only Carpenter's work is now seen as having contributed significantly to knowledge about primates in their natural habitats. He was the first scientist to collect enough ecological data to permit a meaningful definition of the relation between animals' adaptability and their environments.

The Asiatic Expedition

In 1937, a full-scale expedition to study the gibbon in Thailand was initiated by Harold Coolidge, Jr. Sponsored by Harvard, Columbia, and Johns Hopkins universities. The expedition was organized to study and collect primates from Thailand (then Siam) and North Borneo (Sherwood L. Washburn, personal communication 1976), and as such, it constituted the first attempt to study both the behavior and morphology of primates. Coolidge led the party with the following team: Adolph Schultz, physical anthropologist and anatomist; Augustus Griswold, zoologist in charge of collecting birds and small mammals; Washburn, physical anthropologist and anatomist (later to become a leading influence on the development of primate behavior research); Carpenter, psychologist and by then, veteran primate field-worker; and John Coolidge, III, photographer and artist. The multifaceted aspect of this expedition is reflected in the composition of the group, who spent 4 months in Thai forests, performing anatomical dissection and observing behavior.

The Asiatic Expedition was important to the development of primate behavior for three reasons. First, Coolidge organized the project to study the behavior, ecology, and morphology of free-ranging primates, indeed a wholistically planned endeavor. Second, while participating in this project Carpenter conducted his classic gibbon study. Finally, several participants in the expedition would later have a significant impact on primatology. Carpenter and Washburn became motivating forces in the recognition of the importance of primate behavior research, and Schultz contributed to the knowledge of relationships between living and fossil primates with his careful anatomical studies using the comparative method (e.g., Schultz 1963). Coolidge, who had already plotted the distribution of the pygmy chimpanzee (*Pan paniscus*) (1933) and made field expeditions that resulted in the revision of the genus *Gorilla* (Coolidge 1929, 1930, 1936), was, in great part, the impetus for George Schaller's subsequent field research on the mountain gorilla.

Cayo Santiago

One other important event occurred during this early period that has had a lasting effect on primate research in the United States. In 1938, Carpenter arranged for the purchase of over 500 rhesus monkeys (*Macaca mulatta*) in India, which he then released on Cayo Santiago, an island near Puerto Rico (Carpenter 1942a). Originally owned by Columbia University's School of Tropical Medicine at San Juan, Puerto Rico, the colony is now part of the Caribbean Primate Research Center with facilities that include rhesus on the islands of Guayacan, La Cueva (Vandenberg 1967), and Tesecheo (Morrison and Menzel 1972).

The Cayo Santiago colony has been studied almost continuously since its establishment. Carpenter observed the animals intermittently, reporting on group formation and reproductive behavior (1942a, 1942b, 1942c) and on the methodology for observing and analyzing behavior (1945, 1964). When World War II interrupted his research, Carpenter ceased his primate studies for a time and became active in the United States Navy Education programs.

Early Anthropological Interest

Yerkes was not alone in his enthusiasm for studying nonhuman primates. Two eminent anthropologists, Earnest A. Hooton and Alfred L. Kroeber, recognized the importance of primate research to the study of human evolution, although neither man undertook his own primate study. Hooton's interest is reflected in his book, *Man's Poor Relations* (1942), dedicated to "Robert Mearns Yerkes, Student of Primates, Teacher of Primatologists." In it, Hooton wrote: "I may be an apostate from anthropology when I assert that it seems to be that the study of individual and group behavior among the infrahuman primates may offer nearly as much to the student of man as does the investigation of the social life and psychology of contemporary savages [1942:323]." Hooton's interest is further indicated in an article published posthumously entitled "The Importance of Primate Studies in Anthropology" (1955).

Kroeber, a leading figure in the development of the study of cultural anthropology in the United States, also understood the importance of nonhuman primates, and, like Hooton, was interested in them as a vehicle for understanding human culture and behavior. He was clearly impressed with the research results of Yerkes, Köhler (1925), Kohts (1923), and others who had experimented on ape intelligence, and in his article, "Sub-Human Culture Beginnings" (1928), Kroeber applied what little was known about nonhuman primates to the origin of culture. He suggested that one of the main routes to understanding the origin of culture would come from a comparison with "those of the infra-human animals most likely to manifest anticipations of cultural activity [1928:326]." It was Kroeber's aim to understand several aspects of human behavior and culture from studying nonhuman primates; specifically, by examining primate social behavior, he hoped to determine whether primate behavioral repetoires exhibited those kinds of behavior he attributed to "culture." Using such criteria as religion and ethics, he decided chimpanzees were "cultureless" but had "reactions and faculties closely akin to our own, and manifesting at least some measure of the basal psychic ingredients which enter into culture [1928:341]."

There is no doubt that Kroeber was calling for research on nonhuman primates with the anthropological goal of understanding culture. His view evidently was not shared by many other anthropologists at this time since anthropological research on primates did not begin until much later, three decades after Kroeber made his 1928 comparisons.

The Formative Stage 1950–1959

Following Carpenter's gibbon study in 1937, field studies on primates ceased until the 1950s. Between 1948 and 1952, some information on primates came from epidemiological investigations in the tropics—from research on yellow fever, in particular. Sponsored by the Virus Research Institute at Entebbe, Uganda, field research was conducted on the African redtail monkey (*Cercopithecus ascanius schmidti*) with brief reports on other African cercopithecines (Buxton 1951, 1952; Haddow 1952; Haddow *et al.* 1947; Lumsden, 1951). Although these studies did not focus on primate behavior, they are interesting from an historical point of view because they represent information collected as a result of military influence due to World War II. They also are the first examples of nonanecdotal field information on African monkey behavior and ecology, although categories of behavior were delineated almost causally: "[The] dominance, threat, submission and frankly sexual activities so obvious in baboons" could not be observed in the behavioral repertoire of the redtail (Haddow 1952). Haddow made no mention of intentional observations on baboon behavior but his comparison of two species constitutes one of the first to appear in the literature on primates in the wild. As is often the case with field studies on forest-dwelling primates, ecological observations greatly outnumber behavioral ones, with facts such as band size, feeding activity, breeding seasons, activity peaks, and occasional sightings of solitary males being the main categories of data gathered. This was also true of Haddow's study. Two rare nocturnal studies were conducted by Lumsden (1951) and Buxton (1951); both men reported seeing solitary redtails.

Several developments during the period between Carpenter's gibbon study and the decade of the 1950s affected the subsequent growth of primate studies. The publication in 1942 of Julian Huxley's *Evolution, The Modern Synthesis* and the writings of Theodosius Dobzhansky (1944, for example), Ernst Mayr (1942), George Gaylord Simpson (1949), and other evolutionists had an impact on physical anthropology. The new synthesis provided a long-needed unifying paradigm for physical anthropologists, that is, a strong evolutionary perspective that was systematically organized (Brew 1968). Explicit in the new perspective was the importance of behavior in the evolutionary process, which indirectly opened the way for naturalistic studies of primates.

It was during this period that fossil remains of early hominids were becoming increasingly important. In 1940, W. E. Le Gros Clark agreed that the South African skull Raymond Dart had found in 1924 (Dart 1925) was more human than ape (Le Gros Clark 1940) and the australopithecines gained widespread acceptance as early hominids. Another australopithecine, found by Louis and Mary Leakey in East Africa (Leakey 1959), confirmed a fairly wide distribution of early hominids in Africa more than a million years ago, and interest in reconstructing human evolution gave rise to paleoanthropology, which became a major subarea within physical anthropology. In order to reconstruct the lifeways of early hominids, living primates were used as models for the extinct australopithecines (Washburn 1961).

Under cosponsorship of Section H (Anthropology) and Section l (Psychology), a symposium on the contributions of the study of nonhuman primates to an understanding of human evolution was held at the annual meeting of the American Association for the Advancement of Science at Boston on December 27, 1953. At this session, William Straus made a plea for further research on nonhuman primates, stating "I know of no aspect of anthropology that is likely to yield richer dividends to the investigator. [1955:126]."

Seemingly unrelated advances in another area, medicine, in fact had great importance to the conduct of anthropological fieldwork. Directly related to military research during the war, developments in antiseptics and improvements in hygiene made fieldwork less hazardous. Of critical importance was the discovery and use of vaccines, usable sera, antibiotics, and sulfa drugs as well as the treatment and prevention of certain tropical diseases such as malaria, cholera, and yellow fever (Zuckerman 1966).

The 1950s may be characterized as the formative stage in the development of primate behavior research. Previously, little baseline data had been gathered on primates in their natural habitats. Thus, the few studies from this period were general in an attempt to gather as much information as possible.

Research in Japan

In 1948, shortly after the end of World War II, Japanese scientists who had previously studied free-ranging deer, rabbits, and semi-free-ranging horses began to study the behavior and ecology of the Japanese macaque, *Macaca fuscata* (Sugiyama 1965). Under the direction of Denzaburo Miyadi and Kinji Imanishi, a Primate Research Group was formed at Kyoto University (Frisch 1959). Since Japan was recovering from the effects of war and financial assistance for ecological and behavioral studies was unavailable, Miyadi, Imanishi, and their colleagues settled on studying the Japanese macaque (*Macaca fuscata*), an animal locally available. It had never been studied and would entail relatively little expense to research (Imanishi 1960). These studies constitute the earliest, ongoing research on nonhuman primates anywhere in the world.

Because the Japanese researchers considered the wild monkeys too "shy" to be observed naturally, they developed a method of provisioning whereby "food was thrown at them" enabling observations at close range (Sugiyama 1965). This method became widely used in Japanese studies (Kawai 1963; Carpenter and Nishimura 1969; Frisch, 1959) and provoked drastic increases in macaque populations. For example, in his review of the Mount Takasaki monkeys, Itani (1975) stated the estimated total population in 1953 was one troop of approximately 220 monkeys. In 1975, approximately 1400 monkeys, organized into three troops, inhabited the isolated area. Itani realized the extreme effects of provisioning on the animals but justified the methodology by stating:

> If no provisioning had been undertaken, monkeys on Mount Takasaki could have long ago been classified by the government as harmful animals and therefore eliminated. And, in fact, provisioning has resulted in intensifying crop damage to farms immediately adjacent to the feeding ground. But because provisioning has attenuated the nomadic range of these monkeys, the overall amount of farm acreage damage has decreased [1975:118].

Certainly provisioning changes the status of a troop from natural to seminatural, but perhaps the method is justified in a country like Japan where strong competition exists between human and nonhuman primates. In 1947, the Japanese

Ministry of Agriculture and Forestry banned the hunting of monkeys, but the prohibition has become less rigid in recent years, and special hunting permits have been issued where crop damage is "beyond control (Itani 1975)."

Individual recognition of animals in most of the 30 feeding grounds in Japan was accomplished using provisioning methods (Itani 1975), with observations emphasizing social structure, group formation, interindividual behavior, and behavior development. These subjects, among others, formed part of the goals that prompted the establishment of the Japan Monkey Centre in 1956 at Inuyama, Aichi. Commencing publication of the journal *Primates* in 1957, the Japan Monkey Centre helped to establish Japan as one of the major areas for research on nonhuman primate behavior (Sugiyama 1965). Initially, there were unfortunate linguistic barriers between Japanese research and much of the Western world, but in 1957, Imanishi published an article in English on social behavior in Japanese macaques, thus providing for an exchange of information that has continued to the present. Reports by Frisch (1959, 1963) and Simonds (1961) also enabled contact between Japan and the West.

The most striking result of early Japanese research was the observation of newly acquired behaviors by Japanese macaques on Koshima Island (Kawai 1963; *et al.* 1965) that have been interpreted as "protocultural behavior" by Japanese scientists. Monkeys were given tests in which sweet-potato washing, dabbling in water and swimming, placer-mining selection of wheat, erect posture, bipedal, and "give-me-some" behaviors were considered protocultural. An example from Kawai follows.

> One of the foods given the monkeys is wheat. When wheat is scattered over the beach it is so easily buried under the sand that is is difficult for them to find it. Until a couple of years ago they had been picking up the grains one by one, but recently they have begun to scoop them up with the sand and carry the mixture to the sea or to a stream of water. There they wash the sand away and then eat the wheat. This is called the "Placer-Mining Selection Method" and 14 monkeys act it at present. It is interesting to note that their fear of water was overcome as a result of their becoming skillful in washing sweet potatoes [1963:114].

Whether the animals understood wheat is lighter in weight than sand and will float on top of water is highly questionable. However, the practice of "placer-mining selection of wheat" became fairly standard practice among many animals in the group, especially among young ones who learned it in the course of normal development.

The scope of Japanese primate research has broadened to include other primate species. Motivated by an interest in primate evolution, both human and nonhuman, and the need for comparative material, Japanese researchers have observed nonhuman primates on the continents of Asia and Africa. In Africa, extensive observations have been made on gorillas (*Gorilla gorilla*) (Kawai and Mizuhara 1962) and chimpanzees (e.g., Azuma 1966; Azuma and Toyoshima 1961–1962, 1965; Itani 1979; Itani and Suzuki 1967; Kano 1972; Nishida 1968; Sugiyama 1965, 1968, 1969; Suzuki 1969).

Elsewhere in Asia, research on the hanuman langur (*Presbytis entellus*) and the bonnet macaque (*Macaca radiata*) was conducted as part of the Japan–India Joint Project in Primates Investigation (JIPI) (Miyadi 1964). It was necessary to understand the ecology of monkey habitats to determine the route of infection of kyasanur forest disease, borne by ticks to both humans and monkeys. The assistance of Japanese primatologists was enlisted "to train Indian researchers so as to root primate socioecology in India [Miyadi 1964]."

There can be no doubt that early Japanese research represents a pioneering effort in primate behavior studies; it was the first fieldwork to occur since the early studies by Bingham, Nissen, and Carpenter. Even though provisioning may be criticized on many grounds, particularly that it changes the nature of the free-living troop and increases population, results of studies on Japanese macaques include valuable insights into the process of culture acquisition and group formation.

Research by Western Scientists

The subject of howler monkey research is not within the direct scope of this paper on Old World monkeys and apes. However, a consideration of the early research on them is important in the general development of primate field studies. Not only were the howlers on Barro Colorado among the first to be scientifically observed in the early 1930s by Carpenter (1934), they were the first to be studied in the period that characterizes the postwar interest in primate field studies. Many fieldworkers who later made significant contributions to knowledge of primates first conducted fieldwork on the howler population at Barro Colorado.

In the United States, zoology student Charles Southwick and his professor, Nicholas Collias, were the first Western scientists to resume active fieldwork on primates by reexamining the behavior and ecology of the howlers Carpenter had observed 20 years earlier (Collias and Southwick 1952). Shortly after completing this research Southwick, inspired by German biologist Angela Nolte's 2-week survey of primates in India (Nolte 1955), surveyed populations of rhesus monkeys (*Macaca mulatta*) in northern Indian villages, towns, and temples (Southwick 1961; Southwick *et al.* 1965). The rhesus was well known in captivity, but very little about its free-ranging behavior had been recorded. Southwick's interest in rhesus was as a result of his research on them as vectors for diseases affecting human populations. Southwick edited the first collection of articles on nonhuman primates that was devoted totally to social behavior, Primate Social Behavior (1963). In June 1981, Southwick began his twenty-third year of field seasons on the same rhesus populations (C. H. Southwick, personal communication 1981).

Another zoologist, Stuart Altmann, became actively involved in primate research during its formative stage. In 1955, he observed the howlers on Barro Colorado (Altmann 1959), but whereas the purpose of the Collias and Southwick study was to gather census information, Altmann specifically studied social behavior.

Described as one of the most mathematically elegant primate field studies ever conducted (Hutt and Hutt 1970), Altmann's research also consisted of observations from 1956 to 1958 on rhesus monkeys at Cayo Santiago, the colony established by Carpenter in 1938. An outstanding feature of Altmann's work is the inventory of behavioral categories derived from field observations. In his analysis of rhesus behavior, Altmann employed Markov chain analysis, a mathematical technique used to indicate the presence of sequentially dependent behaviors (Altmann 1965). From his research on the howlers and rhesus, Altmann became a forerunner in developing methods for quantification and statistical analysis of behavioral events.

In 1959, Carl Koford continued Altmann's observations of the rhesus on Cayo Santiago, focusing mainly on reproductive behavior (Koford 1963a, 1963b, 1965).

During the latter part of the 1950s, western scientists began field research on African primates. Under the sponsorship of L. S. B. Leakey, two independent investigations on the behavior of mountain gorillas (*Gorilla gorilla beringia*) in Uganda were begun in 1957 by Rosalie Osborn (1963) and Jill Donisthorpe (1958). Both studies were extremely short and are mentioned because of their historical importance as two of the earliest attempts to study gorilla behavior after Bingham's also brief fieldwork. Field conditions were problematical as they had been for Bingham 28 years earlier. Locating the elusive animals was difficult because of lush vegetation, thick afternoon fog, rain, and hailstorms. Very few contact hours were logged, and little information on gorilla social behavior was obtained. Kawai and Mizuhara (1962) from the Japan Monkey Centre spent 3 months in the same area in 1959, mainly gathering ecological data.

Harold J. Coolidge, leader of the Asiatic Expedition in 1937, had long been interested in gorillas, had participated in expeditions to several parts of Africa, and was responsible for much of the taxonomic classification of gorillas (Coolidge 1929, 1930, 1936). In 1959, he arranged funding for a long-term field study of gorilla behavior. At Coolidge's request, John T. Emlen, zoologist at the University of Wisconsin, and his student, George Schaller, undertook the project, and for the first 6 months of the study, Emlen and Schaller surveyed gorilla populations in several areas to obtain an overall view of gorilla ecology and to locate a study site (Emlen and Schaller 1960). Emlen returned to the United States while Schaller remained in the area of the Virunga Volcanoes of Zaire (then the Congo), where he conducted the first long-term field study on a gorilla population (Schaller 1963). In fact, this was the first time any great ape had been studied for longer than 3 months in the wild; almost nothing was known of their behavior outside captivity. Unfortunately, because of political turmoil of the Congo, Schaller's fieldwork was cut short after 1 year. Nevertheless, the study yielded heretofore unknown information about gorilla behavior, and it was the first time any great ape was studied without the security of a rifle (Schaller 1963, 1965).

The first physical anthropologist to become involved in field studies on non-human primates was Sherwood L. Washburn. Washburn led the way in getting field research established within the discipline; in this respect, he may be regarded as a prime mover (as was Yerkes much earlier). Although he did not conduct extensive fieldwork after his initial baboon study with his student, Irven DeVore

(Washburn and DeVore 1961a), he was responsible for making people interested enough in nonhuman primates for them to grant research funds (T. E. Rowell, personal communication 1977; see also Baker and Eveleth, in the present volume). This is evidenced by the large number of students Washburn subsequently sponsored in field research.

There are several reasons for Washburn's interest in nonhuman primates. He was among the first students to earn a doctoral degree in physical anthropology at Harvard University under Hooton. Hooton's interest in primates has already been discussed. The influence of Zuckerman must have had an effect on Washburn. As a young student, Washburn spent several months in England as a laboratory assistant for Zuckerman studying captive primates. At that time, it was apparent to Washburn that data from such a group might be skewed by the captive condition (personal communication 1977).

As a member of The Asiatic Expedition, Washburn was not directly involved in behavioral research, but his involvement with primates and their implications for understanding human evolution was taking form. The experience of The Asiatic Expedition, together with the influence of Hooton and Zuckerman, must have had an affect on his developing interest in primates, an interest that revolutionized the field of physical anthropology (Washburn and DeVore 1961a, 1961b).

Washburn taught anatomy to medical students at Columbia University from 1939 until 1947. At that time he moved to the University of Chicago where he remained for the next decade before going to Berkeley. By applying experimental morphology to the solution of developmental problems, Washburn showed how modification of bone can come about as a result of muscle action; this constituted a breakthrough in the analysis of functional morphology (Washburn 1947). It was during this general time period (1947 to the early 1950s) that Washburn made several trips to East Africa, where the presence of numerous monkey troops caught his scientific attention; he began to realize the potential of combining functional anatomy with behavior and was among the first physical anthropologists to show the relationship between functional morphology and locomotor adaptations (Washburn and Avis 1958). It was a short step from there to behavioral studies with a focus on social rather than anatomical functions, although Washburn has never failed to integrate the whole animal. In this sense, he has been a synthesizer of both nonhuman primate and human evolution (Washburn 1977).

Achievements that attract adherents and provide a model or frame of reference for collecting and organizing data to solve new problems are noteworthy, according to Kuhn (1970), for they establish a new paradigm for scientific inquiry. In this same sense, Washburn's influence at the start of the tremendous growth and proliferation of field studies on nonhuman primates has had profound significance in the fields of anthropology, zoology, and psychology. Although these disciplines have slightly different perspectives, primate field studies did not really begin in full in any of them until Washburn showed through his own research and that of his students, his initiation of an early symposium on the necessity for field studies, through his writings, which indicated the relevance and importance of primate behavior to human evolution research (1961, 1973), and his ability to obtain funding for field research.

Prior to the late 1950s, anthropologists had not conducted research on primate behavior to any great extent. The 1965 edition of T. K. Penniman's *A Hundred Years of Anthropology* did discuss Zuckerman's research on the London Zoo colony of hamadryas baboons, but it is surprising that at that late date, Zuckerman's theory of sociality in primates was still given as valid.

In a recent analysis, Haraway states Washburn's premier importance to the development of fieldwork: "Perhaps the key to Washburn is that he has produced a fundamental theory with tremendous implications for the practice of many sciences and for the rules in speculative evolutionary reconstruction. In Kuhnian terms, Washburn seems to have something basic to do with scientific paradigms [1978:54]." Washburn incorporated the discovery of hominid fossils and new possibilities for the earliest human ancestor(s) into a larger scientific body of data on human evolution by providing a new route for understanding early hominid adaptations as well as contemporary human behavior. On the basis of differences and similarities between nonhuman and human primates, an entirely new way of thinking about human adaptations was created. Although this technique has sometimes been used incorrectly, such as for simplistic extrapolations from nonhuman to human primate behavior, it has nevertheless opened a new area for research for a deeper understanding of *Homo sapiens*.

As part of his basic philosophy, Washburn (1977) has espoused the experimental method in primate behavior research. His views concerning the major contributions of primatology are illustrated by the following ways to consider primate research:

(1)   A fundamental challenge to the notion that there are different levels of knowledge and that the social should be studied without reference to the biological.

(2)   A repudiation of the "black box" philosophy, and an insistence that the study of behavior must include an effort to understand internal mechanisms, including emotions.

(3)   A repudiation of the thought that man is a rational animal and that the brain offers any simple road to truth. We, too, are primates, carrying the advantages and limitations of our evolutionary history and indoctrinated in a particular primitive culture [Washburn 1973:182].

In his closing to the above article, Washburn tells why he believes primate behavior is so important, particularly for anthropological research:

Truth is a very restless thing. The promise of primatology lies in being animal oriented, problem oriented, and experimental. The less we trust the past, the more likely we are to be useful in the present. The more we can borrow techniques which probe far beneath superficial description, the more likely we are to make substantial progress. If we would understand the primates, we cannot accept the view of rational, scientific man which is deeply imbedded in our culture. We are primates, products of the evolutionary process, and the promise of primatology is better understanding of the peculiar creature we call man [Washburn 1973:182].

At the suggestion of Washburn, DeVore, then a graduate student in social anthropology, observed olive baboons (*Papio anubis*) in Kenya in order to get a different perspective on human social institutions (S. L. Washburn, personal communication 1976). Washburn also observed for part of the study, and with DeVore, published the first article on savanna baboon behavior in 1961 (Washburn and DeVore 1961a). The results of this baboon study (DeVore 1963, 1965) stood for a long time as the basic model, not only for all baboon behavior but for other primate species as well. Not until the late 1960s and early 1970s, after several studies on other baboon troops and on other primates were conducted, did the variability in behavior characteristic of primates become known.

At the same time Washburn sent DeVore to observe baboons in East Africa, Phyllis Dolhinow (Jay), also a student of Washburn, went to India where she observed langurs (*Presbytis entellus*) (Jay 1962, 1963, 1965). Her research constitutes one of the first long-term studies on a member of the Colobinae and remains a major work on that species. Both Dolhinow and DeVore stressed the importance of the group in primate social systems and mother–infant relations.

In addition to sponsoring the fieldwork of DeVore and Dolhinow in the late 1950s, Washburn was part of a team that established a primate research colony. With psychologist Frank Beach and zoologist Peter Marler, Washburn obtained funding for an experimental animal behavior station to be located at the University of California at Berkeley. Among the first of its kind, the station contained a primate colony that was used for basic research and for training students in physical anthropology who would later conduct fieldwork on free-ranging primates.

Concurrent with the growth of interest in primates in the United States, K. Ronald L. Hall went to South Africa from England as a field biologist, although he was a psychologist by training. He believed "that fieldwork should begin at dawn and continue as long as there was sufficient light to make observation possible [Gartlan 1968:1]." In England, he had had a strong interest in bird behavior and was influenced by the methods of ethologist Niko Tinbergen. Hall's careful, systematic work on chacma baboons (*P. ursinus*) (Hall 1962a, 1962b, 1963, 1965a), patas monkeys (*Erythrocebus patas*) (Hall 1965b; Hall *et al.* 1965), and vervet monkeys (*Cercopithecus aethiops*) (Hall and Gartlan 1965; Hall and Goswell 1964; Hall and Mayer 1967) greatly influenced physical anthropologists in the United States. The literature abounds with tributes to Hall by several American primatologists who worked with him (DeVore 1965; Altmann 1967; Jay 1968). Perhaps one of the reasons for his broad appeal was his eclectic approach, which drew from anthropology, ethology, and ecology, as well as his own discipline of psychology. Unfortunately, his life was cut short in 1965 by Herpes B virus, carried by cercopithecus monkeys and possibly by members of his own captive colony (Gartlan 1968).

The laboratory research of ethologists and those in animal behavior such as Robert Hinde, Yvette Spencer-Booth, Harry Harlow, and Peter Klopfer (just a few among many) certainly deserves a place in the development of primate studies.

The exclusion of experimental laboratory research is in no way intended to diminish its importance, but that area is beyond the scope of this paper and will be considered elsewhere in a lengthier review.

By the close of 1959, a period of active research on primates in the field had begun that marked the formation of a new and expansive era of scientific studies on primate behavior.

The Prolific Period 1960 to ?

Research activity begun in the 1950s not only continued in the late 1960s but proliferated, resulting in a growth rate faster than in scientific research as a whole (Altmann 1967). This trend appears to have continued until today, although a quantitative study for the period from 1970 to 1981 has not been completed; we cannot yet say if the "Prolific Period" has ended. By the mid–1960s, the study of nonhuman primates had become a separate, *bona fide* area of research for anthropologists as well as zoologists and psychologists from many parts of the world. Fieldwork conducted during this period is so extensive that the research of only a few primatologists is discussed in this chapter. Emphasis is on those observations conducted during the 1960s since that research provided the basis from which current primate studies have fully developed. An evaluation of primate behavior research for 1970–1981 is in preparation.

Archaeological research began to yield an abundance of fossil hominids beginning in 1959 (McCown and Kennedy 1971), and at approximately the same time, primate studies were beginning to increase at a rapid rate. Understanding the origins of behavior became a goal of both primatologists and paleoanthropologists, evidenced by a New York Academy of Sciences conference held in 1962. Entitled "The Relatives of Early Man: Modern Studies of the Relation of the Evolution of Nonhuman Primates to Evolution," the conference formally brought together two physical anthropology subdisciplines in that papers on early hominids as well as on field studies of living primates were presented (Buettner-Janusch 1962). Also in 1962, the Wenner-Gren Foundation for Anthropological Research held a conference on the classification of fossil hominids (Washburn 1963) at which Hall (1963) and DeVore (1963) presented papers on primate behavior.

Simultaneous to the "Relatives of Early Man" conference, was a symposium held in London devoted entirely to primate research. The developing widespread interest in primates is indicated by the fact that the symposium was sponsored by three organizations: The Zoological Society of London; the Anatomical Society of Great Britain and Ireland; and the Society for the Study of Human Biology. Edited by John Napier, *The Primates* (1963) is based on the London symposium.

Numerous conferences have been held since the early 1960s and have been supported by several organizations, including the Wenner-Gren Foundation for

Anthropological Research, the International Primatological Society, and the American Society of Primatologists. Sessions on primate behavior have become established at various professional meetings, such as those of the American Association of Physical Anthropologists and the American Anthropological Association. Other disciplines, such as the American Psychological Association, also have sessions on primate behavior at annual and regional meetings.

Field Research

Most of the physical anthropologists in the United States who conducted primate field studies during the 1960s were students of Washburn. Dolhinow and DeVore comprise the "first generation," while others included in the group are as follows (with limited references): John Ellefson (1968), gibbons (Hylobates lar); Judy Shirek-Ellefson (1967), crab-eating macaques (*Macaca fascicularis*); Jane Lancaster (1971), vervets (*Cercopithecus aethiops*); Donald Lindburg (1971), rhesus macaques (*M. Mulatta*); Michael MacRoberts (1968), barbary ape (*M. sylvana*); Suzanne Ripley (1967), Ceylon gray langur (*P. entellus*); Donald Sade (1965), rhesus macaques; Paul Simonds (1965), bonnet macaques (*M. radiata*); and Andrew Wilson (1968), rhesus macaques.

The aforementioned are not the only people who conducted field research in the 1960s, but they are an impressive list of students for one person to have had; it is an achievement that Washburn attracted so productive a group, which he, in turn, helped in reaching their goals. Many of these primatologists have since given rise to another generation of fieldworkers; directly and indirectly, Washburn has been responsible for more students going to the field than any other single person.

Behavioral patterns of many Old World free-ranging primates were known for the first time. The following is not an exhaustive list of references but is representative of the species observed by the end of the 1960s: *Papio papio* (Bert *et al.* 1967a, 1967b), *P. ursinus* (Stoltz and Saayman 1970), *P. anubis* (Hall and DeVore 1965), *P. cynocephalus* (DeVore and Washburn 1963), and *P. hamadryas* (Kummer 1968); *Mandrillus leucophaeus* (Gartlan 1969); *Theropithecus gelada* (Crook 1966); *Erythrocebus patas* (Hall 1965b); *Cercopithecus aethiops* (Struhsaker 1967); *Miopithecus talapoin* (Gautier-Hion 1966); *Cercocebus albigena* (Chalmers, 1968a, 1968b, 1968c); *Pan troglodytes* (Goodall 1968); *Gorilla gorilla* (Fossey 1970); *Pongo pygmaeus* (Horr 1977); *Colobus polykomos* (Sabater Pi 1973), *Presbytis entellus* (Yoshiba 1968), *P. rubicundus* and *P. aygula* (MacKinnon 1969), *P. melalophos* and *P. obscurus* (Bernstein 1967a); *Nasalis larvatus* (Kawabe and Mano 1972); *Macaca mulatta* (lindburg 1971), *M. fuscata* (Itani 1972), *M. fascicularis* (Shirek-Ellefson 1967) and *M. nemestrina* (Bernstein 1967b).

The major concern early in the decade of the 1960s was to describe norms of behavior among free-ranging primates (Jay 1968). Similar to those of the late 1950s, the early 1960s studies were general. Almost all field studies in the volume *Primate Behavior: Field Studies of Monkeys and Apes* (DeVore 1965), are broad in terms of the kinds of information they report. By 1967 (Altmann 1967) and 1968 (Jay 1968), it was apparent that variation in behavior exists not only between species but within the same species from one location to another. Notions about what type of results were possible from long (versus short) field studies had changed from earlier expectations (Jay 1968). The value of the long-term study that spans at least one annual cycle, and ideally, more than one generation, is its potential for more accurately understanding the entire behavioral repetoire of a species.

Beginning in 1960 and continuing intermittently to the present, Jane Goodall has conducted field research on the same population of chimpanzees (e.g., 1965, 1968, 1975). One of Goodall's most exciting discoveries was that chimpanzees not only use but manufacture and transport tools (1964). The length of Goodall's research has been valuable in demonstrating how important long-term research is for a complete picture of species' behavior patterns. Although her early observations provided what was thought to be the basic behavior repertoire of the chimpanzee, her more recent investigations indicate the presence of heretofore unknown behaviors, such as violence and cannibalism (Goodall 1979).

Problem-oriented studies have more recently become the most important focus of primatology (Sussman 1979), but one early study deserves to be mentioned, that of Swiss developmental physiologist Hans Kummer. Spanning both the "Formative" and "Prolific" periods, Kummer (1968) demonstrated the use of controls in field research with his field experimentation on hamadryas baboons. He was the first to denote synchrony in female baboons and the tripartite structure of hamadryas social organization. His theories of causality (1971) provided a new way of looking at primate societies.

British zoologist Thelma Rowell conducted several studies, one of which was of forest-living baboons (*P. anubis*), which she simultaneously compared with a colony of captive baboons (Rowell 1966, 1967, 1969). Rowell's mentor was Robert Hinde, who had been a student of Niko Tinbergen, thus providing an example of the indirect influence of Tinbergen on the growth of primate studies (T. E. Rowell, personal communication 1977).

The above-mentioned are only two examples of many problem-oriented studies conducted in the Prolific period. The trend toward this kind of research is exemplified by Robert Sussman's *Primate Ecology: Problem-Oriented Studies* (1979), a volume that includes field studies and theoretical papers.

Conclusions and Summary

Primate field studies began slowly, but once interest was renewed in them after World War II, they rapidly increased, with more than 100 field studies conducted before 1970. Futher research to determine whether or not this trend continued through the 1970s is in preparation. Nevertheless, going from zero field studies before 1929 to 100 by 1970 represents a qualitatively new research endeavor rather than a specialization of some previously existing discipline.

In the initial phase, only psychologists were directly involved in field research. The Formative was ushered in by zoologists who were soon joined by anthropologists. Washburn was particularly important in the Formative and the Prolific periods in that he was responsible for establishing primate behavior as a subdiscipline of physical anthropology.

When understanding the origins of human behavior became more possible due to the increasing abundance of fossil hominids, it is not surprising that anthropologists, with their long tradition of field research on human social systems, began field studies on nonhuman primate social systems. Early studies were general, whereas the trend of more recent field research has been to conduct problem-oriented fieldwork.

For the convenience of the reader, the following chronological summary of events in the history of Old World primate field research is given:

1. 1929: Yerkes sent Bingham to observe free-ranging gorillas and Nissen to observe free-ranging chimpanzees.

2. 1930s: Carpenter conducted field studies on howler and spider monkeys and on gibbons.

3. 1938: Carpenter established a rhesus macaque colony on Cayo Santiago.

4. 1948: Japanese primatologists began studying free-ranging Japanese macaques, research that continues to the present.

5. 1952: Collias and Southwick conducted a field study on Barro Colorado, the first primate field research to be conducted by western scientists since 1937.

6. 1956: Altmann observed macaques on Cayo Santiago, the first Old World primate study by a western scientist.

7. 1958–1959: Dolhinow and DeVore, two of Washburn's students, conducted long-term field studies; they were the first anthropologists to conduct fieldwork on free-ranging primates.

8. 1960: A period of rapid growth in field studies began with anthropologists, zoologists, and psychologists contributing to the development of the multidisciplinary field of primatology that currently exists.

Acknowledgments

I wish to thank the Humboldt State University Foundation for their financial assistance, which enabled me to attend the 1981 annual meeting of the American Association of Physical Anthropologists where this paper was delivered in abbreviated form. The information provided by Sherry Washburn has been invaluable. Working with Frank Spencer, organizer of the symposium on which this volume is based, has been delightful, and I thank him for his patience. I also wish to thank Mrs. Judy Hampton for her excellent assistance in the preparation of this manuscript. Last but not least, I am deeply grateful for the continued support of Bertha Siegel and Barry Douglas.

References

Altmann, S. A.
  1959   Field observations on a howling monkey society. *Journal of Mammalogy* **40**:317–330.
  1965   Sociobiology of rhesus monkeys. II. Stochastics of social communication. *Journal of Theoretical Biology* **8**:490–522.
  1967   (editor) *Social communication among primates.* Chicago: University of Chicago Press.
Azuma, S.
  1966   Ecological study of wild chimpanzees in Tanganyika. *Abstract Proceeding of the International Meeting of the Anthropological Society of Nippon and Japanese Society of Ethnology* **19**:34.
Azuma, S., and A. Toyoshima
  1961–   Progress report of the survey on chimpanzees in their natural habitat, Kabogo Point area,
  1962   Tanganyika. *Primates* **3**:61–70.
  1965   Chimpanzees in Kabogo Point area, Tanganyika. In *Monkeys and Apes*, edited by S. Kawamura and J. Itani. Tokyo: Chuokoron. Pp. 127–183.
Bernstein, I. S.
  1967a   Intertaxa interactions in a Malayan community. *Folia Primatologica* **7**:198–207.
  1967b   A field study of the pigtail monkey (*Macaca nemestrina*). *Primates* **8**:217–228.
  1968   The lutong of Kuala Selangor. *Behaviour* **32**:1–16.
Bert, J., A. Ayats, A. Martino, and H. Collomb
  1967a   Le sommeil nocturne chez le babuin *Papio papio:* observation en milieu naturel et donnes électrophysiologiques. *Folia Primatologica* **6**:38–43.
  1967b   Note sur l'organisation de la vigilance sociale chez le babuin *Papio papio* dan l'est Senegalais. *Folia Primatologica* **6**:44–47.
Bingham, H. C.
  1932   Gorillas in a native habitat. *Carnegie Institution of Washington: Publication No.* **426**.
Brew, J. O. (editor)
  1968   *One hundred years of anthropology.* Cambridge, Massachusetts: Harvard University Press.
Buettner-Janusch, J.
  1962   The relatives of man: modern studies of the relation of the evolution of nonhuman primates to human evolution. *Annals of the New York Academy of Sciences* **102**(2):181–514.
Buxton, A. P.
  1951   Further observations on the night resting habits of monkeys in a small area on the edge of the Semliki Forest, Uganda. *Journal of Animal Ecology* **20**:31.
  1952   Observations on the diurnal behaviour of the redtail monkey (*Cercopithecus ascanius Schmidti* Matschie) in a small forest in Uganda. *Journal of Animal Ecology* **21**:25–58.
Carpenter, C. R.
  1934   A field study of the behavior and social relations of howling monkeys (*Alouatta palliata*). *Comparative Psychology Monographs* **10**(2):1–168.
  1935   Behavior of the red spider monkey (*Ateles geoffroyi*) in Panama. *Journal of Mammalology* **16**:171–180.
  1940   A field study in Siam of the behavior and social relations of the Gibbon (*Hylobates lar*). *Comparative Psychology Monographs* **16**(5):1–212.
  1942a   Sexual behavior of free-ranging rhesus monkeys (*Macaca mulatta*). I. Specimens, procedures and behavioral characteristics of estrus. *Journal of Comparative Psychology* **33**:113–142.
  1942b   Sexual behavior of free-ranging rhesus monkeys (*Macaca mulatta*). II. Periodicity of estrus, homosexual, autoerotic and non-conformist behavior. *Journal of Comparative Psychology* **33**:143–162.
  1942c   Societies of monkeys and apes. *Biological Symposia* **8**:177–204.
  1945   Concepts and problems of primate sociometry. *Sociometry* **8**:56–61.

1964   *Naturalistic behavior of nonhuman primates.* University Park: Pennsylvania State University Press.

Carpenter, C. R., and A. Nishimura
1969   The Takasakiyama colony of Japanese macaques (*Macaca fuscata*). *Proceedings of the 2nd International Congress of Primatology, 1968* 1:16–30.

Chalmers, N. R.
1968a   Group composition, ecology and daily activities of free-living mangabeys in Uganda. *Folia Primatologica* 8:247–262.
1968b   The social behaviour of free-living mangabeys in Uganda. *Folia Primatologica* 8:263–281.
1968c   The visual and vocal communication of free-living mangabeys in Uganda. *Folia Primatologica* 9:258–280.

Collias, N., and C. H. Southwick
1952   A field study of population density and social organization in howling monkeys. *Proceedings of the American Philosophical Society* 96:143–156.

Collidge, H. J.
1929   A revision of the genus *Gorilla. Memoirs of the Harvard Museum of Comparative Zoology* 50:293–381.
1930   Notes on the gorilla. In *The African Republic of Liberia and the Belgian Congo*, edited by R. P. Strong, II. Cambridge, Massachusetts: Harvard University Press. Pp. 623–635.
1933   *Pan paniscus*, pygmy chimpanzee from south of the Congo River. *American Journal of Anthropology* 18:1–59.
1936   Zoological results of the George Vanderbilt African expedition of 1934. Part IV. Notes on four gorillas from the Sanga River region. *Proceedings of the Academy of Natural Sciences of Philadelphia* 88:479–501.

Crook, J. H.
1966   Gelada baboon herd structure and movement—a comparative report. *Symposia of the Zoological Society of London* 18:237–248.

Dart, R. A.
1925   *Australopithecus africanus*: the man–ape of South Africa. *Nature (London)* 115:195–199.

DeVore, I.
1963   Comparative ecology and behavior of monkeys and apes. In *Classification and human evolution*, edited by S. L. Washburn. Chicago: Aldine. Pp. 301–319.
1965   (editor) *Primate behavior: field studies of monkeys and apes.* New York: Holt.

DeVore, I., and K. R. L. Hall
1965   Baboon ecology. In *Primate behavior: field studies of monkeys and apes*, edited by I. DeVore. New York: Holt. Pp. 20–52.

DeVore, I., and S. L. Washburn
1963   Baboon ecology and human evolution. In *African ecology and human evolution*, edited by F. C. Howell and F. Bourliere. Chicago: Aldine. Pp. 335–367.

Dobzhansky, T.
1944   On species and races of living and fossil man. *American Journal of Physical Anthropology* 2:251–265.

Donisthorpe, J.
1958   A pilot study of the mountain gorilla. *South African Journal of Science* 54:195–217.

Ellefson, J. O.
1968   Territorial behavior in the common white-handed gibbon, *Hylobates lar* Linn. In *Primates: studies in adaptation and variability*, edited by P. C. Jay. New York: Holt. Pp. 180–189.

Emlen, J. T., and G. B. Schaller
1960   Distribution and status of the mountain gorilla (*Gorilla gorilla beringei*)—1959. *Zoologica* 45(1):41–52.

Fossey, D.
1970   Making friends with mountain gorillas. *National Geographic Magazine* 137:48–68.

Frisch, J. E.
  1959   Research on primate behavior in Japan. *American Anthropologist* **61**:584–596.
  1963   Japan's contribution to modern anthropology. In *Studies in Japanese culture*, edited by J.
          Roggendorf. Tokyo: Sophia University. Pp. 225–244.
Gartlan, J. S.
  1968   K. R. L. Hall: a memoir. In *Primates: studies in adaptation and variability*, edited by P. C. Jay.
          New York: Holt. Pp. 1–3.
  1969   *Evolutionary implications of the social structure and organization of the drill*, Mandrillus
          leucophaeus. *Wenner–Gren Symposium on Primates* No. 43. New York: Wenner-Gren
          Foundation for Anthropological Research.
Gautier-Hion, A.
  1966   L'écologie et l'ethologie du talapoin, *Miopithecus talapoin talapoin*. Biologica Gabonica
          2(4):311–329.
Gee, E. P.
  1961   The distribution and feeding habits of the golden langur, *Presbytis geei* Gee (Khajivia,
          1956). *Journal of the Bombay Natural History Society* **58**:1–12.
Goodall, J.
  1964   Tool-using and aimed throwing in a community of free-living chimpanzees. *Nature*
          (London) **201**:1264–1266.
  1965   Chimpanzees of the Gombe Stream Reserve. In *Primate behavior: field studies of monkeys and
          apes*, edited by I. DeVore. New York: Holt. Pp. 425–473.
  1968   The behaviour of free-living chimpanzees in the Gombe Stream Reserve. *Animal Behaviour
          Monograph* **1**:161–311.
  1975   Chimpanzees of Gombe National Park: thirteen years of research. In *Hominisation and
          Verhalten*, edited by I. Eibesfeldt. Stuttgart: Fischer. Pp. 74–136.
  1979   Intercommunity Interactions in the chimpanzee population of the Gombe National Park.
          In *The great apes*, edited by D. A. Hamburg and E. R. McCown. Menlo Park, California:
          Benjamin/Cummings. Pp. 13–53.
Gregory, W. K.
  1922   *The origin and evolution of the human dentition*. Baltimore, Maryland: Williams and Wilkins.
Haddow, A. J.
  1952   Field and laboratory studies on an African monkey, *C. ascanius schmidti* Matschie.
          Proceedings of the Zoological Society of London **122**(II):297–394.
Haddow, A. J., K. G. Smithburn, A. F. Mahaffy, and J. C. Bugher
  1947   Monkeys in relation to yellow fever in Bwamba County, Uganda. *Transactions of the Royal
          Society of Tropical Medicine and Hygiene* **40**:677–700.
Hall, K. R. L.
  1962a   Numerical data, maintenance activities and locomotion of the chacma baboon, *Papio
          ursinus*. *Proceedings of the Zoological Society of London* **139**:181–220.
  1962b   The sexual, agonistic and derived social behaviour patterns of the wild chacma baboon,
          Papio ursinus. *Proceedings of the Zoological Society of London* **139**:283–327.
  1963   Some problems in the analysis and comparison of monkey and ape behavior. In
          Classification and human evolution, edited by S. L. Washburn. Chicago: Aldine, Pp. 273–300.
  1965a   Experiment and quantification in the study of baboon behavior in its natural habitat. In *The
          baboon in medical research*, edited by H. Vagtborg. Austin: University of Texas Press. Pp. 29–
          42.
  1965b   Behaviour and ecology of the wild patas monkey, *Erythrocebus patas*, in Uganda. *Journal of
          Zoology* **148**:15–87.
Hall, K. R. L., and I. DeVore
  1965   Baboon social behavior. In *Primate behavior: field studies of monkeys and apes*, edited by I.
          DeVore. New York: Holt. Pp. 53–110.
Hall, K. R. L., and Gartlan, J. S.

1965   Ecology and behaviour of the vervet monkey, *Cercopithecus aethiops*, Lolui Island, Lake Victoria. *Proceedings of the Zoological Society of London* **145**:37–56.

Hall, K. R. L., and M. J. Goswell
1964   Aspects of social learning in captive patas monkeys. *Primates* **5**(3–4):59–70.

Hall, K. R. L., and B. Mayer
1967   Social interactions of a group of captive patas monkeys (*Erythrocebus patas*). *Folia Primatologica* **5**:213–236.

Hall, K. R. L., R. C. Boelkins, and M. J. Goswell
1965   Behaviour of patas, *Erythrocebus patas*, in captivity, with notes on the natural habitat. *Folia Primatologica* **3**:22–49.

Haraway, D.
1978   Animal sociology and a natural economy of the body politic. Part II. The past is the contested zone; human nature and theories of production and reproduction in primate behavior studies. *Signs* **4**(1):37–60.

Hooton, E. A.
1942   *Man's poor relations*. New York: Doubleday.
1955   The importance of primate studies in anthropology. In *The nonhuman primates in human evolution*, edited by J. A. Gavan. Detroit, Michigan: Wayne University Press. Pp. 1–10.

Horr, D.
1977   The borneo orang-utan. In *Primate ecology: problem-oriented field studies*, edited by R. W. Sussman. New York: Wiley. Pp. 317–321.

Hutt, S. J., and C. Hutt
1970   *Direct observation and measurement of behavior*. Springfield, Illinois: Thomas.

Huxley, J. S.
1942   *Evolution, the modern synthesis*. London: Allen and Unwin.

Imanishi, K.
1957   Social behavior in Japanese monkeys, *Macaca fuscata*. *Psychologia* **1**:47–54.
1960   Social organization of sub-human primates in their natural habitats. *Current Anthropology* **1**(5–6):393–407.

Itani, J.
1972   The social structure of primates. In *Ecology*, Vol. 2, edited by S. Morishita *et al.* Tokyo: Kyoritsu-Shuppan. Pp. 1–161. (J)
1975   Twenty years with Mount Takasaki monkeys. In *Primate utilization and conservation*, edited by G. Bermant and D. G. Lindburg. New York: Wiley. Pp. 101–125.
1979   Distribution and adaptation of chimpanzees in an arid land. In *The great apes*, edited by D. Hamburg and E. R. McCowan. Menlo Park, California: Benjamin/Cummings. Pp. 55–71.

Itani, J., and A. Suzuki
1967   The social unit of wild chimpanzees. *Primates* **8**:355–381.

Jay, P. C.
1962   Aspects of maternal behavior among langurs. *Annals of the New York Academy of Sciences* **102**:468–476.
1963   The Indian langur monkey. In *Primate social behavior*, edited by C. H. Southwick. Princeton, Van Nostrand-Reinhold. Pp. 114–123.
1965   The common langur of North India. In *Primate behavior: field studies of monkeys and apes*, edited by I. DeVore. New York: Holt. Pp. 197–249.

Jay, P. C. (editor)
1968   *Primates: studies and adaptation and variability*. New York: Holt.

Kano, T.
1971   The chimpanzees of Filabanga, western Tanzania. *Primates* **12**:229–246.
1972   Distribution and adaptation of the chimpanzee on the eastern shore of Lake Tanganyika. *Kyoto University, African Studies* **7**:37–129.

Kawabe, M., and T. Mano

1972   Ecology and behavior of the wild proboscis monkey (*Nasalis larvatus* Wurmb) in Sabah, Malaysia. *Primates* **13**:213–228.

Kawai, M.
1963   On the newly-acquired behavior of the natural troop of Japanese monkeys on Koshima Island. *Primates* **4**:113–115.

Kawai, M., and H. Mizuhara
1962   An ecological study of the wild mountain gorilla (*Gorilla gorilla beringei*). *Primates* **2**:1–42.

Kawai, M., A. Tsumori, and R. Motoyoshi
1965   Delayed response of wild Japanese monkeys by the sand-digging method (I). *Primates* **6**(2):195–212.

Klein, L., and D. Klein
1973   Observations on two types of neotropical primate intertaxa associations. *American Journal of Physical Anthropology* **38**:649–653.

Koford, C.
1963a   Group relations in an island colony of Rhesus monkeys. In *Primate social behavior,* edited by C. H. Southwick. Princeton, New Jersey: Van Nostrand-Reinhold. Pp. 136–152.
1963b   Rank of mothers and sons in bands of rhesus monkeys. *Science* **141**:356–357.
1965   Population dynamics of rhesus monkeys on Cayo Santiago. In *Primate behavior: field studies of monkeys and apes,* edited by I. DeVore. New York: Holt. Pp. 160–174.

Kohler, W.
1925   *The mentality of apes.* London: Kegan Paul.

Kohts, N.
1923   *Untersuchungen uber die Erkenntnisfahigkeiten des Schimpansen* (in Russian with German translation of summary). Moscow: Museum Darwinianum.

Kroeber, A. L.
1928   Sub-human culture beginnings. *Quarterly Review of Biology* **3**:325–342.

Kuhn, T. S.
1970   *The structure of scientific revolutions* (second edition). Chicago: University of Chicago Press.

Kummer, H.
1968   *Social organization of Hamadryas baboons: a field study.* Chicago: University of Chicago Press.
1971   *Primate societies: group techniques of ecological adaptation.* Chicago: Aldine-Atherton.

Lancaster, J. B.
1971   Play-mothering: the relations between juvenile females and young infants among free-ranging vervet monkeys (*Ceropithecus aethiops*). *Folia Primatologica* **15**:161–182.

Lancaster, J. B., and R. B. Lee
1965   The annual reproductive cycle in monkeys and apes. In *Primate behavior: field studies of monkeys and apes,* edited by I. DeVore. New York: Holt. Pp. 486–513.

Leakey, L. S. B.
1959   A new fossil skull from Olduvai. *Nature* (*London*) **201**:967–970.

Le Gros Clark, W. E.
1940   Palaeontological evidence bearing on human evolution. *Biological Review of the Cambridge Philosophical Society* **15**:202.

Lindburg, D.
1971   The rhesus monkey in North India. In *Primate behavior: developments in field and laboratory research,* edited by L. A. Rosenblum. New York: Academic Press. Pp. 2–106.

Lumsden, W. H. R.
1951   The night resting habits of monkeys in a small area on the edge of the Smeliki Forest, Uganda. A study in relation to the epidemiology of sylvan yellow fever. *Journal of Animal Ecology* **20**:11–30.

McCown, T. D., and K. A. R. Kennedy
1972   *Climbing man's family tree.* Englewood Cliffs, New Jersey: Prentice-Hall.

MacKinnon, J.

1969 The Oxford University expedition to Sabah 1968. *Oxford University Explorers Club Bulletin* **17**(4):53–70.

MacRoberts, M. H.
 1968 The social organization of Barbary apes. (*Macaca sylvana*). Ph.D. thesis, University of California at Berkeley.

Marler, P.
 1969 *Colobus gureza*: territoriality and group composition. *Science* **163**:93–95.

Mayr, E.
 1942 *Systematics and the origin of species.* New York: Columbia University Press.

Miyadi, D.
 1964 Report on the activity of the Japan–India Joint Project in Primates Investigation. *Primates* **5**(3–4):1–6.

Morrison, J. A., and E. W. Menzel, Jr.
 1972 Adaptation of a free-ranging rhesus monkey group to division and transplantation. *Wildlife Monographs* **31**:1–78.

Napier, J.
 1963 *The Primates. Zoological Society of London No.* **10**. London: Zoological Society of London.

Nishida, T.
 1968 The social group of wild chimpanzees in the Mahali Mountains. *Primates* **9**:167–224.

Nissen, H. W.
 1931 A field study of the chimpanzee. *Comparative Psychology Monographs* **8**(1):1–122.

Nolte, A.
 1955 Field observations on the daily routine and social behavior of common Indian monkeys, with special reference to the Bonnet Monkey (*Macaca radiata* Geoffroy). *Journal of the Bombay Natural Historical Society* **53**:177–184.

Osborn, R.
 1963 Behaviour of the mountain gorilla. *Symposia of the Zoological Society of London* **10**:29–37.

Penniman, T. K.
 1965 *A hundred years of anthropology.* New York: International Universities Press.
 1974 *A hundred years of anthropology.* New York: William Morrow.

Poirier, F. E.
 1968a The Nilgiri langur (*Presbytis johnii*) mother-infant dyad. *Primates* **9**:45–68.
 1968b Nilgiri langur (*Presbytis johnii*) territorial behavior. *Primates* **9**:351–364.

Poirier, F. E.
 1968c The ecology and social behavior of the Nilgiri langur (*Presbytis johnii*) of South India. Unpublished Ph.D. dissertation, Department of Anthropology, University of Oregon, Eugene.

Ripley, S.
 1967 Intertroop encounters among Ceylon gray langurs (*Presbytis entellus*). In *Social communication in primates*, edited by S. A. Altmann. Chicago: University of Chicago Press.

Rowell, T. E.
 1966 Forest living baboons in Uganda. *Journal of Zoology* **149**:344–364.
 1967 A quantitative comparison of the behaviour of a wild and a caged baboon group. *Animal Behaviour* **15**:499–509.
 1969 Long-term changes in a population of Ugandan baboons. *Folia Primatologica* **11**:241–254.

Sabater Pi, J.
 1973 Contribution to the ecology of *Colobus polykomos satanas* (Wasterhouse 1838) of Rio Muni, Republic of Equatorial Guinea. *Folia Primatologica* **19**:193–207.

Sade, D.
 1965 Some aspects of parent-offspring and sibling relations in a group of rhesus monkeys, with a discussion of grooming. *American Journal of Physical Anthropology* **23**:1–18.

Schaller, G. B.

1963   *The mountain gorilla: ecology and benavior.* Chicago: University of Chicago Press.
1965   The behavior of the mountain gorilla. In *Primate behavior: field studies of monkeys and apes,* edited by I. DeVore. New York: Holt. Pp. 324–367.

Schultz, A. H.
1963   Age changes, sex differences and variability as factors in the classification of primates. In *Classification and human evolution,* edited by S. L. Washburn. Chicago: Aldine. Pp. 85–115.

Shirek-Ellefson, J.
1967   Visual communication in *Macaca irus.* Unpublished Ph.D. dissertation, Department of Anthropology, University of California at Berkeley.

Simonds, P. E.
1961   The Japan Monkey Centre. *Current Anthropology* 3(3):303–305.
1965   The bonnet macaque in South India. In *Primate behavior: field studies of monkeys and apes,* edited by I. DeVore. New York: Holt. Pp. 175–196.

Simpson, G. G.
1949   *The meaning of evolution.* New Haven, Connecticut: Yale University Press.

Southwick, C. H.
1961   Social behavior of rhesus monkeys in a temple habitat in northern India. *American Zoologist* 1(3):390.

Southwick, C. H. (editor)
1963   *Primate social behavior.* Princeton, New Jersey: Van Nostrand-Reinhold.

Southwick, C. H., M. A. Beg, and M. R. Siddiqi
1965   Rhesus monkeys in North India. In *Primate behavior: field studies of monkeys and apes,* edited by I. DeVore. New York: Holt. Pp. 111–159.

Stoltz, L. P., and G. S. Saayman
1970   Ecology and behaviour of baboons in the northern Transvaal. *Annals of the Transvaal Museum* 26:99–143.

Straus, W. L. Jr.
1955   Closing remarks. In *The nonhuman primates and human evolution,* edited by J. A. Gavan. Detroit: Wayne State University Press. Pp. 126–134.

Struhsaker, T. T.
1967   Behavior of vervet monkeys (*Cercopithecus aethiops*). *University of California, Berkeley, Publications in Zoology* 82:1–74.

Sugiyama, Y.
1965   Short history of the ecological and sociological studies on nonhuman primates in Japan. *Primates* 6:457–460.
1968   Social organization of chimpanzees in the Budongo forest, Uganda. *Primates* 9:225–258.
1969   Social behavior of chimpanzees in the Budongo forest, Uganda. *Primates* 10:197–225.

Sussman, R. W.
1979   *Primate ecology: problem-oriented field studies.* New York: Wiley.

Suzuki, A.
1969   An ecological study of chimpanzees in a savanna woodland. *Primates* 10:103–148.

Thorndike, E. L.
1901   The mental life of monkeys. *Psychological Review Monographs, Supplement No.* 15.

Ullrich, W.
1961   Zur biologie und Soziologie der Colobusaffen. *Der Zoologische Garten* 25(6):305–368.

Vandenberg, J. G.
1967   The development of social structure in free-ranging rhesus monkeys. *Behaviour* 29:179–194.

Washburn, S. L.
1947   The relation of the temporal muscle to the form of the skull. *Anatomical Record* 99(3):239–248.
1961   *Social life of early man.* Chicago: Aldine.
1963   Behavior and human evolution. In *Classification and human evolution,* edited by S. L. Washburn. Chicago: Aldine. Pp. 91–105.

1973   The promise of primatology. *American Journal of Physical Anthropology* **38**:177–182.

1977   Field study of primate behavior. In *Progress in ape research,* edited by G. H. Bourne. New York: Academic Press. Pp. 231–242.

Washburn, S. L., and V. Avis

1958   Evolution of human behavior. In *Behavior and evolution,* edited by A. Roe and G. G. Simpson. New Haven, Connecticut: Yale University Press. Pp. 421–436.

Washburn S. L., and I. DeVore

1961a   The social life of baboons. *Scientific American* **204**(6):63–71.

1961b   Social behavior of baboons and early man. *Viking Fund Publications in Anthropology* **31**:91–104.

Wilson, A. P.

1968   Social behavior of free-ranging rhesus monkeys with an emphasis on aggression. Unpublished Ph.D. Dissertation, Department of Anthropology, University of California at Berkeley.

Yerkes, R. M., and A. W. Yerkes

1929   *The great apes.* New Haven, Connecticut: Yale University Press. (Republished, 1970, New York: Johnson Reprint).

Yoshiba, K.

1968   Local and intertroop variability in ecology and social behavior of common Indian langurs. In *Primates: studies of adaptation and variability,* edited by P. C. Jay. New York: Holt. Pp. 217–242.

Zuckerman, S.

1932   *The social life of monkeys and apes.* London: Routledge and Kegan Paul. A second edition of Zuckerman's *Social life of monkeys and apes* was published in 1981 by Routledge and Kegan Paul. This edition is identical to the first, but has a number of appendixes in which the author continues to explore topics begun in the first. Additionally, it includes survey articles on the behavior of various nonhuman primates written by experts in the field.

1966   *Scientists and war.* New York: Harper.

4

Primate Neuroanatomy:
An Evolutionary Perspective[1]

Dean Falk

My task is to review the progress of research in primate neuroanatomy during the past 50 years. This is a large subject that spans cortical mapping studies; comparative neurology; endocasts and cranial capacities from extant and fossil primates, including hominids; descriptions of brains representing various human groups as well as nonhuman primates; and methods of quantitative analysis, including those used in allometric investigations. Because the data are so extensive, I have organized this report on a decade-by-decade basis and have attempted to confine it as much as possible to the perspective of the physical anthropologist.

The 1930s

Although much of the paleoneurological literature that was published during the 1930s was descriptive, important foundations for future brain research were established during this decade in the areas of gross morphology of nonhuman primate brains, cortical mapping studies, and morphology or cortices (endocasts) of extant and fossil human groups. The most widely studied fossil hominid of the 1930s was *Homo erectus* (*Sinanthropus*), and an important paleoneurological "institution" was established in America with the initiation of the James Arthur lectures on human brain evolution.

---

[1]This paper is dedicated to the memory of George Sacher (1917–1981) whose research on quantitative analyses of mammalian brain evolution ended much too soon.

A HISTORY OF AMERICAN
PHYSICAL ANTHROPOLOGY, 1930–1980

During the early 1930s, gross descriptions of ape brains were published, and brain indices were provided for apes (Connolly 1932, 1933). Fulton (1938) described the cytoarchitecture of the gorilla brain. Among apes, the brain of the chimpanzee was favored with published descriptions of the configuration of the cerebral hemispheres (Walker and Fulton 1936) and the arterial supply of the cerebral cortex (Shellshear 1930), and in a comparative study of endocasts and corresponding brains from six chimpanzee skulls (Le Gros Clark *et al.* 1936). This latter important study showed that endocasts prepared from chimpanzee skulls do not reliably reproduce the central, caudal portions of Sylvian, lunate, and temporal sulci.

The brains of nonhominoid primates were also examined during the 1930s. Mettler (1933) described the brain of *Macaca* from the Old World; von Bonin (1938), the sulcal pattern and cytoarchitecture of the cerebral cortex of *Cebus* from the New World. In 1936, Connolly published an article on the fissural patterns of primate brains in the *American Journal of Physical Anthropology* (*AJPA*) that would later be incorporated into his monograph (1950) on brains, which spanned the primate order.

Important data regarding the organization of the cerebral cortex were gathered during the 1930s for both nonhuman and human primates. Methods used to determine cortical maps, using the term *mapping* in the broad sense (Welker 1976), included excision of cerebral substance, application of strychnine solution on the cortex, electrical stimulation, electrocorticograms, evoked potentials, and cyto-architecture. Motor representations for tails were mapped for several genera of monkeys, including prehensile tailed *Ateles* (Fulton and Dusser De Barenne 1933). The functional organization of the sensory cortex was also described for *Macaca* (Dusser De Barenne and McCulloch 1938), as was the organization of the primate thalamus (Walker 1938). In 1939, Klüver and Bucy conducted a preliminary analysis of functions of the temporal lobe in monkey and Dusser De Barenne and McCulloch mapped the sensory cortex of the chimpanzee.

Pioneer work during the 1930s that resulted in cortical maps of human brains was conducted most notably by Wilder Penfield and his associates. Clinical studies and the surgical treatment of epilepsy inspired much of this research (Penfield and Boldrey 1939). Thus, Penfield investigated the mechanism of intracranial pain (1935), somatic motor and sensory representations in the human cerebral cortex (Penfield and Boldrey 1937), the cerebral cortex and consciousness (Penfield 1938), and the role of the frontal lobe in humans (Penfield and Evans 1935). The somatic sensory cortex in humans was also studied by Bard (1938) and by Evans (1935), and Cohn and Papez (1930) examined the striate cortex in humans. Motor representations of leg muscles were investigated by Woolsey (1938), and the human motor cortex was further discussed in light of epilepsy (Foerster 1936).

The 1930s is noteworthy for numerous publications describing brains that represent extant human races (Connolly 1931). Articles were published on the brains (or portions thereof) of Chinese (Wen 1933), Koreans (Shibata 1936), Kanja natives (Vint 1934), Bushmen (Shellshear 1934), Jakuts (Bushmakin 1936),

Australian Aborigines (Shellshear 1937), and South African Blacks (Schepers 1938). Levin (1937) studied "inferiority characters" such as exposed insulas, lunate sulci, and continuous callosomarginalis sulci, in racial groups and compared their incidences to those manifested in hemispheres from "great personalities". He concluded that "most of the 'inferiority signs' have no justification to be regarded as such. Studies on the brains of the so-called inferior human races are as yet, inconclusive [1937]." Levin's findings would be confirmed much later by Tobias (1970).

By the onset of the 1930s, representatives of *Australopithecus, H. erectus,* and Neandertal and Upper Paleolithic hominids had been discovered. Because an international team had excavated numerous hominid remains at Choukoutien in China in the 1920s and 1930s, much attention was focused on *Sinanthropus (H. erectus)* during the 1930s. Its endocast was described (Black 1933) and compared to endocasts of other *H. erectus* individuals (Dubois 1933; Weidenreich, 1937, 1938), Neandertals (Ariëns Kappers 1933) and apes (Shellshear and Elliot Smith 1934; Weidenreich 1936). In his comparative study, Weidenreich (1936) provided a detailed description of endocasts of *Sinanthropus* and showed that most of the sulcal pattern, including the lunate sulcus, was not reproduced on these endocasts. He stressed the importance of endocast shape, however, and determined that height–length indices varied from *H. erectus* to Neandertal to *H. sapiens* endocasts. Additional *H. erectus* endocasts were described during the 1930s. These included endocasts of Solo skulls (Ariëns Kappers 1936) and endocasts of *Pithecanthropus* from Java (Ariëns Kappers and Bouman 1939). Based on his comparative study of endocasts, Weidenreich (1936) determined that *Sinanthropus* and *Pithecanthropus* should be palced in the same taxon, preceding that of the Neandertals.

In addition to those of *H. erectus,* endocasts of more recent hominids were prepared and described during the 1930s. These include Neandertal (Ariëns Kappers 1933), Kanjera I from Kenya (Leakey 1935), Ehringsdorf from Germany (Ariëns Kappers 1936), Skhul V from Mount Carmel (Keith and McCown 1939), Swanscombe from England (Le Gros Clark 1938), and Florisbad from South Africa (Dreyer 1936; Drennan 1937).

As noted by Weidenreich (1936) and Le Gros Clark *et al.* (1936), endocasts prepared from hominoid skulls do not usually reproduce details of sulcal pattern. Thus, the 1930s publications on fossil hominid endocasts relied on gross descriptive techniques, such as estimating cranial capacity, determining indices related to endocast shape, describing expansions in certain areas, and noting asymmetries.

One endocast from a relatively small-brained early hominid of the genus *Australopithecus* was described during the 1930s (Le Gross Clark *et al.* 1936). The Taung specimen was a natural endocast (i.e., it was formed as the result of natural processes in a lime-rich environment of South Africa). This specimen reproduces a surprising amount of sulcal pattern for a hominid, as do several of the six other available South African natural australopithecine endocasts (Falk 1980a). Based on surface features, proportions, and contours, Le Gros Clark *et al.* (1936) showed that the endocast of humans, as Dart (1925) had suggested. As noted above, Le Gros

Clark *et al.*'s study was a careful one based on comparisons of six chimpanzee brains with six corresponding endocasts (i.e., from the same skulls that produced the brains), and it is ironic that Le Gros Clark would later (1947) incorrectly (Falk 1980a) reverse his opinion regarding the Taung endocast (see the discussion in the next section).

Paleoneurological work done in the 1930s was largely descriptive. Inspired by the wide attention given Peking Man (*Sinanthropus*), physical anthropologists emphasized hominid endocasts and brains in their paleoneurological investigations. However, the 1930s produced little in the way of the sophisticated quantification that would later characterize the 1960s and 1970s. Two articles investigated the relationship between brain (endocast) size and skull size in humans (Pickering 1930; Ariëns Kappers 1932) and two others discussed methods of determining cranial capacities (Stewart 1933, 1937). Von Bonin (1937) provided brain weights and body weights for various adult mammals, including primates. Roginsky's (1933) quadratic index foreshadowed later attempts to establish measures of relative brain size that would control for the allometric scaling due to body size.

Finally, an important contribution to American paleoneurology during the 1930s was the establishment by the American Museum of Natural History of the annual James Arthur lecture series on human brain evolution. The inaugural lecture, given by Frederick Tilney in 1932, was titled "The Brain in Relation to Behavior."

The 1940s

Interest in the brains of fossil and extant humans continued during the 1940s, although with less intensity than was apparent during the 1930s. Endocasts of Saccopastore I and II (Sergi 1942, 1944) and the relatively recent Tepexpan Man (DeTerra *et al.* 1949) were described, and the *Sinanthropus* specimens continued to be interpreted by Weidenreich (1941, 1943). During the 1940s, there was a new emphasis on the relationship between brains and skulls as well as a fledgling interest in quantitative techniques for analyzing primate brain evolution.

If *Sinanthropus* was the center of attention during the 1930s, the fossil hominid that was the focus of most paleoneurological investigation during the 1940s was *Australopithecus africanus* from South Africa (Broom and Schepers 1946; Clark 1947; Broom and Robinson 1948). In particular, Schepers described natural endocasts of several South African australopithecines and stated that their sulcal pattern appeared to be human-like rather than pongid-like. This assertion was in keeping with Dart's (1925) claim that the lunate sulcus of the Taung specimen occupied a caudal position similar to that of the lunate sulcus in humans. Le Gros Clark (1947) agreed with Broom and Schepers, thus reversing his early opinion (Le Gros Clark *et al.* 1936). The Broom and Schepers description of australopithecine cortices as "human-like" influenced thinking on human brain evolution through the 1970s. For example, according to Holloway, the "minimal interpretation" of the caudal position of the lunate sulcus is that "by the time of the Taung child, the hominid brain was already reorganized in a human direction, regardless of the chimpanzee-like size [1972b:198]."

Recently, I redescribed the available South African australopithecine natural endocasts, including the Taung specimen (Falk 1980a), and came to the conclusion that, contrary to the literature, these endocasts reproduce an overall ape-like rather than human-like sulcal pattern. In particular, the position of the lunate sulcus could not have been caudal to the lambdoid suture (because of its position relative to the lateral calcarine sulcus), and, as others have suggested, it may have been as far forward as the indentation that Broom and Schepers (1946) labeled the "parieto–occipital sulcus."

The 1940s descriptions of australopithecine endocasts must be viewed in an historical context. After his announcement of the discovery of the Taung specimen and naming of *Australopithecus africanus* in 1925, Dart had to defend his assertion that "the specimen is of importance because it exhibits an extinct race of apes intermeditate between living anthropoids and man [1925:195]." Perhaps it was in response to critics who dismissed the importance of these fossils, that early workers such as Broom and Schepers emphasized the human-like attributes of the "ape-men" and downplayed their apelike features.

Researchers continued to describe the brains of extant human groups during the 1940s. Connolly (1940) discussed in the ontogentic development of sulci, and Stewart (1943) reported on the variability in cranial capacities and other indices in skulls of Native Americans and Caucasians. Sulcal patterns were described for a large series of Chinese brains (Chi and Chang 1941), and Packer (1949) compared the endocast and brain of an Australian Aborigine. Several publications explored race differences in curvature (Woo 1949) and sulcal pattern (Connolly 1941, 1942) in various lobes of the human brain. Most of these publications were purely descriptive (i.e., they did not attempt to interpret functionally group differences in brain morphology when they were shown to exist). (However, see Gamble [1944] for an attempt to correlate causally racial types with certain psychoses!)

Cortices of extant humans were studied in further detail. The frontal lobe was of interest from the point of view of surgical experiments and speech functions (Penfield and Rasmussen 1949) as well as prefrontal lobotomies (Meyer *et al.* 1947). Research on epilepsy continued to play an important role in determining cerebral functions (Penfield and Erickson 1941), and cytoarchitecture was becoming more widely used to map primate brains (von Bonin 1944; Lashley and Clark 1946).

Cytoarchitecture involves delimiting cortical areas based on the arrangement of cells in a nervous structure. This method was used by Brodmann, whose cortical maps are still used today. Subjective and nonreproducible descriptions of minute morphological differences in lamina or cell structure became common during the early 1900 (Zilles *et al.* 1981), and this development led to the publication of papers, such as Lashley and Clark's (1946), that were severely critical of cytoarchitectonic investigations. However, today it is known that areas obtained by cytoarchitecture analyses "tend to correlate well with those obtained by neurophysiological mapping and by studies of cortical fiber connectivity [Galaburda and Pandya 1981 2:204]."

Researchers continued to publish functional maps of nonhuman primate cortices during the 1940s. Numerous maps of the sensory cortices of monkeys (Dusser De Barrene *et al.* 1941; Marchall *et al.* 1945; Woolsey 1944; Woolsey *et al.* 1942) as well as the visual cortices of monkeys (Lashley 1948; Solnitzky and Harman 1946) were provided. The sensory cortex was also mapped for the chimpanzee (Bailey *et al.* 1940; Woolsey *et al.* 1943). Sperry (1947) discussed cerebral control of motor functions in monkey, and Baily *et al.* (1943) compared long association fibers in the cerebral hemispheres of monkey and chimpanzee. The neocortex was described for *Galago* (von Bonin 1945), *Callithrix* (Peden and von Bonin 1947), *Macaca* (von Bonin and Bailey 1947), and numerous genera of platyrrhine monkeys (Anthony 1946).

Besides the expected papers on human brain weight (Appel and Appel 1942) and techniques for determining cranial capacity (Tildesley and Datta-Majunder 1944), there was, during the 1940s a keen interest among researchers in the relationship between the brain and the skull. Weidenreich (1941, 1947) concluded that the increase in brain size that occurred during human evolution was an "orthogenetic development," and that concomitant transformations of hominid skulls were an inevitable result of these changes in brain size. Von Bonin (1942) was also interested in the relationship between skull and brain, as was Le Gros Clark (1945), who suggested that the sulcal patterns of primate brains may partially be the result of resistance to expansion of the cortex caused by extrinsic mechanical factors, such as large orbits.

Weidenreich's work (1941, 1947), along with Schultz's (1940), provided basic data on allometry in primates. Schultz's (1941) article on relative cranial capacity in primates presented data on ontogenetic and phylogenetic curves of relative brain size. These data would much later play an important part in our understanding of "encephalization quotients" and other indices related to allometry. Along similar lines, basic brain weight–body weight data for mammals were published by Crile and Quiring (1940) and Count (1947). These data were destined to become a mainstay of allometric studies in the 1970s and 1980s.

Hirschler (1942) published a detailed monograph comparing anthropoid and human endocasts. His concern with detecting curvatures and asymmetries of various parts of endocasts, as well as general endocast shape, foreshadowed more recent work, such as that of Kochetkova (1978). Von Bonin (1941) also manifested a concern with primate brain shape as described by indices determined directly from brains (encephalometry). Despite the seeds of quantitative analysis that were sown in the 1940s by Weindenreich, Schultz, and von Bonin, the decade was generally characterized by simplistic approaches for understanding brain evolution. For example, Keith (1948) elucidated his theory of the cerebral "rubicon" (i.e., his belief that a critical mass of 750 cc of brain was required to attain human status). Keith's theory inspired lively discussion in the subsequent literature about the meaning of brain size, and during the 1950s, much energy was expended determining cranial capacities of fossil and extant hominids.

The 1950s

The 1950s was truly an in-between decade for the paleoneurological research of the past 50 years. The number of purely descriptive studies of primate brains subsided relative to previous years, and the studies of brains representing extant human races, which were so prevalent in the 1930s and 1940s, ceased. Many of the data on the morphology and functional organization of primate, including human, cortices that were published during the previous two decades were summarized in monographs during the 1950s. In addition to culminating earlier descriptive work, the 1950s also provided important foundations for future investigations regarding the significance of brain size. It was during this decade that paleoneurology became an international topic of research, especially in France and Germany (Kochetkova 1978).

Researchers continued to publish descriptions of endocasts of fossil hominids, including australopithecines (Broom *et al.* 1950), *Homo erectus* (Singer 1954; Drennan 1955; Arambourg 1955) and Neandertals (Bunak 1951; Jakimov 1952; for further references, see also Kochetkova 1978:Table 1). According to Kochetkova (1978), international symposia were held in 1952 and 1958 in order to discuss the morphology and position among hominids of the natural endocast from Gánovce (now regarded as a Neandertal). The position of australopithecines relative to pongids and to *Homo* was also discussed in light of brain size and morphology during the 1950s (Ashton 1950; Dart 1956; Ashton and Spence 1958).

Although individual mapping studies (Bernhard *et al.* 1953; Bucy and Klüver 1955; Cose *et al.* 1957; Hirsch and Coxe 1958; Woolsey 1958; Powell and Mountcastle 1959) on cerebral cortices of monkeys continued to be published, the 1950s produced numerous monographs summing up the work of the 1930s and 1940s on morphology and the functional organization of the cerebral cortex in humans (Penfield and Rasmussen 1950; Bailey and von Bonin 1951; Penfield and Roberts 1959), chimpanzees (Bailey *et al* 1950), and prosimian and anthropoid primates (Connolly 1950). Connolly's monograph is particularly useful because it contains numerous descriptions and illustrations of brains spanning the entire primate order as well as discussions about endocasts.

There were few papers on paleoneurological methods published in America during this decade, although various European scientists (see Kochetkova 1978), including Hofer (1953a, 1953b), were concerned with the mechanisms governing the imprint of gyri on intracranial surfaces. An important paper describing a method for producing latex endocasts from whole skulls was published in the American Journal of Physical Anthropology (Tugby 1953). This method was used by Radinsky (1968) and myself (Falk 1978c) to study primate cortices.

The study of brain size was a central theme during the 1950s. Jorgensen and Quaade (1956) published a method for estimating cranial capacity from external cranial measurements, and Ashton and Spence (1958) discussed age changes in cranial capacities in hominids in addition to providing basic data on australopithecine cranial capacities (Ashton 1950). Although workers in previous decades had computed cranial capacities for various fossil hominid groups, researchers in the 1950s began to think in terms of size of the cortex relative to brain size (Tower 1954). Such thinking provided the foundation for much work done in the 1960s and 1970s. For example, Shariff's (1953) paper on cell counts in the primate cerebral cortex is still used by investigators.

The relationship between brain size and intelligence was also a concern during this decade (Jerison 1955; Rensch 1956). Referring to Dubois's earlier work, Jerison (1955) discussed regressions on log-transformed brain and body weight data for mammals, including primates. Besides assuming the expected allometric size relationship between brain and body weight, Jerison formulated another assumption that foreshadowed his later work (1963) on "extra neuron" indices: "The evolution of the mammals, characterized by increasing intelligence, involved the differentiation of additional cerebral tissue. The amount of this tissue is correlated with the evolution of intelligence and is unrelated to the body weight [1955]." In a less traditional approach than Jerison's to the allometric study of brain size in mammals, Sacher's (1959) important work showed that life span depends on brain weight and is related to basal metabolic rate.

As Kochetkova points out, there was much discussion in the 1950s about the relationship between brain development (size) and culture, thought, and speech (e.g., Dart, 1956, 1957,; Mettler 1956; see Kochetkova 1978, for other references). These studies were highly speculative and contributed to the belief (that has yet to be substantiated) that the increase in brain size that occurred during human evolution resulted from selection for certain aspects of intelligence. Such thinking was unscientific and would eventually culminate in the 1970s in so-called prime mover theories to account for the increase in brain size (Falk 1980c).

The 1960s

During the 1960s, vision became a major topic within primate mapping studies, and there was a resurgence of interest in comparative neurology. The fossil hominid of the 1960s was *Homo habilis*, and there was much speculation about the taxonomic meaning of brain size in this hominid as well as the significance of brain size in general. The bases for future allometric investigations were developed during this decade.

Maps of sensory and/or motor cortices of primates, including prosimians and apes, were published during the 1960s (Woolsey *et al.* 1960; Sanides and Krishnamurti 1967; Werner and Whitsel 1968; Whitsel *et al.* 1969), and information on cortical localization as defined by evoked potential and electrical stimulation studies was summarized (Woolsey 1964). Although workers were still concerned with the pattern of the primate cerebral cortex (von Bonin and Bailey 1961; further discussion follows), publications appeared on corticocortical (Kuypers *et al.* 1965), commissural (Myers 1965), and thalamic (Bowsher 1961) connections in monkeys. Noback and Moskowitz (1962) stressed the importance of relating cortical to subcortical structures from an evolutionary perspective.

Much research was carried out on the visual cortex of primates during this decade. The sudden interest in primate vision was inspired in party by the important neurophysiological research of Hubel and Wiesel (1968), who studied the receptive fields and functional architecture of monkey striate cortex. Based on the kinds of visual stimuli detected, Hubel and Wiesel (1969) determined that there are three types of neurons in monkey visual cortex: simple, complex, and hypercomplex. The authors also demonstrated that the visual cortex is organized into cylindrical columns. Other workers (Daniel and Whitteridge 1961; Cowey 1964; Iwai and Mishkin 1969; Zeki 1969; Cragg 1969) studied the projection of visual fields onto the cerebral cortex of primates. Hassler (1966) compared visual systems in nocturnal and diurnal monkeys, and Stephen (1969) conducted a quantitative analysis of primate visual structures.

Homologous sulci were identified in dogs and monkeys (Kreiner 1968), and the physiological significance of sulci as boundaries of functional areas in the somatosensory cortex was established for procyonids (Welker and Compos 1963). This latter study would eventually be varified for slow loris among primates (Krishnamurti *et al.* 1976) and would contribute considerably to the theoretical bases for "reading" primate endocasts (Radinsky 1972; Falk 1978c, 1981). Crosby, Humphrey, and Lauer's *Correlative Anatomy of the Nervous System* (which is still considered a valuable text) was published in 1962, and, in keeping with the resurgence of interest in comparative anatomy, Ariëns Kappers and coworker's 1936 synthesis on comparative anatomy of the nervous system was reissued in 1960 (Ariëns Kappers *et. al* 1936/1962).

Cortical sulcal patterns were described for brains of extant *Cercopithecus* (Girgis 1968) and *Papio* (Compère 1968) monkeys and for endocasts representing extant prosimians (Radinsky 1968). Descriptions of endocasts of fossil primates from both the Eocene (Gazin 1965) and Oligocene (Hofer and Wilson 1967; Radinsky 1967b) were also published during the 1960s, and Edinger (1964) discussed Hofer's (1953b) description of the endocast of the fossil giant lemur *Megaladapis*. In addition to these descriptive papers, other publications dealt with more speculative aspects of primate brain evolution, such as the question of which parameters (e.g., expanded areas of neocortex, neural density, cell size) are best suited for paleoneurological investigation (Diamond and Hall 1969; Hofer 1969; Holloway, 1966b, 1968, 1969).

Although various European and Russian investigators described endocasts from fossil hominids including and postdating *H. erectus* (Krantz 1961; for additional references, see Kochetkova 1978), American paleontologists were concerned with the cranial capacities of australopithecines in general and of *Homo habilis* in particular. Using Tobias's (1963, 1964) data, workers calculated means, standard deviations, coefficients of variation, and probable ranges of variation for the cranial capacity of South African australopithecines. The cranial capacity of Olduvai Hominid 7 from Bed I at Olduvai Gorge, estimated by Tobias (1968) to be 657 ± 12 cc, was assessed in light of these statistics for South African australopithecines. Was the cranial capacity of OH7 so large that the specimen should be excluded from the australopithecines, that is, did OH7 represent a new species—*Homo habilis?* Tobias (1965) and Pilbeam (1969, 1970) argued that the cranial capacities of australopithecines and OH7 were significantly different; Holloway (1965) and Wolpoff (1969, 1970) thought that OH7 could be another australopithecine. Of all the claims made, Pilbeam's (1969) statement that it seemed unwise to draw firm taxonomic conclusions based solely on the cranial capacity of one specimen was, and is, the most reasonable.

The brains of extant humans were again a topic of investigation in the 1960s, although only one study (Pakkenberg and Voigt 1964) described the brains of a particular group (Danes). Other studies produced new information about human brains. Thus, we know that the human cortex contains an average of 2.6×10^9 cells (Pakkenberg 1966), the human brain does not go through an adolescent growth spurt (Baer and Harris 1969), and the cephalic index appears to be inherited "in a unitary fashion [Sekla and Soukup 1969]!" Schreider (1966) showed that brain weight correlated positively with stature and negatively with age. Interest in cerebral asymmetries was inspired by Sperry's (1968) work on human patients who had sustained commissurotomies of the corpus callosum, and, in an important paper (Geschwind and Levitsky 1968), left–right asymmetries were demonstrated in human temporal lobes.

During the 1960s, publications about the evolution of the human brain varied from the concrete (e.g., von Bonin's 1963 book, which contains valuable data on fossil hominids, endocasts, and the cerebral cortex) to the speculative (see Andrew 1962 for an interesting discussion of relative intelligence in dolphins and humans). Holloway (1966b) elaborated on the concept of neurological reorganization as a major factor during human brain evolution. According to this concept, the human brain underwent significant reorganization in a number of components and subsystems of the entire brain and "by the time of the Australopithecines there was neural reorganization of such an extent as to permit the shift into essentially human behavior [1966b]." Still more speculative were attempts to analyze the human brain in terms of conscious experience (Eccles 1966). Concern with the relationship between brain size, taxonomic status (or phylogenetic level), and intelligence led to papers on comparative intelligence (and testing thereof) in different animals (Andrew 1962; Bitterman 1965; Rensch 1956), and efforts to assess behavior from brain size in fossil hominids continued (Holloway 1967; Krantz 1961, 1968; Witherspoon 1960).

The 1960s produced the expected papers on "new" methods for determining various parameters of brain evolution: cranial capacity (Jorgensen *et al.* 1961; Upenskii 1964), surface features of cranial fossae in closed skulls (Erskine and O'Morchoe 1960), relative brain size (by substituting the area of the foramen magnum for body size [Radinsky 1967a]), and *cerebralization* (by dividing brain weight by spinal cord weight [Krompecher and Lipak 1966]). Radinsky (1968) provided a detailed description of the method for preparing and removing latex endocasts from whole skulls, and, in an important paper, Elias and Schwartz (1969) delineated a method for determining total cortical surface area from the length of exposed gyri in mammalian brains.

Perhaps the most important methodological work carried out in the 1960s was that concerning the allometric relationship between brain and body weight. The significance of the increase in brain size that occurred during human evolution cannot be assessed until "criteria of subtraction" for removing the effects of body size from paleoneurological data have been established (Pilbeam and Gould 1974). Bauchot and Stephan (1966, 1969) and Stephan and Andy (1969) have developed an index of progression (IP) that describes residual factors after body size factors have been subtracted from the brain–body data. Using brain weight–body weight data from basal insectivores, the authors calculated the basic regression equation $\log h = 1.632 + 0.63 \log k$, where h = brain weight and k = body weight. Thus "basal" brain weight can be predicted for a given primate species by substituting its mean body weight into the equation. The ratio between the actual brain weight of the species, progressive size (PrG), and the predicted basal size (BG) equals the IP, or IP = PrG/BG. Jerison's (1961, 1963) encephalization quotient (EQ) and extra neuron index (Nc) have been developed along similar lines (see Holloway 1966a, for a critique of the latter index). This work on allometry greatly influenced paleoneurologists in the 1970s.

The 1970s

The 1970s was an important decade for primate brain studies, as is evidenced by the appearance of five new books related to the subject: *An Illustrated History of Brain Function* (Clarke and Dewhurst 1972), *The Primate Brain* (Noback and Montagna 1970), *The Brain in Hominid Evolution* (Tobias 1971), *Evolution of the Brain and Intelligence* (Jerison 1974), and *Paleoneurology* (Kochetkova 1978). During this decade, the study of endocasts from fossil primates came into its own, as did studies of allometry and cortical asymmetries in primate brains. Mapping of primate cerebral cortices continued to be important during the 1970s. The somatotopic organization of the sensory cortex was determined for spider monkeys (Pubols and Pubols 1971), and the sensory cortex of slow lorises was also mapped using microelectrodes (Krishnamurti *et al.* 1976). Hubel (1979) continued research on the primate visual cortex, and Jones and Powell (1970), using stepwise lesions, studied corticocortical projections in macaques. The work carried out in the 1970s on the organization of visual and somatosensory cortices in primates has been reviewed by Kaas (see Kaas 1978, and Kaas *et al.* 1981, respectively). The reader is referred to Welker (1976) for a discussion of historical trends in mapping studies and to volume 13 of *Brain, Behavior and Evolution* (1976) for a summary of mammalian mapping studies.

As was the case in the 1960s, the brain size of fossil hominids was a topic of interest in the 1970s (Lestrel and Read 1973; Schwidetzky 1976). The taxonomic status of OH7 continued to be argued on the basis of cranial capacity (Pilbeam 1970; Wolpoff 1970), and new endocranial values were provided for australopithecines (Holloway 1970b, 1973), including the Taung specimen (Holloway 1970a). Fossil hominid body weights have been estimated from available fossil skeletal remains (McHenry 1975, 1976; McHenry and Temerin 1979; Reed and Falk 1977), and the brain sizes of hominids have been computed relative to body size (Holloway 1975; Leutenegger 1973; McHenry 1975; Pilbeam and Gould 1974). These data show that both absolute and relative brain sizes increased dramatically during hominid evolution. This finding is of general interest because an increase in relative brain size occurred independently in many groups of mammals (Jerison, 1970, 1974; Radinsky, 1978, 1979). Surprisingly, Radinsky noted that there is "little scientific evidence demonstrating a relationship between brain size and intelligence [1979:24]" (see, however, Passingham 1975a; Van Valen 1974). Nevertheless, efforts to identify specific aspects of intelligence (such as savy in warfare [Pitt 1978] or production of tools [Kochetkova 1978]) that were responsible for selection for increased brain size have been made. See Falk (1980c) for a discussion of these speculative "prime mover" theories.

In addition to size of the brain, workers in the 1970s attempted to elucidate qualitative changes that occurred during hominid brain evolution. Holloway (1972b, 1975, 1979) continued to develop his concept of neurological reorganization (as has been mentioned) and to discuss hominid brain evolution in terms of social behavior. Passingham (1975b) was also concerned with changes in brain organization and assigned special primacy to selection on the neocortex during human evolution (Passingham 1973; Passingham and Ettlinger 1974). However, my recent search (Falk 1980c) for qualitative brain differences that separate fossil and living hominids from pongids proved futile.

During the 1970s, much attention was directed at the morphology of endocasts from extant and fossil primates. Sulcal patterns were described for all genera of extant New World (Hershkovitz 1970; Falk 1980b) and Old World (Falk 1978c; Compère 1971) monkeys. These comparative data were used to analyze brain evolution in New and Old World monkeys (Falk 1978a, 1979a, 1980b). Besides discussing the role of endocasts in primate brain studies, Radinsky (1972, 1975; see also Holloway 1974, 1978 and Jerison 1975) examined the fossil records of *Aegyptopithecus* (Radinsky 1973; see also Gingerich 1977) and of prosimian brain evolution (Radinsky 1970, 1977) and described and summarized the fossil evidence for anthropoid brain evolution in one paper (1974)! Thus, Radinsky has been a main contributor to our understanding of the fossil record of primate brain evolution, and his work on this subject was summarized in the forty-ninth James Arthur lecture (Radinsky 1979). In terms of fossil hominid endocasts, two new australopithecine specimens were described during the 1970s: SK1585 from a presumed robust australopithecine (Holloway 1972a) and STS1017 from a gracile specimen (Falk 1979b).

A new trend developed in the 1970s in response to contemporary literature on the brain, cerebral asymmetries, and language (Geschwind 1970; Sanides 1975). Since asymmetries had earlier been demonstrated in human temporal speech regions (Geschwind and Levitsky 1968), workers began examining nonhuman primate cortices for cerebral asymmetries. Thus, pongid (LeMay and Geschwind 1975) and monkey (Falk 1978b) brains were found to be asymmetrical in their sulcal patterns. Yeni-Komshian and Benson (1976) failed to find cortical asymmetries in monkeys but psychophysical evidence published by Dewson (1977) and Petersen *et al.* (1978) confirm the existence of functional cortical asymmetry in monkeys. Asymmetries have also been demonstrated in endocasts and skulls of fossil hominids (Abler 1976; LeMay 1975). These data on cerebral asymmetries in anthropoid primates, including humans, have been used to support the theory that human language originated in an arboreal habitat and much longer ago than is traditionally believed (Falk 1980d, 1980e). The reader is referred to Galaburda *et al.* (1978) for a review of the literature on brain asymmetries.

Methods used in paleoneurological research during this decade ranged from the simple to the sophisticated. Procedures were published for estimating cranial capacity based on the products of cranial dimensions (Olivier and Tissier 1975) and analysis of roentgenograms (Haack and Meihoff 1971). Other papers reiterated methods for producing endocasts from whole skulls (Murrill and Wallace 1971) and criticized the use of foramen magnum areas in relative brain size indices (Wanner 1971). In his classic paper on the brain and race, Tobias showed how variable methods of determining brain statistics could account for variations in interracial comparisons and concluded that "most published interracial comparisons are invalid [1970:3]." Campbell and Hodos (1970) discussed methods for determining homologies in nervous system structures. Finally, a mathematical model that described the intrinsic mechanical forces responsible for cortical folding in humans was developed by Richman *et al.* (1975).

Stephan (1972) and Stephan *et al.* (1970) continued their work on brain–body scaling, or allometry, in primates. American workers (Gould 1975; Pilbeam and Gould 1974; Sacher 1970) became increasingly interested in allometry during this decade. Gould (1975) called attention to the possible importance of neoteny in accounting for human brain weight–body weight data, and other workers (Epstein 1973; Jordaan 1976; Přívratský 1979) have investigated the brain weight of human neonates. In a departure from traditional allometric studies, Sacher (1975, 1981) on the other hand, studied the relationship between cranial capacity and maturation or longevity.

Various workers have noted that regressions on log-transformed data slope at approximately ⅔ for higher taxa (classes, orders, families) of mammals (Gould 1975; Jerison 1974). However, the exponent of allometry (slope) among closely related species is lower (i.e., approximately 0.3) (Gould 1975). According to Gould (1975), the 0.66 slope for the brain–body data of higher taxa is a general rule that, so far, has been unaccounted for in a functional sense. Some workers question the validity of the ⅔ slope and suggest that it may be nearer to ¾ and, therefore, functionally related to metabolism (Martin 1982). At any rate, workers have begun to investigate basic trends in mammalian brain evolution (Hofer 1971; Sacher 1975) in efforts to unravel allometric factors governing brain evolution in primates. This is a positive approach and one that should be fruitful during the 1980s.

Summary and Conclusions

Because brain evolution is a central theme in the study of primate evolution, research in primate neuroanatomy has provided an important source of data for physical anthropologists through the years. This research has been outlined here on a decade-by-decade basis. Certain trends in neuroanatomical research cut across these decades, however. For example, although mapping the brain has remained a significant research activity during the past 50 years, the fascinating experiments of Penfield and his associates on human surgical patients yielded much basic data on cortical localization during the 1930s and 1940s, whereas mapping of visual areas in nonhuman primates became an important area of mapping research during the 1960s.

Other topics related to primate neuroanatomy have been fashionable at different times during the decades covered. Thus, numerous descriptions of brains representing different human races were published during the 1930s and 1940s, but these publications ceased during the 1950s, at which time papers began appearing that discussed brain size and its significance relative to intelligence, culture, and social behavior. The latter speculative topic is still prevalent in the literature. Similarly, methods for determining *encephalization quotients* and other indices related to allometry were published during the 1960s, and these types of studies are a central theme in brain evolution research today. Again, although endocasts of fossil nonhuman primates had been sporadically described through the 1960s, this type of research did not become prevalent until the 1970s. That decade also saw the beginning of research on cerebral asymmetries in nonhuman primates.

Physical anthropologists and primate neuroanatomists have maintained a keen interest in the brains of fossil hominids throughout the past 50 years. Interest in these studies was initially inspired by widespread public attention to the excavations at Choukoutien during the 1930s. Thus, publications on endocasts of *Sinanthropus* (*H. erectus*) were prevalent at that time. During the 1940s and 1950s, endocasts of australopithecines were described, and the place these hominids would take among hominoids became a controversial subject. The same can be said about *H. habilis* in the 1960s. During the 1970s, no one group of fossil hominids was emphasized over others, but cranial capacities were redetermined for various groups, and speculation continued about the relationship of brain size to intelligence and culture.

In general, research in the earlier decades was basically descriptive, with little in the way of sophisticated techniques for quantitative analyses. However, the 1950s marked a turning point in primate neuroanatomy from the physical anthropologist's point of view. Much of the earlier descriptive work was summarized in monographs, and, as noted previously, certain types of descriptive publications simply ceased. From the 1950s on, quantitative functional analyses became increasingly important to studies of primate brain evolution.

Despite the voluminous amount of research in primate neuroanatomy that has transpired during the past 50 years, physical anthropologists are still not able to provide concrete hypotheses regarding specific qualitative (i.e., not size related) changes in the brain that occurred during primate, including human, evolution (Falk 1980c). However, this may simply reflect the crude nature of the paleoneurological evidence. In 1980, symposia on primate brain evolution were held at the annual meeting of the American Association of Physical Anthropologists in Niagara Falls and the International Primatological Congress in Florence. These symposia brought together comparative neurologists and paleoneurologists (Armstrong and Falk 1982). Although most of the work summarized for the 1970s was carried out by paleoneurologists, comparative neurology is becoming increasingly important in the study of primate brain evolution (e.g., see Armstrong 1979, 1980a 1980b; Haines 1971). It is to be hoped that, with continued communication between subfields as well as development of new quantitative approaches for data analysis, physical anthropologists' understanding of primate brain evolution will improve.

Acknowledgments

I thank Doctor Norman Maldonado, Chancellor of the Medical Sciences Campus of the University of Puerto Rico, for support to travel to libraries on the mainland.

References

Abler, W. L.
    1976   Asymmetry in the skulls of fossil man: evidence of lateralized brain function? *Brain, Behavior and Evolution* **13**:111–115.
Andrew, R. J.
    1962   Evolution of intelligence and vocal mimicking. *Science* **137**:585–589.
Anthony, J.
    1946   Morpologie externe du cerveau des singes Platyrhiniens. *Annales des Sciences Naturelles, Zoologie et Biologie Animale* **8**:1–150.
Appel, F. W. and E. M. Appel
    1942   Intracranial variation in the weight of the human brain. *Human Biology* **14**:48–68, 235–250. ⁴
Arambourg, C.
    1955   Le parietal de l'Atlanthropus mauritanicus. *Comptes Rendus Hebdomadaires des Seances de l'Academie des Sciences* **241**:980–982.
Ariëns Kappers, C. U.
    1932   On some correlations between skull and brain. *Philosophical Transactions of the Royal Society of London* **221**:391–429.
    1933   The fissuration on the frontal lobe of *Sinanthropus pekinensis* Black, compared with the fissuration in Neanderthal men. *Proceedings of the Koninklijke Nederlandse Akademie van Wetenschappen* **36**:802–812.
    1936   The endocranial casts of the Ehringsdorf and *Homo soloensis* skulls. *Journal of Anatomy* **71**:61–76.
Ariëns Kappers, C. U., and K. H. Bouman
    1939   Comparison of the endocranial casts of the *Pithecanthropus erectus* skull found by Dubois and von Koenigwald's *Pithecanthropus* skull. *Proceedings of the Koninklijke Nederlandse Akademie van Wetenschappen* **42**:30–40.
Ariëns Kappers, C. U., G. C. Huber, and E. C. Crosby
    1960   *The Comparative Anatomy of the Nervous System of Vertebrates, Including Man.* New York: Hafner. (Originally published, 1936, New York, Hafner.)
Armstrong, E.
    1979   A quantitative comparison of the hominoid thalamus. I. Specific sensory relay nuclei. *American Journal of Physical Anthropology* **51**:365–382.
    1980a   A quantitative comparison of the hominoid thalamus. II. Limbic nuclei anterior principalis and lateral dorsalis. *American Journal of Physical Anthropology* **52**:43–54.
    1980b   A quantitative comparison of the hominoid thalamus. III. A motor substrate—the ventro-lateral complex. *American Journal of Physical Anthropology* **52**:405–419.
Armstrong, E., and D. Falk
    1982   *Primate brain evolution: Concepts and methods.* New York: Plenum.
Ashton, E. H.
    1950   The endocranial capacities of the Australopithecinae. *Proceedings of the Zoological Society of London* **120**:715–721.
Ashton, E. H., and T. F. Spence
    1958   Age changes in the cranial capacity and foramen magnum of hominoids. *Proceedings of the Zoological Society of London* **130**:169–181.
Baer, M. J., and J. E. Harris
    1969   A commentary on the growth of the human brain and skull. *American Journal of Physical Anthropology* **30**:39–44.
Bailey, P., and G. von Bonin
    1951   *The isocortex of man.* Urbana: University of Illinois Press.
Bailey, P., J. G. Dusser De Barenne, H. W.Garol, and W. S. McCulloch

1940   The sensory cortex of the chimpanzee. *Journal of Neurophysiology* **3**:469–485.
Bailey, P., G. von Bonin, H. Garol, and W. S. McCulloch
1943   Long association fibers in cerebral hemispheres of monkey and chimpanzee. *Journal of Neurophysiology* **6**:129–134.
Bailey, P., G. von Bonin, and W. S. McCulloch
1950   *The isocortex of the chimpanzee.* Urbana: University of Illinois Press.
Bard, P.
1938   Studies on the cortical representation of somatic sensibility. *Bulletin of the New York Academy of Medicine* **14**:585–607.
Bauchot, R., and H. Stephan
1966   Données nouvelles sur l'encéphalisation des insectivores et des prosimiens. *Mammalia* **30**:160–196.
1969   Encéphalisation et niveau évolutif chex les simiens. *Mammalia* **33**:235–275.
Bernhard, C. G., E. Bohm, and I. Peterson
1953   New investigations of the pyramidal systems of *Macaca mulatta. Experientia* **9**:111–112.
Bitterman, M. E.
1965   The evolution of intelligence. *Scientific American* **212**:92–100.
Black, D.
1933   On the endocranial cast of the adolescent *Sinanthropus* skull. *Proceedings of the Royal Society of London* **112**:263–276.
Bowsher, D.
1961   The termination of secondary somatosensory neurons within the thalamus of *Macaca mulatta. Journal of Comparative Neurology* **117**:213–227.
Broom, R., and J. T. Robinson
1948   Size of the brain in the ape-man, *Plesianthropus. Nature* (London) **161**:438.
Broom, R. and G. W. H. Schepers
1946   The South African fossil ape-men: the Australopithecinae. *Transvaal Museum Memoirs* **2**.
Broom, R., J. T. Robinson, G. W. H. Schepers
1950   The Sterkfontein ape-man *Plesianthropus. Transvaal Museum Memoirs* **4**.
Bucy, P. C., and H. Klüver
1955   An anatomical investigation of the temporal lobe in the monkey (*Macaca mulatta*). *Journal of Comparative Neurology* **103**:151–251.
Bunak, W.
1951   Cranial cavity model of Paleolithic child's skull from the Teshik-Tash Grotto, Uzbekistan. *Sbornik Muzeya po Antropologii i Etnografii* **13**:417–479.
Bushmakin, N.
1936   The brain of the Jakuts. *American Journal of Physical Anthropology* **21**:29–37.
Campbell, C. B. G., and W. Hodos
1970   The concept of homology and the evolution of the nervous system. *Brain, Behavior and Evolution* **3**:353–367.
Chi, T. K., and C. Chang
1941   The sulcal pattern of the Chinese brain. *American Journal of Physical Anthropology* **28**:167–211.
Clarke, E., and K. Dewhurst
1972   *An illustrated history of brain function.* Berkeley: University of California Press.
Cohn, H. A., and J. W. Papez
1930   A comparative study of the visuosensory or striate area in the two hemispheres of the human brain. *American Journal of Physical Anthropology* **14**:405–415.
Compère, J.
1968   Superficie du cortex de *Papio cynocephalus kindae*. Etude biométrique. *Mammalia* **32**:690–707.
1971   Morphologie externe du télencéphale de *Papio cynocephalus kindae. mammalia* **35**:471–500.
Connolly, C. J.

1931   Contribution to the anthropology of the brain. *American Journal of Physical Anthropology* **15**:477–491.

1932   Brain indices of anthropoid apes. *American Journal of Physical Anthropology* **17**:57–67.

1933   The brain of a moutain gorilla. *American Journal of Physical Anthropology* **17**:291–307.

1936   The fissural pattern of the primate brain. *American Journal of Physical Anthropology* **21**:301–422.

1940   Development of the cerebral sulci. *American Journal of Physical Anthropology* **26**:113–149.

1941   The fissural pattern in the brain of Negroes and Whites. *American Journal of Physical Anthropology* **28**:133–165.

1942   The fissural pattern in the brain of Negroes and Whites (continued). The parietal and temporal lobes. *American Journal of Physical Anthropology* **29**:41–46.

1950   *External morphology of the primate brain.* Springfield, Illinois: Thomas.

Count, E. W.
1947   Brain and body weight in man: their antecedents in growth and evolution. *Annals of the New York Academy of Sciences* **46**:993–1122.

Cowey, A.
1964   Projection of the retina onto striate and prestriate cortex in the squirrel monkey, *Saimiri sciureus. Journal of Neurophysiology* **27**:366–396.

Coxe, W. S., J. F. Hirsch, R. M. Benjamin, W. I. Welker, R. F. Thompson, and C. M. Woolsey
1957   Precentral and supplementary motor areas of *Ateles. Physiologist* **1**:19 (Abstract).

Cragg, B. G.
1969   The topography of the afferent projections in the circumstriate visual cortex of the monkey studied by the Nauta method. *Vision Research* **9**:733–747.

Crile, G., and D. P. Quiring
1940   A record of the body weight and certain organ and gland weights of 3690 animals. *Ohio Journal of Science* **40**:219–259.

Crosby, E. C., T. Humphrey, and E. Lauer
1962   *Correlative anatomy of the nervous system.* New York: Macmillan.

Daniel, P. M., and D. Whitteridge
1961   The representation of the visual field on the cerebral cortex in monkeys. *Journal of Physiology (London)* **159**:203–221.

Dart, R. A.
1925   *Australopithecus africanus*: the man-ape of South Africa. *Nature (London)* **115**:195–199.

1956   The relationships of brain size and brain pattern to human status. *South African Journal of Medical Sciences* **21**:23–45.

1957   The Osteodontokeratic culture of *Australopithecus prometheus. Transvaal Museum Memoirs* **10**.

DeTerra, H., J. Romero, and T. D. Stewart
1949   Tepexpan Man. *Viking Fund Publications in Anthropology* **11**:1–160.

Dewson, J. H.
1977   Preliminary evidence of hemispherica asymmetry of auditory function in monkeys. In *Lateralization in the nervous system,* edited by S. R. Harnard. New York: Academic Press. Pp. 63–71.

Diamond, I. T., and W. C. Hall
1969   Evolution of neocortex. *Science* **164**:251–262.

Drennan, M. R.
1937   The Florisbad skull and brain cast. *Transactions of the Royal Society of South Africa* **25**:103–114.

1955   The special features and status of the Saldanha skull. *American Journal of Physical Anthropology* **13**:625–634.

Dreyer, T. F.
1936   The endocranial cast of the Florisbad skull, a correction. *Söologiese Navorsing van die Nasionale Museum, Bloemfontein* **1**:21–23.

Dubois, E.

1933   The shape and the size of the brain in *Sinanthropus* and in *Pithecanthropus*. *Proceedings of the Koninklijke Nederlandse Akademie van Wetenschappen* **36**:415–423.

Dusser De Barenne, J. G., and W. S. McCulloch
1938   Functional organization in the sensory cortex of the monkey (*Macaca mulatta*). *Journal of Neurophysiology* **1**:69–85.
1939   The sensory cortex of the chimpanzee. *Proceedings of the Society for Experimental Biology and Medicine* **42**:27–29.

Dusser De Barenne, J. G., J. G. Garol, and W. S. McCulloch
1941   Functional organization of sensory and adjacent cortex in the monkey. *Journal of Neurophysiology* **4**:324–330.

Eccles, J. C.
1966   *Brain and conscious experience*. Berlin, and New York: Springer-Verlag.

Edinger, T.
1964   Recent advances in paleoneurology. *Progress in Brain Research* **6**:147–160.

Elias, N., and D. Schwartz
1969   Surface areas of the cerebral cortex of mammals determined by stereological methods. *Science* **166**:11–13.

Epstein, H. T.
1973   Possible metabolic constraints on human brain weight at birth. *American Journal of Physical Anthropology* **39**:135–136.

Erskine, C. A., and C. C. C. O'Morchoe
1960   Measurement and surface features of the cranial fossae in closed skulls. *American Journal of Physical Anthropology* **18**:97–99.

Evans, J.
1935   A study of the sensory defects resulting from excision of cerebral substance in humans. *Research Publications—Association for Research in Nervous and Mental Disease* **15**:331–370.

Falk, D.
1978a   Brain evolution in Old World monkeys. *American Journal of Physical Anthropology* **48**:315–320.
1978b   Cerebral asymmetry in Old World monkeys. *Acta Anatomica* **101**:334–339.
1978c   External neuroanatomy of Old World monkeys (Cercopithecoidea). *Contributions to Primatology* **15**:1–95.
1979a   Cladistic analysis of New World monkey sulcal patterns: implications for primate brain evolution. *Journal of Human Evolution* **8**:637–645.
1979b   On a new australopithecine partial endocast. *American Journal of Physical Anthropology* **50**:611–614.
1980a   A reanalysis of the South African australopithecine natural endocasts. *American Journal of Physical Anthropology* **53**:525–539.
1980b   Comparative study of the endocranial casts of New and Old World monkeys. In *Evolutionary biology of the New World monkeys and continental drift*, edited by R. L. Ciochon and B. Chiarelli. New York: Plenum. Pp. 275–292.
1980c   Hominid brain evolution: the approach from paleoneurology. *Yearbook of Physical Anthropology* **23**:93–107.
1980d   Language, handedness and primate brains: did the australopithecines sign? *American Anthropologist* **82**:72–78.
1980e   CA* comment on Krantz, G: Sapienization and speech. *Current Anthropology* **21**:780.
1981   Sulcal patterns of fossil *Theropithecus* baboons: Phylogenetic and functional implications. *International Journal of Primatology* **2**:57–69.

Foerster, O.
1936   The motor cortex in man in the light of Hughlings Jackson's doctrines. *Brain* **59**:135–159.

Fulton, J. F.
1938   Cytoarchitecture of the gorilla brain. *Science* **88**:426–427.

Fulton, J. F., and J. G. Dusser De Barenne

1933   The representation of the tail in the motor cortex of primates, with special reference to spider monkeys. *Journal of Cellular and Comparative Physiology* **2**:399–426.

Galaburda, A. M., and D. N. Pandya
1982   Role of architectonics and connections in the study of primate brain evolution. In *Primate brain evolution: Concepts and methods*, edited by E. Armstrong and D. Falk. New York: Plenum. Pp. 203–216.

Galaburda, A. M., M. LeMay, T. L. Kemper, and N. Geschwind
1978   Right–left asymmetries in the brain. *Science* **199**:852–856.

Gamble, D. P.
1944   Physical type and mental characters. Preliminary notes on the study of the correlations between racial types and types of psychotic reaction. *American Journal of Physical Anthropology* **2**:195–220.

Gazin, C. L.
1965   An endocranial cast of the Bridger middle Eocene primate, *Smilodectes gracilis*. *Smithsonian Miscellaneous Collections* **149**:1–14.

Geschwind, N.
1970   The organization of language and the brain. *Science* **170**:940–944.

Geschwind, N., and W. Levitsky
1968   Human brain: Left–right asymmetries in temporal speech region. *Science* **161**:186–187.

Gingerich, P. D.
1977   Correlation of tooth size and body size in living hominoid primates, with a note on relative brain size in *Aegyptopithecus* and *Proconsul*. *American Journal of Physical Anthropology* **47**:395–398.

Girgis, M.
1968   External morphology of the brain of the grivet monkey (*Cercopithecus aethiops aethiops*). *Acta Anatomica* **71**:134–146.

Gould, S. J.
1975   Allometry in primates, with emphasis on scaling and the evolution of the brain. *Contributions to Primatology* **5**:244–292.

Haack, D. C., and E. C. Meihoff
1971   A method for estimation of cranial capacity from cephalometric roentgenograms. *American Journal of Physical Anthropology* **34**:447–452.

Haines, D. E.
1971   The morphology of the cerebellar nuclei of *Galago* and *Tupaia*. *American Journal of Physical Anthropology* **35**:27–42.

Harman, P. J.
1957   *Paleoneurologic, neoneurologic and ontogenetic aspects brain phylogeny. James Arthur Lecture, 1957.* American Museum of Natural History, New York.

Hassler, R.
1966   Comparative anatomy of the central visual systems in day and night active primates. In *Evolution of the forebrain*, edited by R. Hassler and H. Stephan. Stuttgart: Thieme. Pp. 419–434.

Hershkovitz, P.
1970   Cerebral fissural patterns in platyrrhine monkeys. *Folia Primatologica* **13**:213–240.

Hirsch, J. F., and W. S. Coxe
1958   Representation of cutaneous tactile sensibility in cerebral cortex of *Cebus*. *Journal of Neurophysiology* **21**:481–498.

Hirschler, P.
1942   *Anthropoid and human endocranial casts.* Amsterdam: Disser.

Hofer, H.
1953a   Die Paläoneurologie ab Weg zur Erforschung der Evolution des Gehirnes. *Naturwissenschaften* **40**:566–569.

1953b   Über Gehirn und Schädel von *Megaladapis edwardsi* G. Grandidier (Lemuroidea). *Zeitschrift fuer Wissenschaftliche Zoologie* **157**:220–284.

1969   The evolution of the brain in primates: its influence on the form of the skull. *Annals of the New York Academy of Sciences* **167**:341–356.

1971   The evolution of the brain and its importance for physiological research. *Medical Primatology, Selected Papers from the 2nd Conference on Experimental Medicine and Surgery in Primates, 1969* Pp. 304–307.

Hofer, H., and J. A. Wilson

1967   An endocranial cast of an early Oligocene primate. *Folia Primatologica* **5**:148–152.

Holloway, R. L.

1965   Cranial capacity of the hominid from Olduvai Bed. I. *Nature (London)* **208**:205–206.

1966a   Cranial capacity and neuron number: a critique and proposal. *American Journal of Physical Anthropology* **25**:305–314.

1966b   Cranial capacity, neural re-organization, and hominid evolution: a search for more suitable parameters. *American Anthropologist* **68**:103–121.

1967   The evolution of the human brain: some notes toward a synthesis between neural structure and the evolution of complex behavior. *General Systems* **12**:3–19.

1968   The evolution of the primate brain: some aspects of quantitative relations. *Brain Research* **7**:121–172.

1969   Some questions on parameters of neural evolution in primates. *Annals of the New York Academy of Sciences* **167**:332–340.

1970a   Australopithecine endocast (Taung specimen, 1924): a new volume determination. *Science* **168**:966–968.

1970b   New endocranial values for the australopithecines. *Nature (London)* **227**:199–200.

1971a   New australopithecine endocast, SK 1585, from Swartkrans, South Africa. *American Journal of Physical Anthropology* **37**:173–186.

1972b   Australopithecine endocasts, brain evolution in the Hominoidea, and a model of hominid evolution. In *The functional and evolutionary biology of primates*, edited by R. H. Tuttle. Chicago: Aldine. Pp. 185–203.

1973   New endocranial values for the East African early hominids. *Nature (London)* **243**:97–99.

1974   The casts of fossil hominid brains. *Scientific American* **231**:106–115.

1975   *The role of human social behavior in the evolution of the brain. 43rd James Arthur Lecture, 1973.* American Museum of Natural History, New York.

1978   The relevance of endocasts for studying primate brain evolution. In *Sensory systems in primates*, edited by C. R. Noback. New York: Plenum. Pp.181–200.

1979   Brain size, allometry, and reorganization: toward a synthesis. In *Development and evolution of brain size: Behavioral implications*, edited by M. E. Hahn, C. Jensen, and B. C. Dudek. New York: Academic Press. Pp. 59–88.

Hubel, D. H.

1979   The visual cortex of normal and deprived monkeys. *American Scientist* **67**:532–543.

Hubel, D. H., and T. N. Wiesel

1968   Receptive fields and functional architecture of monkey striate cortex. *Journal of Physiology (London)* **195**:215–243.

1969   Anatomical demonstration of columns in the monkey striate cortex. *Nature (London)* **221**:747–750.

Iwai, E., and M. Mishkin

1969   Further evidence on the locus of the visual area in temporal lobe of the monkey. *Experimental Neurology* **25**:585–594.

Jakimov, V. P.

1952   Natural cast of the cranial cavity of Neandertal man from Czechoslovakia. *Sovetskaya Etnografiya* **3**:57–62.

Jerison, H. J.

1955   Brain to body ratios and the evolution of intelligence. *Science* **121**:447–449.
1961   Quantitative analysis of evolution of the brain in mammals. *Science* **133**:1012–1014.
1963   Interpreting the evolution of the brain *Human Biology***35**:263–291.
1970   Brain evolution: new light on old principles. *Science* **170**:1224–1225
1974   *Evolution of the brain and intelligence.* New York: Academic Press.
1975   Fossil evidence of the evolution of the human brain. *Annual Review of Anthropology* **4**:27–58.

Jones, E. C., and T. P. S. Powell
1970   An anatomical study of converging sensory pathways within the cerebral cortex of the monkey. *Brain* **93**:793–820.

Jordaan, H. V. F.
1976   Newborn: Adult brain ratios in hominid evolution. *American Journal of Physical Anthropology* **44**:271–278.

Jorgensen, J. B., and F. Quaade
1956   External cranial values as an estimate of cranial capacity. *American Journal of Physical Anthropology* **14**:661–664.

Jorgensen, J. B., E. Parison, and F. Quaade
1961   The correlation between external cranial volume and brain volume. *American Journal of Physical Anthropology* **19**:317–320.

Kaas, J. H.
1978   The organization of visual cortex in primates. In *Sensory systems of primates*, edited by C. R. Noback. New York: Plenum. Pp. 151–179.

Kaas, J. H., R. J. Nelson, M. Sur, and M. U. Mersenich
1981   Organization of somatosensory cortex in primates. In *The Organization of the cerebral cortex*, edited by F. O. Schmitt, F. G. Worden, G. Adelman, and S. G. Dennis. Cambridge, Massachusetts: MIT Press. Pp. 237–261.

Keith, A.
1948   *A new theory of human evolution.* London: Watts and Company.

Keith, A., and T. D. McCown
1939   *The stone age of Mount Carmel* (Vol 2). London and New York: Oxford University Press (Clarendon).

Klüver, H., and P. Bucy
1939   Preliminary analysis of functions of the temporal lobes in monkeys. *Archives of Neurology and Psychiatry* **42**:979–1000.

Kochetkova, V.
1978   *Paleoneurology.* New York: Wiley.

Krantz, G. S.
1961   Pithecanthropine brain size and its cultural consequences. *Man* **61**:85–87.
1968   Brain size and hunting ability in earliest man. *Current Anthropology* **9**:450–451.

Kreiner, J.
1968   Homologues of the fissural and gyral patterns of the hemispheres of the dog and monkey. *Acta Anatomica* **70**:137–167.

Krishnamurti, A., F. Sanides, and W. I. Welker
1976   Microelectrode mapping of modality-specific somatic sensory neocortex in slow loris. *Brain, Behavior and Evolution* **13**:267–283.

Krompecher, S., and J. Lipak
1966   A simple method for determining cerebralization: brain weight and intelligence. *Journal of Comparative Neurology* **127**:113–120.

Kuypers, H. G., J. M. Szwarcbart, M. Mishkin, and H. E. Rosvold
1965   Occipitotemporal corticocortical connections in the rhesus monkey. *Experimental Neurology* **11**:245–262.

Lashley, K. S.

1948   The mechanism of vision. XVIII Effects of destroying the visual association areas of the monkey. *Genetic Psychology Monographs* **37**:107.

Lashley, K. S., and G. Clark
1946   The cytoarchitecture of the cerebral cortex of *Ateles*: A critical examination of cyto-architectural studies. *Journal of Comparative Neurology* **85**:223–305.

Leakey, L. S. B.
1935   *The stone age races of Kenya.* London: Oxford University Press.

Le Gros Clark, W. E.
1938   *The endocranial cast of the Swanscombe bones. Journal of the Royal Anthropological Institute of Great Britain and Ireland* **68**:61–67.
1945   Deformation patterns in the cerebral cortex. In *Essays on growth and form,* edited by W. E. Le Gros Clark and P. B. Medawar. London and New York: Oxford University Press. Pp. 1–22.
1947   Observations on the anatomy of the fossil Australopithecinae. *Journal of Anatomy* **81**:300–333.

Le Gros Clark, W. E., D. M. Cooper, and S. Zuckerman
1936   The endocranial cast of the chimpanzee. *Journal of the Royal Anthropological Institute of Great Britain and Ireland* **66**:249–268.

LeMay, M.
1975   The language capability of Neanderthal man. *American Journal of Physical Anthropology* **42**:9–14.

LeMay, M., and N. Geschwind
1975   Hemispheric differences in the brain of great apes. *Brain, Behavior, and Evolution* **11**:48–52.

Lestrel, P. E., and D. W. Read
1973   Hominid cranial capacity versus time: a regression approach. *Journal of Human Evolution* **2**:405–411.

Leutenegger, W.
1973   Encephalization in australopithecines: a new estimate. *Folia Primatologica* **19**:9–17.

Levin, G.
1937   Racial and inferiority characters in the human brain. *American Journal of Physical Anthropology* **22**:345–380.

McHenry, H. M.
1975   Fossil hominid body weight and brain size. *Nature* **254**:686–688.
1976   Early hominid body weight and encephalization. *American Journal of Physical Anthropology* **45**:77–84.

McHenry, H. M., and L. A. Temerin
1979   The evolution of hominid bipedalism: evidence from the fossil record. *Yearbook of Physical Anthropology* **22**:105–131.

Marshall, W. H., C. N. Woolsey, and P. Bard
1945   Observations on cortical somatic mechanisms of cat and monkey. *Journal of Neurophysiology* **14**:1–24.

Martin, R. D.
1981   Allometric approaches to the evolution of the primate nervous system. In *Primate brain evolution: Concepts and methods,* edited by E. Armstrong and D. Falk. New York, Plenum. Pp. 39–56.

Mettler, F. A.
1933   Brain of Pithecus rhesus (M. rhesus). *American Journal of Physical Anthropology* **17**:309–331.
1956   *Culture and the structural evolution of the neutral system. James Arthur Lecture, 1956,* American Museum of Natural History, New York.

Meyer, A., E. Beck, and T. McLardy
1947   Prefrontal lobotomy. *Brain* **70**:18–49.

Murrill, R. I., and D. T. Wallace

1971   A method for making an endocranial cast through the foramen magnum of an intact skull. *American Journal of Physical Anthropology* **34**:441–446.

Myers, R. E.
1965   Commissural connections between occipital lobes of the monkey. *Journal of Comparative Neurology* **718**:1–6.

Noback, C. R., and W. Montagna (editors)
1970   *The primate brain* (Vol. I). New York: Appleton.

Noback, C. R., and N. Moskowitz
1962   Structural and functional correlates of "encepalization" in the primate brain. *Annals of the New York Academy of Sciences* **102**:210–218.

Olivier, G., and H. Tissier
1975   Determination of cranial capacity in fossil men. *American Journal of Physical Anthropology* **43**:353–362.

Packer, A. D.
1949   A comparison of endocrania: cast and brain of an Australian aborigine. *Journal of Anatomy* **83**:195–204.

Pakkenberg, H.
1966   The number of nerve cells in the cerebral cortex of man. *Journal of Comparative Neurology* **128**:17–19.

Pakkenberg, H., and J. Voigt
1964   Brain weight of Danes. *Acta Anatomica* **56**:297–307.

Passingham, R. E.
1973   Anatomical differences between the neocortex of man and other primates. *Brain, Behavior and Evolution* **7**:337–359.
1975a   The brain and intelligence. *Brain Behavior and Evolution* **11**:1–15.
1975b   Changes in the size and organization of the brain in man and his ancestors. *Brain, Behavior and Evolution* **11**:73–90.

Passingham, R. E., and G. Ettlinger
1974   A comparison of cortical functions in man and the other primates. *International Review of Neurobiology* **16**:233–299.

Peden, J. K., and G. von Bonin
1947   The Neocortex of Hapale. *Journal of Comparative Neurology* **86**:37–64.

Penfield, W.
1935   A contribution to the mechanism of intracranial pain. *Research Publications—Association for Research in Nervous and Mental Disease* **15**:399–416.
1938   The cerebral cortex in man. I. The cerebral cortex and conciousness. *Archives of Neurology and Psychiatry* **40**:417–422.

Penfield, W., and E. Boldrey
1937   Somatic motor and sensory representation in the cerebral cortex of man as studied by electrical stimulation. *Brain* **60**:389–443.
1939   Cortical spread of epileptic discharge and the conditioning effect of habitual seizures. *American Journal of Psychiatry* **96**:255–281.

Penfield, W., and T. Erickson
1941   *Epilepsy and cerebral localization.* Springfield, Illinois: Thomas.

Penfield, W., and J. Evans
1935   The frontal lobe in man: a clinical study of maximum removals. *Brain* **58**:115–133.

Penfield, W., and T. Rasmussen
1949   Vocalization and arrest of speech. *Archives of Neurology and Psychiatry* **61**:21–27.
1950   *The cerebral cortex of man.* New York: Macmillan.

Penfield, W., and L. Roberts
1959   *Speech and brain mechanisms.* Princeton, New Jersey: Princeton University Press.

Petersen, M. R., M. D. Beecher, S. R. Zoloth, D. B. Moody and W. L. Stebbins

1978   Lateralization of species-specific vocalizations by Japanese Macaques (*Macaca fuscata*). *Science* **202**:324–326.

Pickering, S. P.
1930   Correlation of brain and head measurements and relationship of brain shape and size to shape and size of the head. *American Journal of Physical Anthropology* **15**:1–52.

Pilbeam, D. R.
1969   Early Hominidae and cranial capacity. *Nature* (*London*) **224**:386.
1970   Early hominids and cranial capacities (continued). *Nature* (*London*) **227**:747–748.

Pilbeam, D. R., and S. J. Gould
1974   Size and scaling in human evolution *Science* **186**:892–901.

Pitt, R.
1978   Warfare and hominid brain evolution. *Journal of Theoretical Biology* **72**:551–575.

Powell, T. P. S., and V. B. Mountcastle
1959   Some aspects of the functional organization of the cortex of the postcentral gyrus of the monkey. *Bulletin of the Johns Hopkins Hospital* **105**:132–162.

Přívratský, V.
1979   The brain and neoteny in the process of hominization. In *Natural selection*, edited by V. J. A. Novák, V. V. Leonovich, and B. Pacltová. Praha: Czechoslovak Academy of Sciences. Pp. 303–309.

Pubols, B. H., and L. M. Pubols
1971   Somatopic organization of spider monkey somatic sensory cerebral cortex. *Journal of Comparative Neurology* **141**:63–76.

Radinsky, L. B.
1967a   Relative brain size: A new measure. *Science* **155**:836–838.
1967b   The oldest primate endocast. *American Journal of Physical Anthropology* **27**:385–388.
1968   A new approach to mammalian cranial analysis, illustrated by examples of prosimian primates. *Journal of Morphology* **124**:167–180.
1970   The fossil evidence of prosimian brain evolution. In *The primate brain*, edited by C. R. Noback and W. Montagna. New York: Appleton. Pp. 209–224.
1972   Endocasts and studies of primate brain evolution. In *The functional and evolutionary biology of primates*, edited by R. Tuttle. Chicago: Aldine. Pp. 175–184.
1973   Aegyptopithecus endocasts: oldest record of a pongid brain. *American Journal of Physical Anthropology* **39**:239–248.
1974   The fossil evidence of anthropoid brain evolution. *American Journal of Physical Anthropology* **41**:15–28.
1975   Primate brain evolution. *American Scientist* **63**:656–663.
1977   Early primate brains: fact and fiction. *Journal of Human Evolution* **6**:79–86.
1978   Evolution of brain size in carnivores and ungulates. *American Naturalist* **112**:815–831.
1979   *The fossil record of primate brain evolution. 49th James Arthur Lecture, 1979*. American Museum of Natural History, New York.

Reed, C. A., and D. Falk
1977   The stature and weight of Sterkfontein 14, a gracile australopithecine from Transvaal, as determined from the innominate bone. *Fieldiana, Geology* **33**:423–440.

Rensch, B.
1956   Increase of learning capability with increase of brain size. *American Naturalist* **90**:81–95.

Richman, E. P., R. M. Steward, J. M. Hutchinson, and V. S. Caviness
1975   Mechanical model of brain convolutional development. *Science* **189**:18–21.

Roginsky, Y. Y.
1933   Brain weight index. *Anthropolgicheskii Zhurnalz* 1933 **1–2**.

Sacher, G. A.
1959   Relationship of lifespan to body weight and brain weight of mammals. *Ciba Foundation Colloquia on the Lifespan of Animals* **5**:115–133.

1970   Allometric and factoral analysis of brain structure in insectivores and primates. In *The primate brain* (Vol. I), edited by C. R. Noback and W. Montagna. New York: Appleton. Pp. 245–287.

1975   Maturation and longevity in relation to a cranial capacity in hominid evolution. In *Primate functional morphology and evolution*, edited by R. H. Tuttle. The Hague: Mouton. Pp. 417–441.

1982   The role of brain maturation in the evolution of primates. In *Primate brain evolution: Concepts and methods*, edited by E. Armstrong and D. Falk. New York, Plenum. Pp. 97–112.

Sanides, F.
1975   Comparative neurology of the temporal lobe in primates including man with reference to speech. *Brain and Language* **2**:396–419.

Sanides, F., and A. Krishnamurti
1967   Cytoarchitectonic subdivisions of sensorimotor and prefrontal regions and of bordering insular and limbic fields in slow loris (*Nycticebus coucang coucang*). *Journal für Hirnforschung* **9**:225–252.

Schepers, G. W. H.
1938   The corpus callosum and related structures in the South African Negro brain. *American Journal of Physical Anthropology* **24**:161–184.

Schreider, E.
1966   Brain weight correlations calculated from original results of Paul Broca. *American Journal of Physical Anthropology* **25**:153–158.

Schultz, A. H.
1940   The size of the orbit and of the eye in primates. *American Journal of Physical Anthropology* **26**:389–408.

1941   The relative size of the cranial capacity in primates. *American Journal of Physical Anthropology* **28**:273–287.

Schwidetzky, I.
1976   Postpleistocene evolution of the brain? *American Journal of Physical Anthropology* **45**:605–612.

Sekla, B., and F. Soukup
1969   Inheritance of the cephalic index. *American Journal of Physical Anthropology* **30**:137–140.

Sergi, S.
1942   Sulla morfologia cerebrale del secondo Paleantropo di Saccopastore. *Atti della Accademia Nazionale dei Lincei, Classe di Scienze, Fisiche, Matimatiche e Naturali, Rendiconti* **20**:670–681.

1944   Craniometria e craniografia del primo paleantropo di Saccopastore. Ricerche di Morfologia **20–21**:733–791.

Shariff, G. A.
1953   Cell counts in the primate cerebral cortex. *Journal of Comparative Neurology* **98**:381–400.

Shellshear, J. L.
1930   The arterial supply of the cerbral cortex in the chimpanzee. *Journal of Anatomy (London)* **65**:45–87.

1934   The primative features of the cerebrum, with special reference to the brain of the Bushwoman described by Marshall. *Philosophical Transactions of the Royal Society of London* **223**:1–26.

1937   The brain of the aboriginal Australian. A study in cerebral morphology. *Philosophical Transactions of the Royal Society of London* **227**:293–409.

Shellshear, J. L., and G. E. Elliot Smith
1934   A comparative study of the endocranial cast of *Sinanthropus*. *Philosophical Transactions of the Royal Society of London* **223**:469–487.

Shibata, I.
1936   Brain weight of the Korean. *American Journal of Physical Anthropology* **22**:27–35.

Singer, R.
1954   The Saldanha skull from Hopefield, South Africa. *American Journal of Physical Anthropology* **12**:345–363.

Solnitzky, O., and P. S. Harman
    1946   A comparative study of the central and peripheral sections of the visual cortex in primates, with observations on the lateral geniculate body. *Journal of Comparative Neurology* **85**:313–419.
Sperry, R. W.
    1947   Cerebral regulation of motor coordination in monkeys following multiple transection of sensorimotor cortex. *Journal of Neurophysiology* **10**:275–294.
    1968   Mental unity following surgical disconnection of the cerebral himispheres. *Harvey Lectures* **62**:292–323.
Stephan, H.
    1969   Quantitative investigations on visual structures in primate brains. *Proceedings of the 2nd International Congress of Primatology, 1968.* Pp. 34–42.
    1972   Evolution of primate brains: a comparative anatomical investigation. In *The functional and evolutionary biology of primates,* edited by R. H. Tuttle. Chicago: Aldine. Pp. 155–174.
Stephan, H., and O. J. Andy
    1969   Quantitative comparative neuroanatomy of primates: an attempt at a phylogenetic interpretation. *Annals of the New York Academy of Sciences* **167**:370–387.
Stephan, H., R. Bauchot, and O. J. Andy
    1970   Data on size of the brain and of various brain parts in insectivores and primates. In *The primate brain* (Vol. I), edited by C. R. Noback and W. Montagna. New York: Appleton. Pp. 289–297.
Stewart, T. D.
    1933   Cranial capacity studies. *American Journal of Physical Anthropology* **18**:337–359.
    1937   An examination of the Breitinger method of cranial capacity measurement. *American Journal of Physical Anthropology* **23**:111–125.
    1943   Relative variability of Indian and White cranial series. *American Journal of Physical of Anthropology* **1**:261–270.
Tildesley, M. L., and N. Datta-Majunder
    1944   Cranial capacity data on the techniques of Macdonell and Breitinger. *American Journal of Physical Anthropology* **3**:233–249.
Tobias, P. V.
    1963   Crnial capacity of *Zinjanthropus* and other australopithecines. *Nature (London)* **197**:743–746.
    1964   The Olduvai Bed I hominine with special reference to its cranial capacity. *Nature (London)* **202**:3–4.
    1965   Reply to RL Holloway: cranial capacity of the hominine from Olduvai Bed I. *Nature (London)* **208**:206.
    1968   Cranial capacity in anthropoid apes, *Australopithecus* and *Homo habilis,* with comments on skewed samples. *South African Journal of Science* **64**:81–91.
    1970   Brain-size, grey matter and race—fact or fiction? *American Journal of Physical Anthropology* **32:3–26.**
    1971   *The brain in hominid evolution.* New York: Columbia University Press.
Tower, D. B.
    1954   Structural and functional organization of mammalian cerebral cortex. The correlation of neurone density with brain size. *Journal of Comparative Neurology* **101**:19–53.
Tugby, D. J.
    1953   A new internal casting method. *American Journal of Physical Anthropology* **11**:437–440.
Uspenskii, S. I.
    1964   A new method for measuring cranial capacity. *American Journal of Physical Anthropology* **22**:115–117.
Van Valen, L.
    1974   Brain size and intelligence in man. *American Journal of Physical Anthropology* **40**:417–424.
Vint, F.
    1934   The brain of the Kanja native. *Journal of Anatomy (London)* **68**:216–223.

von Bonin, G.
    1937   Brain-weight and body-weight of mammals. *Journal of General Psychiatry* **16**:379–389.
    1938   The cerebral cortex of the cebus monkey. *Journal of Comparative Neurology* **69**:181–227.
    1941   On encephalometry. *Journal of Comparative Neurology* **75**:287–314.
    1942   The axis of the forebrain in macaque and man. *American Journal of Physical Anthropology* **29**:41–46.
    1944   Architecture of the precentral motor cortex and some adjacent areas. In *The precentral motor cortex*, edited by P. C. Bucy. Urbana: University of Illinois Press.
    1945   *The cortex of Galago*. Urbana: University of Illinois Press.
    1963   *The evolution of the human brain*. Chicago: University of Chicago Press.
von Bonin, G., and P. Bailey
    1947   *The neocortex of* Macaca mulatta. Urbana: University of Illinois Press.
    1961   Pattern of the cerebral isocortex. *Primatologia* **2**:1–42.
Walker, A. E.
    1938   *The primate thalamus*. Chicago: University of Chicago Press.
Walker, E., and J. F. Fulton
    1936   The external configuration of the cerebral hemispheres of the chimpanzee. *Journal of Anatomy (London)* **71**:105–116.
Wanner, J. A.
    1971   Relative brain size: a critique of a new measure. *American Journal of Physical Anthropology* **35**:255–258.
Weidenreich, F.
    1936   Observations on the form and proportions of the endocranial casts of *Sinanthropus pekinensis* and the great apes: a comparative study of brain size. *Palaeontologia Sinica* **7**:1–50.
    1937   The relationship of *Sinanthropus pekinensis* to *Pithecanthropus, Javanthropus* and Rodesian man. *Journal of the Royal Anthropological Institute of Great Britain and Ireland* **67**:51–65.
    1938   The ramifications of the middle meningeal artery in fossil hominids and its bearing upon phylogenetic problems. *Palaeontologia Sinica* **110**:1–16.
    1941   The brain and its role in the phylogenetic transformation of the human skull. *Transactions of the American Philosophical Society* **31**:321–442.
    1943   The skull of *Sinanthropus pekinensis. Palaeontologia Sinica* **127**:1–486.
    1947   Some particulars of skulls and brains of early hominids. *American Journal of Physical Anthropology* **5**:357–427.
Welker, W. I.
    1976   Mapping the brain. Historical trends in functional localization. *Brain, Behavior and Evolution* **13**:327–343.
Welker, W. I., and G. B. Campos
    1963   Physiological significance of sulci in somatic sensory cerebral cortex in mammals of the family Procyonidae. *Journal of Comparative Neurology* **120**:19–36.
Wen, I. C.
    1933   A study of the occipital region of the Chinese fetal brain. *Journal of Comparative Neurology* **57**:477–506.
Werner, G., and B. L. Whitsel
    1968   Topology of the body representation in somatosensory area I in primates. *Journal of Neurophysiology* **31**:856–869.
Whitsel, B., L. Petrucelli, and G. Werner
    1969   Symmetry and connectivity in the map of the body surface in somatosensory area II of primates. *Journal of Neurophysiology* **32**:170–183.
Witherspoon, Y. T.
    1960   Brain weight and behavior. *Human Biology* **32**:366–369.
Wolpoff, M. H.
    1969   Cranial capacity and taxonomy of Olduvai Hominid 7. *Nature (London)* **223**:5205.

1970   Taxonomy and cranial capacity of Olduvai Hominid 7 (continued). *Nature (London)* **227**:747.

Woo, J.

1949   Racial and sex differences in the frontal curvature and its relationship to metopism. *American Journal of Physical Anthropology* **7**:215–226.

Woolsey, C. N.

1938   Representation in the motor cortex of flexor and extensor muscles of the leg. *American Journal of Physiology* **123**:221–222.

1944   Additional observations on a "second" somatic receiving area in the cerebral cortex of the monkey. *Federation Proceedings, Federation of American Societies for Experimental Biology* **3**:53.

1958   Organization of somatic sensory and motor areas of the cerebral cortex. In *Biological and biochemical bases of behavior*, edited by H. Harlow and C. N. Woolsey. Madison: University of Wisconsin Press. Pp. 63–81.

1964   Cortical localization as defined by evoked potential and electrical stimulation studies. In *Cerebral localization and organization*, edited by G. Schaltenbrand and C. N. Woolsey. Madison: University of Wisconsin Press. Pp. 17–26.

Woolsey, C. N., W. H. Marshall, and P. Bard

1942   Representation of cutaneous tactile sensibility in cerebral cortex of monkey as indicated by evoked potentials. *Bulletin of the Johns Hopkins Hospital* **70**:399–441.

1943   Note on organization of tactile sensory area of cerebral cortex of chimpanzee. *Journal of Neurophysiology* **6**:287–291.

Woolsey, C. N., *et al.*

1960   Organization of pre- and postcentral leg areas in chimpanzee and gibbon. *Transactions of the American Neurological Association* **85**:144–146.

Yeni-Komshian, G. H., and D. A. Benson

1976   Anatomical study of cerebral asymmetry in the temporal lobe of humans, chimpanzees and rhesus monkeys. *Science* **192**:387–389.

Zeki, S. M.

1969   Representation of central visual field in prestriate cortex of monkey. *Brain Research* **14**:271–291.

Zilles, K., H. Stephan, and A. Schleicher

1982   Quantitative cytoarchitectonics of the cerebral cortices of several prosimian species. In *Primate brain evolution: Concepts and methods*, edited by E. Armstrong and D. Falk. New York: Plenum Pp. 177–201.

5

Molecular Anthropology:
Its Development and Current Directions

Morris Goodman and J. E. Cronin

> The persistence of the chemical blood-relationship between the various groups of animals serves to carry us back into geological times, and I believe we have but begun the work along these lines, and that it will lead to valuable results in the study of various problems of evolution.
>
> In view of the crudity of our methods, it is not surprising if certain discrepancies may be encountered in the course of investigations conducted by biological methods, the body of evidence however is perfectly conclusive. The object of my investigation has been to determine certain broad facts with regard to blood-affinities, consequently my studies must be regarded in the light of a preliminary investigation, which will have to be continued along special lines by many workers in the future.
>
> Nuttall 1904:4

The publication in 1904 of G.H.F. Nuttall's famous monograph, *Blood Immunity and Blood Relationship*, occurred many years before it was known that the primary structures of proteins were DNA-encoded amino-acid sequences and that such translated DNA information was the genetic basis for the immunological specificities of animal sera. Nevertheless, the findings described in *Blood Immunity and Blood Relationship* testified that immunological comparisons could help reveal the genealogical relationships that exist among anthropoid primates and other species. This led to the eventual birth of molecular anthropology, which occurred in the summer of 1962 at the Burg-Wartenstein Symposium organized by Sherwood Washburn on "Classification and Human Evolution."

This symposium initiated one of the principal directions of the research in molecular anthropology—an accurate description of the genealogy of the primates. On the basis of extensive immunological and electrophoretic comparisons of serum proteins, it was argued (Goodman 1963a) that the African apes, *Pan* and *Gorilla*, are phylogenetically more closely related to *Homo* than to the Asiatic apes and therefore should be removed from the family Pongidae and placed with man in the family Hominidae. Indeed, this earlier molecular evidence suggested that the chimpanzee and gorilla were each as closely related to man as to one another. At this same Burg-Wartenseinen Symposium, Klinger *et al.* (1963) supported such a taxonomic proposal with chromosomal findings, and Zuckerkandl (1963) reviewed findings from the tryptic peptide analysis of hemoglobin chains, which also pointed to the close genetic relationship of the chimpanzee and gorilla to man. Of particular significance is the fact that Zuckerkandl called his paper "Perspectives in Molecular Anthropology," thereby signifying, in giving this field its name, that the concepts and methods of molecular biology should prove rewarding in the study of human evolution.

The next important development in molecular anthropology occurred in the later 1960s when Sarich and Wilson (1967) applied the molecular clock hypothesis to quantitative immunological measurements of the amounts of divergence among primate albumins. From the results of their clock calculations, they concluded that the lineages to *Homo, Pan,* and *Gorilla* separated from one another in the range of 5 million years ago. By the 1970s sizable amounts of amino-acid sequence data on primate species began to accumulate, and computer procedures, such as the maximum parsimony algorithms, were developed to extract evolutionary information from this data. DNA comparisons of hominoids and other primates had also been progressing. In 1975, at another Burg-Wartenstein Symposium, this time on "Progress in Molecular Anthropology," the mounting molecular evidence on primate phylogeny and the molecular clock controversy concerning hominoid branching times were explored. Although controversy continues as to whether accurate molecular clocks exist, the evidence from molecules for a late ancestral separation of *Homo* from *Pan* and *Gorilla* has been gaining wide support.

Varying rates of change in protein evolution have been noted, even by clock proponents (Cronin and Sarich 1980; Sarich and Cronin 1976; Wilson *et al.* 1977). There is also good evidence that natural selection caused accelerations and decelerations in the rates of molecular evolution of globins and other proteins (Goodman *et al.* 1975; Baba *et al.* 1981; Goodman 1981). The past 40 million years appear to be a period of deceleration, at least for specific proteins and DNA sequences in some anthropoid lineages and, specifically, within the hominoid clade.

The molecular biological revolution of the 1960s, which deciphered the genetic code, provided molecular anthropology with important concepts and tools for studying primate phylogeny and human evolution. The second molecular biological revolution, now in progress and involving the isolation and sequencing of genes, is already having a major impact on the directions of research in molecular anthropology. These current directions of research will produce a more profound understanding of human origins, and they will do so in several ways: (*a*) they will help establish the correct genealogical position of the human lineage within the Hominoidea; (*b*) they will help trace our lineage back to our earliest primate ancestors, indicating our true degrees of genealogical relationship to the other lineages of Primates; (*c*) they will help establish within the time frame of primate phylogeny the date of our ancestral splitting from our closest ape sister group as well as the earlier divergence dates that separate us from more distant primate relatives; and (*d*) they will characterize the tempo and mode of genetic change surrounding human origins and, in so doing, provide insights about the role of natural selection and other forces of evolution, such as genetic drift, during this process.

Genealogical Description of Primate Phylogeny

Toward a Cladistic Classification

As already noted, this central aspect of molecular anthropology had its historical beginnings in the pioneering work of Nuttall (1904). The significance of his work is revealed by the first figure of *Blood Immunity and Blood Relationship*. This figure, reproduced here (Figure 1), is a genealogical tree of the Anthropoidea taken from the paleoanthropologist Dubois. Nuttall stressed that the results of the immunological serum precipitin test pointed to the more remote relationship from man and anthropoid apes "of the Cercopithecidae, but especially of the New World monkeys, as indicated in the tree" of Dubois. A striking feature of the Dubois' phylogenetic tree is that *Anthropithecus* (= *Pan*) and *Gorilla* are closer genealogically to *Homo* than to *Simia* (= *Pongo*), which agrees with the views of molecular anthropologists (Goodman 1975, 1976; Sarich and Cronin 1976). However, the modern evidence from proteins and DNA indicates that within the Hominoidea, there is a relatively long period of common ancestry for *Homo*, *Pan*, and *Gorilla* after the ancestral separation of *Pongo* and not the relatively short period depicted in Dubois's tree. Nor would the modern evidence support a long period of common ancestry for *Pan* and *Gorilla* independent of their common ancestry with *Homo* (Goodman 1975, 1976, 1981; Sarich and Cronin 1976; Cronin and Sarich 1982, Ferris *et al.* 1981).

Other than showing the Dubois tree as the first figure of *Blood Immunity and Blood Relationship*, Nuttall never explicitly discussed the possibility, raised by some of the blood comparisons, that the African apes shared a more recent common ancestor with man than they did with Asiatic apes. Perhaps deterred by the crudity of his methods and artifacts in his results, Nuttall accepted the traditional taxonomic grouping of African and Asiatic apes in the family Simiidae (= Pongidae) as distinct from Hominidae.

By the early 1960s it had been established that the amino-acid sequences of proteins were encoded by nucleotide sequences in genes (Anfinsen 1959; Crick *et al.* 1961; Ingram 1961). This prepared the way for interpreting the closer immunological and electrophoretic correspondence of *Homo*, *Pan*, and *Gorilla* to one another than to *Pongo* or other primates as reflecting the genetic kinship and monophyletic origin of man, chimpanzee, and gorilla (Goodman 1962, 1963a, 1963b). It was concluded that the conventional Pongidae, which grouped *Pan*,

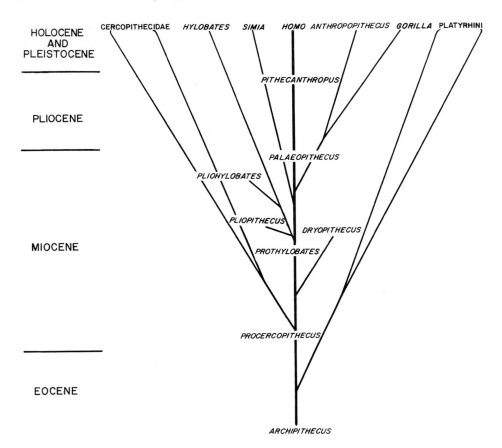

Figure 1   Genealogy of Anthropoidea from G. H. F. Nuttall's famous monograph, "Blood Immunity and Blood Relationships," (1904).

Gorilla, and *Pongo* together in the Ponginae, was a polyphyletic taxon and that a Darwinian approach to taxonomy, which constructed monophyletic groups based on recency of common ancestry, required the grouping of *Pan* and *Gorilla* with *Homo* rather than with *Pongo* (Goodman 1962, 1963a, 1963b). This proposal was rejected by Simpson (1963), who agreed with the genealogy suggested by the protein (e.g., Goodman 1963a; Zuckerkandl 1963) and chromosomal (e.g., Klinger *et al.* 1963) data but not with the proposed revision of the taxonomic classification of hominoid groups. Simpson argued that the extent African and Asiatic apes were termini of conservative lineages. Man, on the other hand, was the offspring of a markedly divergent lineage whose entrance into a radically new adaptive zone justified having *Homo* as the sole extant member of the family Hominidae. Support for the proposal of classifying *Pan* and *Gorilla* with *Homo* rather than with *Pongo* has come from advocates of Hennig's phylogenetic systematics (e.g., Eldridge and

Table 1 A Classification of Extant Primates[a]

Immunodiffusion and protein sequence data[b]	Microcomplement fixation, electrophoretic and protein sequence data[c]
Order Primates	Order Primates
Semiorder Strepsirhini	Semiorder Strepsirhini
Suborder Lemuriformes	Suborder Lemuriformes
Superfamily Lemuroidea	Superfamily Lemuroidea
Family Lemuridae	Family Lemuridae
Lemur (lemur)	*Lemur*
	Hapalemur
	Varecia
Family Indriidae	Family Indriidae
Propithecus (sifaka)	*Propithecus*
	Avahi
Superfamily Cheirogaleoidea	Superfamily Cheirogaleoidea
Family Cheirogaleidae	Family Cheirogaleidae
	Subfamily Cheirogalinae
Cheirogaleus (dwarf lemur)	*Cheirogaleus*
Microcebus (mouse lemur)	*Phaner*
	Subfamily Microcebinae
	Microcebus
Superfamily Daubentonioidea	Superfamily Daubentonioidea
Daubentonia (aye-aye)	*Daubentonia*
Suborder Lorisiformes	Suborder Lorisiformes
Superfamily Lorisoidea	Superfamily Lorisoidea
Family Perodicticidae	Family Perodicticidae
Subfamily Perodicticinae	Subfamily Perodicticinae
Perodicticus (potto)	*Perodicticus*
Arctocebus (angwantibo)	*Arctocebus*
Family Galagidae	Family Galagidae
Galago (bushbaby)	*Galago*
Galagoides (pygmy galago)	*Galagoides*
Family Lorisidae	Family Lorisdae
Loris (slender loris)	*Loris*
Nycticebus	*Nycticebus*
Semiorder Haplorhini	
Suborder Tarsioidea	Semiorder Tarsiiformes
Tarsius (tarsier)	*Tarsius*
Suborder Anthropoidea	Semiorder Anthropoidea
Infraorder Platyrrhini	Infraorder Platyrrhini
Superfamily Ceboidea	Superfamily Ceboidea
Saguinus (marmoset)	Family Cebidae
Aotus (owl monkey)	Subfamily Aotinae
Callicebus (titis)	*Aotus*
Cacajao (uakari)	Subfamily Callicebinae
Chiropotes (sakis)	*Callicebus*
Cebus (capuchin)	Subfamily Pithecinae
Saimiri (squirrel monkey)	*Pithecia*
Alouatta (howler monkey)	*Cacajao*
Ateles (spider monkey)	Subfamily Cebinae
Lagothrix (woolly monkey)	*Cebus*

(Continued next page)

Table 1 *(continued)*

Immunodiffusion and protein sequence data[b]	Microcomplement fixation, electrophoretic and protein sequence data[c]
	Subfamily Atelinae
	Ateles
	Alouatta
	Lagothrix
	Subfamily Saimirinae
	Saimiri
	Family Callithricidae
	Callithrix
	Saguinus
	Leontopithecus
	Callimico
Infraorder Catarrhini	Infraorder Catarrhini
Superfamily Cercopithecoidea	Superfamily Cercopithecoidea
Family Cercopithecidae	Family Cercopithecidae
Subfamily Colobinae	Subfamily Colobinae
Colubus (guerezas)	*Colobus*
Presbytis (langurs)	*Presbytis*
Pygathrix (douc langur)	*Pygathrix*
Nasalis (probiscis monkey)	*Nasalis*
Subfamily Cercopithecinae	Subfamily Cercopithecinae
	Tribe Papionini
Macaca (macques)	*Papio*
Papio (baboon)	*Macaca*
Theropthecus (gelada baboon)	*Cercocebus*
Cercocebus (mangabey)	*Mandrillus*
Erythrocebus (patas monkey)	*Theropithecus*
Cercopithecus (vervet)	Tribe Cercopithecini
	Cercopithecus
	Erythrocebus
Superfamily Hominoidea	Superfamily Hominoidea
Family Hylobatidae	Family Hylobatidae
Hylobates (gibbon)	*Hylobates*
Symphalangus (siamang)	*Symphalangus*
	Nomascus
Family Hominidae	Family Hominidae
Subfamily Ponginae	Subfamily Ponginae
Pongo (orangutan)	*Pongo*
Subfamily Homininae	Subfamily Homininae
Gorilla (gorilla)	*Gorilla*
Pan (chimpanzee)	*Pan*
Homo (human)	*Homo*

[a]Adapted from Goodman (1975:Table 4).
[b]Data collected by M. Goodman.
[c]Data collected by J. E. Cronin.

Cracraft 1980; Nelson and Platnick 1981) in which the idea first enunciated by Darwin (1859), that taxonomic classification should describe primarily the genealogical relationships of the classified organisms, was rigorously followed. The proposed cladistic arrangement, however, is not unanimously accepted. An analysis of morphological data has suggested that *Pongo* is in a monophyletic clade united with the African apes to the exclusion of the human lineage.

It may be that *Pongo* is more similar to the African apes in some features simply because the former has retained more ancestral characters than *Homo* has. Since shared primitive and unique derived characters are not useful in recognizing cladistic relationships, morphological distinctions between these four may not be definitive ways to interpret their relationships. We would suggest that the morphological based conclusion that *Homo* diverged early in hominoid history before *Pongo*, *Pan*, and *Gorilla* lineages had separated from each other is drawn from a phenetic analysis that implicitly assumes a constant rate of morphological change and interprets morphological distinctiveness to mean early branching (Mickevich 1978; Cronin and Meikle 1982). The derived features of humans—bipedal locomotion, cranial and dental size and morphology, etc.—could have risen at any time along this lineage after its separation from the African apes. Similarly, *Pongo* may be plesiomorphic in many traits, but this would not be indicative of a shared recent lineage with *Pan* and *Gorilla*. Table 1, adapted from Table 4 in Goodman (1975), presents such a genealogical classification of extant primates. It follows the main outline of the original scheme (Goodman 1963a) but embraces a larger number of primate genera.

Immunological Evidence

This classification (Table 1) was based on data obtained from thousands of immunodiffusion comparisons performed with antisera to the serum proteins of many different primate genera. The immunodiffusion data were converted by a computer program (Moore and Goodman 1968) into antigenic distance tables, one for each genus of Primates against which antisera had been produced. Then these antigenic distance tables were converted into a dendrogram by the unweighted pair group method of Sokal and Michener (1958). The hypothesis of divergent evolution was used to draw phylogenetic inferences from this unweighted pair group tree by the assumption that the more ancient the common ancestor for a pair of species is, the greater is the genetic distance for that pair of species.

Similarly, during the mid-1960s to the late 1970s, immunological data based on the quantitative technique of "microcomplement Fixation" (MC'F) (Champion *et al.* 1974) was being gathered in the laboratory of A. Wilson by V. Sarich and J. Cronin. Again, thousands of comparisons were made of numerous mammalian species, particularly primates, with antisera directed to the purified serum proteins albumin and transferrin. The raw data were converted into units called *immunological distance*

(ID) *units*, which were subsequently used for phylogenetic tree construction. The tree construction algorithm has been detailed in numerous publications (Sarich 1969; Sarich and Cronin 1976). The algorithm makes *no* a priori assumptions about the rates of evolution of the molecules. In fact, the procedure yields the branching order (cladistics) and the amount of change of the molecule to assign to each branch. Thus, a comparison of the rates of protein evolution within a cluster can be determined by comparing it with the next outside sister taxon or cluster. In this manner, a *relative* rate test can be conducted before any absolute dates are determined through the use of the molecular clock model. The accuracy of the constructed tree can be calculated by means of a measure of deviation of output versus input data, and the tree with the lowest percentage standard error can be chosen (Fitch and Margoliash 1967). The data from MC'F comparisons, gathered by immunodiffusion techniques and presented in Table 1, are remarkably concordant. The main disagreement is in the placement of *Tarsius*. The MC'F data (Cronin and Sarich 1980) depict a trichotomy consisting of the branch to *Tarsius* (Tarsiiformes), the branch to Lemuriformes and Lorisiformes, (i.e., Strepsirhini), and the branch to Anthropoidea, whereas the immunodiffusion data (Dene *et al.* 1976) depict a dichotomy consisting of Strepsirhini and Haplorhini, (i.e., *Tarsius* and Anthropoidea).

Recently, genetic information has been gathered from fossil remains through the use of immunological techniques of radioimmunoassay (RIA). By this technique the serum protein albumin has been detected in the soft tissues of two recently extinct species, the Siberian mammoth (*Mammuthus primigenius*) and the Tasmanian wolf (*Thalacinus cynocephalus*). The former was found to be equidistant from the albumins of the Indian and African elephant species. The Tasmanian wolf is closely related to the dasyuroid complex of Australian marsupials (Lowenstein *et al.* 1981). Lowenstein (1981) has also detected immunologically reactive collagens from *Australopithecus* fossils, including a specimen from *A. robustus*. Clearly this technique holds the potential for discovering the phylogenetical affinities of a number of fossil forms. Particularly of interest will be the possible determination of the relationship of *Ramapithecus* both to other Miocene hominoids and to living apes and humans. Work toward this end is in progress. A caveat is necessary, however. Protein denaturation in the fossil specimens can produce misleading findings unless rigorous controls are employed.

Nucleic Acid Evidence

Studies involving direct comparisons of nucleic acids for primate evolutionary studies date to the end of the 1960s and to the early 1970s. These investigations, which measured the degree of homology between different species' cellular DNA, were expressed as a percentage difference in the nucleotide sequence. The direct measurement, however, involved hybridizing unique sequence DNA from heterologous species and measuring the degree to which the thermal stability of the hybrid molecule is lowered compared to the native species' double stranded DNA. When opposite bases are mispaired in the hybrid molecule, thermal stability is decreased. Especially important studies were those of Kohne (1972), Kohne *et al.* (1975), Hoyer, *et al.* (1972), Benveniste and Todaro (1976), and Bonner *et al.* (1980). In brief, the main finding of primate phylogeny described in the classification in Table 1 was fully confirmed. A monophyletic Anthropoidea subdivides into Platyrrhini and Catarrhini. In turn, Catarrhini bifurcates into Cercopithecoidea and Hominoidea, Hylobatidae separates from Hominidae, and then Hominidae branches into Ponginae (*Pongo*) and Homininae (*Pan, Homo,* and *Gorilla*). The results of Benveniste and Todaro (1976) are of further interest because their comparisons of a specific viral component of catarrhine cellular DNA implicated Asia as a potential geographic area for much of the history of the clade to *Homo*.

Very recently, comparisons of DNA found in the mitochrondria of hominoid species and analyzed through the use of restriction enzymes, (i.e., enzymes that cleave the double-stranded DNA at specific four- or six-base sequences), have yielded quantitative distances within the Hominoidea (Ferris *et al.* 1981). Such data are particularly good for close genetic comparisons—the rate of evolution of mitochondrial DNA is some 10 times the rate of nuclear DNA. The importance of these, as well as nucleic-acid sequence data for the future will be discussed at the end of this chapter.

Electrophoretic Evidence

Although gel electrophoresis has as its forte the discrimination at the lower taxonomic levels (i.e., at the levels of the individual, population, subspecies, and closely related sibling species), it has provided some useful evidence on the broader aspects of hominoid phylogeny. However, since the method discriminates between various proteins solely on the basis of the net change in and the size of the molecules, most of the sequence information at any one locus is lost in electrophoretic comparisons. Thus, the evidence provided on hominoid phylogeny is not as strong as that provided by immunological comparisons or actual amino acid sequencing of proteins. Nevertheless, the extensive electrophoretic comparisons of Bruce and Ayala (1979) suggest that *Pongo* clearly falls within the African ape and human cluster to the exclusion of *Hylobates*. In fact, their analysis could not distinguish *Pongo* from this cluster. In constrast, a cladistic analysis of the electrophoretic data (Cronin and Sarich 1981) indicates an initial bifurcation between *Hylobates* and the great apes; the African hominoids then cluster relative to the orangutan. But, again, the trichotomy between the chimpanzee, gorilla, and human lineages is not resolvable from these data. There do not appear to be any shared derived electrophoretic substitutions along a common clade uniting any two of these lineages to the exclusion of the other.

If any one electrophoretic study can be singled out as having an important impact on thinking about evolution within the hominoid clade that led to *Homo*, it is clearly the study of King and Wilson (1975). On the basis of electrophoretic comparison of 44 loci, they calculated that the average human and chimpanzee genes were 99% identical, a value most people found surprisingly high. In contrast to this great genic similarity, they noted extensive morphological differences between the two species and suggested that evolution was working on two different levels—one genic and the other morphological. To account for this disparity, they suggested that in contrast to the allozymic differences, mutations at putative regulatory loci—whether as point or gene order reorganization—were mainly responsible for the morphological differences, such as large brains that distinguish humans from chimpanzees.

Amino-Acid Sequence Evidence

Amino-acid sequence data of primates began to accumulate in large amounts during the late 1960s and the 1970s. Some of the proteins sequenced included: cytochrome *c* (Fitch and Margoliash 1967), fibrinopeptides (Doolittle *et al.* 1971; Wooding and Doolittle 1972), myoglobin (Romero-Herrera *et al.* 1978), hemoglobin (Goodman 1976), and carbonic anhydrase (Tashian *et al.* 1976). (See Goodman [1981] for an extensive review of this data.) During this period, a much more powerful algorithm and evolutionary hypothesis, the "Red King" or maximum homology hypothesis (Moore 1976), was developed and used to draw phylogenetic inferences from amino-acid sequence data on the primates (Goodman 1976).

The maximum homology hypothesis constructs genealogical trees from amino-acid sequence data by the principle of minimum evolution (Edwards and Cavalli-Sforza 1963; Zuckerkandl 1964; Eck and Dayhoff 1966) or maximum parsimony (Farris 1970; Fitch 1971; Moore *et al.* 1973). The aim of this principle is to account for the evolutionary descent of related sequences by the fewest possible genic changes. To show such minimum evolution, a genealogical arrangement must be found that maximizes the genetic likelinesses associated with common ancestry while minimizing the incident of parallel and back mutations. This can be done by utilizing the genetic code to represent the amino-acid sequences as messenger RNA (mRNA) sequences and by then seeking a tree with the minimum number of nucleotide replacements (NR) (i.e., lowest NR length). Since common ancestry rather than convergent evolution is the most probable explanation for any extensive matching of nucleotide sequences between species, tree reconstruction algorithms based on maximum parsimony offer the way of using Occam's razor to find the preferred genealogical hypothesis. This approach, which is described in detail elsewhere (Goodman *et al.* 1979a; Goodman 1981), adheres to the principles of phylogenetic systematics (Hennig 1966), in that grouping by derived similarity (as revealed by maximizing the number of matching nucleotide sites between ancestral and descendant sequences) determines the branching order of the tree.

In one of the most recent studies of primate phylogeny utilizing the maximum homology hypothesis, genealogical trees were constructed by the maximum parsimony method on amino-acid sequence data from 553 polypeptide chains of 244 species, including 37 primate species (Goodman *et al.* 1981). The polypeptide chains consisted of 94 cytochromes *c*, 46 lens α-crystallins 47 combined A and B sequences, 18 carbonic anhydrases, 29 members of the protein family containing calmodulin, and 268 globins, of which those from jawed vertebrates consisted of myoglobins, β-hemoglobins, and α-hemoglobins. Aside from the separate trees or gene phylogenies for the different types of sequences, species phylogenies were constructed after the different sequences were combined in a tandem alignment as if such sequences were a giant polypeptide chain encoded by an extended gene. These gene and species phylogenies have provided important insights not only on the branching pattern in primate phylogeny but also on the tempo and mode of molecular evolution over the course of vertebrate phylogeny, particularly in that lineage that ultimately descended to present day *Homo sapiens.*

An example of the genealogical findings obtained from amino-acid sequence data by the "Red King" hypothesis is the species tree shown in Figure 2. As can be noted in this cladogram, the primates are a monophyletic assemblage that divide into Strepsirhini (Lorisoidea and Lemuroidea) and Haplorhini (*Tarsius* and Anthropoidea). Within Haplorhini, Anthropoidea is a monophyletic unit that bifurcates to form the sister groups Platyrrhini and Catarrhini. Catarrhini divides into Cercopithecoidea and Hominoidea.

Although Hominoidea always appears as a monophyletic assemblage, parsimony analysis of the tandem alignment of amino-acid sequence data is equivocal in depicting the relationship between Hylobatinae and *Pongo*. There are three equally parsimonious arrangements for the Hominoidea. One of these arrangements joins Hylobatinae and *Pongo* as a single cluster forming the most anciently separated lineage within Hominoidea. Another arrangement (reflecting the influence of myoglobin sequences) depicts *Pongo* as the most ancient lineage followed by Hylobatinae. The third arrangement, seen in Figure 2, supports (reflecting the influence of fibrinopeptides A and B sequences) the immunological, DNA hybridization, and electrophoretic findings previously discussed by placing *Pongo* closer to *Homo* and the African apes. Thus, the amino-acid sequence data support the cladistic classification in Table 1.

Members of the cladistic Homininae (*Homo, Pan,* and *Gorilla*) are always more closely related to one another than to the Asiatic apes (*Pongo, Symphalangus,* and *Hylobates*). Alpha-hemoglobin sequences indicate a slightly closer relationship between *Pan* and *Homo* than between either of these species and *Gorilla*. Whereas the *Gorilla* sequence retains aspartic acid at position 23 (the ancestral hominoid amino acid), both *Pan* and *Homo* have the derived substitution, glutamic acid, at this position. Otherwise, each of the other sets of protein sequences in which *Pan, Homo,* and *Gorilla* are represented depict a trichotomy. High resolution chromosomal G-banding (Yunis *et al.* 1980) shows *Pan* and *Homo* to be more similar (Yunis and Prahash 1982), whereas Miller's (1977) analysis of chromosomal evolution favors a closer relationship of *Homo* and *Gorilla*. Dutrillaux (1975), on the basis of

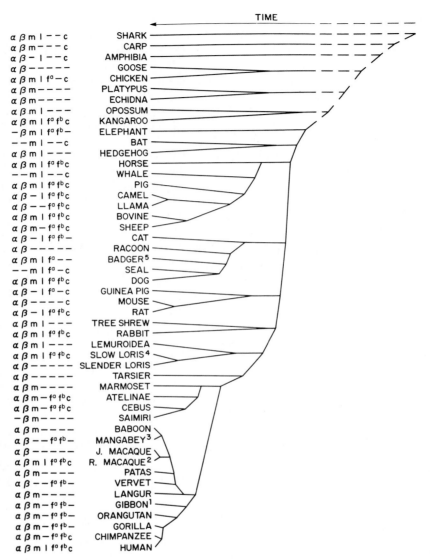

Figure 2   A parsimonious genealogical tree for 49 vertebrate taxa using a tandem alignment of up to seven polypeptide chains: α-hemoglobin (α), β-hemaglobin (β), myoglobin (m), lens α A crystallin (l), fibrinopeptide A (f^a), fibrinopeptide B (f^b), cytochrome c (c). This tree requires 2425 NRs. (1) The only portion of the gibbon α-hemogoblin chain (the first N-terminal 31 positions) that has been sequenced (Boyer *et al.* 1972) is included as part of the sequence data for this OTU. (2) The myoglobin sequence for this OTU comes from the crab-eating macaque; all other sequences come from the rhesus monkey. (3) Fibrinopeptides A and B sequences for this OTU come from the drill; all other sequences are from the mangabey. (4) The lens α A crystallin sequence for this OTU comes from the galago; all other sequences are from slow loris (5) The lens α A crystallin sequence for this OTU comes from mink; all other sequences are from badger.

his analysis of hominoid karyotypes, proposed that after an initial ancestral *Pan-Homo* separation from *Gorilla*, an event of hybridization occurred between the basal *Pan* and basal *Gorilla* lineages. Arnheim *et al.* (1980) found the chromosomal organization of ribosomal genes in hominoid karyotypes to be most alike between *Pan* and *Homo*. Deoxyribonucleic acid hybridization data (Benveniste and Todaro 1976; Hoyer *et al.* 1972) favor a trichotomy or a slightly closer kinship of *Pan* and *Homo*. Ferris *et al.*'s (1981) restriction endonuclease maps of mitochondrial DNA unite *Pan* and *Gorilla*, but it costs only one mutation more to first unite *Pan* with *Homo*. Similarly, immunological and elctrophoretic comparisons are not definitive in resolving this trichotomy into two bifurcations.

Thus, the exact course of genealogical branching within the Hominoidea, especially regarding the divergence topology of *Homo*, *Pan*, and *Gorilla*, has not yet been fully resolved. Nevertheless, the very close genetic relationship of the African apes and humans suggested by all the molecular evidence gathered to data has encouraged reevaluation of hominoid fossil evidence, especially ramapithecine material. The finds from Afar and Laetoli (Johanson and White 1979) are consistent with a relatively late ancestral separation of *Homo*, *Pan*, and *Gorilla* from one another, such as at a date of 5 million years ago as proposed by Sarich and Wilson (1967) when they applied the molecular clock hypothesis to immunologically determined distances among anthropoid albumins.

The gene phylogenies constructed by maximum parsimony for the sequences of single proteins or those of the same family (e.g., globins) yield results that are in general agreement with the species phylogeny in Figure 2. In these gene phylogenies the sequences of African apes and *Homo* always cluster in a monophyletic assemblage. Evidence for the close kinship of *Hylobates* and *Symphalangus*, their grouping within Hylobatinae, is provided by myoglobin and fibrinopeptides A and B sequences.

Within the group of African Hominoidea, the tempo of sequence evolution for these protein chains has been found to be slowest in the lineage to *Homo* (Goodman 1981; Gooman *et al.* 1981). This also appears to be true to mitochondrial DNA sequences (W. M. Brown, personal communication 1981; Ferris *et al.* 1981) especially as revealed by the analysis of Alan Templeton (1981). However, within Hominoidea, as well as within other comparable genealogical groups of higher primates, relatively uniform rates of evolution occur for the molecules albumin and transferrin (Sarich and Cronin 1976, 1976). Nor were any disparities among such lineages noted during analysis of DNA hybridization data (that of Benveniste and Todaro 1976) and electrophoretic data (Sarich and Cronin 1976; Cronin and Sarich 1981). On the other hand, over the much longer period of primate phylogeny, the DNA hybridization data of Bonner *et al.* (1980) do show marked variation in rates of evolution. Anthropoids accumulated less change than both lorisoids and *Tarsius*, whereas lemurs accumulated the least change.

Returning to the evidence from amino-acid sequences, the Asiatic apes (*Pongo*, *Hylobates*, and *Symphalangus*) have proteins that display evolutionary conservatism even more marked than that of *Homo Sapiens* (Darga *et al.* 1981). Hylobates, in particular, might represent a lineage whose morphological and molecular conservatism resulted from remaining in an ecological environment similar to that of the basal hominoids. In turn, the evolutionary conservatism of the proteins and mitochondrial DNA examined in humans might be connected to the process of *hominization* (i.e., the evolutionary transformation from an ape grade of phyletic development to the human grade). Paedomorphical changes in ontogenetic maturation, lengthening generation times, improvements in homeostatis, and increases in generalized adaptability associated with advances in brain evolution might all have served in one way or another to counteract or reduce mutational and environmental selective pressures for genetic change.

Hominization may be viewed as a particularly dramatic example from human biological evolution of a final stage of that larger evolutionary process (which affected many lineages of life) called "aromorphosis" by Severtsov (1939) and "anagenesis" by Huxley (1942) and Rensch (1960). *Anagenesis* is that form of phyletic progress in which organisms evolved to have more complex internal environments and greater independence from and control over perturbances of the external environment (Goodman 1963a, 1976; Huxley 1942; Rensch 1960; Wicken 1980; Zuckerkandl 1976). As a process of molecular evolution, anagenesis increased the density of "lock-and-key-type" recognition sites among macromolecules and, therefore, increased the number of structural constraints that cause most mutations in modern day proteins to be detrimental.

Clarifying the phylogenetic relationships of *Tarsius*, Lorisoidea, and Lemuroidea to one another and to Anthropoidea may be the key to understanding the biochemical direction of anagenesis in the order Primates and, as a result, expose the deeper molecular roots of hominization. In this regard, there is evidence that regulatory changes in the organization of energy metabolism occurred during primate phylogeny. Of the two types of lactate dehydrogenase (LDH), skeletal-muscle type and heart type, a preponderance of skeletal-muscle-type LDH occurs in the brain tissue of lemurs and lorises; conversely, a preponderance of heart-type LDH occurs in the brain tissue of higher primates, especially in hominoid brains: Tarsier brain shows roughly equal quantities of the two types (Goodman *et al.* 1969; and Koen and Goodman 1969). Inasmuch as heart-type LDH services tissues engaged in sustained aerobic metabolism, whereas muscle-type LDH is needed in tissues metabolizing under oxygen deficits, it may be suggested that anagenetic evolution produced anthropoid brains that functioned at higher energy levels than prosimian brains.

An accurate assessment of the tarsier's place within the primates may prove to be especially important to our understanding of anthropoid origins. *Tarsius* today bears many primitive skeletal and soft tissue characters and has a dentition almost identical to the Eocene prosimian Pseudoloris (Simons 1972). If the tarsier is genealogically the most anciently derived member of the higher primate suborder, as is suggested by the cladogram in Figure 2, living tarsiers (excluding their obvious specialization) could reflect important biochemical apsects of the ancestral condition of monkeys, apes, and humans. The debate concerning the replacement of *Tarsius* within the genealogical classification of Primates, however, is far from resolution. On the basis of morphology, Hershkovitz (1974), Szalay (1975), Luckett (1975, 1980), and others argue that extant tarsiers are genealogically closer to Anthropoidea than are extant lemuroids and lorisoids, whereas Gingerich (1976, 1980) argues the opposite view (see Cartmill, in the present volume). Results of immunodiffusion investigations (Dene *et al.* 1976), DNA hybridization comparisons (Hoyer and Roberts 1967; Bonner *et al.* 1980), and maximum parsimony analysis of hemoglobin amino-acid sequences (Goodman *et al*, 1978) have tended to favor a closer sister-group relationship of Anthropoidea to *Tarsius* than to any other extant taxon, whereas the immunological studies of Sarich and Cronin (1976) have not favored this conclusion. In order to resolve further the issue of the tarsier's genealogical position within primates, more discriminating biochemical data are needed, such as can be provided by nucleotide sequencing.

To determine the actual nucleotide sequences of genes, rather than to infer them from the amino-acid sequences of the encoded proteins, allows more accurate data to be used in developing and testing evolutionary hypotheses about the genes and organisms under study. In place of ambiguous or arbitrary choices of mRNA codons mandated by the redundancy of the genetic code, nucleotide sequence data can reveal not only the amino-acid changing base substitutions but also the base substitutions that do not cause amino-acid changes (so-called silent substitutions). The computer approaches that have proved effective in extracting, by the "Red King" hypothesis, evolutionary information from amino-acid sequence data have now been extended to take full advantage of this more precise information in the actual nucleotide sequences. With the aid of the computer, it should be possible to resolve such problematic features of higher primate phylogeny as the *Homo, Pan, Gorilla* branching order once a sufficient body of nucleotide sequence is gathered on evolutionarily corresponding segments of genomic DNA in the six extant hominoid genera and in a range of other primates. Similarly, as already indicated, the genealogical trees constructed from such a body of nucleotide sequence data should decisively resolve the Anthropoidea, *Tarsius*, Lorisoidea, Lemuroidea branching order.

The Tempo and Mode of Molecular Evolution

In this section, as in Table 1, we two authors state separate positions. This time, in contrast to the nearly complete concordance of our respective findings on the genealogical relationships of primates, our views concerning the molecular clock controversy and the Darwinian-versus-non–Darwinian evolution controversy diverge appreciably. It is apparent, however, from our broad overview of molecular anthropology at the beginning of this chapter, that we both agree that Sarich and Wilson made an important contribution in the middle to latter 1960s when they deduced from their immunological albumin data, using the molecular

clock hypothesis of Zuckerkandl and Pauling (1962), that humans and chimpanzees separated from one another much later in primate phylogeny than had
previously been supposed by paleontologists. Moreover, we both agree that useful
information on divergence times in phylogeny can often be obtained by
heuristically applying the molecular clock model to the molecular comparisons.

Nevertheless, one of us, the senior author (M.G.), feels that the genealogical
reconstructions carried out on amino-acid sequence data by the maximum
parsimony method provide strong evidence for nonconstant rates of amino-acid
substitutions during protein evolution. Thus, M.G. questions the general validity
of the clock hypothesis in which the sequences of each type of protein are
supposed to evolve at their own approximately constant rate. M.G. uses the
mutation patterns in the protein genealogical trees (*a*) to challenge the neutral or
non-Darwinian evolution theory (Kimura 1968, 1969, 1979; King and Jukes 1969)
in which almost all evolutionary change in proteins results from random drift of
selectively neutral mutations and (*b*) to argue for the Darwinian thesis that
natural selection is the principle force behind the evolution of molecules and
organisms. In turn, the coauthor (J.C.) has carried out studies that make him an
enthusiastic supporter of the clock model and generally sympathetic to the neutral
theory.

The findings of M.G. are extensively reviewed elsewhere (Goodman 1981) and
the conclusions to be drawn from them are briefly summarized here under the
headings "Clock Dates," "Evolutionary Rates," and "Positive and Stabilizing
Natural Selection." The views of J.C. then follow under the headings "Non-
Darwinian Evolution," "Molecular Clock Model," and "Molecular Clock Dates and
the Fossil Record."

Clock Dates

The dates calculated when the species lineages in the genealogical trees for the
different proteins follow the branching arrangement of the species cladogram in
Figure 2 are listed in Tables 2–4. The first splitting within Eutheria (node A) was
arbitrarily placed at 90 million years before the present, about the earliest date that
could be chosen from the opinions of paleontologists for this first splitting time.
Node A's assigned time span to the present was equated with its average number
of NRs to the present (its NR span) counted over the lineages descending from it.
Then, each remaining node in the phylogeny was dated by extrapolation from the
ratio of each such node's NR span over the a priori dated node's NR span. Clock
calculations were also carried out on genealogical reconstructions in which the
species lineages followed phylogenetically plausible alternative branching arrangements to those in Figure 2, and essentially the same findings were obtained.

Individual proteins are very poor timekeepers because they yield grossly
inconsistent dates for the same nodes in the phylogeny (see examples in Tables 2

and 3). However, when the results from the genealogical reconstructions for the 10 different polypeptide chains are combined, the hypothesized protein clock performs somewhat better (see Table 4). The clock dates for branch times pass the test of internal consistency (i.e., no offspring of a parent node ever has a more ancient clock date than that parent node), and for a majority of the ancestral nodes examined (26 within Amniote, of which 23 are within Eutheria), the clock dates are close to or within the range of dates suggested by paleontological evidence. Nevertheless, several major disagreements with this evidence consistently present themselves. There are far too recent clock dates for higher primate branch times (e.g., the *Homo–Pan* split comes out to only 1.0–1.5 million years ago), too recent Carnivore branch dates, and a gross underestimation of the data of the Aves–Mammalia ancestral split.

Evolutionary Rates

Even using the clock dates, the rates calculated, designated in units of NR% (number of NRs per 100 codons per 10^8 years), showed considerable variation in the different lines of descent. A much sharper picture of variations in the rate of molecular evolution was obtained by not biasing the results with the initial assumption that molecular evolution must proceed in a clocklike manner. In the calculations shown in Table 5 and in Figures 3–5, paleontological evidence on the "branch times" of the species lineages was used to assign dates to a number of ancestral nodes, not just one, in the genealogical trees. Whenever there was a range of dates to choose from for a node, the data chosen tended to minimize the variation in evolutionary rates between the different periods of descent.

Nevertheless, highly elevated rates of protein evolution occurred in the early vertebrates during the emergence of gnathostomes (jawed-vertebrates) and on the stem of early tetrapods (see Table 5 and Figure 3). This was followed by a very slow evolutionary rate between the bird–mammal ancestor (about 300 million years ago) and the eutherian ancestor (about 90 million years ago). Then, a burst of accelerated protein evolution occurred in the early Eutheria during the emergence of Primates and on the stem to the basal Anthropoidea, to be followed by markedly decelerated protein evolution in the lineage to *Homo*. It is worth noting that from the *Pan–Homo–Gorilla* common ancestor to the present, the slowest rate occurred in the lineage to present-day *Homo* (as illustrated in Figure 6 by an example involving *Pan* and *Homo*).

It is also worth noting that the periods of highly elevated protein evolution during the past half billion years of vertebrate phylogeny were also periods of adaptive radiation and major morphological evolution. This synchrony in evolutionary tempos conforms to expectations of Darwinian theory. Intensified selection should occur for new organismal adaptations at molecular and morphological levels in lineages invading new ecological habitats. After the accelerated molecular

Table 2   Clock Dates of 26 Ancestral Nodes Calculated from Unaugmented Nucleotide Replacement

Ancestral node	β-hemoglobin	Myoglobin	lens α crystallin	Fibrinopeptides A and B
Aves–Mammalia	160.3	176.7	148.8	—
Theria	119.6	105.4	123.0	—
Marsupalia	72.9	39.1	37.2	—
Eutheria	90.0	90.0	90.0	90.0
Insectivora–Primates	84.5	81.4	55.5	—
Ungulata–Primates	76.7	74.6	54.4	86.4
Ungulata	69.9	62.4	28.7	68.7
Artiodactyla	68.1	58.7	17.0	73.1
Tylopoda–Pecora	62.0	—	7.1	60.6
Bovidae	41.0	17.4	—	30.4
Carnivora–Primates	70.3	63.2	50.3	86.3
Carnivora	32.6	—	19.1	47.8
Mustelidae–Canidae	18.0	42.4	21.3	—
Rodentia–Primates	67.9	—	31.9	65.4
Rodentia	66.8	—	5.3	—
Lagomorpha–Primates	53.0	62.1	39.4	55.5
Lagomorpha–Tupaia	38.3	39.1	14.1	—
Primates	48.0	65.4	47.8	45.1
Strepsirhini	47.8	50.0	5.3	—
Anthropoidea	17.7	30.1	—	19.4
Cebus–Atelinae	14.8	10.1	—	7.3
Catarrhini	13.8	14.0	15.9	11.8
Macaca–Papio	4.9	2.2	—	12.9
Hominidae[b]	4.8	8.7	—	7.3
Homininae	0.9	2.9	—	0
Homo–Pan	0	2.2	—	0

[a]Dates are in millions of years before the present.
[b]Hominidae in the geneaological classification represents the grouping on Ponginae (*Pongo*) and Homininae (*Homo, Pan,* Gorilla).

evolution in the successful lineages, decelerated evolution should ensue caused by stabilizing selection holding perfected adaptations constant.

Positive and Stabilizing Natural Selection

Proteins evolved at accelerated rates when advantageous mutations were being selected at sites acquiring functions. However, once the new sites were well established and adapted to a multitude of other molecular sites, natural selection slowed evolutionary rates by protecting these coadapted arrays of functional sites from further changes. The evidence for this twofold role of natural selection was obtained from genealogical reconstructions for globins (Goodman *et al.* 1975; Goodman and Czelusniak 1980; Goodman 1981; cytochrome *c* (Baba *et al.* 1981), and the calmodulin family (Goodman *et al.* 1979b; Goodman 1980, 1981), proteins

Values[a]

α-Hemoglobin	Cytochrome C	Carbonic anhydrase			Average clock date
		I	II	III	
150.7	150.8	143.9	—	—	155.2
104.7	85.2	—	—	—	107.6
82.9	—	—	—	—	58.0
—	—	—	—	—	90.0
81.5	72.9	—	—	—	75.2
73.0	73.0	73.0	73.0	73.0	73.0
49.4	38.5	—	—	—	52.9
48.6	21.3	—	—	—	47.8
46.5	18.9	—	—	—	39.0
22.5	0	—	20.9	—	22.0
64.9	95.9	—	—	—	71.8
45.6	—	—	—	—	36.3
25.2	—	—	—	—	26.7
63.1	87.6	—	—	—	63.2
63.2	0	—	—	—	33.8
58.1	105.1	63.7	42.8	—	60.0
52.3	—	—	—	—	36.0
46.2	63.9	—	—	—	52.7
32.6	—	—	—	—	33.9
29.0	48.3	—	14.7	—	26.5
6.8	0	—	—	—	7.8
26.2	9.5	18.8	3.1	—	14.1
19.6	—	—	—	—	9.9
3.5	—	10.9	—	—	7.0
1.9	—	—	—	7.5	2.6
0	0	4.2	—	—	1.1

about which considerable knowledge exists concerning their three-dimensional structures and functional sites.

If the bursts of rapid evolution in these proteins had been simply due to an accumulation of selectively neutral mutations from a relaxation of constraints, as might occur in duplicated genes that were nonexpressed for a period of their history, the mutations should have been randomly distributed over the encoded protein chains. Instead, the bursts of evolution were concentrated in functionally important residue positions. The fact that, later on, such positions evolved at extremely slow rates shows that natural selection caused the earlier fast rate. Logic dictates that wherever strong stabilizing selection acts on a protein, somewhere in the past positive natural selection must have spread the amino-acid substitutions now being conserved.

These findings on the mode and tempo of protein evolution suggest that during the later stages of anagenesis not only did the force of stabilizing selection become stronger, but, due to improvements in homeostasis in organisms such as higher primates, the pressure from the external environment for selection of new

Table 3   Clock Dates of 26 Ancestral Nodes Calculated from Augmented Nucleotide Replacement

Ancestral node	β-Hemoglobin	Myoglobin	lens α crystallin	Fibrinopeptides A and B
Aves–Mammalia	177.2	193.2	149.8	—
Theria	124.1	104.4	124.1	—
Marsupalia	100.3	46.9	49.9	—
Eutheria	90	90	90	90
Insectivora–Primates	84.4	81.0	53.5	—
Ungulata–Primates	77.3	75.0	51.5	86.4
Ungulata	76.4	61.3	25.6	68.3
Artiodactyla	73.7	71.2	14.8	73.3
Tylopoda–Pecora	67.1	—	6.2	60.0
Bovidae	40.7	17.8	—	29.8
Carnivora–Primates	70.5	66.3	47.9	87.6
Carnivora	35.1	—	20.2	50.7
Mustelidae–Canidae	16.0	56.6	23.2	—
Rodentia–Primates	68.7	—	31.0	65.5
Rodentia	71.1	—	4.6	—
Lagomorpha–Primates	53.4	63.0	38.5	55.7
Lagomorpha–Tupaia	50.9	38.9	12.3	—
Primates	48.5	66.6	49.0	45.4
Strepsirhini	65.0	52.5	4.6	—
Anthropoidea	15.3	29.0	—	18.2
Cebus-Atelinae	12.9	9.2	—	6.6
Catarrhini	12.0	12.8	13.8	10.8
Macaca–Papio	4.3	2.0	—	11.8
Homindae	4.1	7.9	—	6.6
Homininae	0.8	2.7	—	0
Homo–Pan	0	2.0	—	0

[a]Dates are in millions of years before the present.

mutations in genes was reduced. Such a reduction in the opportunities for positive selection to transform genes may be greatest in the human species, where the development of advanced technological cultures erected a further buffer against external perturbances. This can help explain why the genealogical reconstructions detected remarkably little protein sequence change during the radiation of the Hominoidea in the lineage that descended to modern human beings. Furthermore, there is evidence, as already noted, that nucleotide sequence evolution of mito-chondrial DNA also slowed in the lineage to present-day *Homo* (W. M. Brown, personal communication 1981; Ferris *et al.* 1981; Templeton 1981). These in-dications of a pervasive deceleration of molecular sequence evolution during hominization can be tested further when the data analyzed are nucleotide sequences of many corresponding nuclear genes from a large number of primates and other vertebrates.

Values[a]

α-Hemoglobin	Cytochrome c	Carbonic anhydrase			Average clock date
		I	II	III	
156.4	166.5	152.9	—	—	166.0
105.8	84.6	—	—	—	108.6
110.5	—	—	—	—	76.9
—	—	—	—	—	90
80.8	73.3	—	—	—	74.6
72.6	72.6	72.6	72.6	72.6	72.6
51.1	40.0	—	—	—	53.8
50.4	18.3	—	—	—	50.3
49.4	16.3	—	—	—	39.8
23.3	0	—	19.4	—	21.8
64.5	89.8	—	—	—	71.1
46.9	—	—	—	—	38.2
25.9	—	—	—	—	30.4
62.4	85.2	—	—	—	62.6
71.5	0	—	—	—	36.8
55.9	102.3	62.7	41l7	—	59.2
63.6	—	—	—	—	41.4
43.5	59.6	—	—	—	52.1
33.3	—	—	—	—	38.9
26.3	47.8	—	12.6	—	24.9
5.9	0	—	—	—	6.9
24.3	8.2	17.2	2.6	—	12.7
19.0	—	—	—	—	9.3
2.9	—	10.0	—	—	6.3
1.6	—	—	—	6.9	2.4
0	0	3.9	—	—	1.0

Non-Darwinian Evolution

The non-Darwinian theory posits that a substantial fraction of evolutionary change is due to random genetic drift in and the fixation of neutral mutations (Kimura 1968; King and Jukes 1969). It also suggests that most polymorphisms are neutral isoalleles. Evidence for the theory mainly derives from consideration of mathematical models and the concept of genetic load (substitutional and balanced) (see Lewontin [1974] and Kimur [1979] for a review).

Neutrality is a relative concept. An allele can only be neutral with respect to another allele. And, neutrality does not mean that each allele has exactly the same fitness of 1.0. Neutrality is a range in which selective differentials are small and are overcome by the effects of chance due to small deme size. The smaller the population, the larger the differential between the two alleles can be and still have the condition of *effective* neutrality.

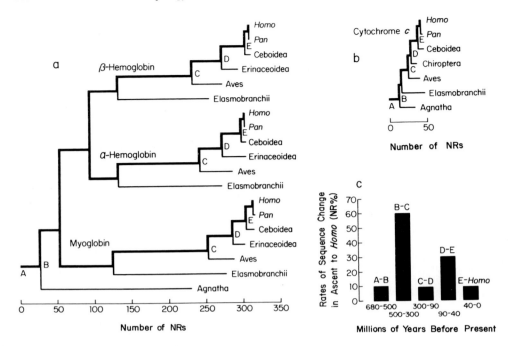

Figure 3   Acceleration–deceleration pattern in rates of sequence evolution. The portions of the globin (a) and cytochrome *c* (b) genealogical trees shown depict the phyletic line to *Homo* from the early vertebrates to the present. The length of each branch equals the average number of NRs, corrected for superimposed replacements, calculated to have occurred along that line of evolution, with the main branches shown being those that circumscribe the accelerated evolution depicted in the bar graph (c) between the vertebrate and bird–mammal ancestor and again between the Eutheria and Anthropoidea ancestor.

In small populations even detrimental alleles can be fixed or maintained at a low frequency. Wright has calculated that in small populations the probability of fixation of a favored allele is twice the selection coefficient (if $S = 0.1, p = 0.2$). We have seen very few alleles in natural populations with a selective advantage in fact this high. When selective coefficients drop below this value, then drift becomes an important factor. Even for infinite population sizes, the initial slope of the probability of fixation is only 2S (Cavalli-Sforza and Bodmer 1971).

Neutralists do not deny the effects of natural selection. It is obvious to geneticists that natural selection is working at the level of the structure of proteins. Even the most ardent "neutralist" believes that a neutral allele has passed through a selective filter at some level. This is readily seen by the fact that a particular amino acid is most likely to be replaced in evolution by one similar in size, in configuration, and/or in charge. The outside surface of a molecule seems to undergo more change than the inside, and the active sites, less than other areas. Different substitutions obviously have differing affects if they alter the structure or function of the

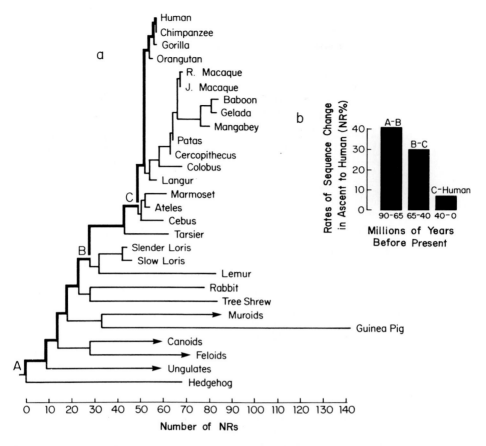

Figure 4 Portions of the eutherian region of the most parsimonious tree (costing 1613 NRs) constructed for 55 contemporary vertebrate taxa from orthologous sets of β- and α-hemoglobin sequences combined in a tandem alignment (a). The length of each branch shown equals the average number of NRs, corrected for superimposed replacements, calculated to have occurred along that line of evolution. The corresponding bar graph (b) depicts the rapid rate of sequence evolution in the early Eutheria and early Primates followed by the slow rate in the Anthropoidea on the phyletic line ascending to *Homo*.

molecule. All of these observations are evidence that selection is working at the level of the gene. What neutralists are concerned with is determining what fraction of genetic change is due to directional selection and what part is due to genetic drift in which one allele among a number of selectivity equivalent alleles is fixed. The realm of new mutations would be in a continuum from "always selected against" through "selectively neutral" to "always selected for." The question that remains is, "What is the form of this distribution?"

The observation of the regularity of molecular evolution is not dependent on the

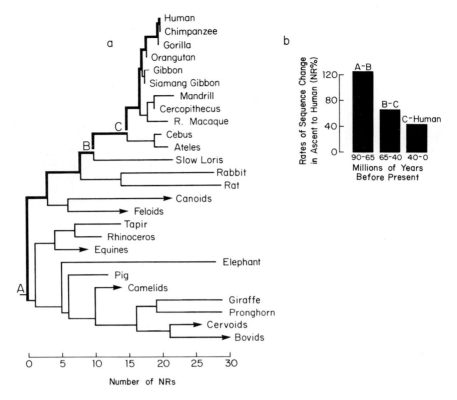

Figure 5 (a) Portions of the eutherian region of the most parsimonious tree (costing 260 NRs) constructed for 47 OTUs from tandemly combined fibronopeptides A and B sequences. The length of each branch shown equals the average number of NRs, corrected for superimposed replacements, calculated to have occurred along that line of evolution. (b) The corresponding bar graph depicts the rapid rate of sequence evolution in the early Eutheria and early Primates followed by the slow rate in the anthropoidea on the phyletic line ascending to *Homo*. The tree used for the calculations in Tables 2–5 (costing 264 NRs) follows the species genealogy depicted in Figure 2 and shows an even faster rate of sequence evolution in the early Eutheria.

neutral mutation hypothesis (Fitch and Langley 1976; Sarich and Cronin 1976). Indeed it is possible to construct a model of directional selection for each substitution. It would, however, be a model with substantial difficulties. Conversely, we cannot prove that each and every substitution is not selected for in some way. What the neutral mutation hypothesis provides is a possible explanation for an empirical observation.

Molecular Clock Model

The molecular clock model is just that, a model. It is neither deterministic nor rigid in its predictions. Natural selection is still the final arbitor of molecular

Table 4   Comparison between Clock Dates and Paleontological Dates on Calculating the Clock Date for Each of the 26 Ancestral Nodes by Equally Weighting the Nucleotide Replacements over All Sequences Represented at that Node[a]

Ancestral node	Clock date from		Paleontological date[b]
	Unaugmented NR span	Augmented NR span	
Aves–Mammalia	161.9	173.8	290–320
Theria	115.3	117.3	80–120
Marsupalia	68.5	92.2	65–100
Eutheria	*90*	*90*	70– 90
Insectivora–Primates	83.4	83.2	65– 85
Ungulata–Primates	*76.4*	*76.4*	65– 85
Ungulata	59.5	61.4	55– 65
Artiodactyla	57.2	61.0	50– 60
Tylopoda–Pecora	50.0	52.7	45– 55
Bovidae	25.7	25.5	15– 20
Carnivora–Primates	71.5	71.5	65– 85
Carnivora	39.5	41.7	45– 60
Mustelidae–Canidae	27.4	29.8	40– 50
Rodentia–Primates	64.8	65.0	65– 85
Rodentia	56.3	62.1	40– 60
Lagomorpha–Primates	57.7	57.0	65– 85
Lagomorpha–Tupaia	42.9	51.7	65– 85
Primates	51.5	51.0	50– 65
Strepsirhini	41.2	48.4	20– 50
Anthropoidea	22.5	20.5	40– 55
Cebus–Atelinae	9.4	8.3	30– 40
Catarrhini	14.7	13.4	25– 40
Macaca–Papio	10.2	9.7	4– 10
Hominidae	7.2	6.3	15– 20
Homininae	2.1	1.8	5– 15
Homo–Pan	1.5	1.3	5– 15

[a]Dates are in millions of years before the present.
[b]The ranges of paleontological dates used for these 26 modes are from Ciochon and Chiarelli (1981), Johanson and White (1979), Joysey and Friday (Perutz *et al.* 1981; Romero-Herrera *et al.* 1978) Lovejoy (1981), Lovtrup (1977), McHenry and Corruccini (1980), Novacek (1981), Pilbeam (1979), Romer (1966), Simons (1976), Szalay and Delson (1979), and Walker (1976).

change, and undoubtedly we see its effects on protein structure, function, and evolution. We should not be surprised to find specific instances where rates of change of proteins are not linearly related to time. Varying rates of change have been noted by clock proponents (Cronin and Sarich 1980; Wilson *et al.* 1977). Such empirical observations of nonregularity do not invalidate the model, much as varying determinations of a specific radiometric data do not invalidate radiometric dating in general. An analysis of the protein sequence data (Fitch and Langley 1976) suggested that the variation in rates of evolution were only twice that to be expected if a clock were perfect. Estimates improved as more molecules were added to the comparison. Some molecules have highly correlated genetic distances between species pairs and, thus, divergence data estimates that are distributed

Table 5 Rates of Globin, Cytochrome *c*, *α*-Lens Crystallin, Fibrinopeptide A and B, and Carbonic

Evolutionary Period	Age[b]	Myoglobin	*α*-Hemoglobin	*β*-Hemoglobin
Vertebrate to gnathastome ancestor	500–425	87.0	107.0	113.4
Gnathostome ancestor[c] to present	425–0	29.0	26.8	30.5
Gnathostome to amniote ancestor	425–300	71.8	53.2	65.3
Amniote ancestor* to present	300–0	12.1	15.5	16.8
Amniote to eutherian ancestor	300–90	10.3	11.7	12.8
Eutherian ancestor* to present	90–0	16.5	28.3	30.1
Eutherian to primate ancestor	90–65	13.1	53.1	43.2
Eutherian to Anthropoidea ancestor	90–40	18.7	36.5	38.3
Primate to Anthropoidea ancestor	65–40	24.4	23.2	33.5
Primate to Catarrhini ancestor	65–25	18.5	18.1	22.6
Anthropoidea ancestor to man	40–0	11.4	7.1	10.6
Catarrhini ancestor to man	25–0	13.1	5.7	14.2
Hominine ancestor to man	5–0	0	14.2	0
Homo–Pan ancestor to man	5–0	0	0	0

Column header note: "Nucleotide replacement per"

[a]Augmented NR values were employed.

[b]Dates are in millions of years before the present as estimated from the paleontological records.

[c]Asterisk indicates use of an average of all lineages descending from this node to the present.

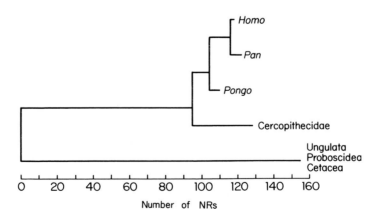

Figure 6 The data set used to determine the branching order depicted in this figure grouped Proboscidea with Ungulata and Cetacea. The later expanded data set used to produce the species tree in Figure 2 (see p. 116) groups the Ungulata-Cetacea branch closer to Primates than to Proboscidea; the latter emerges as the most ancient lineage diverging from the basal eutherian stem in Figure 2.

Anhydrase Evolution

100 codons per 100 million years[a]

Cytochrome c	α A Lens crystallin	Fibrinopeptides A and B	Carbonic anhydrase		
			I	II	III
4.5	—	—	—	—	—
5.3	5.6	—	—	—	—
6.7	11.0	—	—	—	—
4.4	3.1	—	10.0	—	—
1.3	1.5	—	6.3	—	—
6.8	6.3	75.2	17.7	24.1	15.3
41.6	14.8	200.0	—	—	—
22.8		154.1	—	38.6	
7.7	—	74.8	—	—	—
13.2	9.6	55.1	—	—	—
10.8	—	33.3	—	9.4	—
3.8	4.6	40.0	12.8	5.6	—
—	—	0	—	—	0
0	—	0	7.6	—	—

tightly. The differences may be due to the effects of natural selection, the size of the molecule, its rate of evolution, its function, or to the magnitude of the genetic distances involved (sampling error).

Recent analyses of macromolecular data have demonstrated the validity, given certain precautions, of using molecularly derived divergence dates (Corruccini *et al.* 1979, 1980; Cronin and Meikle 1979, 1982; Wilson *et al.* 1977). Corruccini *et al.* (1980) examined molecular data—first, between and within major primate taxa, and second, within only the suborder Anthropoidea. Within the Anthropoidea, there exists a remarkable degree of colinearity of evolutionary rates. It is important

Table 6 A Comparison of Differences between Six Catarrhine Species Pairs by Four Molecular Techniques

Technique	P. anubis– P. cynocephalus	P. cynocephalus– P. hamadryas	Papio– Theropithecus	Papio– Mandrillus	Papio– Macaca	Homo– Pan
Immunological distance[a]	4	6	10	18	26	17
Plasma protein electrophoresis[b]	0.35	0.5	0.8	2.0	2.0	1.6
DNA hybridization (cellular)[c]	0.2	1.1	1.8	2.1	2.6	2.4
DNA hybridization (FRHT)[d]	0.3	0.3	1.0	1.1	1.9–1.6	—

[a]Albumin plus transferrin immunological distance (Sarich and Cronin 1976; Cronin 1975).
[b]Plasma protein electrophoresis D value (Sarich and Cronin 1976; Cronin and Mikle 1979).
[c]ΔTm (°C) (Benveniste and Todaro 1976)
[d]ΔTm (°C) (Gillepsie 1977)

Table 7 Fossil versus Molecular Dates among the Catarrhini

Lineages	Molecular estimate of time of origin	Oldest fossil evidence
Hominoidea	20 ± 3 million years[a,b]	ca. 23 million years[c]
Pongo	9 ± 3 million years[a]	ca. 1–2 million years[c]
Hylobates	12 ± 2 million years[a]	ca.1–2 million years[c]
Australopithecus	5.5 ± 2 million years[a, d]	ca. 5.5 million years[c]
Pan	5.5 ± 2 million years[a, d]	none
Gorilla	5.5 ± 2 million years[a, d]	none
Cercopithecidae	20 ± 3 million years[a, b]	ca. 20 million years[c]
Colobinae and		
Cercopithecinae	12 ± 2 million years[b]	ca. 15 million years[c]
Cercopithecus	7 ± 2 million years[a, b, e]	ca. 3.5 million years[c]
Macaca	7–8 million years[f]	ca. 7–8 million years[c]
Theropithecus	2–4 millionyears[g]	ca. 4 million years[c]

[a]Source: Sarich and Cronin (1976).
[b]Source: Cronin (1975).
[c]Source: Szalay and Delson (1979).
[d]Source: Cronin and Meikle (1982).
[e]Source: Sarich and Cronin (1976).
[f]Source: Cronin et al. (1980).
[g]Source: Cronin and Meikle (1979).

to note that the amount of data is quite extensive for these comparisons. On the other hand, many fewer data points exist for comparisons between the major clades Anthropoidea, Lorisoidea, and Lemuroidea. It is these comparisons that show the most departure from linearity. In the latter comparisons, genetic distances are quite large, a fair amount of each molecule has changed since the time of the last common ancestor (perhaps 50–65 million years ago), and homoplasy is increasing. Thus, the true genetic distance is underestimated as distance increases.

The degree of homoplasy a specific molecule exhibits in different lineages is in part due to its size, function, and rate of evolution. The globin genes (alpha- and beta-hemoglobin and myoglobin) that account for three of the six comparisons of Corruccini *et al.* (1980) have demonstrated (in at least the first two) gene duplications, suppressions, and concerted changes occurring along lineages (Liebhaber *et al.* 1981; Martin *et al.* 1980; Slightom *et al.* 1980; Zimmer *et al.* 1980). We may be faced with comparing paralogous (nonhomologous) globin genes. The more phylogenetically distant the taxa compared, the more homplasy becomes important. Essentially, the study by Corruccini *et al.* (1980) confirms what was expected and has been observed before in macromolecular comparisons (Sarich and Cronin 1976; Wilson *et al.* 1977).

When dealing with small genetic distances and possible recent divergence events (such as 0–3 amino-acid sequence changes or a few percentages of DNA base pair difference) we should expect larger variances in distances between taxa than when comparisons are based on larger genetic distances and more lineages. This is a problem of small sample sizes. Confidence and resolving power increases as sample size increases (Corruccini *et al.* 1980; Cronin 1975). For example, in the human–chimpanzee–gorilla comparisons, there are no differences in the fibrino-peptide sequences; thus, we might predict zero time a divergence. On the other hand, electrophoretic comparisons of humans, chimpanzees, and gorillas yield an estimated branch time of about 4.0 million years ago. The DNA hybridization data yield estimates centering on divergence at around 6.5 million years ago, whereas other sequence data suggest a time of separation of these taxa of about 10 million years ago. The fibrinopeptides are extremely small peptides, some 30 amino acids long. The electrophoretic data is based on 20–25 loci, whereas the DNA hybridi-zation data are based on tens of thousands of base pair differences. Macro-molecules, then, predict a range of from 0–10 million years ago for the human–chimpanzee divergence. The mean time of divergence for all molecular com-parisons is about 5–6 million years, plus or minus 2 million years. Thus, an estimated date of divergence somewhere between 4 and 8 million years ago is quite reasonable, given the limitations just discussed.

Any absolute, rather than relative, date estimated by the molecular clock depends upon a calibration point in the fossil record. Any paleontologically derived date for a specific divergence event is fraught with difficulty. The problem of predicting recent divergence dates based upon calibration point early in mammalian evolution has been discussed before (Sarich and Cronin 1976). First, appearance dates must be used within the addition of time to account for "true" divergence dates. Yet, as calibration points increase in age problems of homplásy increase in the molecular comparisons and may effect divergence date estimates to varying degrees. Recent divergence events, therefore, have a larger percentage component of error (e.g., 5–6 ± 2 million years for hominid origins) (Cronin 1975; Sarich and Cronin 1976; Corruccini *et al.* 1980).

Where data are adequate and interpreted within the constraints of homplasy, gene duplication, suppression, and concerted evolution we should not be surprised to find, as we do, a marked degree of colinearity related to the calibration of rates of molecular evolution. Although it needs to be interpreted within confidence intervals, as any evolutionary model does, the molecular clock model is of great value for calibrating the sequence of divergence events within the order Primates.

Molecular Clock Dates and the Fossil Record

One of the central objections to the molecular clock is that the dates predicted for specific divergences among species pairs are not concordant with, or are greatly at variance with, the interpretation of the fossil evidence. The molecular clock, to be convincing to most paleontologists, must be reconciled with paleontological dates. A recent analysis of molecular and paleontological data in two key areas of debate in primates suggests a molecular range of dates that overlaps with the first appearance of, in one case, an undoubted member of *Australopithecus* and, in the other case, undoubted *Theropithecus* in the fossil record. Each of the two cases stems from a speciation event that eventually resulted in a substantially derived lineage and one or more relatively unchanged lineages. Yet, in each instance, claims of the antiquity of the divergence event extend to at least twice the age of the first certain appearance of the more derived lineage in the fossil record. What follows is a brief account of this analysis (Cronin and Meikle 1979, 1982).

The two key cases of alternative interpretations of the nature and timing of speciation events involves (*a*) origins of the *Australopithecus–Homo* lineage and (*b*) the phyletic position of the gelada baboon (*Theropithecus gelada*). The *Theropithecus* lineage is usually viewed as having originated some 6–8 million years ago, subsequent only to macaque origins within the 42-chromosome complex of Old World monkeys (*Papio, Mandrillus, Macaca, Cercocebus* and *Theropithecus*). Table 6 presents molecular data from immunological, electrophoretic, and DNA hybridization studies. By each comparison, *Papio* and *Theropithecus* are closer to each other than either is to any other genus. Note also that the *Homo–Pan* genetic distances found are relatively close, less than those separating *Papio* from some other papionine genera. This observation is consistent with other evidence of the very great similarity of human and chimpanzee molecules regardless of morphological differences.

Why has the finding that *Theropithecus* and *Papio* differ molecularly from each other little more than do species within *Papio* come as such a surprise? Analogously, why have similar findings in the human–chimpanzee case been such a surprise to some? The gelada, much as the *Australopithecus–Homo* clade, are morphologically uniquely divergent or derived relative to the ancestral condition. We would suggest that traditional conclusions (deriving *Theropithecus* early in papionine evolution and linking *Pongo, Pan,* and *Gorilla* to exclude *Homo*) are drawn from a phenetic analysis that implicitly assumes a constant rate of morphological change and interprets morphological distinctiveness to mean early branching (Michevich 1978).

Can one estimate the respective times at which these separations may have taken place? For the monkeys, the presence of extinct species of *Theropithecus* in the Pliocene and Pleistocene of Africa establishes a minimum age for this event (Delson 1975; Eck 1977; Jolly 1972). The oldest record of *Theropithecus* is a single tooth from Lothagam, Kenya, that is probably about 4 million years old (Behrensmeyer 1976). This tooth possesses the derived dental characters expected in *Theropithecus,* and therefore gives a minimum age for the *Papio–Theropithecus* split (Delson 1975; Cronin and Meikle 1982).

Is a time of separation greater than 4 million years ago compatible with the molecular data? According to the molecular clock hypothesis, one should be able to use these relative distances and calibrated rates of evolution to estimate times of divergence (Sarich and Cronin 1976; Wilson *et al.* 1977). For the *Papio–Theropithecus* divergence, our mean estimate is 3.2 million years B.P., with a standard deviation of 1.3 million years and standard error of 0.46 million years. This is less than one standard deviation from the minimum age established by the fossil record (Cronin and Meikle 1979). Considering the quite small amounts of genetic distance involved, all the macromolecular estimates are consistent and in fairly good agreement (Nei 1978).

Table 6 compares molecular estimates of the times of origin of several living Old World monkey and hominoid lineages with the oldest know fossil records of these lineages. The molecular estimates are consistent with conventional ideas of the cladistic relationships of these lineages. In addition, none of the estimates (except possibly that for the colobine–cercopithecine separation) is directly contradicted by known fossil specimens. The first appearance of the *Theropithecus* lineage in the fossil record may be close to its actual time of origin. Certain models of speciation suggest that rapid divergence of peripheral populations may lead to the sudden appearance of new taxa in the fossil record (Eldredge and Gould 1972; Gould and Eldredge 1977). One implication of these models is that it is not necessary to expect to find a long chain of gradually changing species as fossils; large amounts of morphological change may take place in a geologically short period of time. Therefore, we do not believe it is necessary to add on a large proportion of the known time of existence of the *Theropithecus* lineage to estimate its age. The *Papio–Theropithecus* separation may well have occurred less than 5 million years ago.

What are the implications of this conclusion for the hominid record? Macromolecular data have been quite consistent in showing the close relationship of *Homo* and the African apes (Bruce and Ayala 1979; King and Wilson 1975; Sarich and Cronin 1976). The molecular clock hypothesis suggests a relatively recent time of divergence for these taxa, probably in the range of 4–8 million years ago (Sarich and Cronin 1976; Sarich and Wilson 1967) (See Figure 7). Recent additions to the fossil record have for the first time given a more than fragmentary view of 3–4-million-year-old ancestors of *Homo* (Johanson and White 1979). These specimens are said to display many primitive traits that make them more similar to an apelike ancestor than any other specimens previously known in the *Australopithecus–Homo* clade. The present fossil record of the clade extends to between 5 and 6 million years at Lothagam; older specimens sometimes considered to be in it are either quite fragmentary or otherwise of uncertain status (Pilbeam 1979).

The three different molecular comparisons in Table 7 yield an ancestral divergence time estimate for humans and African apes of approximately 4.6 ± 0.7 million years. This is close to the time of appearance of the 5.5-million-year-old Lothagam specimen.

Consideration of the macromolecular and fossil data together suggests that the human–African ape divergence is very unlikely to have occurred in the area of 15 million years ago and is much more likely to have been in the range of 5–8 million years B.P. A model of either punctuated equilibrium or "rapid gradualism" after speciation, which may explain the sudden appearance of *Theropithecus*, could be applicable to the origins of the *Australopithecus–Homo* clade as well.

The *Theropithecus–Papio* case has been used by some to oppose the use of molecular clocks (Delson 1975; Simons 1976), but his example may instead be consistent with that hypothesis. There appears to be no discrepancy between molecular predictions of when *Theropithecus* and *Papio* separated and the time of

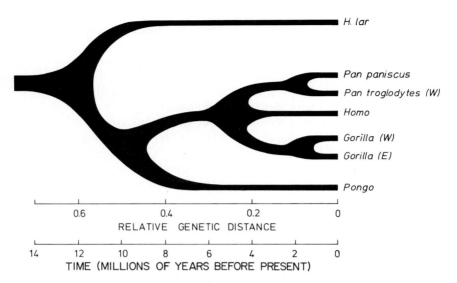

Figure 7 A molecular phylogeny of the Hominoidea based on nucleic acid, immunological, and electrophoretic data. (Cronin and Sarich 1982). No molecular data have been conclusive in determining if any pair of the lineages *Homo, Pan,* and *Gorilla* share a common ancestor to the exclusion of the third species.

appearance of the derived, and therefore diagnostic, form, *Theropithecus.* Similarly, molecular estimates for the human–African ape divergence are not discordant with the time of appearance of the first undisputed *Australopithecus* in the geologic record.

Future Prospects

The techniques that we have discussed, such as immunology, DNA hybridization, electrophoresis, and amino-acid sequencing, will continue to yield important data in human and primate evolution, diversity, and adaptation. Yet, continued advances in nucleic acid technology like we have witnessed over the past 5–10 years are what hold the most promise for evolutionary biologists and students of human evolution in the future. The methods of nucleotide sequencing are advancing rapidly (Maxam and Gilbert 1977; Messing 1979; Messing *et al.* 1981; Sanger *et al.* 1977). As a result of this gene sequencing revolution underway in molecular biology, it is becoming possible to carry out a much more detailed analysis of the evolutionary forces acting on human genes. This analysis can be directed not only at the amino-acid changing base substitutions, but also at the silent base substitutions in the protein encoding portions as well as at evolutionary changes in noncoding portions (cf. Efstratiadis *et al.* 1980). One of the most exciting discoveries is that the nucleotide sequence of a eukaryotic gene encoding a protein chain need not code for this chain in a continous manner. Instead, the gene may be divided into pieces (Gilbert 1978) that are both transcribed into mRNA and translated into amino-acid sequences (exons) and intervening nucleotide sequences that are transcribed into a mRNA that is so rapidly degraded it is not translated (introns). Upstream of the first exon and downstream of the last exon are the flanking regions of the gene, part of which are also transcribed into mRNA, but not translated. Many gene families, such as the α- and non–α-globin gene clusters, also include pseudogenes (i.e., DNA regions that display significant evolutionary homology to functional genes but that bear mutations that prevent expression of any protein chain.

Certainly the globin genes, with their flanking regions and pseudogenes, will continue to be a focus of study for molecular anthropologists. We note that the extensive data on human globin genes have revealed a polarity in their DNA positional organization that reflects the ontogenetic regulation of expression of these genes. For example, in the human non-α cluster, extending over 60 kilobases, the order of positioning of genes (and pseudogenes) progressing from 5'- to 3'-end is $\psi\beta2$, ε, $^G\gamma$, $^A\gamma$, $\psi\beta1$, δ, β with each gene (and each pseudogene) being separated from its nearest neighbor by about 3–20 Kb of noncoding sequence (Fritsch *et al.* 1980) the pseudogenes $\psi\beta2$ and $\psi\beta1$ are, of course nonexpressed. The gene ε is expressed first in early embryonic life; $^G\gamma$ and $^A\gamma$ are expressed next in fetal life; and then δ and β are expressed in postnatal life. Thus, because of this polarity between position and expression, there is reason to suspect that in the noncoding regions there are control sequence elements regulating the differential expression of these globin genes.

An important approach to identifying these control elements lies in the sequencing of the globin gene cluster regions in nonhuman primates and the evolutionary reconstructions that this will permit. It is already apparent that some evolutionary changes occurred in the organization of non–α-globin genes during primate phylogeny. Although the gross organization is essentially identical in baboon, gorilla, and human, the owl monkey (a ceboid) cluster extends over 40 Kb rather than 60 Kb and has one γ locus rather than two. The lemur cluster extends over only 20 Kb, lacking a counterpart of δ and having only one putative γ (Barrie *et al.* 1981). The exciting phenomenon of gene conversion, already characterized to some extent in primate α-hemoglobin genes (Zimmer *et al.* 1980) and human γ-hemoglobin genes (Slightom *et al.* 1980) will also be elucidated. Gene conversion appears to be a process in which tandemly linked genes undergo repeated duplications and deletions with newer duplicates replacing older ones, presumably by unequal homologous crossing over of the DNA strands.

Once the body of nucleotide sequence data embraces a number of corresponding genomic DNA regions in many primate and nonprimate species, the parsimonious genealogical trees constructed from such data should answer some of the key questions concerning human origins and primate phylogeny. Assuming that the previous molecular evidence of a cladistic Homininae consisting of *Pan*, *Homo*, and *Gorilla* will be upheld, the new reconstructions should tell us (*a*) if the closest kinship is between *Pan* and *Homo*, between *Pan* and *Gorilla*, between *Gorilla* and *Homo*, or whether for all practical purposes, an unresolvable trichtomy exists; and (*b*) if the human–African ape branch and the two Asian ape branches (*Pongo* and Hylobatinae) form a trichotomy or if two of these three branches share the closest kinship (present molecular evidence, as mentioned earlier, weakly favors *Pongo* as closest to the human–African ape branch). In addition, these reconstructions will in all likelihood clearly resolve the ancestral order of branching for Lemuroidea, Lorisoidea, *Tarsius*, and Anthropoidea.

The maximum parsimony reconstructions will also provide abundant data for examining clock models of molecular evolution and for using such models heuristically to propose possible dates for the ancestral separation of the human lineage from its nearest extant ape sister group as well as for other important branch points at earlier stages of our evolutionary history. Since the alternating forces of positive and stabilizing natural selection—which accelerate and decelerate rates of amino-acid changing base substitutions—have much less effect on the silent base substitutions in exons, this latter category of substitutions as found in genes for proteins with wide distributions throughout vertebrates and eukaryotes might provide the best basis for a relatively smooth running global molecular clock. In direct pairwise comparisons of contemporary nucleotide sequences, the degree of divergence due to silent base substitutions levels off after a relatively short evolutionary separation because the sites accepting such substitutions soon become saturated with them. This may be the reason that they do not serve as clocks in distant pairwise comparisons (Jukes 1980). However, the maximum parsimony reconstructions carried out for dense arrays of species will detect large numbers of superimposed mutations. Thus, these reconstructions should yield much fuller estimates of nucleotide divergence among anciently separated taxa and thereby allow linear extrapolation between time and molecular divergence to be effectively applied over a considerably broader span of ancestral nodes.

The divergence dates chosen from more firmly established paleontological evidence to evaluate prospects for a global molecular clock and to set the time frames for possible clocks can also be used to deduce how fast or slow rates of molecular evolution were in different periods of primate phylogeny. This will allow us to find out if previous evidence for fast rates in the early primates and slow rates in later lineages of higher primates, such as the human lineage, holds at the nucleotide sequence level and whether it applies only to amino-acid changing base substitutions or also encompasses other kinds of base substitutions. The genealogical reconstructions will provide the framework for analyzing the impact of point mutations, base sequence insertions, deletions, duplications, and gene conversions as well as selection versus random drift in the evolutionary history of human genes. The findings obtained on the evolution of protein-encoding portions of genes and the control mechanisms that regulate their differential expression during ontogeny will elucidate how the transformation during primate phylogeny of these DNA sequences shaped the genetic roots of our species.

Conclusion

Although the field of molecular anthropology is relatively new, less than 20 years old, its *origins* go to the beginning of the century. The rapid accumulation of new data and the development of the newer techniques should allow the resolution of a number of long-standing problems. Although there are a number of controversies inherent in the interpretation of the molecular data, such as the molecular clock debate, we should not lose sight of the fact that the vast majority of the molecular data itself is internally consistent. The areas of differences center mainly on areas where there is a relative paucity of molecular comparisons or, secondly, on areas where the lineages we are trying to measure are brief. One may not be able to detect certain lineages at the molecular level. This may be the case for the trichotomy of *Homo–Pan–Gorilla*. Twenty years of intensive data collection have not yet resolved this important sequence of speciations. Thus, we would stress the fact that we must be judicious in the use of molecular data in phylogenetic reconstructions, just as we must be for any other type of data. But we have confidence in the ability of the macromolecular data to reveal evolutionary history and to serve as a framework around which other types of data can be integrated.

Molecular data may not be as contradictory to the fossil record as some believe. Molecular, fossil, and comparative anatomical data together can be analyzed to minimize the apparent conflicts between the various kinds of evidence. The bodies of data can be concordant. There can be only one true phylogeny.

Finally, we look forward to the next 50 years of molecular studies. If the growth of new data and methodologies continues at the pace of the past 15–20 years, then our knowledge of our own history will be expanded beyond any previous expectations, and certainly much beyond Nuttall's prescient prophecy almost 80 years ago.

Acknowledgments

The more recent studies in molecular anthropology from Morris Goodman's laboratory have been supported by NSF grant DEB 7810717.

We would also like to thank L. Brunker for extensive comments on earlier drafts of this paper.

E. Meikle participated in J. E. Cronin's analysis of the molecular clock and fossil data, which will appear in greater detail in another publication.

References

Anfinsen, L. B.
   1959   *The molecular basis of evolution.* New York: Wiley.
Arnheim, N., R. Krysatl, G. Schmickel, O. Wilson, and E. Zimmer
   1980   Molecular evidence for genetic exchanges among ribosomal genes on nonhomologous chromosomes in man and apes. *Proceedings of the National Academy of Sciences of the United States of America* **77**:7323–7327.
Baba, M. L., L. Darga, and M. Goodman
   1979   Immunodiffusion systematics of the Primates. Part V. The Platyrrhini. *Folia Primatologica* **32**:207–238.
Baba, M. L., L. Darga, M. Goodman, and J. Czelusniak
   1981   Evolution of cytochrome *c* investigated by the maximum parsimony method. *Journal of Molecular Evolution* **17**:197–213.
Barrie, P. A., A. J. Jeffreys, and A. F. Scott
   1981   Evolution of the β-globin gene cluster in man and the primates. *Journal of Molecular Biology* **149**:319–336.
Behrensmeyer, A. K.
   1976   Lothagam Hill, Kanapoi, and Ekora: a general summary of stratigraphy and fauna. In *Earliest man in the Lake Rudolf Basin*, edited by Y. Coppens, F. C. Howell, G. L. Isaac, and R. E. F. Leakey. Chicago: University of Chicago Press. Pp. 163–170.
Benveniste, R. E., and G. J. Todaro
   1976   Evolution of type C viral genes: evidence for an Asian origin of man. *Nature (London)* **261**:101–108.
Bonner, T. I., R. Heinemann, and G. J. Todaro
   1980   Evolution of DNA sequences has been retarded in Malagasy primates. *Nature (London)* **286**:420–423.
Boyer, S. H., A. N. Noyes, C. F. Timmons, and R. A. Young
   1972   Primate hemoglobins: polymorphisms and evolutionary patterns. *Journal of Human Evolution* **1**:515–543.
Bruce, E., and F. A. Ayala
   1979   Phylogenetic relationships netween man and the apes: electrophoretic evidence. *Evolution* **33**:1040–1056.
Cavalli-Sforza, L., and W. F. Bodmer
   1971   *The genetics of human populations.* San Francisco: Freeman.
Champion, A. C., E. M. Prager, D. Wachter, and A. C. Wilson
   1974   Microcomplement fixation. In *Biochemical and immunological taxonomy of animals*, edited by C. A. Wright. New York: Academic Press.
Ciochon, R. L., and A. B. Chiarelli (editors)
   1981   *Evolutionary biology of the New World monkeys and continental drift.* New York: Plenum.
Corruccini, R. S., J. E. Cronin, and R. L. Ciochon
   1979   Scaling analysis and congruence among anthropoid primate macromolecules. *Human Biology* **51**:167–185.
Corruccini, R. S., M. Baba, M. Goodman, R. L. Ciochon, and J. E. Cronin
   1980   Nonlinear macromolecular evolution and the molecular clock. *Evolution* **34**:1216–1219.
Crick, F. H., L. L. Barnett, S. Brenner, and R. J. Watts-Tobin
   1961   General nature of the genetic code for proteins. *Nature (London)* **192**:1227–1232.
Cronin, J. E.
   1975   Molecular systematics of the order primates. Unpublished Ph.D. dissertation, Department of Anthropology, University of California, Berkeley.
Cronin, J. E., and W. E. Meikle
   1979   The phyletic position of *Theropithecus*: congruence among molecular, morphological and

paleontological evidence. *Systematic Zoology* **28**:259–269.

1982   Hominid and gelada baboon evolution: agreement between molecular and fossil time scales. *International Journal of Primatology*, in press.

Cronin, J. E., and V. M. Sarich

1980   Tupaiid and Archonta phylogeny: The macromolecular evidence. In *Comparative biology and evolutionary relationships of tree shrews*, edited by W. P. Luckett. New York: Plenum. Pp. 293–312.

Cronin, J. E., R. Cann, and V. M. Sarich

1980   Molecular evolution and systematics of the genus *Macaca*. In *The macaques: Studies in ecology, behavior and evolution*, edited by D. Lindburg. Princeton, New Jersey: Van Nostrand-Reinhold. Pp. 31–51.

1982   Apes, humans and molecular clocks: a reappraisal. In *New interpretations of ape and human ancestry*, edited by R. Corrucini and R. L Ciochon. New York: Plenum (in press).

Darga, L. L., M. L. Baba, M. Weiss, and M. Goodman

1981   Molecular perspectives on hylobatid evolution. In *The lesser apes: Evolutionary and behavioral biology*, edited by W. Brockelman and N. Creel. Edinburgh: Edinburgh University Press (in press).

Darwin, C.

1859   *The origin of species by means of natural selection or the preservation of favored races in the struggle for life.* Garden City, New York: Doubleday.

Delson, E.

1975   Evolutionary history of the Cercopithecidae. In *Approaches to primate paleobiology*, edited by F. S. Szalay. Basel: Karger. Pp. 167–217.

Dene, H. T., M. Goodman, and W. Prychodko

1976   Immunodiffusion evidence on the phylogeny of the primates. In *Molecular anthropology*, edited by M. Goodman and R. E. Tashian. New York: Plenum. Pp. 171–195.

Doolittle, R. F., G. L. Wooding, Y. Lin, and M. Riley

1971   Hominid evolution as judged by fibrinopeptide structures. *Journal of Molecular Evolution* **1**:74–83.

Dutrillaux, B.

1975   Sur la nature et l'origine des chromosomes humaines. *Monographes en Annalytique Génétique Expansive Science de France* Pp. 51–71.

Eck, F. F.

1977   Diversity and frequency distribution of Omo group Cercopithecoidea. *Journal of Human Evolution* **6**:55–63.

Eck, R. V., and M. O. Dayhoff

1966   *Atlas of protein sequence and structure.* Maryland: National Biomedical Research Foundation.

Edwards, A. W. F., and L. L. Cavalli-Sforza

1963   The reconstruction of evolution. *Annals of Human Genetics* **27**:104.

Efstratiadis, A., J. W. Posakony, T. Maniatis, R. M. Lawn, C. O'Connell, R. A. Spritz, J. K. DeRiel, B. G. Forget, S. M. Weissman, J. L. Slightom, A. E. Blechl, O. Smithies, F. E. Baralle, C. C. Shoulders, and N. J. Proudfoot

1980   The structure and evolution of the human β-globin gene family *Cell* **21**:653–668.

Eldredge, N., and J. Cracraft

1980   *Phylogenetic patterns and the evolutionary process.* New York: Columbia University Press.

Eldredge, N., and S. J. Gould

1972   Punctuated equilibrium: an alternative to phyletic gradualism. In *Models in paleobiology*, edited by J. M. Schopf. San Francisco: Freeman. Pp. 82–115.

Farris, J. S.

1970   Methods for computing Wagner trees, *Systematic Zoology* **19**:83–93.

Ferris, S. D., A. C. Wilson, and W. M. Brown

1981   Evolutionary tree for apes and humans based on cleavage maps of mitochondrial DNA. *Proceedings of the National Academy of Sciences of the United States of America* **78**:2432–2436.

Fitch, W. M.
    1971   Toward defining the course of evolution: minimum change for specific tree topology. *Systematic Zoology* **20**:406–416.
Fitch, W. M., and C. H. Langley
    1976   Evolutionary rates in proteins, neutral mutations and the molecular clock. In *Molecular anthropology*, edited by M. Goodman and R. Tashian. New York: Plenum. Pp. 197–222.
Fitch, W. M., and E. Margoliash
    1967   Construction of phylogenetic trees. *Science* **155**:279–284.
Fritsch, E. F., R. M. Lawn and T. Maniatis
    1980   Molecular cloning and characterization of the human β-like gene cluster. *Cell* **19**:959–972.
Gilbert, W.
    1978   Why genes in pieces (News and Views). *Nature (London)* **271**:501.
Gillespie, F.
    1977   Newly evolved repeated DNA sequences in primates. *Science* **196**:889–891.
Gingerich, P. D.
    1976   Cranial anatomy and evolution of early Tertiary Plesiadapidae (Mammalia: Primates). *University of Michigan Papers on Paleontology* **15**:1–140
    1980   Eocene Adapidae, paleogeography and the origin of South American Platyrrhini. In *Evolutionary biology of the New World monkeys and continental drift* edited by R. Ciochon and B. Chiarelli. New York: Plenum. Pp. 123–138.
Goodman, M.
    1962   Immunochemistry of the Primates and primate evolution. *Annals of the New York Academy of Sciences* **102**:219–234.
    1963a   Man's place in the phylogeny of the primates as reflected in serum proteins. In *Classification and human evolution*, edited by S. L. Washburn. Chicago: Aldine. Pp. 204–234.
    1963b   Serological analysis of the systematics of recent hominoids. *Human Biology* **35**:377–436.
    1975   Protein sequence and immunological specificity: their role in phylogenetic studies in Primates. In *Phylogeny of the primates: A multidisciplinary approach*, edited by W. P. Luckett and F. S. Szalay. New York: Plenum. Pp. 219–248.
    1976   Towards a genealogical description of the Primates. In *Molecular anthropology*, edited by M. Goodman and R. E. Tashian. New York: Plenum. Pp. 321–353.
    1980   Molecular evolution of the calmodulin family. In *Calcium-binding proteins: Structure and function*, edited by F. L. Siegel, E. Carafoli, R. H. Kretsinger, D. H. MacLennan, and R. H. Wasserman. New York: Elsevier/North-Holland. Pp. 347–354.
    1981   Decoding the pattern of protein evolution. *Progress in Molecular Biology* **38**:105–164.
Goodman, M., and J. Czelusniak
    1980   Mode, tempo, and role of natural selection in the evolution of heme proteins. *Protides of the Biological Fluids* **28**:57–60.
Goodman, M., and G. W. Moore
    1971   Immunodiffusion systematics of the Primates. I. The Catarrhini. *Systematic Zoology* **20**:19–62.
Goodman, M., F. N. Syner, C. W. Stimson, and J. J. Rankin
    1969   Phylogenetic changes in the proportions of two kinds of lactate dehydrogenase in primate brain regions. *Brain Research* **14**:447–459.
Goodman, M., G. W. Moore, and G. Matsuda
    1975   Darwinian evolution in the genealogy of haemoglobin. *Nature (London)* **253**:603–608.
Goodman, M., D. Hewett-Emmett, and J. M. Beard
    1978   Molecular evidence on the phylogenetic relationships of *Tarsius*. In *Recent advances in primatology*, edited by D. L. Chivers and K. A. Joysey. New York: Academic Press. Pp. 215–225.
Goodman, M., J. Czelusniak, G. W. Moore, A. E. Romero-Herrera, and G. Matsuda
    1979a   Fitting the gene lineage into its species lineage, a parsimony strategy illustrated by cladograms constructed from globin sequences. *Systematic Zoology* **28**:132–163.

Goodman, M., J. F. Pechére, and J. G. Demaille
    1979b   Evolutionary diversification of structure and function in the family of intracellular calcium-binding proteins. *Journal in Molecular Evolution* **13**:331–352.
Goodman, M., A. E. Romero-Herrera, H. Dene, and R. E. Tashian
    1981   Amino acid sequence evidence on the phylogeny of primates and other eutherians. In *Macromolecular sequences in systematic and evolutionary biology,* edited by M. Goodman. New York: Plenum (in press).
Gould, S. J., and N. Eldredge
    1977   Punctuated equilibrium: the tempo and mode of evolution reconsidered. *Paleobiology* **3**:115–151.
Hennig, W.
    1966   *Phylogenetic systematics.* Urbana: University of Illinois Press.
Hershkovitz, P.
    1974   A new genus of late Oligocene monkey (Ceboidea, Platyrrhini) with notes on postorbital closure and platyrrhine evolution. *Folia Primatologica* **21**:1–35.
Hoyer, B. H., and R. B. Roberts
    1967   Studies of nucleic acid interactions using DNA-agar. In *Molecular genetics: An advanced treatise,* edited by H. Taylor (Part 2). New York: Academic Press. Pp. 425–479.
Hoyer, B. H., N. W. Van de Velde, M. Goodman, and R. B. Roberts
    1972   Examination of hominoid evolution by DNA sequence homology. *Journal of Human Evolution* **1**:645–649.
Huxley, J.
    1942   *Evolution, the modern synthesis.* London: Allen and Unwin.
Ingram, V. M
    1961   Gene evolution and haemoglobin. *Nature (London)* **189**:704–708.
Johanson, D. C., and T. D. White
    1979   A systematic assessment of early African hominids. *Science* **203**:321–330.
Jolly, J. C.
    1972   The classification and natural history of *Theropithecus (Simopithecus)* (Andrews, 1916) baboons of the African Plio-Pleistocene. *Bulletin of the British Museum (Natural History), Geology* **22**:1–123.
Jukes, T. H.
    1980   Silent nucleotide substitutions and the molecular evolutionary clock. *Science* **210**:973–978.
Kimura, M.
    1968   Evolutionary rates at the molecular level. *Nature* **217**:624–626.
    1969   The rate of molecular evolution considered from the standpoint of population genetics. *Proceedings of the National Academy of Science of the United States of America* **63**:1181–1188.
    1979   The natural theory of molecular evolution. *Scientific American* **241**:94–104.
King, J., and T. H. Jukes
    1969   Non-Darwinian evolution: random fixation of selectively neutral mutations. *Science* **164**:788–798.
King, M. C., and A. C. Wilson
    1975   Evolution at two levels in humans and chimpanzees. *Science* **188**:107–116.
Klinger, H. P., J. L. Hamerton, D. Mutton, and E. M. Lang
    1963   The chromosomes of the Hominoidea. In *Classification and human evolution,* edited by S. L. Washburn. Chicago: Aldine. Pp. 235–242.
Koen, A. L., and M. Goodman
    1969   Lactate dehydrogenase isozymes: qualitative and quantitative changes during primate evolution. *Biochemical Genetics* **3**:457–474.
Kohne, D.
    1975   DNA evolution data and its relevance to mammalian phylogeny. In *Phylogeny of the primates: A multidisciplinary approach,* edited by W. P. Luckett and F. S. Szalay. New York: Plenum. Pp. 249–264.

Kohne, D., J. A. Chrision, and B. H. Hoyer
    1972   Evolution of primate DNA sequences. *Human Biology* 1:627–644.
Lewontin, R. C.
    1974   *The genetic basis of evolutionary change.* New York: Columbia University Press.
Liebhaber, S. A., M. Goossens, and Y. W. Kan
    1981   Homology and concerted evolution in the α1 and α2 locus of human αglobin. *Nature*
            (*London*) **290**:26–29.
Lovejoy, C. O.
    1981   The origin of man. *Science* **211**:341–350.
Løvtrup, S.
    1977   *The phylogeny of vertebrata.* New York: Wiley.
Lowenstein, J. M.
    1981   Immunological reactions from fossil material. *Philosophical Transactions of the Royal Society of*
            London **292**:143–149.
Lowenstein, J. M., V. M. Sarich, and B. J. Richardson
    1981   Albumin systematics of the extinct mammoth and Tasmanian wolf. *Nature* (*London*)
            291:409–411.
Luckett, W. P.
    1975   Ontogeny of the fetal membranes and placenta: their bearing on primate phylogeny. In
            Phylogeny of the primates: A multidisciplinary approach, edited by W. P. Luckett and F. S.
            Szalay. New York: Plenum. Pp. 157–182.
    1980   Monophyletic or diphyletic origin of Anthropoidea and hystricognatha: Evidence of the
            fetal membranes. In *Origins of the New World monkeys and continental drift,* edited by R.
            Ciochon and B. Chiarelli. New York: Academic Press. Pp. 347–368.
McHenry, H. M., and R. S. Corruccini
    1980   Late Tertiary hominoids and human origins. *Nature* (*London*) **285**:397–398.
Martin, S. L., E. A. Zimmer, Y. W. Kan, and A. C. Wilson
    1980   Silent δ globin genes in Old World monkeys. *Proceedings of the National Academy of Sciences*
            of the United States of America **77**:3563–3566.
Maxam, A. M., and W. Gilbert
    1977   A new method for sequencing DNA. *Proceedings of the National Academy of Sciences of the*
            United States of America **74**:560–564.
Messing, J.
    1979   A multipurpose cloning system based on the single-stranded DNA bacteriophage M13.
            Recombinant DNA Technical Bulletin 2:43–48.
Messing, J., R. Crea, and P. Seeburg
    1981   A system for shotgun sequencing. *Nucleic Acid Research* 9:309–321.
Mickevich, M. F.
    1978   Taxonomic congruence. *Systematic Zoology* **27**:143–158.
Miller, D. A.
    1977   Evolution of primate chromosomes. *Science* **198**:1116–1124.
Moore, G. W.
    1976   Proof for the maximum parsimony ("Red King") algorithm. In *Molecular anthropology,*
            edited by M. Goodman and R. E. Tashian. New York: Plenum. Pp. 117–137.
Moore, G. W., and M. Goodman
    1968   A set theoretical approach to immunotaxonomy: analysis of species comparisons in
            modified Ouchterlony plates. *Bulletin of Methematical Biophysics* **30**:279–289.
Moore, G. W., J. Barnabas, M. Goodman
    1973   A method for constructing maximum parsimony ancestral amino acid sequences on a
            given network. *Journal of Theoretical Biology* **38**:459–485.
Nei, M.
    1978   Estimation of average heterozygosity and genetic distance from a small number of
            individuals. *Genetics* **89**:583–590.

Nelson, G., and N. Platnick
    1981   *Systematics and biogeography*. New York: Columbia University Press.
Novacek, M. J.
    1981   Information for molecular studies from anatomical and fossil evidence on higher eutherian phylogeny. In *Macromolecular sequences in systematic and evolutionary biology*, edited by M. Goodman. New: Plenum (in press).
Nuttall, G. H. F.
    1904   *Blood immunity and blood relationship*. London and New York: Cambridge University Press.
Perutz, M. F., C. Bauer, G. Gros, F. Lerclercq, C. Vandecasserie, A. G. Schnek, G. Braunitzer, A. E. Friday, and K. A. Joysey
    1981   Allosteric regulation of crocodillan haemoglobin. *Nature (London)* **291**:682–684.
Pilbeam, D.
    1979   Recent finds and interpretations of Miocene hominoids. *Annual Review of Anthropology* **8**:333–352.
Radinsky, L.
    1978   Do albumin clocks run on time? *Science* **200**:1182–1183.
Rensch, B.
    1960   *Evolution above the species level*. New York: Columbia University Press.
Romer, A. S.
    1966   *Vertebrate paleontology*. Chicago: University of Chicago Press.
Romero-Herrera, A. E., H. Lehmann, K. A. Joysey, and A. E. Friday
    1978   On the evolution of myoglobin. *Philosophical Transactions of the Royal Society of London* **283**:61–163.
Sanger, F., S. Nicklen, and A. R. Coulson
    1977   DNA sequencing with chain-terminating inhibitors. *Proceedings of the National Academy of Sciences of the United States of America* **74**:5463–5467.
Sarich, V. M.
    1969   Pinniped phylogeny. *Systematic Zoology* **18**:416–422.
Sarich, V. M., and J. E. Cronin
    1976   Molecular systematics of the Primates. In *Molecular anthropology*, edited by M. Goodman. New York: Plenum. Pp. 141–170.
Sarich, V. M., and A. C. Wilson
    1967   Immunological time scale for hominid evolution. *Science* **158**:1200–1203.
Severtsov, A. N.
    1939   Morfologicheskie Zakonomernosti Evoliustii. Moscow–Leningrad: Izdatel'stvo Akademii Nauk SSSR.
Simons, E. L.
    1972   *Primate evolution: An introduction to man's place in nature*. New York: Macmillan.
    1976   The fossil record of primate phylogeny. In *Molecular anthropology*, edited by M. Goodman and R. E. Tashian. New York: Plenum. Pp. 35–62.
Simpson, G. G.
    1963   The meaning of taxonomic statements. In *Classification and human evolution*, edited by S. L. Washburn. Chicago: Aldine. Pp. 1–31.
Slightom, J. L., A. E. Blechl, and O. Smithies
    1980   Human fetal G γ and A γ globin genes: Complete nucleotide sequences suggest that DNA can be exchanged between these duplicated genes. *Cell* **21**:627–638.
Sokal, R. R., and G. D. Michener
    1958   A statistical method for evaluating systematic relationships. *University of Kansas Science Bulletin* **38**:1409–1438.
Szalay, F. S.
    1975   Phylogeny of primate higher taxa. In *Phylogeny of the primates: A multidisciplinary approach*, edited by W. P. Luckett and F. S. Szalay. New York: Plenum. Pp. 91–125.

Szalay, F. S., and E. Delson
    1979   *Evolutionary history of the primates.* New York: Academic Press.
Tashian, R. E., M. Goodman, R. E. Ferrell, and R. J. Tanis
    1976   Evolution of carbonic anhydrase in primates and other mammals. In *Molecular anthropology,* edited by M. Goodman and R. E. Tashian. New York: Plenum. Pp. 301–319.
Templeton, A.
    1981   Adaptation. Symposium lecture at 1981 Annual Metting of Society for the Study of Evolution. Iowa City, June 29, 1981.
Walker, A.
    1976   Splitting times among hominoids deduced from the fossil record. In *Molecular anthropology,* edited by M. Goodman and R. E. Tashian. New York: Plenum. Pp. 63–77.
Wicken, J. S.
    1980   A thermodynamic theory of evolution. *Journal of Theoretical Biology* **87**:9–23.
Wilson, A. C., S. S. Carlson, and T. J. White
    1977   Biochemical evolution. *Annual Review of Biochemistry* **46**:573–639.
Wooding, G. L., and R. F. Doolittle
    1972   Primate fibrinopeptide: evolutionary significance. *Journal of Human Evolution* **1**:553–563.
Yunis, J. J. and O. Prahtsh
    1982   The origin of man: a chromosomal, pictorial legacy. *Science* **215**:1525–1530.
Yunis, J. J., J. R. Sawyer, and K. Dunham
    1980   The striking resemblance of high-resolution G-banded chromosomes of man and chimpanzee. *Science* **208**:1145–1148.
Zimmer, E. A., S. L. Martin, S. M. Beverley, Y. W. Kan, and A. C. Wilson
    1980   Rapid duplication and loss of genes coding for the α chains of hemoglobin. *Proceedings of the National Academy of the United States of America* **77**:2158–2162.
Zuckerkandl, E.
    1963   Perspectives in molecular anthropology. In *Classification and human evolution,* edited by S. L. Washburn. Chicago: Aldine. Pp. 243–272.
    1964   Further principles of chemical paleogenetics as applied to the evolution of hemoglobin. *Protides of the Biological Fluids* **12**:102–109.
    1976   Programs of gene action and progressive evolution. In *Molecular anthropology,* edited by M. Goodman and R. E. Tashian. New York: Plenum. Pp. 387–447.
Zuckerkandl, E., and L. Pauling
    1962   Molecular disease, evolution and genetic heterogeneity. In *Horizons in biochemistry,* edited by M. Kasha and N. Pullman. New York: Academic Press. Pp. 189–225.

6

Basic Primatology
and Prosimian Evolution

Matt Cartmill

From the time of Darwin and Huxley to the present, the wish to understand man's place in nature has drawn scientists in disproportionate numbers to the study of the relatively small and unsuccessful mammalian order Primates—an order that is, after all, about equal in size and adaptive diversity to the single family of squirrels. Primatologists are more numerous than sciurologists because human beings are primates, and primate biology offers the hope of explaining our own resemblances to and differences from that group of animals to which we are most similar. Providing a historical account of how and why human beings got to be the way they are is probably the most important service to humanity that our profession can perform; and it is particularly important today, when a sectarian religious frenzy has invaded the corridors of power in the United States and threatens to impose a hysterical blindness to biological reality on the schools and textbooks of the nation.

Although the fact that people are primates gives primatology its distinctive humanistic significance (and accounts for its recognition as a discipline), whatever cohesiveness it may have as a system of ideas has been chiefly derived, not from studies of hominids and their close relatives, but from prosimian biology. How we choose to draw the lower boundary of the order Primates obviously determines the scope of primatology; but more importantly, it also largely determines the way we think about the order as a whole and its evolution. During the 50 years commemorated by this volume, two periods of pervasive change in primate biology have resulted from redefining the order. The first began in the late 1920s, when Le Gros Clark introduced the tree shrews into the Lemuriformes. The second came in the 1960s, when Van Valen and others persuaded us that tree shrews were not

A HISTORY OF AMERICAN
PHYSICAL ANTHROPOLOGY, 1930–1980

lemurs after all. The changes set in motion by Le Gros Clark culminated during the 1930s in what I will describe here as the classical primatological synthesis. The gradual disintegration of this synthesis over the past 15 years or so has left primatology a congeries of incommensurable theoretical concerns and brute facts that lack a satisfactory theoretical context. Although the outlines of a new synthesis are not yet discernible, the following brief survey of shifts in fundamental primatological ideas during the past half century can perhaps suggest some of the principles and problems that might confer new form and direction on primate biology in the coming decades.

Although this volume is intended as a survey of American physical anthropology, I have made no effort to write a history of primatology in the United States. Since many of the most significant figures in the development of primatological ideas during the past half-century were either Europeans, Americans trained in Europe (e.g., E. L. Simons), or Britons transplanted to the United States (e.g., Walker and Tattersall), a summary of American primatology per se would have no more intellectual interest than a telephone directory. Any historical treatment of the past 50 years of primate biology that avoided discussing the ideas of Le Gros Clark, Wood Jones, Petter, Napier, Charles-Dominique, Martin, and so on and so forth, could be no more than an exercise in bibliographical compilation, as boring to read as to write. I also have not attempted to provide an exhaustive survey of primatological research since 1930. What follows is mainly an idiosyncratic survey of the development of certain ideas that seem interesting in the realm of what might be called basic or macro-primatology (i.e., large-scale ideas about the order Primates as a whole, its origins, and its early differentiation).

Le Gros Clark and the Origins of Modern Primatology

Studies of primate anatomy are as old as anatomy itself, and the foundations of our understanding of primate evolution were laid far back in the nineteenth century by the major participants in the Darwinian revolution. But in two important respects, it is no exaggeration to say that modern primatology is the creation of Le Gros Clark. First, Le Gros Clark can himself be justly regarded as the first primatologist—that is, the first biologist of repute to devote his entire career to the study of primates. Second, nearly all subsequent primate biologists were trained in an intellectual tradition that was rooted in Le Gros Clark's work in the tree shrews in the late 1920s and transmitted via his classic textbooks of the ensuing four decades (Le Gros Clark 1934a, 1949, 1955, 1959, 1970, 1971).

Le Gros Clark's vision of primate evolution, although based on his own anatomical studies, represented to a large extent a synthesis of what had gone before. Late nineteenth-century authors, including Major (1899, 1901), Tandler (1899), and Winge (1895), had turned their attention to basicranial anatomy and found it useful in sorting out the formless prosimian *Lumpenproletariat* of Huxley

(1863) and Mivart (1873); into three groups—lemurs, lorises, and tarsiers—defined by characteristics of the bulla and carotid arteries. This anatomical tradition culminated in the work of the American paleontologist W. K. Gregory. In a series of brilliant and widely influential publications, beginning with his 1910 review of mammalian systematics and climaxed in the 1920s by his classic monographs on dental evolution and *Notharctus*, Gregory (1910, 1915a, 1915b, 1920, 1922) argued that primates had evolved from arboreal menotyphlan insectivores resembling tupaiids or plesiadapids, both of which he excluded from Primates because of their persistently primitive limb morphology (Gregory 1920:70, 240). The grasping feet and flattened nails that in Gregory's view distinguish primates from Menotyphla first appear in the lemur-like adapids of the Eocene, which Gregory regarded as suitable structural ancestors for lemurs, lorises, and New World monkeys.

Gregory's work was long on anatomical fact and phylogenetic hypotheses but short on grand explanations of primate anatomy and diversity. Such explanations were the peculiar concern of two variously hyphenated British anatomists, G. Elliot Smith and F. Wood Jones. Elliot Smith, a neuroanatomist, had proposed in a series of lectures in 1912 that the primates had differentiated from more primitive, ground-dwelling placental mammals as a result of taking up living in trees, a novel habit that placed a premium on vision, touch, and general intelligence and led to a degeneration of the sense of smell. This move into the trees initiated an inexorable and linear evolutionary process leading from primitive lemurs through tarsiers, monkeys, and apes to culminate in the Nordic race of *Homo sapiens* (Elliot Smith, 1924).

Wood Jones borrowed Elliot Smith's ideas about the evolution of the brain and the tarsioid origins of the Anthropoidea, combining these notions with Matthew's (1904) thesis that primitive placental mammals were not ground-dwellers but arboreal creatures with grasping extremities—an internal contradiction that was to go unremarked for 40 years. The implications of these assumptions were worked out by Wood Jones in some detail in his book *Arboreal Man* (1916), in which he insisted that the arboreal habit gradually led to divergent functional specialization of the forelimbs and hind limbs, a trend culminating in, and preadaptive for, the upright posture of man (see Fleagle and Jungers, in the present volume). Like Elliot Smith, Wood Jones regarded subhuman primates as evolutionary failures whose progress toward humanity had been derailed by various aberrant specializations that worked against the salubrious effects of living in trees.

The synthesis produced by Le Gross Clark represented a fusion of the "arboreal theory" (Howells 1947) of Elliot Smith and Wood Jones with the anatomical work of Gregory and his precursors. Le Gros Clark's work on *Tupaia* and *Ptilocercus* (Le Gros Clark 1924a, 1924b, 1925, 1926) had persuaded him that several features of tree shrews—their orbital mosaic, intrabullar tympanic ring, postorbital bar, incipient tooth comb, and limb muscles—were so diagnostically lemur-like that the tupaiids had to be included in the order Primates, and specifically in Gregory's infraorder Lemuriformes. To Gregory's objection that tree shrews lacked the diagnostic primate characters of flattened nails and a divergent hallux, Le Gros Clark (1936, 1959) replied that the nails of marmosets and *Daubentonia* had retained a claw-like form and histology essentially like those of tree shrews (implying that ancestral primates were clawed) and that the supposed Oligocene tupaiid *Anagale* (Simpson 1931a, 1945), though more primitive than modern tupaiids in lacking a postorbital bar, had developed flattened nails on the manus that helped to bridge the morphological gap.

In the meantime, Wood Jones had also concluded that tree shrews were lemurs. Since it was obvious to him that tree shrews were not primates, it followed that lemurs were not primates either and that the order Primates should be restricted to tarsiers and the Anthropoidea—the Haplorhini of Pocock's (1918) classification. If Wood Jones's corollary to Le Gros Clark's insight had been generally accepted, the history of primatology would have been very different. Unfortunately for Jones, his classificatory notions were discredited by their association with his notorious "tarsioid" theory of human evolution.

Wood Jones's thesis that arboreal habits tended to liberate the forelimb from the job of propelling and supporting the body had led him to conclude that all apes and monkeys must be degenerately specialized descendants of a more bipedal ancestor resembling *Tarsius* and that the hominids had independently descended from this tarsioid ancestor without dirtying their hands with specializations for quadrupedalism or brachiation. This theory was not acceptable to other primatologists, and it was rendered doubly unacceptable because Wood Jones had had the poor taste to promulgate it first, not in a scientific journal, but in a pamphlet printed up by the Society for Promoting Christian Knowledge (Wood Jones 1918).

After enduring a 1919 symposium convened by the Zoological Society to debate his ideas, which were universally rejected even by Pocock (1919) and Elliot Smith (1919), Wood Jones withdrew to Australia to study marsupials and work on a book defending the tarsioid hypothesis. This book, *Man's Place Among the Mammals* (Wood Jones 1929a), was answered 5 years later by Gregory's crushing retort, pointedly entitled *Man's Place Among the Anthropoids* (Gregory 1934; cf. Gregory 1930; Wood Jones 1929b). The tarsioid theory was relegated to an occasional mention in the larger textbooks, and Wood Jones made no further major contributions to primate biology. However, he continued to be influential as a teacher and mentor, most conspicuously of Osman Hill and A.J.E. Cave, whose work on primates represents in large part an attempt—and ultimately a successful attempt—to restore *Tarsius* to a central place in accounts of primate evolution.

The inclusion of tupaiids and *Anagale* in the Lemuriformes meant that the order Primates now lacked defining characteristics. It became a central axiom of the primatological synthesis that no such characteristics existed (Davis 1955; Simpson 1955). The primates were to be defined instead by a set of evolutionary trends—by a vector rather than a perimeter. These trends, as summarized by Le Gros Clark (1934a), included Elliot Smith's neurological trends toward enhanced vision and reduced olfaction; Wood Jones's trends toward liberation and increased prehensility of the forelimb, with correlated reduction of the grasping snout; and several other trends noted by Le Gros Clark, including the development of binocular vision and consequent tendencies toward convergence and enclosure of the orbits. All of these trends were explained by Le Gros Clark as the results of progressive adaptation to arboreal life. Virtually the only contemporary dissenter from these doctrines was E.A. Hooton (1930), whose alternative theories were vague, orthogenetic, and universally ignored.

Simpson and the Primatological Synthesis

The most influential convert to Le Gros Clark's vision of the primates was George Gaylord Simpson, whose classic works of the next two decades reiterated Le Gros Clark's ideas and lent them the stamp of Simpson's great authority as a paleontologist and evolutionary theorist. Simpson's early (1925a, 1925b, 1926, 1928, 1929) work on Mesozoic mammals had persuaded him that the class Mammalia was what we would now call polyphyletic, with different groups of mammals having arisen in parallel from different families of reptiles. Nevertheless, he still wished to recognize Mammalia as a taxon; and he accordingly evolved a philosophy of systematics (Simpson 1945) that permitted higher taxa to be defined by multiple parallelisms. He was correspondingly predisposed to join Le Gros Clark in regarding the order Primates as a collection of lineages bound together by shared evolutionary trends, lacking defining characteristics or a distinctive basal adaptation.

Simpson's 1935 study of the fossil remains of *Plesiadapis* invokes Le Gros Clark explicitly in arguing for the inclusion of plesiadapids in the order Primates (contra Matthew and Gregory). In Simpson's view, Le Gros Clark had conclusively shown that tupaiids are primates. But Simpson found the limb bones of *Plesiadapis* to be more primate-like than those of tupaiids, and he accepted Gidley's (1923) conclusion that the cheek teeth of *Plesiadapis* resembled those of primitive notharctines in minute detail. Therefore, Simpson reasoned, "If the tupaioids are primates, then the plesiadapids are necessarily primates also [Simpson 1935:25]." He concluded that plesiadapids were specifically allied to the Lemuriformes, representing an intermediate stage between tupaioids and primitive lemurs like *Notharctus*.

In 1940, Simpson reviewed the systematic position of the families of early primates and concluded that no satisfactory division of them into tarsioids and lemuroids was possible. Although specifically lemur-like forms (*Plesiadapis*, *Notharctus*) and tarsier-like forms (*Necrolemur*, *Tetonius*) could be distinguished, the lemur-like postcranial remains of the supposed tarsioid *Hemiacodon* convinced Simpson that early prosimian radiations comprised many parallel lineages diverging more or less simultaneously from a primitive lemuroid ancestry, so that attempting to sort them out into groupings above the family level was essentially futile. *Tarsius*, Simpson suggested, should be thought of in this light "as an aberrant and peculiarly specialized lemuroid... [rather] than... as representing a separate major division of the primates [1940:197]" as urged by Gregory (1915b). In his 1945 classification of the mammals, Simpson still tried to group extinct prosimian families into infraorders; but in his 1955 monograph on the Phenacolemuridae, he abandoned the attempt and declared that all Paleocene and Eocene primate families should henceforward be regarded simply as Prosimii *incertae sedis*. He was followed in this by Patterson (1954) and by Barth (1950), who went so far as to insist that parallelism had been so pervasive in early primate evolution that morphological features could not be used in determining the affinities of early primates. As Barth remarked with considerable understatement, this "constitutes an important limitation upon the comparative method [1950]."

Anyone undertaking a historical survey of prosimian biology must be struck by the fact that the stream of publications on primitive primates, which had flowed so freely in the first 30 years of this century and became an untameable cataract from the late 1960s onward, dwindled to a trickle between 1935 and 1960. Many factors contributed to this hiatus of a quarter-century (World War II not least among them), but it seems reasonable to attribute it in part to the morphological Pyrrhonism inherent in the canonical synthesis developed by Le Gros Clark and Simpson. This body of theory, in its mature form, proclaimed that the primate order and its major subdivisions were not definable by morphological character-istics but by complexes of evolutionary trends variously manifested in multiple parallel lineages. Such postulates, though not universally accepted, made it seem unprofitable to search for phylogenetic affinities between early and later primates and so tended to discourage research. Little progress was made beyond this point until the 1960s, when cracks began to appear in the foundations of the classical primatological synthesis.

Simons and Russell: New Light on Old Bones

Although the first glimmerings of the coming revolution in primate biology could be discerned during the 1950s in Osman Hill's revival of the haplorhine–strepsirhine distinction and his exclusion of tree shrews from the order (1953, 1955), Hill's atheoretical compendia of facts represented no real threat to the prevailing vision of the order and its evolution. The new direction in primatology was more clearly evident in the work of E. L. Simons in the early 1960s. In a short paper on the cranial anatomy of *Necrolemur* that appeared in 1960, Simons and D. E. Russell concluded that this European Eocene primate showed clear signs of phylogenetic affinity to *Tarsius*. This conclusion, which reaffirmed those of Stehlin (1916), Hill (1955), Gazin (1958), and others, was not novel; but the paper departed from the prevailing tradition in two significant respects. First, in explicitly attacking Hürzeler's (1948) conclusion that the ear region of this otherwise tarsier-like fossil resembled that of lemurs, Simons and Russell undercut one of Simpson's

(1955) chief reasons for thinking that suprafamilial distinctions could not be made among early primates. Second, and more importantly, this paper sounded the theme that was to predominate in the subsequent work of Simons and his students: a determination to replace the vague phylogenetic skepticism of classical primatology with concrete links between modern primates and their most probable fossil antecedents. In Simons's articles of the 1960s, question marks on phylogenetic trees sprouted into hard black lines stretching back from *Oreopithecus* toward *Apidium* (Simons 1960), from *Tarsius* toward *Necrolemur* and *Pseudoloris* (Simons 1961a), from *Hylobates* toward *Aeolopithecus* (Simons 1961b), from ceboids toward *Ourayia* and *Omomys* (Simons 1961c), from galagos and lorises toward *Anchomomys* (Simons 1962a), from cercopithecids toward *Parapithecus* (Simons 1969a, 1969b), and, mostly importantly, from *Homo* back toward *Ramapithecus* (Simons 1961d) and maybe all the way back to *Propliopithecus haeckeli* (Simons 1965). None of these ideas represents a break with the past. Many of them had already been tentatively advanced by Gregory (1922), Simpson (1931b, 1940), Gazin (1958), and Le Gros Clark (1959); and in affirming the ubiquity of parallelism in the evolution of early primates and the resulting necessity for tolerating paraphyletic and polyphyletic primate taxa, Simons (1962b) remained firmly in the Simpsonian tradition. But taken as a whole, Simon's work in the early 1960s clearly expresses that hankering after bold, precise phylogenetic hypotheses that was to dominate primatology in the succeeding two decades.

While Simons was busy imposing an un-Simpsonian phylogenetic order on what he was later (Simons 1972) to call "primates of modern aspect," his collaborator D. E. Russell was laying the groundwork for a redefinition of the order through his studies of more archaic primates. In 1964, Russell published a monographic study of the Paleocene mammals of Europe that described new specimens of *Plesiadapis*, including a crushed skull (described briefly by Russell [1960]) and extensive postcranial remains. These remains differed startingly from those of typical primates. The skull was low and flat, with small, laterally facing orbits lacking any trace of postorbital ossifications; and the terminal phalanges had obviously borne large recurving claws.

In 1940, neither of these discoveries would have seemed disturbing. After all, tree shrews also had claws and laterally directed orbits, and a postorbital bar was not only absent in such supposed tupaioids as *Anagale* and the apatemyids but was also thought to be lacking in the otherwise modern-looking late Eocene prosimian *Pronycticebus* (Le Gros Clark 1934b). In the context of the classical synthesis, the new fossils of *Plesiadapis* could have been seen—and were, by Simons (1962b) —as one more bit of evidence for a pervasive parallelism in early primate evolution.

But by the mid-1960s, this was no longer entirely persuasive. McKenna had demonstrated in 1963 that the apatemyids were not primates or close primate relatives and that *Anagale* had no affinities to tupaiids (McKenna 1963a, 1963b). Simons himself (1962a) had correctly noted that the postorbital bar of *Pronycticebus* was broken off and lost rather than simply absent. These clarifications opened the way for a redefinition of the order in terms of shared derived characters.

The Eviction of the Tree Shrews

Such a redefinition of Primates was promptly undertaken by Van Valen (1965) in a seminal paper that represented the first fundamental attack on the classic primatological synthesis. Inverting Simpson's arguments of 1935, Van Valen showed that almost all of the few reported resemblances between tree shrews and lemurs were either spurious, primitive for Eutheria, or not found in *Plesiadapis*. Thus, if Simpson was right in admitting *Plesiadapis* to the order Primates, it followed that nonprimitive traits shared by the tree shrews and lemurs had to be convergent similarities. Inclusion of tupaiids in a polyphyletic order Primates would still have been possible, but this was ruled out by Van Valen's radical rejection of polyphyletic taxa. Simpsonian systematics had tolerated low degrees of polyphyly because of Simpson's reluctance to abandon the traditional boundaries of the class Mammalia in the face of evidence for mammalian polyphyly; but Van Valen did not shrink from declaring that if Mammalia was polyphyletic as presently defined, then either some mammals would have to be returned to the reptiles or some reptiles would have to be recognized as mammals (as Van Valen had already proposed in 1960). Similarly, if the lemur-like traits of tree shrews were not found in *Plesiadapis*, then no justification existed for regarding the tree shrews as primates. Van Valen's study of ontogenetic series of skulls persuaded him that the ento-tympanic bulla of tupaiids was not homologous with the petrosal bulla of primates, and that their last common ancestor must accordingly have been something close to a generalize placental mammal.

Van Valen's conclusions, seconded by McKenna (1966), were soon bolstered by Luckett's (1968, 1969) studies of tree-shrew placentation and by C.B.G. Campbell's (1966, 1974) neurological investigations, neither of which found tupaiids to be primate-like in any significant respect. More recent analyses of tupaiid osteology (MacPhee 1977, 1979, 1981; Novacek 1980; Cartmill and MacPhee 1980), dentitions (Butler 1980), reproductive anatomy and physiology (Martin 1967; Luckett 1980), and amino-acid sequence data (Dene *et al.* 1980) have arrived at similar conclusions. But Szalay's studies of tarsal morphology (Szalay 1977; Szalay and Drawhorn 1980) and the immunological work of Sarich and his colleages (Cronin and Sarich 1980) continue to suggest that tree shrews may be close allies of plesiadapoids and primates of modern aspect (see Goodman and Cronin, in the present volume).

New Definitions of Primates

With the tree shrews removed from the order, definition of the Primates wholly in terms of evolutionary trends was no longer workable— especially since none of Le Gros Clark's trends was evident in *Plesiadapis*. The new systematic principles made explicit by Van Valen, reinforced and augmented by those set forth in Hennig's (1966) *magnum opus*, demanded a redefinition of the order Primates and a reexamination of its origin and early differentiation. This task was undertaken in the late 1960s by three young investigators—R. D. Martin, F. S. Szalay, and M. Cartmill—whose doctoral theses (Martin 1967; Szalay 1969; Cartmill 1970) all dealt with the problem of the definition of Primates and the insectivore–primate transition. Although all three followed Van Valen in excluding the tupaiids and in regarding the petrosal bulla as a hallmark of the order, they agreed in little else.

Martin's early work marks the first introduction of the language and concepts of Hennig into the literature of primatology and was largely concerned with purely phyletic questions of the sort amenable to Hennigian analysis. In studying the behavior and taxonomy of tree shrews, Martin (1967, 1968a) had come to appreciate the considerable morphological and adaptive diversity of the family Tupaiidae. He was accordingly dismayed by the way in which Le Gros Clark had selectively marshalled his evidence for the lemuroid affinities of tupaiids, pointing to primate-like features present in the brain and carotid arteries of *Tupaia* but not *Ptilocercus*, in the molars and orbits of *Ptilocercus* but not *Tupaia*, in the incisors of *Anathana* but not *Tupaia* or *Ptilocercus*, and so on. Martin's grasp of cladistic principles made this kind of procedure intolerable to him, and he argued with great force that this distribution simply proved that none of these primate-like traits could have been present in the ancestral tupaiids (Martin 1968b). Martin went on to suggest that many of the primate characters that Le Gros Clark had analyzed as specialized adaptations to arboreal life were primitive for the class Mammalia and that tree shrews were not primitive but specialized (and thus un-primate-like) in having complex olfactory apparatus and in relying on sharp claws rather than grasping feet in climbing trees. The corollary of this argument is that *Plesiadapis* and its allies cannot be primates, either.

Szalay's paleontological studies of suspected early primate relatives led him to seek his definition of the order and its basal adaptation in features of the dentition. Examining the cheek teeth of picrodontids for signs of primate affinities, he concluded that they could have been derived from those of early paromomyids by selection for reduction of shearing functions and increase of crushing ability (Szalay 1968a). This observation led him to the broader conclusion (Szalay 1968b) that the similar but less pronounced specializations distinguishing all archaic primates from primitive insectivores could be explained in the same way. In his authoritative papers of 1968 and 1969, Szalay suggested that the origin of the Primates had involved a shift from a diet of insects to a predominantly herbivorous diet, and that this represented an adaptive transition that defined the order's lower boundary.

A different adaptive shift was proposed as definitive of the order Primates by Cartmill, whose attempts to correlate orbital and cranial morphology with arboreal habits in extant mammals led him to conclude that divergent orbits, keen noses, and sharp claws were no handicap to tree-dwelling mammals—and that arboreality per se could therefore not be invoked in explaining the loss of these primitive mammalian traits in modern primates (Cartmill 1970, 1972, 1974a, 1974b). Cartmill proposed instead that convergent orbits and grasping feet had originally evolved as adaptations for visually directed predation on insects in the shrub layer and canopy of tropical forests, and that early primates of modern aspect should in effect be regarded as placental mammals convergent with chameleons. Taking these features of the skull and feet as markers of the order's basal adaptation, he urged the removal of Van Valen's (1969) superfamily Microsyopoidea, including *Plesiadapis* and the other archaic primates, to the Insectivora (Cartmill 1972). Starting with assumptions and concerns much like those of Szalay, Cartmill had arrived at the same definition of the order as that proposed by Martin.

Prosimian Field Studies and Their Evolutionary Implications

In the early decades of modern primatology, conceptions of prosimian behavior and ecology were derived chiefly from travellers' tales, collectors' notes, and casual observation of captive animals. Fossil prosimians were studied with care; living ones were generally ignored. Even as late as the late 1940s, American writers of textbooks on human evolution tended to dismiss modern "Lemuroidea" (i.e., strepsirhines) as an undifferentiated band of nocturnal, insect-eating Eocene holdovers lacking stereoscopic vision and guided chiefly by an acute sense of smell. The last lines of Hooton's (1946) verse "The Lemur," quoted in some of the textbooks of the 1940s and 1950s, sum up the prevailing attitude:

> He is arboreal and omnivorous;
> From more about him, Lord deliver us!

Hooton's prayers proved inefficacious. Field and laboratory studies of the ecology and biology of lemurs and other extant prosimians burgeoned during the 1960s in France, where they centered around J.-J. Petter, and in the United States, where they centered principally around J. Buettner-Janusch.

Buettner-Janusch's prosimian colonies at Yale University provided material and experimental animals for a host of basic biological studies of prosimians in the early 1960s. These studies included not only the work on serum proteins carried out by Buettner-Janusch and his collaborators and students (e.g., Buettner-Janusch 1962, 1963a, 1967, 1970; Buettner-Janusch and Buettner-Janusch 1964; Buettner-Janusch and Hill 1965), but also studies of prosimian behavior (Buettner-Janusch and Andrew 1962; Buettner-Janusch 1964; Andrew 1964; Bishop 1964), immunology (Goodman 1962; Williams 1962, 1964), and karyology (Chu and Bender 1961; Chu and Swomley 1961; Bender and Chu 1963). Montagna's prosimian colonies at Brown University, which were originally established in cooperation with Buettner-Janusch, provided subjects for a long series of papers on primate dermatology, beginning in the early 1960s (e.g., Montagna and Ellis 1959, 1963; Montagna and Yun 1962). In the late 1960s, the prosimian colonies established by Buettner-

Janusch and Montagna were moved to the Duke University and Oregon Regional Primate Research Centers respectively, where they have furnished material for a continuous stream of scientific publications too numerous to mention here.

Field studies of Malagasy lemur ecology and behavior were begun in the late 1950s by Petter, who soon established his own prosimian colonies at the University of Paris to facilitate investigations (e.g., by Petter-Rousseaux 1958, 1962, 1964) of physiological questions raised by field observations. Petter's 1962 monograph summarizing his early fieldwork provided the first solid understanding of the scope and diversity of lemur adaptations, and new concepts of early primate evolution based on Petter's findings soon began to appear in print.

On the basis of his field observations, Petter (1962) distinguished two types of locomotor adaptation among lemurs: (a) a specialized leaping type represented by the indriids and *Lepilemur*, and (b) a seemingly more primitive quadrupedal type represented by the other Malagasy primates. Animals in the specialized group seemed to Petter to be relatively clumsy and maladroit at everything except leaping between and clinging to large vertical supports, and he was unable to think why such a specialization might have evolved in the absence of significant predators. Petter's remarks, taken together with the wide distribution among prosimians of specializations for leaping, suggested to J. R. Napier's student A. C. Walker (1967) that this vertical clinging and leaping habit might be a primitive retention among Malagasy lemurs, rather than a maladaptive specialization. In 1967, Napier and Walker (1967a, 1967b) proposed that the earliest primates of modern aspect had been indriid-like or galago-like leaping animals, and that other primate locomotor patterns represented modifications of this ancestral specialization. The skulls and limb bones of Eocene prosimians, in the opinion of Napier and Walker, resembled those of indriids, galagos, and tarsiers in several features related to leaping and vertical posture, and similar locomotor habits could accordingly be inferred for these early primates.

This hypothesis, subsequently criticized with varying degrees of ferocity by Cartmill (1970, 1972, 1974b), Szalay (1972a), Stern and Oxnard (1973), and Hershkovitz (1977), was received sympathetically by Simons (1967) and Martin (1972b). Martin and Pierre Charles-Dominique, comparing notes on their respective field studies of *Microcebus murinus* in Madagascar (Martin 1972a, 1973a) and five lorisiform species in Gabon (Charles-Dominique 1971, 1977), were struck by the detailed similarities between *Microcebus* and *Galago demidovii* in locomotion, reproduction, communication, and foraging behavior. In a joint paper, Charles-Dominique and Martin (1970) suggested that these resemblances represented a common inheritance and that all tooth-comb strepsirhines had been derived from a small *Microcebus*-like or *Galago*-like animal exhibiting what Martin (1972b) was to call "hindlimb-dominated" locomotion— a somewhat less upright and saltatory version of the sort of ancestral primate envisioned by Napier and Walker. Charles-Dominique and Martin suggested more tentatively that the similarities between galagos and mouse lemurs could be retentions from the ancestral primates, which implied that *Plesiadapis* might have to be removed from the order along with the tree shrews—a step taken without hesitation by Martin in 1972 (Martin 1972b).

Fieldwork in Madagascar by American primatologists began with Jolly's monographic study of *Lemur* and *Propithecus* in southwestern Madagascar (Jolly 1966), which represents the first detailed and quantified report of lemur feeding habits and social behavior. The 1970s saw a great influx of American and British field-workers into Madagascar, including Budnitz and Dainis (1975), Harrington (1975), McGeorge (1978), Pollock (1975, 1977), Richard (1974a, 1974b, 1977), Russell (1977), Sussman (1974, 1975), and Tattersall (1976, 1977a, 1977b; Tattersall and Sussman 1975). Like its predecessors, this new wave of fieldwork on prosimians led to the proposal of a new concept of ancestral primate adaptations. On the basis of observations of nectar- and flower-eating among several Malagasy prosimians, Sussman (1978; Sussman and Raven 1978) suggested that nectar was an important element in the diet of early primates, and that the reduced claws and grasping extremities that characterize primates of modern aspect had evolved, as in the nectar-eating marsupial *Tarsipes*, to make it easier to feed from flowers in terminal branches.

A great deal remains to be learned about the behavior and ecology of the living prosimians. One third of the 33 extant prosimian species recognized by Napier and Napier (1967) have not yet been the object of a significant field study, and different reports give conflicting pictures of the basic facts about some of the others (e.g., *Lepilemur mustelinus* [cf. Charles-Dominique and Hladik 1971; Hladik and Charles-Dominique 1974; Russell 1977]). It is to be expected that further fieldwork on the extant prosimians of Africa, Asia, and Madagascar will continue to provide surprising insights into the adaptations and radiations of the early primates.

Among the most exciting recent field studies of prosimians have been three brief reports on the ecology and behavior of tarsiers (Fogden 1974; Niemitz 1979; MacKinnon and MacKinnon 1980), which have established that these enigmatic insect-eaters forage both on the ground and in trees, live in monogamous family units like marmosets, and defend territories that are maintained by complex vocal duets resembling those of hylobatids. Future investigations of tarsiers in the field may yield bold new hypotheses about the population biology of ancestral haplorhines—at least for those primatologists who believe that there were such things as ancestral haplorhines. Unfortunately, primatology today is torn by deep-seated disagreements on this and other fundamental issues in primate phylogeny and systematics.

The Collapse of Classical Primate Systematics

The basic classification of the primates derived from the classical synthesis is that proposed by Simpson (1945) and worked out in minute detail by Piveteau (1957), Buettner-Janusch (1963b), and Napier and Napier (1967). In this classification, which enjoyed canonical status during the 1950s and early 1960s, the order was divided into the suborders Prosimii and Anthropoidea; the former a paraphyletic or "wastebasket" taxon able to accomodate Paleogene families of uncertain affinities, and the latter a gradistic taxon suspected by many systematists of being polyphyletic at the low level permitted by Simpsonian systematics (Simpson 1945, 1949; Patterson 1954; Gazin 1958; Romer 1966; Simons 1972). Three prosimian infraorders were distinguished by Simpson, following Gregory (1915b): Lemuriformes (in which Simpson included *Anagale*, tupaiids, and plesiadapids), Lorisiformes, and Tarsiiformes (including paromomyids). Within the Anthropoidea, three superfamilies of approximately equal antiquity and uncertain infraordinal affinities were recognized: Cercopithecoidea, Ceboidea, and Hominoidea. Simpson's classification is an elegant expression of the phylogenetic agnosticism inherent in classical primatology. Today, not one actively working primate systematist would regard it as an acceptable classification of the order. Unfortunately, no alternative commands general acceptance, and so practically every nomen above the generic level now has to be expressed as a trinomial of which the middle term is *sensu*.

From the mid-1960s until the early 1970s, a fragile near-consensus obtained among most primate systematists. The primate classifications offered during this period by Romer (1966), Van Valen (1969), and Simons (1972) resembled each other and differ from Simpson's in several novel features that reflect ideas then prevailing about early primate evolution. All three remove the tree shrews from Primates. All three establish a new taxon at the infraordinal level or its equivalent (Van Valen's superfamilies, Romer's suborders) into which the archiac primates are consolidated in recognition of their distinctively primitive cranial and digital anatomy. Romer and Van Valen discard the Lorisiformes and simply lump the lorises in with the other lemuroids as a separate family, anticipating Charles-Dominique and Martin (1970) in suspecting close phyletic ties between the two groups of tooth-comb prosimians. All three classifications remain persistently Simpsonian, however, in making no attempt to postulate strictly monophyletic suborders: Van Valen and Simons retain Simpson's gradistic suborders, whereas Romer simply throws up his hands and names five suborders corresponding to Van Valen's superfamilies.

The generally similar classifications of Primates offered by systematists of the late 1960s proved to be only a momentary lull in the post-Simpsonian turmoil. During the 1970s, the division of the order into prosimians and anthropoids was almost universally discarded, to be replaced by other schemes thought by their conflicting partisans to be better expressions of phylogenetic relationships. The most popular scheme from the early 1970s on has been Pocock's (1918) division of the order into Haplorhini and Strepsirhini, with the addition of a third suborder, Plesiadapiformes, for the reception of *Plesiadapis* and its relatives (McKenna 1975; Szalay and Delson 1979). Although the division of living primates into haplorhines and strepsirhines is supported by extensive evidence drawn from cranial anatomy (Pocock 1918; Cave 1967; Szalay 1975a, 1976; Martin 1978; Cartmill and Kay 1978; Cartmill 1980a; Rosenberger and Szalay 1980), reproductive anatomy (Luckett

1975; Luckett and Szalay 1978), and biochemistry (Hoyer and Roberts 1967; Goodman et al. 1978), it is not yet clear that fossil primates can be similarly divided with confidence (Simons 1974; Cartmill and Kay 1978).

The most important challenge to the haplorhine–strepsirhine dichotomy in primate systematics has been that proposed by Gingerich (1973, 1975a, 1975b, 1976, 1978, 1980; Gingerich and Schoeninger 1977). Gingerich's work on Paleogene primates, including important new basicranial material of Plesiadapis and the Fayum anthropoids, convinced him that the ear region of Plesiadapis resembled that of Necrolemur and that early anthropoids resembled adapids in having a lemur-like tympanic anulus, a fused mandibular symphysis, and vertically implanted spatulate incisors. The enlarged incisors and somewhat omomyid-like cheek teeth of many archaic primates, which had led earlier investigators to classify them as tarsioids before their cranial anatomy was known, were cited by Gingerich as further evidence for a phyletic connection between the plesiadapoids and omomyids. He accordingly proposed that all extant primates except Tarsius are decended from adapids and that Tarsius is the terminus of an independent line of descent leading back through the Eocene tarsioids to the paromomyids. Gingerich's division of the order into suborders Simiolemuriformes and Plesitarsiiformes has been supported, on radically different grounds involving novel theories of dental homology, by Schwartz and his co-workers (Schwartz and Krishtalka 1977; Schwartz et al. 1978; Schwartz, 1978a, 1978b, 1980), and has been corroborated indirectly by recent biomolecular studies (Sarich and Cronin 1980; Cronin and Sarich 1980) that indicate that lemurs are at least as closely related to anthropoids as tarsiers are. However, Gingerich's most recent paper on this subject (1981) concedes that present evidence favors the hypothesis that primates of modern aspect constitute a monophyletic group.

Novel and discordant phylogenetic hypotheses at lower taxonomic levels among prosimian primates also proliferated in the 1970s. Among the most widely accepted has been the rejection or modification of Gregory's (1915b) division of the tooth-comb primates into Lemuriformes and Lorisiformes. This division was first questioned by Charles-Dominique and Martin (1970), who noted the possibility that the features shared by Galago demidovii and Microcebus murinus might be interpreted as evidence for a relatively recent common ancestry of lorisiforms and cheirogaleids rather than (as they preferred to think) as ancient retentions from the common ancestry of all lemurs and lorises. In an unusual example of multiply parallel scientific investigation, four studies of prosimian cranial anatomy—carried out independently by Mahé (1972), Szalay and Katz (1973), Schwartz (1974), and Cartmill (1975)—arrived at a single conclusion: that cheirogaleids and lorises are phyletic sister groups. The evidence presented in these studies undercuts the arguments of Charles-Dominique and Martin favoring a Microcebus-like ancestor for the extant strepsirhines; and recent formal classifications of the Primates (Schwartz et al. 1978; Szalay and Delson 1979) have abandoned Gregory's scheme and transferred the cheirogaleids to the Lorisiformes. Other unconventional views of prosimian phylogeny, which have been less favorably received, include the hypothesis of Tattersall and Schwartz (1974, 1975; Schwartz *et al.* 1978; Schwartz and Tattersall 1979) that the phyletic divisions between indriids, *Lemur* and *Lepilemur* are of great antiquity (probably antedating the separation of Madagascar from the African mainland) and the hypothesis of Cartmill and Kay (1978; Cartmill 1980a) that *Tarsius* is the phyletic sister of the Anthropoidea.

Although biomolecular and immunological approaches to primate phylogeny have during the past two decades become increasingly more detailed and sophisticated as technology has mushroomed and data have accumulated, they have so far failed to realize the hopes expressed at their birth in the late 1950s by providing an objective and reliable means of determining phylogenetic relationships. In the most controversial areas of primate systematics, molecular evidence has been either internally contradictory or else in conflict with the weight of morphological evidence, exacerbating rather than solving the problems (see Goodman and Cronin, in the present volume). Almost all morphologists that have studied tree shrews recently (with the important exception of Szalay) have agreed that no anatomical evidence links tupaiids to primates; yet most studies of immunology and macromolecular sequence data indicate that tupaiids and primates are closely related (Goodman 1975; Cronin and Sarich 1980; Sarich and Cronin 1976). The morphological evidence for a cheirogaleid–lorisiform clade is persuasive; but the biomolecular evidence contradicts it (Goodman 1975), thereby providing support for the theories advanced by Charles-Dominique and Martin. Morphologists disagree on whether *Tarsius* is the most distant or the closest relative of the Anthropoidea among the living primates; but so, unfortunately, do the molecular studies (Sarich and Cronin 1980; Goodman 1975; Dene *et al.* 1976; Goodman *et al.* 1978; Baba *et al.* 1980).

After Phylogeny, What?

In primatology, as in other areas of evolutionary biology, the 1970s were characterized by the progressive spread of Hennigian phylogenetic systematics, which was soon modified by various American workers into an axiomatized system complete with attached philosophy of science. The steely-eyed dogmatism manifested in the writings of some proponents of this neocladistic school has tended to evoke a red-eyed incoherence in the ripostes of more traditional evolutionary systematists, and many disciplines have tended to split into two mutually hostile and contemptuous camps. This is to some extent true of primatology, although oddly enough the most divergently polarized students of primate phylogeny have agreed in accepting Gingerich's radical phylogenetic assumptions. Schwartz and his co-workers, perhaps the most rigorous and aggressive proponents of the cladistic approach in primatology, defend Gingerich's phylogeny using cladistic procedures and assumptions abhorrent to Gingerich. Gingerich, for his part, goes beyond most traditionalists in rejecting cladistic methods in phylogeny reconstruction altogether and instead urges a "stratophenetic" approach (Gingerich and Schoeninger 1977; Gingerich 1978, 1979), in which ancestor–descendant relationships are inferred from phenetic similarity and spatiotemporal proximity.

All parties in this and related disputes have shared a preoccupation with patterns of phyletic relationship. As we have seen, this preoccupation became manifest before the general spread of cladistic procedures in systematics and phylogeny reconstruction, and may have been conducive to that spread as well as being reinforced by it. The primatology of the last two decades has been distinguished from the classic synthesis that preceded it by a trend toward continually greater precision in making and framing phylogenetic hypotheses. It seems unlikely that this trend will continue much longer. The net result of these 20 years of increasingly strident insistence on phylogenetic rigor has been the production of ever more numerous and more divergent hypotheses concerning primate phylogeny; and there seems little hope that the introduction of new anatomical, paleontological, and molecular data can be expected to lead to a genuine consensus on these issues in the immediate future. It seems increasingly likely that conflicting phylogenetic hypotheses cannot always be resolved with great precision, for several reasons. Parallel and convergent evolution appear to be extremely common, at least among primates, and this prevalence of parallelisms renders the assumptions of cladistic methodology and character analysis correspondingly suspect. In a recent study of strepsirhine phylogeny utilizing 60 morphological and behavioral characters, R. H. Eaglen (1980) has demonstrated that at least 80% of these 60 characters have exhibited parallel evolutionary change within the Strepsirhini, and that the most parsimonious phylogenetic hypothesis implies that 10 of these characters have evolved in parallel six or more times. Eaglen, Joysey (1978), Cronin and Sarich (1980), and others have found that when a sufficiently large data base is utilized, widely different phylogenetic schemes often differ little in degree of parsimony—which is what would be expected if parallelisms and convergences are about as common as synapomorphies. It has recently been shown that anatomical terminology itself is not neutral with respect to phylogeny and that different phylogenies can be supported by the use of different systems of terminology to describe the same facts, even when those systems have identical information content (Cartmill 1980b, in press). The significance of these findings should not be exaggerated; obviously, we have adequate grounds for rejecting many phylogenetic schemes and adopting certain others. But it begins to appear as if Simpson's phylogenetic agnosticism of the 1940s and 1950s was grounded in a realistic assessment of the prevalence of parallel evolution and the difficulty of detecting it.

If phylogenetic analysis does not persist as the dominant motif in primate biology, what can be expected to replace it? I suspect that the central concern of primatology in this century's last decades will prove to be the same one that preoccupied the thinking of Elliot Smith, Wood Jones, Le Gros Clark, and other founders of modern primatology: explaining the origins of the major grades of primate organization. This problem is, to a large extent, separable from the phylogenetic squabbles that have bedeviled primatology in the 1970s. The discreteness of the two sorts of issues is clearly shown, for example, in the work of Cachel (1976, 1979), who has advanced an elaborate and comprehensive explanation of the origin of Anthropoidea, yet believes that the anthropoid grade was attained independently by different prosimian lineages in the New and Old Worlds. Grades, in short, are not clades; and it is often possible to investigate the origins of either one without having any opinion about the existence of the other. Indeed, proving that a grade is polyphyletic only enhances the likelihood that its origins had intelligible adaptive causes, rather than resulting from drift, macromutation, or other transient and random processes now effectively beyond the reach of scientific inquiry.

In the classical primatological synthesis, the origins of the major grades of primate adaptation from tree shrews to ancestral hominids were covered by a single explanation: life in trees produces trends toward ape-like morphology, and these trends are preadaptive for the appearance of man—or, as Hooton (1930) phrased it, "The only prerequisites of intellect are prehensile limbs and a convenient tree." During the 50 years commemorated by this volume, accumulated studies of primates and other arboreal mammals have revealed that there are many equally profitable ways of making a living in the trees and that monkeys and apes are not necessarily always better off than galagos and squirrels. As a result, it is no longer clear just what a squirrel-like plesiadapoid would have gained by evolving into a lemur, or how an early tarsioid might have benefitted by acquiring anthropoid features. Explaining these and similar transitions presents a problem. I suggest that this problem may represent the central, unifying question in a grade-oriented, neo-Simpsonian primatology of the near future.

Because of their relevance to human origins, four morphological grade transitions in primate evolution assume particular interest for us: (*a*) the origins of the order Primates, (*b*) the origins of primates of modern aspect, or primates *sensu stricto*, (*c*) the origins of Anthropoidea, and (*d*) the pongid–hominid transition. (An intelligent indriid would find other transitions of equal interest: but then, so would we, if there were intelligent indriids.) The first three of these transitions fall within the purview of prosimian biology, and I wish to conclude by summarizing the unresolved issues in each and by suggesting the lines that future research may take. The fourth transition, which has deservedly attracted more attention and thought than the other three put together, is dealt with elsewhere in this volume (see Fleagle and Jungers, Chapter 7).

Primate Origins: The Problem of Functional Inference

If the morphological novelties that distinguish major grades of organization have been produced by natural selection and reflect the appearance of a new adaptive mode, explaining how they came to be requires that we understand the adaptive significance of both the novel morphology and its more primitive antecedents. (For example, if the last common ancestor of primates and tree shrews was adapted to life in the trees, the distinctive traits of primates cannot be explained as the results of a shift from terrestrial to arboreal life.) To explain primate origins, we must therefore be able to make inferences from morphology to mode of life both for early primates and for their proximate ancestors. In some cases, the comparative anatomy of living animals permits inferences about ancestral morphology; however, since all living primates are primates of modern aspect, no anatomical facts about more archaic primates can be inferred from comparative primate anatomy, and attempts to explain the adaptive shift underlying the origin of the plesiadapoids must accordingly be based entirely on paleontological information.

The general problem of inferring function from structure in extinct animals is involved in any attempt to explain morphological evolution. This problem has been approached in two different ways, which reflect different sets of presuppositions about the way evolution works. The most common, most obvious, and intuitively most appealing approach is to assume that biomechanically and physiologically intelligible correlations found to obtain between structure and function in living animals also obtained in extinct ones (Kay 1980a; Kay and Cartmill 1977; Savage and Waters 1978). This approach involves the assumption that morphology usually alters rapidly and efficiently to adapt to small changes in environment and habits, so that present habits can be read more or less accurately from present morphology. The alternative approach is to assume that "evolutionary adaptations result from interactions between many (sometimes conflicting) selection pressures and heritage features [Seligsohn 1977:6]," which implies that changes in morphology are likely to lag behind changes in habit. It follows from this that "inferences on the mode of life of a given fossil taxon must necessarily be based on derived character states," because "primitive character states may only represent adaptations of a precursor [Szalay 1975b:384]." In the study of early primates, the first approach has been associated principally with Simons and his students, especially R. F. Kay and his co-workers; the second, with Szalay and his students. The differences between the two approaches are not profound, but they have significant implications for attempts to explain primate origins.

Most primatologists nowadays would agree that the first primates were *Plesiadapis* and its relatives, and the few who prefer to exclude them from the order do so for different and conflicting reasons (Martin, 1972b; Cartmill 1972, 1974a, 1974b; Hershkovitz 1977). If we accept the prevailing definition of the order, then explaining primate origins is equivalent to figuring out the adaptive significance of the evolutionary novelties seen in the earliest plesiadapoids.

Plesiadapoids (or plesiadapiforms *sensu* Szalay and Delson 1979) are thought to be distinguished from their nonprimate ancestors by a petrosal bulla, loss of the lateral incisor, reduction of the stylar shelf and associated shearing edges on the molar crowns, and various features of the limb joints indicating habitual inversion of the foot and a general enhancement of limb mobility (Szalay 1968b, 1969, 1972a,

1972b; Szalay and Decker 1974; Szalay *et al.* 1975). Attempts to identify the shift in adaptation underlying these novelties have been due principally to Szalay, whose work as a whole exemplifies in this respect what I suggest will be the predominant concern of primatology in the years ahead. Szalay's early studies of dental morphology in primitive primates (Szalay 1968b, 1969, 1972a) led him to postulate that the adaptive shift defining the order involved an increase of plant materials in the diet, reflected in the reduction of shearing in molar occlusion. Subsequent work on tarsal bones attributed to *Plesiadapis* and other early Tertiary placentals convinced Szalay (Szalay 1974, 1975c; Szalay and Decker 1974; Szalay and Delson 1979:32–33; Szalay *et al.* 1975) that the order's origins also involved a shift from life on the ground to life in the trees. This proposal was soon undercut by Szalay himself, who has recently proposed that almost all of the arboreal adaptations he describes in plesiadapoid limb bones date back to the last common ancestor of tree shrews, colugos, primates, and bats (Szalay 1977; Szalay and Drawhorn 1980), from which he infers that a shift to arboreality was the basal adaptation of Gregory's (1910) superorder Archonta, not of the order Primates.

The shift to herbivory that Szalay postulates for the basal primates has been accepted as ordinally definitive by some paleoprimatologists (Van Valen 1971; Rose and Fleagle 1981). Others have argued against both of the adaptive shifts hypothesized by Szalay. Simons (1974) disputed the thesis that ancestral plesiadapoids had a "predominantly frugivorous–herbaceous diet [Szalay 1969:323]," noting the resemblance of early paromomyid molars to those of *Tarsius* and other insectivorous modern prosimians. Biometrical and experimental evidence bearing on this issue has been assembled over the last decade by Kay, whose studies of living primates demonstrate the existence of a complex interdependence between body size, molar dimensions, shearing features of the molars, and the proportions of chitin and structural carbohydrates in the diet (Kay 1973, 1975, 1978; Kay and Hylander 1978; Kay and Sheine 1979; Kay *et al.* 1978; Sheine and Kay 1977). Applying Kay's findings to the dental anatomy of early plesiadapoids, Kay and Cartmill (1977) concluded that ancestral plesiadapoids were predominantly insectivorous.

It is also not universally accepted that early plesiadapoids were arboreal. Again, arguments against Szalay's position rest on analogies with living mammals. Gingerich (1976) infers from the bones and proportions of the limbs of *Plesiadapis* that these animals were ground-dwellers with habits resembling those of marmots. The large numbers and the paleoecological contexts in which fossils of *Plesiadapis* occur have also suggested to several paleontologists that they were not typically arboreal animals (Teilhard de Chardin 1922; Russell 1962; Van Valen 1971; Gingerich 1976). The diminutive, widely separated orbits and large infraorbital foramina of the more primitive plesiadapoid *Palaechthon nacimienti* are regarded by Kay and Cartmill (1977) as metrical (and, by inference, functional) similarities to extant primitive erinaceids. Kay and Cartmill conclude that *Palaechthon* was a beady-eyed, whiskery snuffler after insects on the ground, resembling *Hylomys* or *Monodelphis* in general habits.

As noted above, the disagreements between Szalay and his critics partly reflect disagreements about the principles that should be utilized in inferring adaptation from morphology. It is undoubtedly true, as Szalay (1975b) insists, that some features of any animal's anatomy are retentions that reflect its ancestor's adaptations rather than its own. The rejoinder of Kay and Cartmill (1977; Kay 1980a), that inferring an extinct animal's adaptations solely from its nonprimitive characters is epistemologically (as well as biologically) unsound, remains to be critically evaluated. Our understanding of primate origins, and of other important transitions in primate evolutionary history, depends on a resolution of this methodological dispute.

Finally, it should be noted that for the insectivore–primate transition, unlike the other major gradistic transitions in primate history, there is no consensus on the placement of the lower boundary of the higher grade. Microsyopidae, which lack a petrosal bulla and certain other features typical of plesiadapoids, have been regarded as primitive lepticid-like Plesiadapoidea by most primate systematists of late (Van Valen 1965; Szalay 1969; Bown and Gingerich 1973; Simons 1974; Rose and Gingerich 1976; Schwartz *et al.* 1978; Rose and Fleagle 1981), but others suspect that they may be primitive Dermoptera (Szalay and Drawhorn 1980; McKenna 1981). Until this cladistic issue is resolved, no explanatory account of primate origins is likely to be generally accepted.

Primates of Modern Aspect

The conspicuous distinguishing features of modern primates—large, frontally directed eyes, eye sockets encircled by bone, grasping feet with divergent first digits that bear flattened nails instead of sharp claws—first appear in the primate fossil record in the Eocene families Adapidae and Omomyidae (*sensu* Szalay and Delson 1979). Explaining the origin of primates of modern aspect (the "Euprimates" of Hoffstetter [1977]) involves figuring out the original adaptive significance of these novelties.

Classical primatological theory explained these features as products of trends brought about by life in the trees. Given the inclusion of tree shrews and *Anagale* in the Lemuroidea, and the apparent absence of a postorbital bar in the adapid *Pronycticebus*, it seemed obvious that the features of the orbits, hands, and feet that distinguish modern primates had been acquired many times in parallel, and it was correspondingly reasonable to infer that these features were the all-but-inevitable fruits of arboreality. In Le Gros Clark's view, grasping extremities and flattened nails are superior to claws "for animals which find it necessary to indulge in arboreal acrobatics, for by their greater pliability they can be adapted with much more precision to surfaces of varying shape [1959:174]." The frontation and convergence of the orbits characteristic of modern primates were explained by Collins (1921) as adaptations permitting stereoscopic estimation of distance in leaping from branch to branch. This explanation became imbedded in the classical primatological synthesis (Le Gros Clark 1949; Simons 1962b; Napier and Napier 1967) along with the more general assertions of Elliot Smith (1924) about the relative importance of vision in arboreal life.

The principal difficulty with this account is that other acrobatic arboreal mammals have retained laterally facing, widely separated orbits and sharp claws like those seen in the plesiadapoids. Noting several such counterexamples, Cartmill (1970, 1972, 1974a) concluded that arboreality per se could not explain the distinctive cranial features of modern primates and proposed instead that orbital and optic convergence in prosimians originated as an adaptation to visually directed predation, as in cats, owls, hawks, and salticid spiders. This proposal has been elaborated by Allman (1977), who suggests that the forward rotation of the eyes and orbits in early prosimians and other visually directed predatory mammals was not to permit stereoscopic vision (an apparently ancient mammalian attribute found in mammals with little visual-field overlap), but to improve the optic quality of the frontal visual field's retinal projection by aligning the frontal visual axis with the axis of the eye's lens system. Allman suggests further that this rotation would be selected for chiefly in nocturnal predators, since a diurnal animal can improve image quality more cheaply by stopping down the aperture of the iris than by rearranging the parts of its head. Allman's analysis accords well with the anatomical and paleontological evidence that implies nocturnal habits for the early omomyids and the ancestral strepsirhines (Martin 1973b, 1978; Kay and Cartmill 1977; Cartmill 1980a). It also makes sense of the otherwise anomalous semilaterad orientation of the eyes in hawks and mongooses; being diurnal, these visual predators are partly exempted from the optical considerations that have demanded visual-field constriction and overlap in cats, owls, and primates.

Any explanation of claw loss in primates is forced to deal in one way or another with the fact that most arboreal mammals, including *Daubentonia* and the callitrichids, have sharp claws. Almost every account of claw loss so far advanced runs afoul of the callitrichid counterexample. It has frequently been suggested that claws are a hindrance in leaping from branch to branch and that early primates of modern aspect lost their claws as part of a saltatory locomotor adaptation (Le Gros Clark 1959; Napier and Walker 1967b; Szalay and Delson 1979; Szalay and Drawhorn 1980) but callitrichids leap about on trunks and branches with consummate ease, claws and all (Thorington 1968; Kinzey *et al.* 1975; Garber 1980). From published field observations of callitrichids and other clawed arboreal acrobats, and from theoretical biomechanical considerations, Cartmill (1974b) concluded that claws are generally superior to flattened nails for climbing trees. Cartmill proposed that claw loss in primates must have originated in a small, insect-eating prosimian that climbed around on thin branches in forest undergrowth, where claws would be disadvantageous because they tend to "interfere with full phalangeal flexure," as suggested by Hershkovitz (1970). However, since many callitrichids forage for insects among the twigs of shrubs, it is obvious that nails are not a prerequisite for this sort of adaptation (Garber 1980). The general callitrichid habit of clinging to, and eating gums that ooze from, large tree trunks

(Kinzey *et al.* 1975; Coimbra-Filho and Mittermeier 1976, 1978; Neyman 1978; Garber 1980) may insulate these primates from selection pressures that would otherwise promote claw loss, which complicates attempts to use them in testing explanations of claw loss in ancestral modern primates.

Many of the current hypotheses concerning the origin of modern primates are sufficiently precise and well formulated to be refuted by the discovery of appropriate fossils. For example, if the terminal phalanges of omomyids prove to have borne claws (as Szalay and Delson's [1979] thesis that gum-eating was widespread and perhaps primitive among omomyids suggests), then any explanation of modern primate origins that involves claw loss will be vitiated, and the likelihood that callitrichid claws are a primitive retention will be increased accordingly. If, as Szalay and Drawhorn (1980) propose, some plesiadapoids have divergent, grasping halluces, then the hypothesis that grasping feet represent an adaptation to vertical clinging and leaping (Napier 1967) becomes untenable. If the orbital morphology that characterizes modern primates was first acquired by animals too large or too bunodont to have been chiefly insectivorous, then predatory habits cannot explain the acquisition of this morphology. What we need to know is whether the suite of "euprimate" traits evolved as a complex—or, if not, in what order the various traits were added to the suite.

Anthropoid Origins

The origins of the higher primates represent one of the most important and least understood events in primate evolution. Recent debate has centered around three issues: the phyletic relationships of anthropoids, the zoogeography of early catarrhines and platyrrhines, and the basal adaptation of anthropoids.

The first issue has been intermittently touched on in preceding pages. Three candidate sister groups of anthropoids have been proposed: omomyids (Gazin 1958; Simons 1961c; Hoffstetter 1969, 1974, 1980; Szalay 1975a), adapids (Gingerich 1973, 1975a, 1980; Schwartz *et al.* 1978), and *Tarsius* (Cartmill and Kay 1978; Cartmill 1980a; MacPhee and Cartmill 1981). Dental morphology has proved to be of little help in resolving this issue (Kay 1980b), although the lingering debate over whether the dental and mandibular anatomy of *Amphipithecus* identify it as an adapid or an anthropoid (Simons 1965, 1971; Szalay 1970, 1972c; Szalay and Delson 1979; Gingerich 1980) in itself provides some support for the adapid hypothesis. Most of the phylogenetic controversy has involved supposed basicranial similarities between anthropoids and their three would-be sister groups. Partisans of each of the three schools have identified similarities favoring their respective positions and have urged that the resemblances stressed by the other two schools represent convergences, symplesiomorphies, false homologies, or misattribution of fossils (Hershkovitz 1974; Schwartz *et al.* 1978; Schwartz 1978a; Szalay 1975a; Szalay and Delson 1979; Luckett and Szalay 1978; Cartmill and Kay 1978; Rosenberger and Szalay 1980;

Delson and Rosenberger 1980; Cartmill *et al.* 1981). More paleontological, embryological, and biochemical evidence will be needed to arrive at a generally persuasive answer to this problem.

The zoogeographic problem is likely to prove even more intractable. The earliest undoubted anthropoids are those from the early Oligocene Fayum deposits of Egypt; probable anthropoids are known from about the same time in South America (*Branisella*) and slightly earlier in Burma (*Pondaungia, Amphipithecus*). No anthropoids are known from other geographic regions until the Miocene. Since South America appears to have been separated from other habitable continents by substantial stretches of ocean during the Paleogene (McKenna 1980; Tarling 1980), this distribution of Oligocene anthropoids must mean one of four things: (*a*) early anthropoids were carried to or from South America across the open sea on rafts of floating vegetation; (*b*) early anthropoids reached (or dispersed from) South America via transient islands travelling or appearing between continents as a result of continental drift; (*c*) ancestral anthropoids predate the final breakup of Gondwanaland, and the catarrhine–platyrrhine split was produced by the splitting apart of Africa and South America; or (*d*) there were no ancestral anthropoids; Anthropoidea is a polyphyletic grade, attained independently by different New and Old World prosimian lineages that diverged in the mid-Cretaceous. Although each of these hypotheses has its partisans, the arguments produced by those partisans for rejecting competing hypotheses seem in each case more convincing than the arguments they give for supporting their own (Sarich 1970; Hoffstetter 1971, 1972, 1974, 1977; Conroy and Bown 1974; Szalay 1975d; Simons 1976; Hershkovitz 1974, 1977; Conroy 1978; Cachel 1976, 1979; Gingerich 1980; McKenna 1980; Delson and Rosenberger 1980; Ciochon and Chiarelli 1980; Cartmill *et al.* 1981). All four alternatives seem extremely unlikely. The best we can do without additional paleontological and paleogeographical information is to argue that three of the four are impossible, and that the fourth (being merely preposterous) must therefore be true.

Explaining why (as opposed to where, when, and from what) anthropoids originated involves divining some adaptive mode that could have been expected to select for the pecularities of anthropoids. Living anthropoids are distinguished from contemporary prosimians by a number of shared derived features that strongly argue against the hypothesis that New and Old World anthropoids have separate prosimian antecedents. All anthropoids require vitamin C in their diets; some and possibly all prosimians do not (Elliott *et al.* 1966). The brains of anthropoids are as a rule larger than those of prosimians of similar body weight and exhibit enlarged temporal and occipital lobes and a central sulcus separating the motor cortex from the primary somatic sensory cortex (Radinsky 1972, 1975; Falk 1980). Anthropoid retinas lack a tapetum lucidum and (except for that of *Aotus*) have a fovea; those of strepsirhine prosimians usually have the former and invariably lack the latter (Martin 1973b; Cartmill 1980a; contra Pariente 1975, 1979). Several minutely detailed similarities of reproductive anatomy and placentation, including amniogenesis by cavitation, formation of both primary and secondary yolk sacs, and the simplex condition of the uterus, link Old and New World anthropoids and distinguish them from tarsiers and other prosimians (Luckett 1980). A few minor features of the postcranial skeleton (e.g., absence of the third trochanter of the femur [Ford 1980]—appear to distinguish anthropoids from other primates; however, most of the diagnostic skeletal traits of anthropoids are specializations of the skull. These include fusion of the two halves of the mandible shortly after birth, loss of the metopic suture, formation of a more or less complete postorbital septum, and a distinctive pattern of vascular canals and air sinuses surrounding the middle-ear cavity (Simons 1959, 1972, Szalay 1975a; Cartmill 1980a; Cartmill *et al.* 1981).

The adaptive significance of some of these traits is negligible or obscure, but others permit limited inferences about the ancestral anthropoid way of life. Loss of ascorbic acid biosynthesis suggests that the ancestral anthropoids may have been fruit-eaters, an inference supported by the morphology of the Fayum anthropoids (Kay and Simons 1980). Fusion of the mandibular symphysis appears functionally related to use of the masticatory muscles of both sides in chewing food (Hylander 1979), suggesting that early anthropoids fed on resistant substances requiring powerful mastication. Partial symphyseal fusion is seen among extant leaf-eating prosimians (Beecher 1977), but early anthropoid teeth (and the molar morphologies inferred for ancestral catarrhines and platyrrhines) do not look like those of folivores (Kay 1977, 1980b; Kay and Simons 1980). Comparison with bats suggests that symphyseal fusion may represent an adaptation for eating unripe fruit (Beecher 1979). It is plausible that such a diet would favor bringing all the available masticatory muscles into play during chewing. Cachel (1976, 1979) has interpreted the postorbital septum as a means of providing additional origin for an enlarged anterior temporalis muscle, developed in the ancestral anthropoids as an adaptation to frugivory. An alternative interpretation is that the septum developed in connection with the evolution of a retinal fovea, and originally served to insulate the eyeball from mechanical disturbance by the masticatory muscles (Cartmill 1980a). Experimental studies of eye motion during mastication in prosimians and anthropoids, and metric comparisons of the relative size of various parts of the temporalis muscle in animals with and without a postorbital septum, could lead to the refutation of either or both interpretations of these anatomical peculiarities of higher primates.

Prosimian Adaptations, Anthropoid Parallels, and Evolutionary Theory

The fundamental adaptations of the order Primates are those of prosimians. For this reason, studies of prosimian anatomy, behavior, ecology, and evolution have generated most of this century's ideas about the order's general evolutionary

Chu, E. H. Y., and B. A. Swomley
    1961   Chromosomes of lemurine lemurs. *Science* **133**:1925–1926.
Ciochon, R. L., and A. B. Chiarelli
    1980   Paleobiogeographic perspectives on the origin of the Platyrrhini. In *Evolutionary biology of the New World monkeys and continental drift*, edited by R. L. Ciochon and A. B. Chiarelli. New York: Plenum. Pp. 459–493.
Coimbra-Filho, A. F., and R. A. Mittermeier
    1976   Exudate-eating and tree-gouging in marmosets. *Nature* (*London*) **262**:630.
    1978   Tree-gouging, exudate-eating, and the "short-tusked" condition in *Callithrix* and *Cebuella*. In *The biology and conservation of the Callitrichidae*, edited by D. G. Kleiman. Washington, D.C.: Smithsonian Institution Press. Pp. 105–115.
Collins, E. T.
    1921   Changes in the visual organs correlated with the adoption of arboreal life and with the assumption of the erect posture. *Transactions of the Ophthalmological Society of the United Kingdom* **41**:10–90.
Conroy, G. C.
    1978   Candidates for anthropoid ancestry: some morphological and palaeogeographical considerations. In *Recent advances in primatology* (Vol. 3), edited by D. J. Chivers and K. A. Joysey. New York: Academic Press. Pp. 27–41.
Conroy, G. C., and T. M. Bown
    1974   Anthropoid origins and differentiation: the Asian question. *Yearbook of Physical Anthropology* **18**:1–6.
Cronin, J. E., and V. M. Sarich
    1980   Tupaiid and Archonta phylogeny: the macromolecular evidence. In *Comparative biology and evolutionary relationships of tree shrews*, edited by W. P. Luckett. New York: Plenum. Pp. 293–312.
Davis, D. D.
    1955   Primate evolution from the viewpoint of comparative anatomy. In *The non-human primates and primate evolution*, edited by J. A. Gavan. Detroit, Michigan: Wayne State University Press. Pp. 33–41.
Delson, E., and A. L. Rosenberger
    1980   Phyletic perspectives on platyrrhine origins and anthropoid relationships. In *Evolutionary biology of the New World monkeys and continental drift*, edited by R. L. Ciochon and A. B. Chiarelli. New York: Plenum. Pp. 445–458.
Dene, H. T., M. Goodman, and W. Prychodko
    1976   Immunodiffusion evidence on the phylogeny of the primates. In *Molecular anthropology*, edited by M. Goodman and R. Tashian. New York: Plenum. Pp. 171–195.
Dene, H., M. Goodman, W. Prychodko, and G. Matsuda
    1980   Molecular evidence for the affinities of Tupaiidae. In *Comparative biology and evolutionary relationships of tree shrews*, edited by W. P. Luckett. New York: Plenum. Pp. 269–291.
Eaglen, R. H.
    1980   The systematics of living Strepsirhini, with special reference to the Lemuridae. Ph.D. thesis, Duke University, Durham, North Carolina.
Elliot Smith, G.
    1919   On the zoological position and affinities of Tarsius. *Proceedings of the Zoological Society of London* **1919**:465–475.
    1924   *The evolution of man*. London and New York: Oxford University Press.
Elliott, O., N. J. Yess, and D. M. Hegsted
    1966   Biosynthesis of ascorbic acid in the tree shrew and slow loris. *Nature* (*London*) **212**:739–740.
Falk, D.
    1980   Comparative study of the endocranial casts of New and Old World monkeys. In *Evolutionary biology of the New World monkeys and continental drift*, edited by R. L. Ciochon and A. B. Chiarelli. New York: Plenum. Pp. 275–292.

Fogden, M. P. L.
    1974   A preliminary field study of the Western tarsier, *Tarsius bancanus* Horsefield. In *Prosimian biology*, edited by R. D. Martin, G. A. Doyle, and A. C. Walker London: Duckworth. Pp. 151–165.
Ford, S. M.
    1980   Phylogenetic relationships of the Platyrrhini: the evidence of the femur. In *Evolutionary biology of the New World monkeys and continental drift*, edited by R. L. Ciochon and A. B. Chiarelli. New York: Plenum. Pp. 317–329.
Garber, P. A.
    1980   Locomotor behavior and feeding ecology of the Panamanian tamarin (*Saguinus oedipus geoffroyi*, Callitrichidae, Primates). *International Journal of Primatology* **1**:185–201.
Gazin, C. L.
    1958   A review of the Middle and Upper Eocene Primates of North America. *Smithsonian Miscellaneous Collections* **136**(1):1–112.
Gidley, J. W.
    1923   Paleocene primates of the Fort Union with discussion of relationships of Eocene primates. *Proceedings of the United States National Museum* **63**:1–38.
Gingerich, P. D.
    1973   Anatomy of the temporal bone in the Oligocene anthropoid *Apidium* and the origin of the Anthropoidea. *Folia Primatologica* **19**:329–337.
    1975a   A new genus of Adapidae (Mammalia, Primates) from the late Eocene of southern France, and its significance for the origin of higher primates. *Contributions from the Museum of Geology (Paleontology), University of Michigan* **24**:163–170.
    1975b   Systematic position of *Plesiadapis*. *Nature (London)* **253**:111–113.
    1976   Cranial anatomy and evolution of early Tertiary Plesiadapidae (Mammalia, Primates). *Papers on Paleontology, University of Michigan Museum of Paleontology* **15**:1–140.
    1978   Phylogeny reconstruction and the phylogenetic position of *Tarsius*. In *Recent advances in primatology* (Vol. 3), edited by D. J. Chivers and K. A. Joysey New York: Academic Press. Pp. 249–255.
    1979   The stratophenetic approach to phylogeny reconstruction in vertebrate paleontology. In *Phylogenetic analysis and paleontology*, edited by J. Cracraft and N. Eldredge. New York: Columbia University Press. Pp. 41–77.
    1980   Eocene Adapidae, paleobiogeography, and the origin of South American Platyrrhini. In *Evolutionary biology of the New World monkeys and continental drift*, edited by R. L Ciochon and A. B. Chiarelli. New York: Plenum. Pp. 123–138.
Gingerich, P. D., and M. Schoeninger
    1977   The fossil record and primate phylogeny. *Journal of Human Evolution* **6**:483–505.
Goodman, M.
    1962   Immunochemistry of the primates and primate evolution. *Annals of the New York Academy of Sciences* **102**:219–234.
    1975   Protein sequence and immunological specificity: their role in phylogenetic studies of primates. In *Phylogeny of the primates: A multidisciplinary approach*, edited by W. P. Luckett and F. S. Szalay. New York: Plenum. Pp. 219–248.
Goodman, M., D. Hewett-Emmett, and J. M. Beard
    1978   Molecular evidence on the phylogenetic relationships of *Tarsius*. In *Recent advances in primatology* (Vol. 3), edited by J. Chivers and K. A. Joysey. New York: Academic Press. Pp. 215–224.
Gregory, W. K.
    1910   The orders of mammals. *Bulletin of the American Museum of Natural History* **27**:1–524.
    1915a   On the relationship of the Eocene lemur *Notharctus* to the Adapidae and to other Primates. *Geological Society of America Bulletin* **26**:419–425.

1915b   On the classification and phylogeny of the Lemuroidea. *Geological Society of America Bulletin* **26**:426–446.

1920   On the structure and relationships of *Notharctus*, an American Eocene primate. *Memoirs of the American Museum of Natural History, New Series* **3**:49–243.

1922   *The origin and evolution of the human dentition.* Baltimore: Williams and Wilkins.

1930   A critique of Professor Frederick Wood-Jones's paper: "Some landmarks in the phylogeny of the Primates." *Human Biology* **2**:99–108.

1934   *Man's place among the anthropoids.* London and New York: Oxford University Press.

Harrington, J. E.

1975   Field observations of social behavior of *Lemur fulvus fulvus* E. Geoffroy 1812. In *Lemur Biology,* edited by I. Tattersall and R. W. Sussman. New York: Plenum. Pp. 259–279.

Hennig, W.

1966   *Phylogenetic systematics.* Urbana: University of Illinois Press.

Hershkovitz, P.

1970   Notes on Tertiary platyrrhine monkeys and description of a new genus from the late Miocene of Columbia. *Folia Primatologica* **12**:1–37.

1974   The ectotympanic bone and origin of higher primates. *Folia Primatologica* **22**:237–242.

1977   *Living New World monkeys (Platyrrhini), with an introduction to primates* (Vol. 1). University of Chicago Press, Chicago.

Hill, W. C. O.

1953   *Primates. Comparative anatomy and taxonomy. I. Strepsirhini.* Edinburgh: Edinburgh University Press.

1955   *Primates. Comparative anatomy and taxonomy. II. Haplorhini: Tarsioidea.* Edinburgh: University of Edinburgh Press.

Hladik, C. M. and P. Charles-Dominique

1974   The behaviour and ecology of the sportive lemur (*Lepilemur mustelinus*) in relation to its dietary peculiarities. In *Prosimian biology,* edited by R. D. Martin, G. A. Doyle, and A. C. Walker. London: Duckworth. Pp. 23–37.

Hoffstetter, R.

1969   Un Primate de l'Oligocéne inférieur sud-americain: *Branisella boliviana* gen. et sp. nov. *Comptes Rendus Hebdomadaires des Sciences de l'Academie des Sciences, Série D* **269**:434–437.

1971   Le peuplement mammalien de l'Amérique du Sud. Rôle des continents austraux comme centres d'origine, de diversification et de dispersion pour certains groupes mammaliens. *Anais Academia Brasileira de Ciencias* **43**(Suppl.):125–144.

1972   Relationships, origins, and history of the ceboid monkeys and caviomorph rodents: a modern reinterpretation. *Evolutionary Biology* **6**:323–347.

1974   Phylogeny and geographical deployment of the primates. *Journal of Human Evolution* **3**:327–350.

1977   Phylogénie des Primates: confrontation des résultats obtenus par les diverses voies d'approche de problème. *Bulletins et Mémoires de la Societé Anthropologique de Paris, Série 13* **4**:327–346.

1980   Origin and deployment of New World monkeys emphasizing the southern continents route. In *Evolutionary biology of the New World monkeys and continental drift,* edited by R. L. Ciochon and A. B. Ciarelli. New York: Plenum. Pp. 103–122.

Hooton, E. A.

1930   Doubts and suspicions concerning certain functional theories of primate evolution. *Human Biology* **2**:223–249.

1946   *Up from the ape.* New York: Macmillan.

Howells, W. W.

1947   *Mankind so far.* Garden City, New York: Doubleday.

Hoyer, B. H., and R. B. Roberts
    1967   Studies of nucleic acid interactions using DNA-agar. *Molecular genetics* **2**:425–479.
Hürzeler, J.
    1948   Zur Stammesgeschichte der Necrolemuriden. *Abhandlungen der Schweizerischen Palaeon-tologischen Gesellschaft* **66** (3):1–46.
Huxley, T. H.
    1863   *Evidence as to man's place in nature.* London: Williams and Norgate.
Hylander, W. L.
    1979   Mandibular function in *Galago crassicaudatus* and *Macaca fascicularis*: an in vivo approach to stress analysis of the mandible. *Journal of Morphology* **159**:253–296.
Jolly, A.
    1966   *Lemur behavior.* Chicago: University of Chicago Press.
Jolly, C.
    1970   *Hadropithecus*, a lemuroid small-object feeder. *Man, New Series* **5**:619–626.
Joysey, K. A.
    1978   An appraisal of molecular sequence data as a phylogenetic tool, based on the evidence of myoglobin. In *Recent advances in primatology* (Vol. 3), edited by D. J. Chivers and K. A. Joysey. New York: Academic Press. Pp. 57–67.
Jungers, W. L.
    1977   Hindlimb and pelvic adaptations to vertical clinging and leaping in *Megaladapis*, a giant subfossil prosimian from Madagascar. *Yearbook of Physical Anthropology* **20**:508–524.
Kanagasuntheram, R., and A. Krishnamurti
    1965   Observations on the carotid rete in the lesser bush baby (*Galago senegalensis senegalensis*). *Journal of Anatomy* (*London*) **99**:861–875.
Kay, R. F.
    1973   Mastication, molar tooth structure and diet in primates. Ph.D. thesis, Department of Geology, Yale University, New Haven, Connecticut.
    1975   The functional adaptations of primate molar teeth. *American Journal of Physical Anthropology* **43**:195–216.
    1977   The evolution of molar occlusion in the Cercopithecidae and early catarrhines. *American Journal of Physical Anthropology* **46**:327–352.
    1978   Molar structure and diet in extant Cercopithecidae. In *Development, function, and evolution of teeth,* edited by P. M. Butler and K. A. Joysey. New York: Academic Press. Pp. 309–339.
    1980a   Paleoprimatology—documenting our antecedents. *Paleobiology* **6**:517–520.
    1980b   Platyrrhine origins: A reappraisal of the dental evidence. In *Evolutionary biology of the New World monkeys and continental drift,* edited by R. I. Ciochon and A. B. Chiarelli. New York: Plenum. Pp. 159–188.
Kay, R. F., and M. Cartmill
    1977   Cranial morphology and adaptations of *Palaechthon nacimienti* (Plesiadapoidea, ?Primates), with a description of a new genus and species. *Journal of Human Evolution* **6**:19–53.
Kay, R. F., and W. L. Hylander
    1978   The dental structure of mammalian folivores with special reference to Primates and Phalangeroidea (Marsupialia). In *The ecology of arbortal folivores,* edited by G. G. Montgomery. Washington, D.C.: Smithsonian Institution Press. Pp. 173–191.
Kay, R. F., and W. S. Sheine
    1979   On the relationship between chitin particle size and digestibility in the primate *Galago Senegalensis. American Journal of Physical Anthropology* **50**:301–308.
Kay, R. F., and E. L. Simons
    1980   The ecology of Oligocene African Anthropoidea. *International Journal of Primatology* **1**:21–37.
Kay, R. F., R. W. Sussman, and I. Tattersall
    1978   Dietary and dental variations in the genus *Lemur*, with comments concerning dietary-dental correlations among Malagasy primates. *American Journal of Physical Anthropology* **49**:119–128.

Kinzey, W. G., A. L. Rosenberger, and M. Ramirez
    1975   Vertical clinging and leaping in a neotropical anthropoid. *Nature (London)* **255**:327–328.
Le Gros Clark, W. E.
    1924a   The myology of the tree-shrew (*Tupaia minor*). *Proceedings of the Zoological Society of London* **1924**:461–497.
    1924b   On the brain of the tree-shrew (*Tupaia minor*). *Proceedings of the Zoological Society of London* **1924**:1053–1074.
    1925   On the skull of *Tupaia*. *Proceedings of the Zoological Society of London* **1925**:559–567.
    1926   On the anatomy of the pen-tailed tree-shrew (*Ptilocercus lowii*). *Proceedings of the Zoological Society of London* **1926**:1179–1309.
    1934a   *Early fore-runners of man*. London: Baillière.
    1934b   On the skull structure of *Pronycticebus gaudryi*. *Proceedings of the Zoological Society of London* **1934**:19–27.
    1936   The problem of the claw in primates. *Proceedings of the Zoological Society of London* **1936**:1–24.
    1949   *History of the primates: An introduction to the study of fossil man* (first edition). London: British Museum (Natural History).
    1955   *The fossil evidence for human evolution*. Chicago: University of Chicago Press.
    1959   *The antecedents of man: An introduction to the evolution of the primates* (first edition). Edinburgh: Edinburgh University Press.
    1970   *History of the primates: an introduction to the study of fossil man* (tenth edition). London: British Museum (Natural History).
    1971   *The antecedents of man: An introduction to the evolution of the primates* (third edition). Edinburgh: Edinburgh University Press.
Luckett, W. P.
    1968   Morphogenesis of the fetal membranes and placenta of the tree shrews (Family Tupaiidae). *American Journal of Anatomy* **123**:385–428.
    1969   Evidence for the phylogenetic relationships of tree shrews (Family Tupaiidae) based on the placenta and foetal membranes. *Journal of Reproduction and Fertility, Supplement* **6**:419–433.
    1975   Ontogeny of the fetal membranes and placenta: Their bearing on primate phylogeny. In *Phylogeny of the primates*, edited by W. P. Luckett and F. S. Szalay. New York: Plenum. Pp. 157–182.
    1980   The use of reproductive and developmental features in assessing tupaiid affinities. In *Comparative biology and evolutionary relationships of tree shrews*, edited by W. P. Luckett. New York: Plenum. Pp. 245–266.
Luckett, W. P., and F. S. Szalay
    1978   Clades versus grades in primate phylogeny. In *Recent advances in primatology* (Vol. 3), edited by D. J. Chivers and K. A. Joysey. New York: Academic Press. Pp. 227–235.
MacKinnon, J. and K. MacKinnon
    1980   The behavior of wild spectral tarsiers. *International Journal of Primatology* **I**:361–379.
MacPhee, R. D. E.
    1977   Auditory regions of strepsirhine primates, tree shrews, elephant shrews, and lipotyphlous insectivores: an ontogenetic perspective on character analysis. Ph.D. thesis, Department of Anthropology, University of Alberta.
    1979   Entotympanics, ontogeny, and primates. *Folia Primatologica* **31**:23–47.
    1981   Auditory regions of primates and eutherian insectivores: Morphology, ontogeny, and character analysis. *Contributions to Primatology* **18**:1–282.
MacPhee, R. D. E., and M. Cartmill
    1981   Further evidence for a tarsier-anthropoid clade within Haplorhini. *American Journal of Physical Anthropology* **54**:248.
Mahé, J.
    1972   Craniometrie des Lémuriens: analyses multivariables—phylogénie. Dissertation, Sciences Naturelles, Université de Paris.

Major, C. I. F.
    1899   On the skulls of some Malagasy lemurs. *Proceedings of the Zoological Society of London* **1899**:987–988.
    1901   On some characters of the skull in the Lemurs and Monkeys. *Proceedings of the Zoological Society of London* **1901**:129–153.
Martin, R. D.
    1967   Behaviour and taxonomy of tree shrews (Tupaiidae). Ph.D. thesis, Department of Anthropology, Oxford University.
    1968a   Reproduction and ontogeny in tree-shrews (*Tupaia belangeri*), with reference to their general behaviour and taxonomic relationships. *Zeitschrift fuer Tierpsychologie* **25**:409–495, 505–532.
    1968b   Towards a new definition of primates. *Man, New Series* **3**:377–401.
    1972a   A preliminary field study of the lesser mouse lemur (*Microcebus murinus* J. F. Miller 1777). *Zeitschrift fuer Tierpsychologie, Beiheft* **9**:43–89.
    1972b   Adaptive radiation and behaviour of the Malagasy lemurs. *Philosophical Transactions of the Royal Society of London, Series B* **264**:295–352.
    1973a   A review of the behaviour of ecology and the lesser mouse lemur (*Microcebus murinus*, J. F. Miller 1777). In *Comparative ecology and behaviour of primates*, edited by R. P. Michael and J. H. Crook. New York: Academic Press. Pp. 1–68.
    1973b   Comparative anatomy and primate systematics. *Symposia of the Zoological Society of London* **33**:301–337.
    1978   Major features of prosimian evolution: A discussion in the light of chromosomal evidence. In *Recent advances in Primatology* (Vol. 3), edited by D. J. Chivers and K. A. Joysey. New York: Academic Press. Pp. 3–26.
Matthew, W. D.
    1904   The arboreal ancestry of the Mammalia. *American Naturalist* **38**:811–818.
McGeorge, L. W.
    1978   Influences on the structure of vocalizations of three Malagasy prosimians. In *Recent advances in primatology* (Vol. 3), edited by D. J. Chivers and K. A. Joysey. New York: Academic Press. Pp. 103–108.
McKenna, M. C.
    1963a   New evidence against tupaioid affinities of the mammalian family Anagalidae. *American Museum Novitates* **2158**:1–16.
    1963b   Primitive Paleocene and Eocene Apatemyidae (Mammalia, Insectivora) and the primate-insectivore boundary. *American Museum Novitates* **2160**:1–39.
    1966   Paleontology and the origin of the primates. *Folia Primatologica* **4**:1–25.
    1975   Toward a phylogenetic classification of the Mammalia. In *Phylogeny of the primates: A multidiscipinary approach*, edited by W. P. Luckett and F. S. Szalay. New York: Plenum. Pp. 21–46.
    1980   Early history and biogeography of South America's extinct land mmals. In *Evolutionary biology of the New World monkeys and continental drift*, edited by R. L. Ciochon and A. B. Chiarelli. New York: Pp. 43–77.
    1981   Review of W. P. Luckett (editor), *Comparative biology and evolutionary relationships of tree shrews. International Journal of Primatology* **2**:97–101.
Mivart, St. G.
    1873   On *Lepilemur* and *Cheirogaleus* and on the zoological rank of the Lemuroidea. *Proceedings of the Zoological Society of London* **1873**:484–510.
Montagna, W., and R. A. Ellis
    1959   The skin of primates. I. The skin of the potto (*Perodicticus potto*). *American Journal of Physical Anthropology* **17**:137–162.
    1963   New approaches to the study of the skin of primates. In *Evolutionary and genetic biology of primates* (Vol. 1), edited by J. Buettner-Janusch. New York: Academic Press. Pp. 179–196.
Montagna, W., and J. S. Yun

1962   The skin of primates. VII. The skin of the great bushbaby (*Galago crassicaudatus*). *American Journal of Physical Anthropology* **20**:149–165.

Napier, J. R.
1967   Evolutionary aspects of primate locomotion. *American Journal of Anthropology* **27**:333–342.

Napier, J. R., and P. H. Napier
1967   *A handbook of living primates.* New York: Academic Press.

Napier, J. R., and A. C. Walker
1967a   Vertical clinging and leaping in living and fossil primates. In *Neue Ergebnisse der Primatologie*, edited by D. Starck, R. Schneider, and H.-J. Kuhn. Stuttgart: Fischer. Pp. 66–69.

1967b   Vertical clinging and leaping—a newly recognized category of locomotor behaviour of primates. *Folia Primatologica* **6**:204–219.

Neyman, P.
1978   Aspects of the ecology and social organization of free-ranging cotton-top tamarins (*Sanguinus oedipus*) and the conservation status of the species. In *The biology and conservation of the Callitrichidae*, edited by D. G. Kleiman. Washington, D.C.: Smithsonian Institution Press. Pp. 39–71.

Niemitz, C.
1979   Outline of the behavior of *Tarsius bancanus*. In *The study of prosimian behavior*, edited by G. A. Doyle and R. D. Martin New York: Academic Press. Pp. 631–660.

Novacek, M. J.
1980   Cranioskeletal features in tupaiids and selected Eutheria as phylogenetic evidence. In *Comparative biology and evolutionary relationships of tree shrews*, edited by W. P. Luckett. New York: Plenum. Pp. 35–93

Pariente, G. F.
1975   Observation ophtalmologique de zones fovéales vraies chez *Lemur catta* et *Hapalemur griseus*, Primates de Madagascar. *Mammalia* **39**:487–497.

1979   The role of vision in prosimian behavior. In *Studies of prosimian behavior*, edited by G. A. Doyle and R. D. Martin. New York: Academic Press. Pp. 411–459.

Patterson, B.
1954   The geologic history of non-hominid primates in the Old World. *Human Biology* **26**:191–209.

Petter, J.-J.
1962   Recherches sur l'écologie et l'éthologie des Lémuriens malgaches. *Memoires du Museum National d'Histoire Naturelle, Serie A (Paris)* **27**:1–146.

Petter-Rousseaux, A.
1958   Variations cycliques de la morphologie des organes génitaux externes femelles chez certains Strepsirhini. *Comptes Rendus des Seances de la Societé de Biologie et de Ses Filiales* **152**:951–953.

1962   Recherches sur la biologie de la reproduction des Primates inférieurs. *Mammalia* **26**(Suppl. 1):1–87.

1964   Reproductive physiology and behavior of the Lemuroidea. In *Evolutionary and genetic biology of primates* (Vol. 2), edited by J. Buettner-Janusch. New York: Academic Press. Pp. 91–132.

Piveteau, J.
1957   *Traité de Paléontologie. VII. Primates: Paléontologie humaine*, Paris: Masson.

Pocock, R. I.
1918   On the external characters of the lemurs and of *Tarsius*. *Proceedings of the Zoological Society of London* **1918**:19–53.

1919   On the zoological position and affinities of *Tarsius*. *Proceedings of the Zoological Society of London* **1919**:494–495.

Pollock, J. I.
1975   Field observations on *Indri indri*: a preliminary report. In *Lemur Biology*, edited by I. Tattersall and R. W. Sussman. New York: Plenum. Pp. 287–311.

1977   The ecology and sociology of feeding in *Indri indri*. In *Primate ecology: Studies of feeding and ranging behaviour in lemurs, monkeys and apes*, edited by T. H. Clutton-Brock. New York: Academic Press. Pp. 37–69.

Radinsky, L.
1972   Endocasts and studies of primate brain evolution. In *The functional and evolutionary biology of primates*, edited by R. H. Tuttle. Chicago: Aldine. Pp. 175–184.
1975   Primate brain evolution. *American Scientist* **63**:656–663.

Richard, A.
1974a   Intra-specific variation in the social organization and ecology of *Propithecus verreauxi. Folia Primatologica* **22**:178–207.
1974b   Patterns of mating in *Propithecus verreauxi verreauxi*. In *Prosimian biology*, edited by R. D. Martin, G. A. Doyle, and A. C. Walker. London: Duckworth. Pp. 49–74.
1977   The feeding behaviour of *Propithecus verreauxi*. In *Primate ecology: studies of feeding and ranging behaviour in lemurs, monkeys and apes*, edited by T. H. Clutton-Brock. New York: Academic Press, Pp. 71–96.

Romer, A. S.
1966   *Vertebrate paleontology* (third edition). Chicago: University of Chicago Press.

Rose, K. D., and J. G. Fleagle
1981   The fossil history of nonhuman primates in the Americas. In *Ecology and behavior of neotropical primates* (Vol. 1), edited by A. F. Coimbra-Filho and R. A. Mittermeier. Rio de Janeiro: Academia Brasileira de Ciências. Pp. 111–167.

Rose, K. D., and P. D. Gingerich
1976   Partial skull of the plesiadapiform primate *Ignacius* from the early Eocene of Wyoming. *Contributions from the Museum of Geology (Paleontology), University of Michigan* **24**:181–189.

Rosenberger, A. L., and F. S. Szalay
1980   On the tarsiiform origins of Anthropoidea. In *Evolutionary biology of the New World monkeys and Continental drift*, edited by R. L. Ciochon and A. B. Chiarelli. New York: Plenum. Pp. 139–157.

Russell, D. E.
1960   Le crâne de *Plesiadapis*: note préliminaire. *Bulletin de la Geologique Societé de France Serie 7* **1**:312–314.
1962   Essai de reconstitution de la vie Paléocène au Mont de Berru. *Bulletin Musée Nationale d'Histoire Naturelle* **34**:101–106.
1964   Les Mammifères paléocènes d'Europe. *Mémoires du Muséum National d'Histoire Naturelle, Série C(Paris)* **13**:1–321.

Russell, R. J.
1975   Body temperatures and behavior of captive cheirogaleids. In *Lemur biology*, edited by I. Tattersall and R. W. Sussman. New York: Plenum. Pp. 193–206.
1977   The behavior, ecology and environmental physiology of a nocturnal primate, *Lepilemur mustelinus* (Strepsirhini, Lemuriformes, Lepilemuridae). Ph.D. thesis, Department of Anatomy, Duke University, Durham, North Carolina.

Sarich, V. M.
1970   Primate systematics with special reference to Old World monkeys: A protein perspective. In *Old World monkeys:* Evolution, systematics, and behavior, edited by J. R. Napier and P. H. Napier. New York: Academic Press. Pp. 175–226.

Sarich, V. M., and J. E. Cronin
1976   Molecular systematics of the primates. In *Molecular anthropology*, edited by M. Goodman and R. E. Tashian. New York: Plenum. Pp. 141–170.
1980   South American mammal molecular systematics, evolutionary clocks, and continental drift. In *Evolutionary biology of the New World monkeys and continental drift*, edited by R. L. Ciochon and A. B. Chiarelli. New York: Plenum. Pp. 399–421.

Savage, D. E., and B. T. Waters
  1978   A new omomyid primate from the Wasatch Formation of southern Wyoming. *Folia Primatologica* **30**:1–29.
Schwartz, J. H.
  1974   Dental development and eruption in the prosimian and its bearing on their evolution. Ph.D. thesis, Department of Anthropology, Columbia University.
  1978a   If *Tarsius* is not a prosimian, is it a haplorhine? In *Recent advances in primatology* (Vol. 3), edited by D. J. Chivers and K. A. Joysey. New York: Academic Press. Pp. 195–202.
  1978b   Dental development, homologies, and primate phylogeny. *Evolutionary Theory* **4**:1–32.
  1980   A discussion of dental homology with reference to primates. *American Journal of Physical Anthropology* **52**:463–480.
Schwartz, J. H., and L. Krishtalka
  1977   Revision of Picrodontidae (Primates, Plesiadapiformes): dental homologies and relationships. *Annals of the Carnegie Museum* **46**:55–70.
Schwartz, J. H., and I. Tattersall
  1979   The phylogenetic relationships of Adapidae (Primates, Lemuriformes). *Anthropological Papers of the American Museum of Natural History* **55**:271–283.
Schwartz, J. H., I. Tattersall, and N. Eldredge
  1978   Phylogeny and classification of the primates revisited. *Yearbook of Physical Anthropology* **21**:95–133.
Seligsohn, D.
  1977   Analysis of species-specific molar adaptations in strepsirhine primates. *Contributions to Primatology* **11**:1–116.
Sheine, W. S., and R. F. Kay
  1977   An analysis of chewed food particle size and its relationship to molar structure in the primates *Cheirogaleus medius* and *Galago senegalensis* and the insectivoran *Tupaia glis*. *American Journal of Physical Anthropology* **47**:15–20.
Simons, E. L.
  1959   An anthropoid frontal bone from the Oligocene of Egypt: The oldest skull fragment of a higher primate. *American Museum Novitates* **1976**:1–16.
  1960   *Apidium* and *Oreopithecus*. *Nature* (*London*) **186**:824–826.
  1961a   Notes on Eocene tarsioids and a revision of some Necrolemurinae. *Bulletin of the British Museum* (*Natural History*), *Geology* **5**:45–69.
  1961b   An anthropoid mandible from the Oligocene Fayum beds of Egypt. *American Museum Novitates* **2051**:1–5.
  1961c   The dentition of *Ourayia*: its bearing on relationships of omomyid prosimians. *Postilla* **54**:1–20.
  1961d   The phyletic position of *Ramapithecus*. *Postilla* **57**:1–9.
  1962a   A new Eocene primate genus, *Cantius*, and revision of some allied European lemuroids. *Bulletin of the British Museum* (*Natural History*), *Geology* **7**:1–36.
  1962b   Fossil evidence relating to the early evolution of primate behavior. *Annals of the New York Academy of Sciences* **102**:282–294.
  1965   New fossil apes from Egypt and the initial differentiation of Hominoidea. *Nature* (*London*) **205**:135–139.
  1967   Fossil primates and the evolution of some primate locomotor systems. *American Journal of Physical Anthropology* **26**:241–254.
  1969a   Miocene monkey (*Prohylobates*) from northern Egypt. *Nature* (*London*) **223**:687–689.
  1969b   The origin and radiation of the primates. *Annals of the New York Academy of Sciences* **167**:319–331.
  1971   Relationships of *Amphipithecus* and *Oligopithecus*. *Nature* (*London*) **232**:489–491.
  1972   *Primate evolution: An introduction to man's place in nature*. New York: Macmillan.

1974   Notes on early Tertiary prosimians. In *Prosimian biology*, edited by R. D. Martin, G. A. Doyle and A. C. Walker. London: Duckworth. Pp. 415–433.

1976   The fossil record of primate phylogeny. In *Molecular anthropology*, edited by M. Goodman and R. E. Tashian. New York: Plenum. Pp. 35–62.

Simons, E. L., and D. Russell

1960   Notes on the cranial anatomy of *Necrolemur*. *Museum of Comparative Zoology (Harvard) Breviora* **127**:1–14.

Simpson, G. G.

1925a   Mesozoic Mammalia. I. American triconodonts. *American Journal of Science, Series 5* **10**:145–165, 334–358.

1925b   Mesozoic Mammalia. III. Preliminary comparison of Jurassic mammals except multi-tuberculates. *American Journal of Science, Series 5* **10**:559–569.

1926   Mesozoic Mammalia. IV. The multituberculates as living animals. *American Journal of Science, Series 5* **11**:228–250.

1928   *A catalogue of the Mesozoic Mammalia in the Geological Department of the British Museum.* British Museum (Natural History), London.

1929   American Mesozoic Mammalia. *Memoirs of the Peabody Museum at Harvard* **3**:1–171.

1931a   A new insectivore from the Oligocene, Ulan Gochu horizon, of Mongolia. *American Museum Novitates* **505**:1–22.

1931b   A new classification of mammals. *Bulletin of the American Museum of Natural History* **59**:259–293.

1935   The Tiffany fauna, Upper Paleocene. II. Structure and relationships of *Plesiadapis*. *American Museum Novitates* **816**:1–30.

1940   Studies on the earliest primates. *Bulletin of the American Museum of Natural History* **77**:185–212.

1945   The principles of classification and a classification of the mammals. *Bulletin of the American Museum of Natural History* **85**:1–350.

1949   *The meaning of evolution.* New Haven, Connecticut: Yale University Press.

1955   The Phenacolemuridae, new family of early primates. *Bulletin of the American Museum of Natural History* **105**:411–442.

Stehlin, H. G.

1916   Die Säugetiere des schweizerischen Eocaens. VII (2): *Caenopithecus, Necrolemur,— Microchoerus, Nannopithex, Anchomomys, Periconodon, Amphichiromys—Heterochiromys,* Nachträge zu *Adapis*—Schlussbetrachtungen zu den primaten. *Abhandlung der schweizerischen paläontologischen Gesellschaft* **41**:1299–1552.

Stern, J. T., Jr., and C. E. Oxnard

1973   Primate locomotion: Some links with evolution and morphology. *Primatologia* **4**(11):1–93.

Sucklin, J. A., Sucklin, E. E., and A. Walker

1969   Suggested function of the vascular bundles in the limbs of *Perodicticus potto. Nature (London)* **221**:379–380.

Sussman, R. W.

1974   Ecological distinctions in sympatric species of *Lemur*. In *Prosimian biology*, edited by R. D. Martin, G. A. Doyle, and A. C. Walker. London: Duckworth. Pp. 75–108.

1975   A preliminary study of the behavior and ecology of *Lemur fulvus rufus* Audebert 1800. In *Lemur biology*, edited by I. Tattersall and R. W. Sussman. New York: Plenum. Pp. 237–258.

1978   Nectar-feeding by prosimians and its evolutionary and ecological implications. In *Recent advances in Primatology* (Vol. 3), edited by D. J. Chivers and K. A. Joysey (eds.) New York: Academic Press, Pp. 119–125.

Sussman, R. W., and P. H. Raven

1978   Pollination by lemurs and marsupials: an archaic coevolutionary system. *Science* **200**:731–736.

Szalay, F. S.
   1968a   The Picrodontidae, a family of early primates. *American Museum Novitates* **2329**:1–54.
   1968b   The beginnings of primates. *Evolution* **22**:19–36.
   1969   Mixodectidae, Microsypoidae, and the insectivore-primate transition. *Bulletin of the American Museum of Natural History* **140**:193–330.
   1970   Late Eocene *Amphipithecus* and the origins of catarrhine primates. *Nature (London)* **227**:355–357.
   1972a   Paleobiology of the earliest primates. In *The functional and evolutionary biology of primates*, edited by R. H. Tuttle. Chicago: Aldine. Pp. 3–35.
   1972b   Cranial morphology of the early Tertiary *Phenacolemur* and its bearing on primate phylogeny. *American Journal of Physical Anthropology* **36**:59–76.
   1972c   *Amphipithecus* revisited. *Nature, (London)* **236**:179–180.
   1974   A review of some recent advances in paleoprimatology. *Yearbook of Physical Anthropology* **17**:39–64.
   1975a   Phylogeny of primate higher taxa: The basicranial evidence. In *Phylogeny of the primates: A multidisciplinary approach*, edited by W. P. Luckett and F. S. Szalay. New York: Plenum. Pp. 91–126.
   1975b   Phylogeny, adaptations, and dispersal of the tarsiiform primates. In *Phylogeny of the Primates: A multidisciplinary approach*, edited by W. P. Luckett and F. S. Szalay. New York: Plenum. Pp. 357–404.
   1975c   Where to draw the nonprimate-primate taxonomic boundary. *Folia Primatologica* **23**:158–163.
   1975d   Haplorhine phylogeny and the status of the Anthropoidea. In *Primate functional morphology and evolution*, edited by R. H. Tuttle. The Hague: Mouton. Pp. 3–22.
   1976   Systematics of the Omomyidae (Tarsiiformes, Primates): Taxonomy, phylogeny, and adaptations. *Bulletin of the American Museum of Natural History* **156**:157–450.
   1977   Phylogenetic relationships and a classification of the eutherian Mammalia. In *Major patterns in vertebrate evolution*, edited by M. K. Hecht, P. C. Goody, and B. M. Hecht. New York: Plenum. Pp. 315–374.
Szalay, F. S., and R. L. Decker
   1974   Origins, evolution, and function of the tarsus in late Cretaceous Eutheria and Paleocene primates. In *Primate locomotion*, edited by F. A. Jenkins, Jr. New York: Academic Press. Pp. 223–259.
Szalay, F. S., and E. Delson
   1979   *Evolutionary history of the primates.* New York: Academic Press.
Szalay, F. S., and G. Drawhorn
   1980   Evolution and diversification of the Archonta in an arboreal milieu. In *Comparative biology and evolutionary relationships of tree shrews*, edited by W. P. Luckett. New York: Plenum. Pp. 133–169.
Szalay, F. S., and C. C. Katz
   1973   Phylogeny of lemurs, galagos and lorises. *Folia Primatologica* **19**:88–103.
Szalay, F. S., I. Tattersall, and R. L. Decker
   1975   Phylogenetic relationships of *Plesiadapis*—postcranial evidence. *Contributions to Primatology* **5**:136–166.
Tandler, J.
   1899   Zur vergleichenden Anatomie der Kopfarterien bei den Mammalia. *Denkschriften der kaiserlichen Akademie der Wissenschaften* Wien, mathematisch-naturwissenschaftliche Classe, **67**:677–784.
Tarling, D. H.
   1980   The geologic evolution of South America with special reference to the last 200 million years. In *Evolutionary biology of the New World monkeys and continental drift*, edited by R. L. Ciochon and A. B. Chiarelli. New York: Plenum. Pp. 1–41.

Tattersall, I.
    1976   Group structure and activity rhythm in *Lemur mongoz* (Primates, Lemuriformes) on Anjouan and Moheli Islands, Comoro Archipelago. *Anthropological Papers of the American Museum of Natural History* **53**:367–380.
    1977a   Distribution of the Malagasy lemurs. Part I. The lemurs of northern Madagascar. *Annals of the New York Academy of Sciences* **293**:160–169.
    1977b   Ecology and behavior of *Lemur fulvus mayottensis* (Primates, Lemuriformes). *Anthropological Papers of the American Museum of Natural History* **54**:421–432.
Tattersall, I., and J. H. Schwartz
    1974   Craniodental morphology and the systematics of the Malagasy lemurs (Primates, Prosimii). *Anthropological Papers of the American Museum of Natural History* **52**:139–192.
    1975   Relationships among the Malagasy lemurs: the craniodental evidence. In *Phylogeny of the primates: A multidisciplinary approach,* edited by W. P. Luckett and F. S. Szalay. New York: Plenum. Pp. 299–312.
Tattersall, I., and R. W. Sussman
    1975   Observations on the ecology and behavior of the mongoose lemur *Lemur mongoz mongoz* Linnaeus (Primates, Lemuriformes), at Ampijoroa, Madagascar. *Anthropological Papers of the American Museum of Natural History* **52**:193–216.
Teilhard de Chardin, P.
    1922   Les Mammifères de l'éocène inférieur francais et leurs gisements. *Annals de Paléontologie* **11**:9–116.
Thorington, R. W. Jr.
    1968   Observations of the tamarin *Saguinus midas. Folia Primatologica* **9**:95–98.
Van Valen, L.
    1960   Therapsids as mammals. *Evolution* **14**:304–313.
    1965   Tree shrews, primates, and fossils. *Evolution* **19**:137–151.
    1969   A classification of the primates. *American Journal of Physical Anthropology* **30**:295–296.
    1971   Adaptive zones and the orders of mammals. *Evolution* **25**:420–428.
Walker, A. C.
    1967   Locomotor adaptations in Recent and fossil Madagascan lemurs. Ph.D. thesis, Department of Anthropology, University of London.
    1974   Locomotor adaptations in past and present prosimian primates. In *Primate locomotion,* edited by F. A. Jenkins, Jr. New York: Academic Press. Pp. 349–381.
Williams, C. A., Jr.
    1962   Discussion of biochemical and immunochemical approaches to the study of protein evolution in the Primates. *Annals of the New York Academy of Sciences* **102**:249–252.
    1964   Immunochemical analysis of serum proteins of the primates: A study in molecular evolution. In *Evolutionary and Genetic biology of primates* (Vol. 2), edited by J. Buettner-Janusch. New York: Academic Press. Pp. 25–74.
Winge, H.
    1895   Jordfundne og nulevende aber (Primates) fra Lagôa Santa, Minas Geraes, Brasilien. *E Museo Lundii* (Copenhagen) **2**(3):1–45.
Wood Jones, F.
    1916   *Arboreal man.* London: Arnold.
    1918   *The problem of man's ancestry.* London: Society for Promoting Christian Knowledge.
    1929a   *Man's place among the mammals.* London: Arnold.
    1929b   Some landmarks in the phylogeny of the Primates. *Human Biology* **1**:214–228.

7

Fifty Years of Higher Primate Phylogeny

John G. Fleagle and William L. Jungers

Primate phylogeny has been a central area of interest among members of the American Association of Physical Anthropologists (AAPA) from the very first meeting in 1930 to the present time. The evolutionary history of prosimians and hominids is considered in other contributions to this volume. This chapter deals specifically with the phylogeny of nonhuman higher primates. Although we will touch briefly on most of the issues in higher primate phylogeny that have been actively investigated and discussed over the past 50 years, we will concentrate on the topic that has received the most persistent interest—the relationship of humans to the living and (more recently) to the fossil apes.

The history of primate phylogeny is not just a history of conclusions; more importantly, it is a history of arguments, of available data, and of methods and analysis. In the past half century, many issues have been resolved to almost everyone's satisfaction, and a number of new, unanticipated questions have arisen. From 1930 until the present, there have been those who felt that only one type or source of information could be used to answer questions of phylogeny, and others along the way who were certain that they had found the magic data set. Likewise, there have been repeated announcements that a particular methodological insight has resolved all apparent contradictions and differences of opinion; yet years later the same problems remain unsolved. A history of primate phylogeny is a history of all of these views. Most of all, it is a history of debate. In general, scientists do not write extensively about those issues that have been resolved to everyone's satisfaction; they write about issues that remain unresolved but approachable. Debate is a sign of interest, and primate phylogeny has never lacked interest.

Any history of a discipline is bound to be biased by the author(s)'s own training and interests, and this one is no exception. Interpretation is also heavily influenced by the perspective of time. It is often difficult to grasp clearly the subtle implications of an argument written in 1928, particularly if the issue being heatedly discussed appears to have been satisfactorily resolved by 1980. Fortunately, there are few such issues. In addition, we realize that our perspective on the 1970s is colored unquestionably by both the recency of the decade and our own personal participation. We can only state our awareness of these sources of bias.

Prelude

In retrospect the years immediately preceding the formal organization of the AAPA in 1930 were a seminal period for ideas in primate phylogeny. Many of our current ideas and theories of primate phylogeny are quite clearly the result of the work of such talented, insightful, and prolific scientists as W. K. Gregory, Adolph Schultz, Dudley Morton, and William Straus—all of whom were charter members of the society.

In addition to the strong personalities of the individuals of the time, there are at least two other reasons why interest in primate phylogeny flourished in the 1920s in the United States. In the late nineteenth century, American paleontology dealt largely with collecting and describing fossils from the western United States. Most work on primate evolution was restricted to the numerous prosimians from the Paleocene and Eocene of this continent (e.g., Cope 1885). During the first third of this century, however, American vertebrate paleontology became much more cosmopolitan. Nowhere was this more true than at the American Museum of Natural History (AMNH) under the directorship of Henry Fairfield Osborn. Between 1900 and 1930, the AMNH conducted paleontological expeditions in North Africa, India, China, and Patagonia. American paleontology had clearly become international in scope.

American interest in primate phylogeny at this time was also strongly influenced by the great excitement among a number of British scientists over primate phylogeny. This hubbub in part was a result of the "discovery" and implications of the Piltdown skull (Dawson and Smith Woodward 1913; Miller 1918; Hrdlička 1922). Sharing a common language has clearly played a very important role in the development and exchange of ideas between the American and British scientific communities. Accordingly, in primate phylogeny, as in other areas of physical anthropology, it has been nearly impossible throughout this century to separate the ideas of British and American scientists; the influence of French and German scholarship has not been nearly as strong.

In 1930, the major issue in primate phylogeny was man's place among the primates. The most hotly debated question was whether man had evolved from a brachiating ape or separately, from a lineage that was distinct from that of the living apes. In fact, the actual arguments involved much more detailed issues, and each of the active scientists had somewhat different views of the subject. W. K. Gregory (who, incidentally, was Osborn's protege at the AMNH) was the major proponent of the "brachiationist," anthropoid ape view of human phylogeny (Gregory 1922, 1927a, 1927b, 1928a, 1928b, 1929, 1930). Drawing heavily from Keith's detailed work on higher primate musculature (Keith 1902, 1911, 1912, 1920, 1923), on Elliot Smith's studies of primate brains (Elliot Smith 1918, 1924, 1931), from Morton's study of foot anatomy (Morton 1922, 1924a, 1924b, 1926, 1927), and from his own detailed knowledge of primate dental, cranial, and skeletal anatomy, Gregory argued that man was more closely related to the African great apes, the chimpanzee and the gorilla, than to any other group of primates. Furthermore, the similarities between man and the African apes, he said, were due to a common heritage of brachiation during their evolution (Gregory 1934). As his critics were quick to point out, Gregory often wrote extensively about the close relationship between man and the African apes but was usually less explicit in the phylogenies he drew. The branching point that would define either a human–African ape lineage or an all-pongid clade is curiously vague. One might infer a three-way split among human, African ape, and orangutan lineages on the basis of Gregory's diagrams alone (see Figure 1b), but the human lineage was invariably placed adjacent to that of the African apes.

Schultz and Morton agreed with Gregory, Keith, and Elliot Smith that man's closest relatives were the great apes. Indeed, from time to time both called attention to particularly close anatomical similarities between man and African apes, especially the gorilla (Schultz 1927; Morton 1922, 1924a, 1927). However, when it came to constructing a phylogenetic tree, both quite explicitly expressed their feelings that the living apes were all very specialized. Although man was regarded as having shared a common ancestry with the stock that gave rise to the great apes, both felt that this common ancestor of man and the great apes was probably more like a gibbon morphologically than like either a great ape or a human (see Figure 3 on page 194 and Figure 4a on page 197). W. D. Matthew, also from the AMNH, appears to have held a similar opinion. According to Matthew, man was clearly related to the great apes but not to any particular lineage. At the Smithsonian, G. S. Miller (1920, 1929) also expressed serious reservations about the feasibility of deriving man from a form similar to extant apes.

The anthropoid theory of human evolution had two very able, but radically different, opponents: the British anatomist Frederic Wood Jones and the American vertebrate paleontologist Henry Fairfield Osborn. On the basis of his own extensive studies in mammalian comparative anatomy and his analysis of other authors' studies, Wood Jones felt that humans were anatomically more primitive than any other Old World higher primate, either monkey or ape. Accordingly, he argued that the human lineage diverged from that leading to other higher primates before the appearance of either Old World monkeys or apes—specifically, from an animal that he identified as an advanced tarsioid (Wood Jones 1918, 1923, 1926, 1929, 1948). Wood Jones's reconstruction of this human ancestor varied somewhat

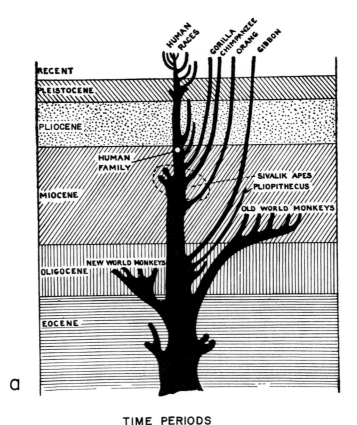

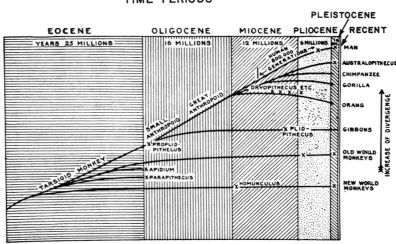

Figure 1 Phylogenetic trees constructed by Elliot Smith (1924) (a) and Gregory (1927) (b) indicating a close evolutionary relationship between the great apes and humans. According to the "brachiationist" perspective, humans were basically made-over apes.

through the years. By 1929, his views were considerably less radical than they had been earlier:

> The bulk of the evidence to be derived from comparative anatomy justifies the belief that the proto-human stock separated from the stem of the other members of the primates before the definite pithecoid specializations had become stereotyped in the cynomorpha, and to a lesser degree, in the anthropomorpha. We are justified in assuming that the proto-human stock arose from a tarsioid form that had not developed the specializations seen in the living Tarsiers; but which possessed all those primitive haplorhine characters which underlie the specializations attained by the modern *Tarsius spectrum*. We are further justified in assuming that there had been a development from this primitive tarsioid stage in the general direction of a primitive gibbon—a gibbon that had not achieved any definite pithecoid specializations [1929:356].

Wood Jones's many anatomical arguments about the primitive features found in humans but not in other apes clearly had a very important, if sometimes unacknowledged, influence on his contemporaries and on later views of primate phylogeny. However, his own phylogenetic reconstructions, because they were so closely tied to the living tarsier, were widely cited but equally widely dismissed as idiosyncratic (e.g., Hooton 1931).

In America, there is no doubt that Osborn's views of primate phylogeny carried much more clout, owing to his powerful position as the director of the AMNH and his reputation as one of the leading scientific authorities in America. Osborn's "Dawn-Man" theory was inspired by a reconnaissance expedition with Roy Chapman Andrews to Mongolia and was first presented to a group of Chinese scientist in Peking (Osborn 1923, 1924, 1926, 1927a, 1927b). Based on his vision in the wilderness of Mongolia, he argued that the lineage leading to man had been separate from that leading to apes since the Eocene and that, in contrast with apes who had evolved in jungles, humans had evolved in the high-altitude steppes of Asia (See Figure 2). In contrast to Wood Jones, Osborn rarely bothered with detailed anatomical arguments, relying more on dramatic contrasts between ape and human behavior as evidence for distant and distinct heritages (Osborn 1927a, 1929). He placed particularly strong emphasis on the irreversibility of evolution and maintained that specialized creatures, such as living apes, could never give rise to such a vastly different specialized group as humans.

Not surprisingly, Wood Jones and Osborn frequently cited each other in support of a nonanthropoid origin for humans, despite their widely differing views about which methods were appropriate for the interpretation of human phylogeny. In Wood Jones's view, only comparative anatomy could provide enough information to allow an accurate reconstruction of phylogenetic relationships among primates or any other animals. For Osborn, all of the answers lay in the fossil record.

In contrast to the extensive debate over the proper phylogeny of man and other higher primates, there was relatively little disagreement about the interpretation and affinities of the fossil primates known in 1930. Virtually everyone agreed that *Parapithecus* and *Propliopithecus* (less clearly, *Apidium*) from the Oligocene of Egypt were the earliest higher primates. *Parapithecus* was the more primitive of the two

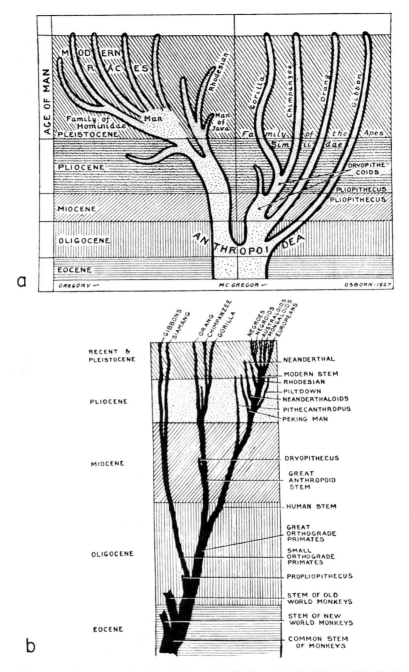

Figure 2 Phylogenetic trees put forth by Osborn (1927) (a) and Keith (1915, 1934) (b). From 1927 onward, Osborn argued for a very early separation of the lineages leading to man and the remaining hominoids. Keith's early position (ca. 1900) was quite similar to Gregory and Elliot Smith, but subsequently he reconsidered the evidence and figured a tree more similar to that of Osborn.

and appeared to be an early catarrhine with some primitive tarsioid affinities. *Propliopithecus* was regarded as a very primitive anthropoid ape, even more primitive than the modern gibbon but probably near the origin of the gibbon lineage. From the Miocene of Europe, *Pliopithecus* was viewed as an ancestral gibbon, and the various dryopithecines from Europe and Asia were seen as pongids variously related to extant great apes.

In 1930, the fossil record mainly provided dates for the evolutionary appearance of modern groups. For some scientists, it also provided corroboration of their branching sequences for primate phylogeny, with the *Propliopithecus–Pliopithecus–Hylobates* lineage appearing first, followed by the radiation of great apes in the Miocene, and finally, the appearance of humans in the Pleistocene or, possibly, the Pliocene. For Gregory, this temporal sequence confirmed his phylogeny. Those who disagreed with Gregory's phylogeny nevertheless accepted this chronological interpretation of the fossil record. They did argue vigorously, however, about which fossil primates had been the last common ancestor of humans and apes.

According to Wood Jones and Osborn, the human lineage probably diverged from that of the apes before or at about the time of *Propliopithecus*, with the intermediate forms between the Oligocene and Pleistocene currently unknown. As both Osborn and Wood Jones noted, such gaps are not unusual; for example, there was no record of tarsiers between their major radiation in the Eocene and their present-day distribution in Southeast Asia. The main reason for this general agreement about the fossils is that, with very few exceptions, most authors regarded the fossils (known almost entirely from jaws and teeth) as being virtually identical with their purported living descendants. Thus, *Pliopithecus* and *Propliopithecus* were, to most people, just like modern gibbons, and *Dryopithecus* was very much like a great ape.

In the 1920s, there was very little discussion of the methods used in reconstructing phylogenies. As noted previously, there were certainly preferences as to the type of data to be used—Osborn argued that only fossils could provide the answers, whereas Wood Jones and Gregory felt that comparative anatomy provided more complete information than did the fossil record. In general, however, most workers were quite eclectic, using whatever data were available. Keith frequently cited comparative information on blood groups, and Wilder (1926) published a phylogeny from Schmelgenhaufer based on dermatoglyphics of the sole. Both Gregory and Osborn occasionally cited behavioral observations from Yerkes's contemporary work (Yerkes and Yerkes 1929), whereas much of Schultz's information was based on embryological investigations.

In the late 1920s, what we now call *functional morphology* was an integral part of phylogeny. Argument for a close phyletic relationship between humans and great apes was synonymous with argument for the evolution of humans from a "large-bodied brachiator." As a result, arguments over phylogeny were arguments over the functional pathways that led to human structure. This integration of function and phylogeny is quite clear in the work of Keith, Gregory, and Morton. Thus

Morton's phylogeny is both a phylogeny of animals and a phylogeny of locomotor adaptations (see Figure 3).

Just as fossils were generally viewed as petrified versions of living forms, what scholars of today would call *evolutionary models* or *ancestral morphotypes* were usually limited in the 1920s to actual living primates. Again, this is clearly indicated in the work of Keith, who, in his early years, at least, felt that gibbons and African apes represented both functional and phyletic stages in our evolution. Morton, on the other hand, was less bound by living forms and actually constructed a hypothetical ancestor with a combination of features from numerous living apes.

The main theoretical issue surrounding phylogeny reconstruction was the irreversability of evolution. Osborn held that evolution is totally irreversible and, therefore, that apes with short thumbs, long arms, and big canines could never give rise to humans with long thumbs, long legs, and small canines. To him, it followed logically that the common ancestor had to be a much more generalized animal. Wood Jones used the same arguments, and apparently more moderate anthropoid supporters, such as Schultz and Morton, were also worried about the specializations found in the great apes. In spite of his close friendship with Osborn, Gregory fought against this irreversability argument time and time again, arguing that although the hypothesis was true as a general rule, it was certainly not a valid reason to discount apes from human ancestry. The argument that the numerous specializations of the great apes barred them from direct human ancestry was

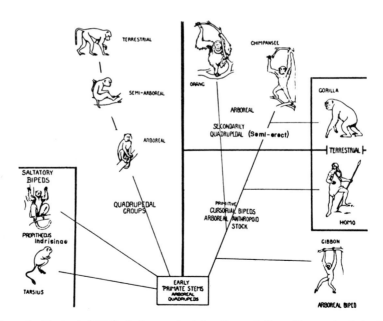

Figure 3   Morton's (1926) phylogeny depicting the evolution of locomotor behavior.

usually accompanied by the suggestion that many of the undeniable similarities between humans and great apes were due to parallelism (see Footnote 2). For the more moderate anthropoid avocates, ape human similarities could still be due to primitive retentions from a common stock, but for more radical phylogenies, such as that of Wood Jones, one had to invoke considerable parallelism. Thus, just as Gregory argued for extensive evolutionary reversal and flexibility, Wood Jones argued for the widespread nature of parallelism, with his major example being the parallel evolution of New and Old World monkeys. Most authors in the 1920s felt that New World monkeys were independently derived from a separate prosimian ancestor (largely, one suspects, because of the "primitive" nature of marmosets). In any case, the fossil record of the group was trivial, consisting of a single taxon, *Homunculus patagonius*, and there was virtually no discussion of the evolutionary history of the platyrrhines.

1930–1950: Moderation and Parallelism

The first decade of the AAPA began with the Gregory–Osborn debate in full force. They argued in public, in the newspapers, on the pages of countless journals, and, so the stories read, in the halls of the AMNH—all the while keeping up a warm and mutually respectful personal relationship. It was the paragon of gentle manly debate. Although the debate continued relentlessly until Osborn's death in 1935, it seems that by the early 1930s, Osborn's views were only given lip service because of his immense reputation. Gregory's views were those that appeared in the major textbooks (e.g., Hooton 1931). Likewise, Wood Jones rarely received more than a token mention after about 1930, and Gregory's 1934 rebuttal, *Man's Place Among the Anthropoids*, appears to have convinced most workers of the period that humans and anthropoid apes were indeed closely related.

Although the most direct and most vocal opposition to the Gregory view of primate phylogeny largely disappeared during the first half of the 1930s, the view of primate phylogeny that gained acceptance during the decade was not that of Gregory but the more moderate views of workers such as Schultz and Morton. By the early 1940s, Gregory's phylogeny, which showed a close relationship between man and the great apes based on a common heritage of brachiation, was definitely a minority position, supported primarily by Hans Weinert (1932) in Germany.

By 1940, few doubted that man was more closely related to the living great apes than to any other group of living primates (be they tarsiers, Old World monkeys, or whatever), but few believed, as Gregory did, that man was descended from an animal that could be called a great ape on morphological criteria. Many seemed to question whether it was either possible or correct to draw a phylogeny linking man with any particular group of apes, and most authorities explicitly stated that they felt man's divergence from the living apes occurred somewhere near the origin of the entire group (see Figure 4).

   The evidence against Elliot Smith's and Gregory's phylogeny, which explicitly linked humans with great apes, came not from paleontologists such as Osborn, but from comparative anatomists, for example, Schultz and Straus at Johns Hopkins and Le Gros Clark in England. Whereas Schultz (1930, 1936) continued to support a divergence of man from the other apes at about the grade of gibbons, Straus (1940, 1941, 1949) felt that man was more primitive than any extant ape and that both the lineage leading to humans and the lineage leading to living apes diverged at a pre-ape stage. Neither Schultz nor Straus was as insistent on reconstructing phylogeny as Gregory, nor were they as prolific, but their persistent demonstration of human primitiveness had a persuasive effect (see Figure 4 a and b).

   In contrast with Schultz and Straus, Le Gros Clark was very interested in reconstructing the history of primate evolution on the basis of both the anatomy of the living species and the fossil record. In *Early Forerunners of Man* (1934), he produced his major synthesis of primate evolution that, as Cartmill has noted (in Chapter 6), largely dominated ideas about primate phylogeny for more than 30 years. Working his way through the anatomy of primates, system by system, he demonstrated (as Huxley [1863] had observed 70 years before) that the living primates exhibit a progressive scale of being (*échelle des êtres*) from tree shrews, which were little more than a generalized mammal with primate inclinations, through lemurs, tarsiers, New World monkeys, Old World monkeys (maybe), apes, and finally, humans. The fossil record appeared to show that this structural scale largely conformed to the timing of the various groups' appearances.

   Although this scale more or less accounted for the major patterns he found in primate evolution, Le Gros Clark also saw that at each particular stage, there was a diverse radiation with marked specializations in individual genera. Like almost everyone, he, too, was worried about evolutionary reversals and realized that because of all the crosscutting specializations, it was impossible to line up primates in a perfectly linear evolutionary sequence. Ancestors with one set of specializations could not give rise to descendants with more primitive features without invoking evolutionary reversals. As a result, he argued that here must have been enormous amounts of parallel evolution both within and between different evolutionary radiations (Le Gros Clark 1935, 1936, 1939). In the face of such rampant parallelism, simple phylogeny reconstruction becomes impossible, which is why Le Gros Clark placed so much emphasis on grades rather than on branching relationships. It was this parallelism, rather than common descent, that Le Gros Clark invoked to account for the similarities between great apes and humans.[1]

   By 1940, Le Gros Clark's view that the extant great apes showed too many specializations to have shared a recent common ancestry with man had become the majority opinion. According to this view, man and great apes must have split early

---

[1]These two major findings, a step-by-step, orderly structural progression through time from tree shrews to humans, together with large amounts of parallelism within grades, convinced Le Gros Clark (1934) that primate evolution was much more direction-oriented than one would expect from the "randomness" of natural selection. He thus argued strongly that orthogenesis was a real phenomenon and that there must be some real direction inherent in the germ plasm of organisms.

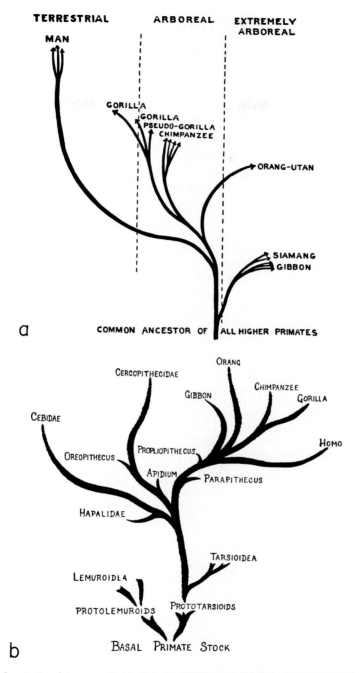

Figure 4 Phylogenetic schemes posited by Schultz (1930, as modified by Keith, 1934) (a) and Le Gros Clark (1934) (b). Apes were viewed as close relatives of humans, but a relatively early divergence of the two lineages was posited, and similarities between the two were regarded as the products of extensive parallel evolution.

from a common stem, before the development of brachiation. Any similarities between humans and apes were either due to some prebrachiation heritage or to parallelism (see Footnote 2 on page 206). Paleontologically, this placed the ape-human divergence at the base of or even before the dryopithecine radiation (depending upon how much "apeness" was allowed in human heritage). Le Gros Clark felt that the known fossil record gave "strong support to the thesis that the ancestors of the Hominidae are to be sought in some branch of the early Miocene Dryopithecinae [1940:207]." The known dryopithecines from the later parts of the Miocene were universally regarded as pongids, however, some being related to chimpanzees, some to gorillas, and others to orangutans. In terms of behavior, this meant to most that the last common ancestor of apes and humans was not a large-bodied brachiator, but a small-bodied, more generalized monkey-like form of "ground-ape."

Earnest A. Hooton, the great popularizer and synthesizer very clearly records this change in consensus between the first (1931) and second (1946) editions of his book, *Up From the Ape* (see Figure 5a and b). In 1931, Hooton's view of ape and human evolution was that of Keith, and particularly, of Gregory: Man is a made-over brachiator, evolved from the stem that gave rise to the chimpanzee and gorilla. Only in a footnote does he cite the opposing view:

> A small but vociferous minority of paleontologists and anatomists refuse to admit that man has developed from the *Dryopithecus* stock, or any other fossil anthropoid stock, but maintain that our ancestors were small terrestrial primates which took to the ground and developed along their own individual line before there were any anthropoid apes or even Old World monkeys. Notable among these dissenters are Frederic Wood-Jones and Henry Fairfield Osborn. The former, obsessed with man's tarsioid affinities, would remove Lemuroidea from the primates, exclude even the most generalized anthropoid ape ancestors from the line of human descent, and bring man straight down the ages from some tarsioid ancestor. For this writer the intimate resemblances which exist between man and the giant apes are of no significance except as examples of "convergent adaptation", a term which is little more than scientific jargon for "coincidence". To Wood-Jones the anthropoid apes show many pithecoid or catarrhine specializations which make him refuse to recognize them as relatives, although man occasionally, in individual cases, exhibits these same features. The narrow specializations of *Tarsius*, whom he regards as our nearest primate relative, divergent from human development as they are, disturb him no whit. He strains at the anthropoid gnat and swallows the tarsioid camel. Professor Osborn's opinion seems to be compounded from a desire to compromise with Christianity and an aristocratic aversion from the anthropoid apes. No one can assert that these two distinguished authorities are wrong: but I do not think they are right. If it comes to a matter of credulity and preference, I find it easier to believe and more palatable to swallow the theory that man has evolved from some large and brutal arboreal ape than from a pop-eyed, swivel-necked, rat-like tarsioid [1931:104–105].

By 1946, although Hooton still adhered to much the same view he had argued earlier, he also acknowledged that this was now a minority view. He added a new section, entitled "Were Man's Ancestors Arboreal Arm-Swingers or Pronograde Ground Apes," in which he listed the evidence for both views and then summarized:

> On the whole, the evidence pro and con seems to be often equivocal and generally inconclusive. In recent years, there has been a strong trend toward the small ground ape theory and away from the giant brachiator hypothesis. An imposing list of authorities inclines to the belief that the

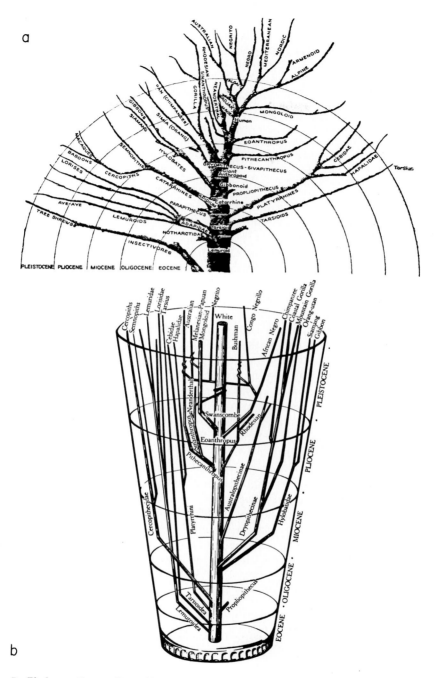

Figure 5 Phylogenetic trees figured by Hooton in 1931 (a) and 1946 (b). The changes in opinion about the human–ape relationship over this period are chronicled in the shifting positions of fossils and modified branching points. (Reprinted with permission of Macmillan Publishing Co., Inc., from *Up from the Ape* by Earnest A. Hooton: (a) First Edition, copyright © 1931 by Macmillan Publishing Co., Inc., renewed 1959 by Mary C. Hooton: and (b) Revised Edition, copyright © 1946 by Macmillan Publishing Co., Inc., renewed 1974 by Newton W. Hooton.)

human stock separated from the common anthropoid–humanoid trunk at about the same time that the gibbon family branched off or possibly only slightly later. Such a separation prior to the development of the giant primates would have to be referred to the Oligocene period, or, at latest, the lower Miocene, and would postulate a divergence beginning some 27 millions of years back. It necessitates the belief that the detailed resemblances of man to the great apes are largely to be referred to the evolutionary phenomenon called "convergence". Among the students who adhere to this view, or something close to it are: F. Wood Jones, Sir Arthur Keith, Adolph H. Schultz, W. L. Straus, Jr., Le Gros Clark. They constitute an eminent and influential majority. The principal adherent of the giant brachiator theory are W. K. Gregory and Hans Weinert. None of these students of human evolution except Wood-Jones has the slightest doubt of man's descent from an ape stock, and all except him recognize the closeness of human relationship with the great apes [1946:132–133].

Hooton's 1946 phylogeny (see Figure 5b) clearly reflects this shift in consensus. It is much more vague and shows relationships between subfamilies rather than between genera. Humans do not branch from the chimpanzee—gorilla trunk, but from the base of the dryopithecine trunk, almost immediately after the divergence of the gibbons. The radiation of living pongids takes place well after the initial appearance of this pongid lineage.

As early as 1915, Keith had begun to move away from the position that apes and humans had shared a relatively recent common ancestry, and, as Hooton noted, by 1940 Keith's view more closely resembled that of Osborn. Keith speculated that when gibbons were in their early stages of evolution (perhaps late Oligocene) and were still developing orthograde brachiating specializations, "two other modes of orthograde posture were also being evolved in the same stock [1940:285]." In one, the ancestral form of African apes, arms and legs were being used almost equally, whereas in the other, the "ancestral human orthograde stock," the lower limbs were becoming the dominant organs of support and locomotion. All three lines were regarded as "arboreal in habitat."

Although many were apparently satisfied with Le Gros Clark's (and Wood relationship, Gregory never wavered. Throughout the 1930s, as evidence accumulated that seemed to make the great apes too specialized to have been human ancestors, Gregory, together with Milo Hellman of the AMNH and G. Edward Lewis of Yale University, was documenting the dental anatomy of new collections of dryopithecine fossils from northern India (including what is now Pakistan). These fossils confirmed their views that this group of large fossil anthropoids gave rise to humans (Gregory *et al.* 1938). One genus in particular, *Ramapithecus,* was depicted as so human–like, Lewis argued, that it could be placed with either apes or humans (Lewis 1934).

Although many were apparently satisfied with Le Gros Clark's (and Wood Jones's) arguments that the similarities between humans and great apes were the result of parallel evolution and not a common heritage, Gregory would not accept this "explanation." He never actually wrote a rebuttal to the parallelism explanation for ape–human similarities, but the extensive marginalia in his personal copies of Le Gros Clark's papers provide eloquent and dramatic testimony to his disagreement. Like many comparative anatomists, Gregory was very uncomfortable with measurements, but he felt that the extensive qualitative similarities between chimpanzees and humans were unequivocal evidence for a common heritage involving "primitive brachiation" and that suggestions of extensive parallelism to account for these similarities were based on little more than vague analogies (Gregory 1938).

By the mid-1940s, debate over the phyletic relationship between humans and apes had died down, but apparently it was not really totally resolved in anyone's mind. In a passage that seems depressingly familiar, Le Gros Clark, in a paper entitled "The Scope and Limitations of Physical Anthropology," observed:

> The question now arises whether we are likely to gain any more certain knowledge regarding the genetic affinities of Man and the anthropoid apes by further comparative anatomical studies of existing forms. The answer to this is—probably not. There has already been accumulated a great store of information concerning the anatomy of the higher Primates, and on the basis of this material it is possible to draw certain inferences in respect of the probable genetic affinities of one group with another. No doubt there is a great amount of data of this kind still to be recorded by patient investigation, but it now seems unlikely that such studies by themselves will clarify further the phylogenetic problem, simply because of the inherent difficulty or impossibility of distinguishing between anatomical resemblances due to a true relationship and those resulting from parallelism. Comparative physiological studies are complicated by the same issue. For example, it has been found that the blood-serum and the red corpuscles of the anthropoid apes contain group isoagglutinins and group iso-agglutinogens which are identical with those of human blood, yet, according to Zuckerman, there is suggestive evidence that Man and the apes evolved their several blood groups independently. From this kind of evidence, therefore, we reach conclusions similar to those based on morphological data; namely, that these higher primates possess certain features in common which indicate a community of origin at some phase in their evolution, but many of the resemblances shown by different genera may be the result of evolutionary parallelism. This is perhaps as far as it is possible to get on the evidence of the comparative anatomy and comparative physiology of existing Primates. For further progress in the study of phylogenetic problems, we must in the future rely on the evidence which accumulates from the study of the fossil record [Le Gros Clark 1939:5].

It should also be noted that by the mid-1940s, there were other more pressing priorities, like World War II and the Australopithecines, which, thanks to Raymond Dart and Robert Broom, were becoming increasingly well known. To Le Gros Clark, at least, this was the type of fossil evidence that would hopefully resolve the now perennial questions in primate phylogeny.

1950–1960: Fossils and the Evolutionary Synthesis

The picture of primate phylogeny provided by comparative anatomy changed very little during the 1950s. Straus's classic paper, "The Riddle of Man's Ancestry," (1949) presented a comprehensive and detailed argument for a prehominoid divergence of humans. As late as 1962, Straus still saw no reason to change his opinion, and even today, his statement remains the definitive version of that position. Schultz's 1951 perspective on primate phylogeny was essentially identical to the one he provided in 1930, and he offered no substantive modifications in later years. In 1951, Sherwood L. Washburn, then working at the University of Chicago, took up the brachiationist torch directly from his former colleague Gregory (1949, 1951), and argued that position with an eloquence and assuredness that had been sorely lacking in the previous decade.

The major changes in the study of primate phylogeny in the 1950s were largely the result of an almost unimagined wealth of new fossils, including the long-awaited information about the locomotor skeleton of fossil apes. In a review of that decade, Simons observed that "the years since 1950 stand as the most productive of new finds and reports of any decade since the first fossil primate, *Adapis*, was described by Cuvier in 1821 [1960a:179]." With these new fossils in hand, a very different approach to primate phylogeny emerged, as did a variety of claims for a new synthesis between comparative anatomy and paleontology that purported to resolve the differences of opinion from the previous decade.

The first of the new fossils and the first attempts at synthesis appeared very early in the decade when Le Gros Clark and Leakey (1950, 1951) described the extensive new material of fossil apes (*Proconsul, Limnopithecus*) from the early Miocene of Kenya that had been collected on the British East Africa expeditions (Le Gros Clark 1947). These fossils, like *Dryopithecus* and *Pliopithecus* from Europe, were almost universally accepted as early pongids and hylobatids, respectively. Yet these new finds, first of *Limnopithecus* (Le Gros Clark and Thomas 1951), then *Pliopithecus* (Zapfe 1952, 1958, 1960) and *Proconsul* (Napier and Davis 1959), showed that their cranial and skeletal anatomy was in many ways not precisely like that of living great apes or gibbons.

Le Gros Clark confidently asserted that the Kenya finds were unequivocal proof that the primitive apes of the Miocene "had not yet developed the peculiar proportions of modern apes" but rather "possessed limbs of more generalized proportions, such as those possessed by tailed monkeys of today [1950:38]." The implications of these findings for human evolution were very clear to Le Gros Clark. Given a branching of the human lineage from the other hominoids in the Miocene, "the contrast in limb proportions between man and the modern apes can no longer form a serious argument against the inference that they have been derived from a common ancestry [1950:38]."

In Le Gros Clark's view and throughout the decade (e.g., Howells 1951; Heberer 1956; Napier and Davis 1959), the finding that early pongids lacked the specializations of their living descendants enabled one to support a derivation of hominids from the great apes without having to support their evolution from actual brachiators. Superficially, this would appear to resolve many of the conflicts of the past decade (Howells 1951), but as Le Gros Clark (1950, 1955) clearly realized, this "synthesis" required a rather different view of an ape than the one debated by earlier anatomists:

> It may be argued that anthropoid apes are, by definition, creatures with long arms adapted for brachiation and, therefore, that the Miocene apes were not really apes at all. But this would only be a verbal quibble, which ignores the well-recognised principle that zoological classifications must

take into account the dynamic element of evolutionary development. The category of "anthropoid ape" should be taken to indicate, not only the evolutionary end-products of this group which exist today, but also all those intermediate types which have come into existence since the progenitors of the group first became segregated in their evolutionary history from other groups. This principle of zoological classification and definition may be illustrated by reference to the well-established history of the horse family. So far as existing animals are concerned, a horse might be defined as a large animal with only one toe on each foot. But, as the fossil record has become more and more complete, the definition of "horse" has necessarily become greatly extended, and now even includes the little *Eohippus* (with several toes on each foot) which about sixty million years ago represented the ancestral stock of all modern horses. *Eohippus* must have looked very different indeed from the horse of today, but is commonly termed a "primitive horse" and is actually included by zoologists in the same family—the Equidae. The question of the definition of "anthropoid ape" is a close parallel; the primitive anthropoid apes of the Miocene age are still to be regarded as anthropoid apes, even though they had not at that time developed the specializations shown by the end-products of simian evolution which exist today [1950:39].

To Straus (1954, 1962), these finds corroborated his earlier argument that humans evolved from a generalized catarrhine. The skeletal evidence, he argued, showed that the Miocene apes were apes in teeth only. Evolution of the human lineage from a Miocene ape was evolution of humans from the primitive pre-brachiator that he had long been supporting. Straus felt less constrained by the laws of dental taxonomy than most. He did not believe that it mattered "whether we regard *Proconsul* as a generalized anthropoid ape or as a somewhat advanced monkey [1954:89]." Animals with the limb proportions of Miocene forms could, in Straus's mind, give rise to long-armed brachiators, on the one hand, and the "immediate forerunners of the Hominidae," on the other. To Straus, this also implied that man's lineage never passed through a brachiating phase.

Although Le Gros Clark and Straus believed that the new fossils were supportive of a very distant (morphological) split between humans and apes, Patterson (1954) argued that there were other possible interpretations. He suggested that the "primitive" morphology of the early dryopithecines was not incompatable with a brachiating heritage in the ancestors of humans if the divergence between hominids and pongids occurred much later:

The generalized locomotor apparatus of later Tertiary hominoids has been hailed as showing that man's ancestry did not pass through a brachiating state, hailed almost with relief, as though brachiating were some deadly sin. I submit that this is going too far and that there is no real evidence for it.. The objections to such a stage perhaps stem in part from old views and may also be in part semantic—the word brachiation being associated with the extreme conditions in living pongids. There would seem to be nothing in the known structure of the earlier pongids to indicate that they did not brachiate to some extent, and, as Gregory has long insisted, a moderate amount of brachiation seems to be the best explanation of how the hominid line got up on its hind legs. Our ancestors, however, unlike those of the living pongids, were able to take their brachiation or leave it alone. The extreme degree of this adaptation shown by hylobatines and pongines today may be as recent an event in primate history as acquisition of the upright gait.
Some recent authors who favor an origin of the human stock from the pongid, branch us off in the Early Miocene, if not earlier, again perhaps in an effort to avoid the demon brachiation. In [my view] this event is postulated to have occurred considerably later [1954:152]; reprinted from the Geologic History of Non-Hominid Primates in the Old World. *Human Biology* **26**(3) by Bryan Patterson by permission of Wayne State University Press.

Thus Patterson recognized that the new fossils of Miocene apes did not really resolve the argument of earlier decades, as Le Gros Clark (1950) and Howells (1951) had hoped. Their real effect was to provide concrete evidence about the limb morphology of early Miocene apes and to "recalibrate" the old arguments about phylogeny. Since the fossils from the early Miocene of East Africa were clearly not like living apes in their limb morphology, those who supported a close relationship between humans and living apes through a brachiating ancestry (e.g., Gregory 1949; Washburn 1951, 1960; Patterson 1954; Remane 1952, 1956) were forced to argue for a much more recent divergence of apes and humans than they had suggested earlier. Those who felt that there was little anatomical evidence for a close evolutionary relationship between humans and living great apes, and had previously argued for a predryopithecine divergence, now found the skeletal morphology of the Miocene apes suitably primitive to be ancestral to both humans and living apes. This recalibrated debate was clearly diagramed by Heberer (1959 c/1962) (Figure 6).

As Simons (1960a) emphasized, the new fossil apes (*Limnopithecus, Dryopithecus, Pliopithecus*) were not the only important higher primate fossils described during the 1950s. This decade also provided, from the Miocene of Colombia, the most complete fossils of New World monkeys ever found (Stirton and Savage 1951). However, in contrast with the Miocene catarrhines from Kenya, these fossil platyrrhines were very much like living forms and led to no extensive discussion about higher primate phylogeny. Patterson (1954), like Gregory and Wood Jones before him, argued that platyrrhines and catarrhines quite likely were derived independently from different prosimian ancestors, whereas Le Gros Clark (1959) still maintained that the many anatomical similarities between New and Old World higher primates suggested a monophyletic origin for Anthropoidea.

This decade also saw the most extensive debate over the phylogenetic position of another fossil anthropoid—*Oreopithecus*. Since its discovery and description in 1872 by Gervais, this form was regarded by most authorities as an abherent cercopithecoid (e.g., Schlosser 1887). In 1949, Hürzeler reexamined the material and decided that *Oreopithecus* was a hominoid, a position taken earlier by Schwalbe (1915). Later Hürzeler (1958, 1960) relabeled the specimen a primitive hominid, an opinion accepted by numerous (mostly European) authors (Heberer 1956; Kalin 1955; Piveteau 1957; Schultz as cited in Heberer 1959/1962:230). Others remained loyal to the early assessment that it was a cercopithecoid (von Koenigswald 1955; Remane 1956; Robinson 1956). By the end of the decade, its phyletic and systematic positions were very unsettled.

The 1950s also saw the incorporation of the Neo-Darwinian "evolutionary synthesis" into the study of primate phylogeny, as emphasized by the Cold Spring Harbor Symposium (e.g., Howells 1951). Le Gros Clark appears to have been particularly influenced. Although his picture of primate phylogeny in the 1950s actually changed very little from those he had presented in the middle and late 1930s, the proposed mechanism did change. He no longer considered the

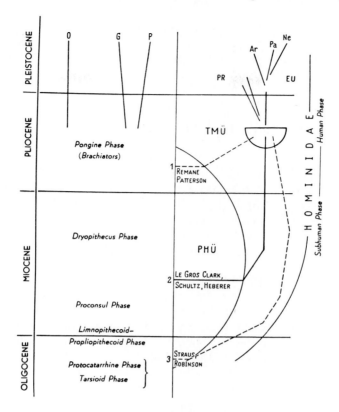

Figure 6 Heberer's (1959/1962) tree illustrates the different views concerning human origins in the late 1950s. The brachiationists now support a Pliocene divergence, whereas the prebrachiationists derive hominids from an animal like *Proconsul*.

progressive grade changes and extensive parallelisms in primate evolution evidence for orthogenesis. Instead, he saw the apparent pattern as the result of a retrospective, human-biased viewpoint. (Le Gros Clark 1959). Likewise, his new emphasis on defining a group on the basis of the initial appearance of a few diagnostic characters suggests a strong paleobiological influence because it was frequently supported by reference to horse evolution—Simpson's classic example (e.g., Simpson 1949, 1951).

It is this new role of fossils that characterized approaches to primate phylogeny during the 1950s. Although changes in thinking began with the recovery of new, more complete fossils, the associated methodological changes had more far-reaching effects. For the first time, primate fossils had to be dealt with not as old evidences of living forms, but as evidence of different types of primates. Fitting these new fossils into the phylogenies based on comparative anatomy of the living forms led, on the one hand, to debate over the timing of the phyletic divergence of apes and humans and, on the other hand, to debate over the anatomical criteria used to identify phyletic groups in the fossil record.[2]

1960–1970 Fossil Phylogenies

These two issues—timing of the ape–human divergence and the identification of early monkeys, apes, and humans in the fossil record—carried over as major themes for the 1960s. Most of the earlier debate about phylogeny based on the comparative anatomy of living primates receded into the background. It appears that the fossils of the 1950s convinced most people that primate phylogeny was really a historical study that could not be resolved by the study of living species (cf. Simpson 1963, 1966).

Le Gros Clark's (1959, 1962) argument for an early, prebrachiation separation of ape and human lineages was the generally accepted view found in textbooks (e.g., Howells 1959, 1967; Campbell 1966; Buettner-Janusch 1966) (see Figure 7a and b), and for much of the decade, there was a definite emphasis on identifying the earliest fossil representatives of modern lineages. In America, the major contributor to our understanding of the primate fossil record was Elwyn Simons of Yale, who, in the course of the decade, discovered, rediscovered, described, and classified scores of fossil primates. Neither Simons's views on higher primate phylogeny nor his approach to interpreting the affinities of fossil primates were radically different from those articulated by his mentor, Le Gros Clark, in the previously decade. Where Simons, Louis Leakey, and later David Pilbeam differed from earlier students of primate phylogeny was in their repeated attempts to link specific fossil taxa with living lineages.

Phylogenies of the 1950s tended to be vague, were frequency composed of numerous parallel lines, and usually located fossils on the side branches (a tendency noted by Patterson 1954), evidently reflecting both the old fear of evolutionary reversals and the newly recognized problem of fossil primates that were often not at all like living taxa. The primate paleontologists of the 1960s were much less reserved. By contrast, they confidently placed fossil species at the base of

---

[2]One evolutionary issue that was occasionally mentioned but never actively discussed was the much touted "parallelism" between apes and humans that had once been used to account for the similarities between them. Howells (1951) noted that parallelism was the development of similar morphologies in different, related lineages through similar selective pressures. As such, it could be used to describe ape and human similarities only if one were postulating independent brachiating ancestry for the two lineages. If human similarities to apes were the result of different selection pressures, this was convergence. Inexplicably, no one except Washburn (1963) ever made much of this inconsistency in Le Gros Clark's and others' continued argument for extensive parallelism in primate evolution; nor did anyone offer an argument for convergence.

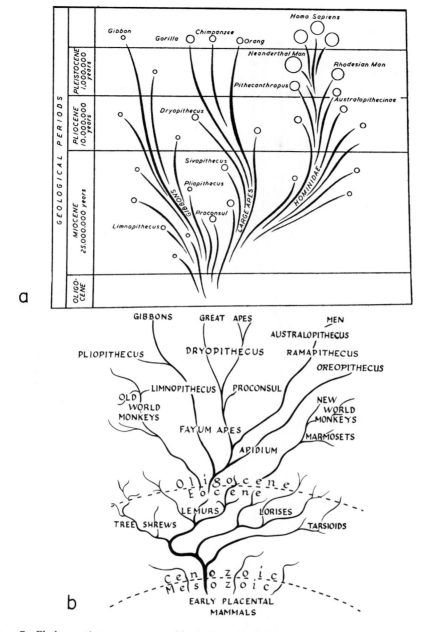

Figure 7 Phylogenetic trees constructed by Le Gros Clark (1959) (a) and Howells (1967) (b). An early divergence between pongid and hominid lineages was clearly the majority opinion. Le Gros Clark saw primate phylogeny as a series of grades with many parallel lines. Fossils generally appear as collateral lines. Howells's tree reflects the influence of fossil phylogeny in the mid-1960s. Fossil groups occupy central ancestral positions. (Figure 7a is reprinted here with permission of Edinburgh University Press; Figure 7b is a diagram from an original drawing by Janis Cirulis in William Howells, *Mankind in the Making*, Doubleday 1959, 1967).

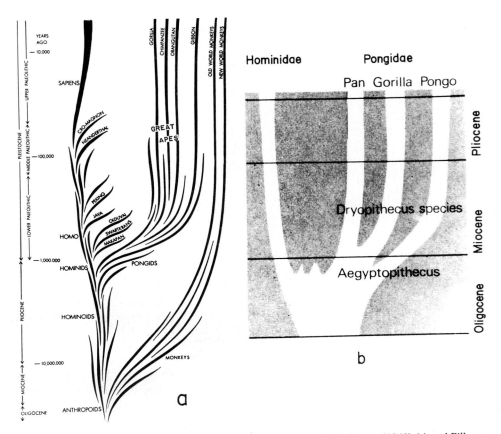

Figure 8   Two of the most divergent phylogenies of the 1960s. Both Washburn (1960) (a) and Pilbeam (1970) (b) view hominids as an integral part of the radiation of pongids, but they differ drastically in the timing of this radiation. (Figure 8a from "Tools and Human Evolution" by Sherwood L. Washburn, copyright © 1960 by Scientific American, Inc., all rights reserved; Figure 8b

modern radiations, and phylogenetic diagrams included lines both between fossils and between fossils and living forms (compare Figure 7a with Figures 7b, 8b, and Figure 9a. Thus, *Ramapithecus* (Pilbeam 1967, 1968, 1970; Simons, 1961, 1964, 1968, 1969a; also see Figure 9b), *Kenyapithecus* (Leakey 1967), or *Propliopithecus* (Pilbeam 1967, 1970) was the earliest hominid. *Aeolopithecus* (Simons 1965) became the earliest gibbon in a lineage that extended through, not around, *Limnopithecus* and *Pliopithecus*. The living African apes were extended back to separate species of *Proconsul* (Pilbeam 1969; Simons 1967a). *Oreopithecus* lost its hominid status, becoming instead a separate branch of hominoids (Straus 1963), possibly linked with *Apidium* (Simons 1960b, 1967a). The origin of Old World monkeys was to be found in the parapithecids of Egypt (Simons 1967b, 1969b), and the divergence of colobines and cercopithecines was nailed down on the basis of two specimens from the early Miocene of Uganda (Pilbeam and Walker 1968). Neither the timing of these phylogenetic divergences nor the allocations of previously known fossils were actually very different in most cases from those proposed earlier (see, for example, Gregory 1922, or Le Gros Clark 1950). What was distinctive about the phylogenies of the 1960s was the integral way in which the fossils were incorporated—not as indicators of a grade of evolution or as possible structural models but as actual animals to be fitted into an evolutionary scheme on an equal basis with living species. These were true *fossil phylogenies*.

Indeed, one gets the very strong impression that during this period primate paleontologists—such as Simons, Leakey, Pilbeam, and others—were not really involved with the issues that had occupied primate phylogeny during the first half of the century. Questions about the exact phyletic relationship between humans and living ape genera or the extent to which the hominid lineage had passed through a brachiating stage were not being posed. Rather, these researchers' primary task was to place the newly found fossils in their proper phyletic and systematic positions.

In direct contrast with the paleontologists who posited an early appearance of the human lineage from a dryopithecine stock, Washburn argued persistently throughout the decade for a very late separation of the hominid line from the one leading to living apes—placing this divergence somewhere in the late Pliocene (see Figure 8a on page 208). While Simons, Leakey, and Pilbeam repeatedly emphasized the hominid or pongid-like features in particular species of the Miocene (or even Oligocene) apes as evidence for an ancient divergence (see Figures 8b, and 9a), Washburn (1960, 1963, 1968) emphasized instead the numerous musculoskeletal features shared by living apes and humans (but apparently not by dryopithecines) and the ape-like features in *Australopithecus*. To Washburn, this was evidence for a very late separation of the hominid line, and the critical evidence resided in locomotor behavior and in the limb skeleton. Thus, in contrast with virtually all English-speaking primatologists since the beginning of the century, he saw the gibbons as an integral part of a late hominoid radiation, rather than as an early branch (see Figure 8a on page 208). For most of a decade dominated by fossil phylogenies, Washburn was almost the sole supporter of a late divergence of hominids and apes and the sole heir to the "brachiationist" arguments of Gregory and early Keith. In 1968, he carried this argument to its most extreme position to date by arguing that not only were humans more closely related to chimpanzees than to any other living primates, but that the last common ancestor of humans and apes was like the living African apes, a knuckle-walker. Man was very much a made-over ape. By the late 1960s the reservations of the 1930s and 1940s about phylogenetic speculations and the reversibility of evolution had weakened—and had vanished entirely in Washburn's evolutionary scheme.

Major support for Washburn's rather daring arguments for a close relationship between humans and apes, in the face of a paleontological front that pressed insistently for an older and older separation, came from the emergence of molecular biology as a major and very vocal force in the study of primate

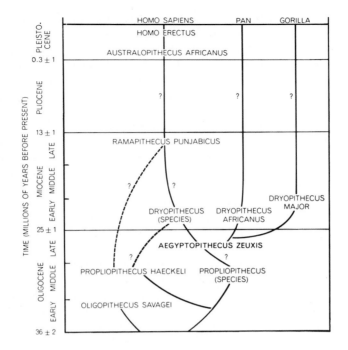

a

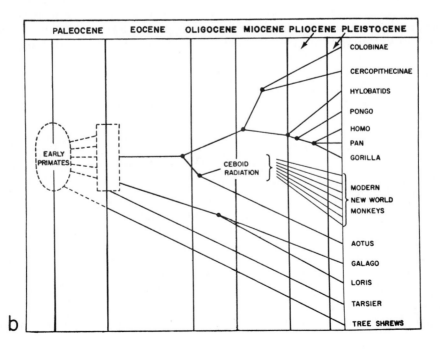

b

phylogeny (see Goodman and Cronin, in Chapter 5). Goodman (e.g., 1963) was in the vanguard in employing serum proteins to study primate phylogeny, and like workers from earlier in the century, he found that blood proteins suggested that man was more closely related to chimpanzees and gorillas than to any other primate; orangutans were next, followed by gibbons and then Old World monkeys. Although these findings supported the old arguments of Elliot Smith and Gregory for a close relationship between humans and African apes, Goodman saw no discrepancy between his results and the early separations of humans from apes suggested by the fossil record. To Goodman, the close molecular similarity between humans and apes was evidence that molecular evolution has slowed down in the hominoid lineage as a result of changes in the fetal membranes.

Sarich and Wilson (1966, 1967) reconstructed a very similar phylogeny of living primates based on immunodiffusion of serum albumins but offered a substantially different interpretation of its significance for understanding the timing of events in primate evolution. Assuming that protein evolution had taken place at an essentially constant rate in all primates and using a single calibration point, they developed a "molecular clock" to time the divergences between groups of living primates.

Like their Berkeley colleague, Washburn, they argued for a very recent split between humans and living apes (Sarich and Wilson 1967, 1968; Sarich 1968). Their data suggested divergence dates throughout primates evolution that were consistently later than those suggested by paleontologists (see Figure 9b). If the molecular clock was right, virtually all fossil phylogenies were wrong. The decade that opened basking in the wealth of new fossil discoveries (Simons 1960a) ended in a hard, and often bitter, debate over where they actually fit in primate phylogeny (Simons 1969b).

1970–1980: Diversity and Debate

Interest and activity in the study of primate phylogeny was greater in the 1970s than at any time since the 1920s and early 1930s. There was active, ongoing study of the phylogeny of virtually every group in living and fossil primates and an equally great diversity of opinion about the proper ways to study phylogeny and the timing of primate evolutionary events. In contrast with the 1960s, firm opinions

Figure 9 Phylogenetic relationships according to Simons (1967) (a) and Sarich (1968) (b). Simons was the champion of "fossil phylogenies" that placed fossils directly into evolving lineages, linking fossils with other fossils and with extant groups. Fossil phylogenies were challenged directly by biochemical data and the "molecular clock" of Sarich and co-workers. Almost all branching points were placed later in time by the molecular phylogeneticists than by the primate paleontologists. (Figure 9a from "The Earliest Apes" by Elwyn L. Simons, copyright © 1967 by Scientific American, Inc., all rights reserved; Figure 9b from *Perspectives on Human Evolution* by S. L. Washburn and P. C. Jay (editors). Copyright © 1968 by Holt, Rinehart and Winston, all rights reserved.

about the fossil record were increasingly rare in this decade. Many authors offered multiple phylogenies based on the same data, and some even questioned the possibility of reconstructing primate phylogeny at all!

Amidst, and perhaps despite, the diversity of opinion generated in the 1970s by the fossil record, an almost unanimous agreement has been achieved, largely as a result of the molecular studies, with regard to the overall phylogenetic relationships among major groups of living primates, and those among the extant hominoids in particular. The phylogeny of living hominoids, which was supported by Huxley, early Keith, Elliot Smith, and Gregory and which shows a close relationship between humans and the African apes, has again become the majority position (e.g., see Figure 10a). Alternative schemes still exist, however. For example, Tuttle (1975) clearly supports an alternate phylogeny, arguing for a separation of the human lineage from a great ape stock before the divergence of African apes and the orangutan (see Figure 10b). Rather than being concerned with the phylogeny of living taxa, most of the discussion about catarrhine phylogeny in the past 10 years has been about the timing of evolutionary events, the position of fossils within this generally accepted phylogeny, and the actual behavior of the fossil species themselves.

The debate over the validity of the molecular clock for calibrating events in primate phylogeny continued throughout the decade. In addition to its inconsistency with paleontological interpretations (e.g., Uzzell and Pilbeam 1971; Simons 1972, 1976a; Walker 1976), numerous theoretical and methodological objections were raised against the validity of the clock (Read and Lestrel 1970; Lovejoy et al. 1972: Lovejoy and Meindl 1973; and Radinsky, 1978; Baba et al. 1980), including, most damningly, the observation that different molecules keep different time (Corruccini *et al.* 1980). Nevertheless, numerous workers have strongly supported the validity of the molecular clock, and either implicitly (e.g., Corruccini and McHenry 1980) or explicitly (e.g., Greenfield 1980) have attempted to coordinate their interpretations of the primate fossil record with the divergence dates proposed by the clock. Even among paleontologists who have argued strongly against the clock, there has been a general tendency to support later divergence times throughout the past decade, making the interpretations more in concordance with those suggested by the clock (cf. Pilbeam 1970, 1972; Pilbeam et al. 1977; Jacobs and Pilbeam 1980).

Much of the debate about higher primate phylogeny during the past decade has been based on reinterpretations of the morphology of Oligocene and Miocene hominoids and the relationship of these animals to living taxa. Simons (1972) and others (Simons and Pilbeam 1972; Pilbeam 1970, 1972; Simons and Fleagle 1973; Andrews and Simons 1977; Simons 1976b) continued to argue, following the model of Le Gros Clark, that the dryopithecines (including *Dendropithecus* and *Pliopithecus*) gave rise to distinct lineages leading to modern gibbons, great apes, and hominids because of mainly dental similarities to later forms. Others, following Washburn, argued that because the Miocene apes were "monkey-like" in their skeleton, the radiation of modern hominoids came much later. In a long series of

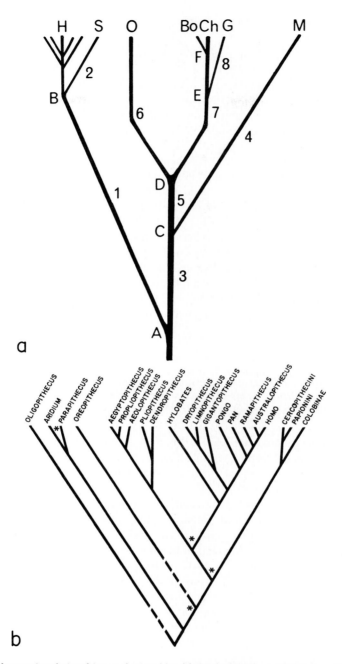

Figure 10 Phylogenetic relationships as depicted by (a) Tuttle (1975) and (b) Delson (1977). Tuttle's branching sequence represents a minority view, with the human lineage (4) branching off before the diversification of great apes (D). Delson's cladistic version of catarrhine relationships includes the current consensus that African apes and humans share a common ancestor subsequent to the bifurcation of orangutans.

papers (including Corruccini *et al.* 1976; Morbeck 1975; O'Connor 1976), it was repeatedly found that on the basis of multivariate and morphological analyses of the limb skeleton, all Miocene apes were rather monkey-like. Accordingly, it was argued that the radiation of living hominoids occurred after the dryopithecines rather than within the radiation, a view that has been endorsed increasingly by paleontologists (e.g., Pilbeam et al. 1977; Pilbeam 1979; Szalay and Delson 1979).

Likewise, although Simons (e.g., 1972, 1976b, 1977; Simons and Pilbeam 1978) and others (Pilbeam *et al.* 1977; Pilbeam 1979; Andrews 1971; Walker and Andrews 1973; Szalay and Delson 1979) have continued to support the hominid status of *Ramapithecus*, others have questioned the hominid-like nature of *Ramapithecus* and/or the distinctiveness of that taxon (Eckhardt 1972; Frayer 1976; Pilbeam *et al.* 1977; Greenfield 1974, 1977, 1979, 1980; Wolpoff 1980). So unsettled are the views of many primate paleontologists about Miocene apes that their opinions change considerably, from paper to paper or even within the same paper. It is not unusual to find several alternate phylogenies offered in the same study as well as phylogenetic diagrams that differ considerably from the position stated in the text (see Pilbeam 1978; Pilbeam *et al.* 1977; Delson and Andrews 1975; Szalay and Delson 1979). For example, regarding the affinities of *Ramapithecus*, Pilbeam observes:

> The taxonomy of this group is in a rather confused state, which newer material from Pakistan will hopefully help clarify. Isolated teeth of *Ramapithecus* and *Sivapithecus* are very difficult to distinguish except on the basis of size; *Ramapithecus* teeth are smaller. It is possible that one very dimorphic species is being sampled, but that seems unlikely for a number of reasons, including differences in enamel histology (which are of uncertain value). [1979:346].

Although Miocene apes have been the most extensively analyzed and discussed primate fossil during the past decade (see Figure 11a and b), most other groups have also been the subject of new investigations. Simons (1970), Simons and Delson (1978), and Delson (1975, 1977) have discussed the fossil record of cercopithecoid monkeys and debated the cercopithecoid affinity of parapithecids. Delson (1979) and Szalay and Delson (1979) have also renewed the issue of *Oreopithecus* by returning that genus to the Old World monkeys. New material of Oligocene higher primates from Egypt has increased our knowledge of the skeletal and dental morphology of these early anthropoids, and, like the new material of Miocene apes that appeared 20 years earlier, has shown them to be extremely primitive (Conroy 1976; Fleagle *et al.* 1980; Kay *et al.* 1981). Likewise, the new material has abolished any remaining arguments for distinct lineages to either gibbons or hominids from the Oligocene taxa.

After being ignored for many years, the phylogeny of New World monkeys has recently become a topic of extraordinary interest and debate from the perspective of both comparative anatomy and paleontology. There is active discussion over both the geographic and the phyletic origin of the entire radiation (see Hoffstetter 1972, 1974; Ciochon and Chiarelli 1980 and references therein). Rosenberger (1980) and Szalay and Delson (1979) have offered dramatically and inevitably

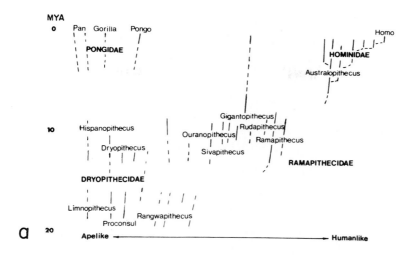

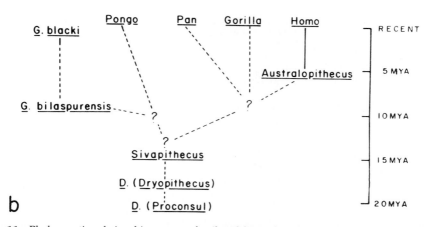

Figure 11 Phylogenetic relationships among fossil and living hominoids as envisioned by Pilbeam (1979) (a) and Greenfield (1980) (b). Pilbeam's assessment here is much more cautious than his views in the 1960s and earlier 1970s (compare with Figure 8b); very few taxa are connected directly to other fossil taxa or to living species. Greenfield's late divergence hypothesis accords well with both cladistic and molecular phylogenies, but question marks remain. (Figure 11a is reproduced with permission from the *Annual Review of Anthropology* Volume 8, copyright © 1979 by Annual Reviews Inc., figure 11b is reproduced with permission of Alan R. Liss, Inc.)

controversial new phylogenies of the genera within platyrrhines, whereas Hershkovitz (1977) and Ford (1980) have debated the evolutionary position of marmosets and tarmarins with respect to the other taxa. The issue of monophyly or polyphyly of higher primates also continues to generate opposing points of view (Ciochon and Chiarelli 1980).

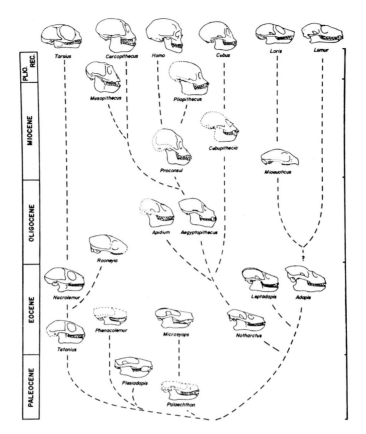

Figure 12   This tree by Gingerich and Schoeninger (1977) reflects the authors' methodological position that primate phylogeny should be reconstructed by phenetic linking of animals in a stratigraphic order. Compare with Figure 10, which has no time dimension.

Although most of the debate over primate phylogeny during the past decade has been broadly comparative in that it involved comparisons of fossil specimens with a wide range of extant taxa, there were also important studies based more heavily on the soft anatomy of living species. For example, Luckett (1974, 1975, 1976) has reanalyzed most issues of primate phylogeny using evidence from the fetal membranes, whereas Lewis (2972a, 1972b) has reanalyzed the joint morphology of the wrist, and more recently, the ankle of living primates (Lewis 1980a, 1980b, 1980c) in an attempt to interpret both the function and the phylogenetic affinities of various fossil taxa (but see Tuttle 1974; Jenkins and Fleagle 1975; Morbeck 1977).

Drawing on his own studies of hand and foot musculature, as well as the results of numerous other workers, Tuttle (1972, 1974, Tuttle and Basmajian 1974; Tuttle *et al.* 1979) has summarized the current evidence from comparative anatomy regarding the relationship of hominids to extant apes, and especially the morphology and locomotor habits of the last common ancestor of apes and humans. Tuttle argues for an origin of hominids from a small, gibbon-like ancestor, much like Morton's hylobatian ancestor, whereas others have argued for an ancestor that was a more like a great ape. Tuttle lables Washburn's model "troglodytian" because of its emphasis on the similarity between humans and chimpanzees and Stern's (1976), "orangutanian" because of the posited similarities between humans and orangutans. More recently, several authors have supported the origin of hominids from an animal like the pygmy chimpanzee, *Pan paniscus* (Zihlman *et al.* 1978; Zihlman 1979). This issue is nowhere near resolution at present (cf. Johnson 1981 and comments).

As in the early part of this century, many of the "evolutionary models" of the 1970s are usually also phylogenies. Thus, in their "chimpanzee" models of human evolution, both Washburn and Zihlman suggest the evolution of hominids from an ancestor that is literally a chimpanzee. Similarly, Tuttle's hylobatian model is quite explicitly linked to a phylogeny that separates humans from a pre-pongid stock (see Figure 10a). Only Stern (1976) offers a functional model of human evolution without a definite phylogeny.

The surge of interest in the details of primate evolution and phylogeny during the past 10 years has also been associated with increased debate over the proper method of phylogeny reconstruction. As in previous decades, opinions range from those who feel that only molecular data based on living taxa can be used confidently in phylogeny reconstruction to others (e.g., Gingerich 1976, 1977; Gingerich and Schoeninger 1976) who argue that true phylogenetic relationships can only be reconstructed from the information in the fossil record. The vast majority of scientists are, as usual, more catholic in their use of available data (e.g., Delson and Andrews 1975; Szalay 1977; Szalay and Delson 1979; Cronin and Meikle 1979, Greenfield 1980).

Even more extensive than the debate over the proper data to be used in understanding primate phylogeny has been that over the proper analytical approach. Some have argued for a strict adherence to the principles of phylogenetic systematics developed by Hennig (1966) (cf. Luckett 1975; Eldredge and Tattersall 1975; Tattersall and Eldredge 1977; Delson *et al.* 1977; Schwartz *et al.* 1978) with no consideration of chronological position (see Figure 10b). In direct contrast, Gingerich and Schoeninger (1976; Gingerich 1977) have argued that phylogeny should be reconstructed by phenetic linking of stratigraphically arranged fossil taxa (see Figure 12). Again, the methods used by most scientists have been more eclectic than either of the extreme positions. Throughout the decade, scientists have become more conscious of the distinctions between primitive and derived features in the construction of phylogenies (perhaps the most important contribution made by phylogenetic systematics), but biochronology continues to play an important role in the evaluation of phylogeny (see, for example, Kay 1977; Szalay and Delson 1979).

The 1970s began with the debate between the fossil phylogenies proposed by the paleontologists of the 1960s and the biochemical phylogenies proposed by advocates of the molecular clock. The debate continues, but there has been little discussion about the phylogeny of living higher primates; in this regard, the molecular phylogeny has been widely accepted. In stark contrast, there has been no consensus (or even much of a consistent viewpoint) about the phylogenetic position of many fossil groups, most notably the Miocene apes and the earliest hominids.

Overview

In the previous sections, we discussed the history of primate phylogeny in a more or less chronological order. For a different perspective and overview of this history, we briefly consider the past 50 years from a topical, rather than a chronological, view. The following are some of the more striking changes that have taken place in the discipline during this time period.

Paleontology and Phylogeny

In the 50 years since the founding of the AAPA, the role of paleontology in the interpretation of primate phylogeny has changed considerably. In the early years (up to 1950), fossils played no substantial part in considerations of phylogeny per se—despite Osborn's assertion of their primacy. They provided a rough time scale and general confirmation that Huxley's scale of nature reflected a chronological pattern of primate evolution. However, because the fossils generally seemed to conform to the scale, they were more often than not treated as old examples of living taxa. Phylogenies were constructed of living animals, and the fossils provided the calibration.

In the 1950s this situation changed considerably. With more complete material it became clear that fossils were not just ancient representatives of living animals (at least in the Old World) but that they frequently combined attributes of several living groups. Most of the debate in primate phylogeny throughout the past 30 years has been over the placement of fossils vis-á-vis living taxa, and primate phylogeny has become increasingly the realm of paleontologists, like Simons and Leakey. For Le Gros Clark, intermediate taxa merely confirmed his gradistic view of primate evolution. For others, the critical question was which features were deemed significant in attempts to align an intermediate or possibly unique fossil with one of the living groups. "Are dental apes really apes, and are dental hominids really hominids even if the remainder of their skeleton looks otherwise?" Le Gros Clark in the 1950s and Simons, Pilbeam, and Leakey in the 1960s felt that the answer was "yes." Straus and Washburn argued that the evidence from the limb skeleton was more diagnostic. The issue is far from being resolved.

Historically, the important change is that primate phylogeny is now irrevocably fossil phylogeny. It is no longer acceptable to tack fossil primates onto living taxa with the assumption that they are identical or to place all of them on side branches and pretend they have nothing to do with the evolution of the living forms. Accordingly, the diversity of primates that must be incorporated into discussions of primate phylogeny has increased dramatically since 1930 and will certainly continue to increase in the future.

Comparative Anatomy and Phylogeny

Fifty years ago, the study of primate phylogeny was almost totally based on comparative anatomy. The giants in primate phylogeny (Elliot Smith, Keith, Gregory, Wood Jones, Le Gros Clark, Morton, Straus) were not primarily paleontologists, like Osborn, but scientists steeped in the details of the comparative anatomy of living mammals. Both Gregory and Wood Jones felt strongly that the fossil record would never provide adequate data to change this situation. However, by 1940, comparative anatomy had clearly proved insufficient for the task—the contradiction in details was overwhelming, and many workers were yearning for a better fossil record to resolve the issues. With the improved fossil record of the 1950s and 1960s, comparative anatomy gave way to paleontology as the primary evidence for the study of primate phylogeny. Although most workers still gave lip service to Keith, Gregory, and Straus, for the most part, the real evidence lay in the fossils.

In the 1960s, comparative primate anatomy was more concerned with function than with phylogeny. How could the comparative anatomy of primates be related to their locomotion and diet? Like Le Gros Clark, John Napier and others (e.g., Napier and Napier 1967; Simons 1967b) saw the locomotor behavior of primates as a series of trends but did not link locomotor behavior and skeletal anatomy as closely with phylogeny as had Washburn (e.g., 1963).

In the 1970s, comparative anatomists began to deal again more directly with questions of phylogeny. Luckett's work on fetal membranes is almost exclusively concerned with phylogeny, whereas the comparative anatomy studies of Lewis, Szalay, Gingerich, Tuttle, Corruccini, Ciochon, McHenry, and Oxnard seek information about both function and phylogeny. Oxnard (1979; Ashton et al. 1976) has argued that the sum of the results of individual functional studies frequently is taxonomy, or perhaps, phylogeny. Primate phylogeny has always been heavily based on functional models to account for evolutionary changes, and the line between function and phylogeny remains very thin (Szalay 1981). Experimental studies that are functional in design may have important implications for phylogeny (Fleagle et al. 1981), but usually the emphasis is on reconstructing behavior rather than phylogeny.

The mass of information and apparent phylogenetic contradictions that bedeviled comparative anatomists of the late 1930s have reappeared again in the 1970s. Cartmill's (Chapter 6) laments about the confounding effects of rampant parallelism sound remarkably similar to those of Le Gros Clark in 1939. Likewise, the seemingly endless search for the one magic character set that will resolve all issues of phylogeny remains unfulfilled (Fleagle 1981). In both comparative anatomy and in paleontology, as new information accumulates, so does the difficulty of analysis.

Molecular Biology and Primate Phylogeny

If there has been a magic character or source of data discovered in the past 50 years of primate phylogeny, it has been the development of molecular systematics. Although the molecular clock has proved at best very controversial and at worst very unreliable, the phyletic relationships of living primates based on molecular data of all sorts have been widely accepted. The debate over the phyletic position of humans relative to other hominoids, which was the major issue in primate phylogeny from 1930 to 1960, is now regarded by most people as having been resolved through molecular systematics. The detailed resolution that has been produced in the analysis of human and great ape phylogeny (e.g., Bruce and Ayala 1979; Ferris *et al.* 1981) has not yet been applied to most other groups at the generic level, and it remains to be seen if the wholehearted endorsement of molecular results will continue.

Progress and Prognosis

A large number of very competent scientists have been actively working on the problems of primate phylogeny for well over 50 years, yet the unresolved problems of today vastly outnumber those of a half a century ago. Has there been any progress in the past 50 years, and is there any hope for the future? In both cases we feel the answer is unequivocally yes. Although members of the AAPA have been debating primate phylogeny for 50 years, only in the most general sense have they been debating the same issues. The most pressing issue of 1930—Are humans descended from a pongid-like ancestor?—has been resolved to almost everyone's satisfaction in the affirmative. Likewise, many of the current "hot topics," such as the relationship of dryopithecines to living apes, were not even debated issues 50 years ago.

As Boaz (in the present volume) correctly emphasizes, progress in primate phylogeny has rarely come about through either the superior intelligence or the greater analytical abilities of succeeding generations. Few primate phylogeneticists will ever match such giants as W. K. Gregory in their personal knowledge of primate form and relationships. Progress in primate phylogeny during the past 50 years has come about largely through increased information from the fossil record and, more recently, from molecular biology. The results from comparative anatomy were largely established by the beginning of the AAPA, and methodological revolutions in phylogeny have thus far proved short lived (see Cartmill in the present volume).

If the unresolved issues in primate phylogeny seem more numerous today than they were 50 years ago, it is not due to lack of progress. It is because primate phylogeny must reflect our increasing knowledge about the details of primate evolution. Fifty years ago, the meager record of fossil primates only provided a rough time scale for phylogeny. Today, as Pilbeam notes, "We are perhaps reaching the stage where the fossils can be treated virtually as though they were living species: they must now be taken fully into account in theory-building [1980:270]." Our knowledge of primate phylogeny will certainly get more complicated in future years, new fossils will bring new surprises, and parallelism and convergence will never go away. For these reasons, primate phylogeny will always be an area of intense interest and equally intense debate in physical anthropology. This is not justification for a nihilistic view of progress in primate phylogeny, but rather just a realistic appraisal of evolutionary biology. As Patterson so wisely observed halfway through the past 50 years,

> In any survey of a history it is very proper to state what the gaps are and where they occur, but is equally proper to go on and do as well as possible with what is in hand. Every primate fossil is a precious relic that contributes its bit to the history of the order. True, the evidence thus far contributed is often capable of conflicting interpretations, but sooner or later matters iron out; new discoveries permit new perspectives, and progress, however halting, is made [1954:141].

Acknowledgments

We thank Frank Spencer for inviting us to contribute this paper, albeit on rather short notice, and for his leniency with deadlines. We are especially indebted to the Osborn Library of the American Museum of Natural History for access to their extensive collection of reprints. We are grateful to Judy Nimmo for typing and correcting numerous versions of the manuscript. We profited greatly from discussions with Jack Stern and Norman Creel and from unpublished manuscripts kindly given to us by Matt Cartmill and Noel Boaz. This work was funded in part by funds from BNS 7924149 and BNS 7924070 from the National Science Foundation.

References

Andrews, P.
    1971   *Ramapithecus wickeri* mandible from Fort Ternan, Kenya. *Nature (London)* **228**:192–194.
Andrews, P., and E. L. Simons
    1977   A new African Miocene gibbon-like genus, *Dendropithecus* (Hominoidea, Primates) with distinctive postcranial adaptations: Its significance to origin of Hylobatidae. *Folia Primatologica* **28**:161–170.
Ashton, E. H., R. M. Flynn, C. E. Oxnard, and T. F. Spence
    1976   The adaptive and classificatory significance of certain quantitative features of the forelimb in primates. *Journal of Zoology* **179**:515–556.

Baba, M., L. Darga, and M. Goodman
    1980   Biochemical evidence on the phylogeny of Anthropoidea. In *Evolutionary biology of the New World monkeys and continental drift,* edited by R. L. Ciochon and A. B. Chiarelli. New York: Plenum. Pp. 1–10.

Bruce, E. J., and F. J. Ayala
    1979   Phylogenetic relationships between man and the apes: electrophoretic evidence. *Evolution* **33**:1040–1056.

Buettner-Janusch, J.
    1966   *Origins of man.* New York: Wiley.

Campbell, B. G.
    1966   *Human evolution.* Chicago: Aldine.

Ciochon, R. L., and A. B. Chiarelli
    1980   Preface. In *Evolutionary Biology of the New World Monkeys and Continental Drift,* edited by R. L. Chiochon and A. B. Chiarelli. New York: Plenum. Pp. vii–ix.

Conroy, G. C.
    1976   Primate postcranial remains from the Oligocene of Egypt. *Contributions to Primatology* **8**:1–134.

Cope, E. D.
    1885   The Lemuroidea and the Insectivora of the Eocene period of North America. *American Naturalist* **19**:457–471.

Corruccini, R. S., and H. M. McHenry
    1980   Cladometric analysis of Pliocene hominids. *Journal of Human Evolution* **9**:209–221.

Corruccini, R. S., R. Ciochon, H. M. McHenry
    1975   Osteometric shape relationships in the wrist joint of some anthropoids. *Folia Primatologica* **24**:250–274.
    1976   The postcranium of Miocene hominoids: were Dryopithecines merely "dental apes"? *Primates* **17**:205–223.

Corruccini, R. S., M. Baba, M. Goodman, R. Ciochon, and J. Cronin
    1980   Nonlinear macromolecular evolution and the molecular clock. *Evolution* **34**:1216–1219.

Cronin, J. E., and W. E. Meikle
    1979   The phyletic position of *Theropithecus*: congruence among molecular, morphological, and paleontological evidence. *Systematic Zoology* **28**:259–269.

Dawson, C., and A. Smith Woodward
    1913   On the discovery of a Palaeolithic human skull and mandible in flint-bearing gravel overlying the Wealden (Hastings Beds) at Piltdown, Fletching (Sussex). *Quarterly Journal of Geological Society of London* **69**:117–151.

Delson, E.
    1975   Evolutionary history of the Cercopithecidae. *Contributions to Primatology* **5**:167–217.
    1977   Catarrhine phylogeny and classification: principles, methods and comments. *Journal of Human Evolution* **6**:433–459.
    1979   *Oreopithecus* is a cercopithecoid after all. *American Journal of Physical Anthropology* **50**:431–432 (Abstract).

Delson, E., and P. Andrews
    1975   Evolution and interrelationships of the Catarrhine primates. In *Phylogeny of the primates: a multidisciplinary approach,* edited by W. P. Luckett and F. S. Szalay. New York: Plenum. Pp. 405–446.

Delson, E., N. Eldredge, and I. Tattersall
    1977   Reconstruction of hominid phylogeny: a testable framework based on cladistic analysis. *Journal of Human Evolution* **6**:263–278.

Eckhardt, R. B.
    1972   Population genetics and human origins. *Scientific American* **226**:94–103.

Eldredge, N., and I. Tattersall
    1975   Evolutionary models, phylogenetic reconstruction and another look at hominid phylogeny. *Contributions to Primatology* **5**:218–242.
Elliot Smith, G.
    1918   *The evolution of man.* London and New York: Oxford University Press.
    1924   *Essays on the evolution of man.* London and New York: Oxford University Press.
    1931   *The search for man's ancestors.* London and New York: Oxford University Press.
Ferris, S. D., A. C. Wilson, and W. M. Brown
    1981   Evolutionary tree for apes and humans based on cleavage maps of mitochondrial DNA. *Proceedings of the National Academy of Sciences of the United States of America* **78**:2432–2436.
Fleagle, J. G.
    1981   The eternal search. *Evolution* **35**:1029–1031.
Fleagle, J. G., R. F. Kay, and E. L. Simons
    1980   Sexual dimorphism in early anthropoids. *Nature (London)* **287**:328–330.
Fleagle, J. G., J. T. Stern, W. L. Jungers, R. L. Susman, A. K. Vangor and J. P. Wells
    1981   Climbing: a biomechanical link with brachiation and bipedalism. In Vertebrate locomotion, edited by M. H. Day. New York: Academic Press. Pp. 359–375.
Ford, S. M.
    1980   Callitrichids as phyletic dwarfs, and the place of the Callitrichidae in Platyrrhini. *Primates* **21**:31–43.
Frayer, D. W.
    1976   A reappraisal of *Ramapithecus. Yearbook of Physical Anthropology* **18**:19–30.
Gingerich, P. D.
    1976   Paleontology and phylogeny: patterns of evolution at the species level in early Tertiary mammals. *American Journal of Science* **276**:1–28.
    1977   Patterns of evolution in the mammalian fossil record. In Patterns of evolution, edited by A. Hallam. Amsterdam: Elsevier. Pp. 409–499.
Gingerich, P. D., and M. Schoeninger
    1977   The fossil record and primate phylogeny. *Journal of Human Evolution* **6**:483–505.
Goodman, M.
    1963   Man's place in the phylogeny of the primates as reflected in serum proteins. In Classification and human evolution, edited by S. L. Washburn. Chicago: Aldine. Pp. 204–234.
Greenfield, L. O.
    1974   Taxonomic reassessment of two *Ramapithecus* specimens. *Folia Primatologica* **22**:97–115.
    1977   *Ramapithecus* and early hominid origins. Unpublished Ph.D. thesis, Department of Anthropology, University of Michigan, University Microfilms, Ann Arbor.
    1979   On the adaptive pattern of "*Ramapithecus.*" *American Journal of Physical Antropology* **50**:527–548.
    1980   A late divergence hypothesis. *American Journal of Physical Anthropology* **52**:351–365.
Gregory, W. K.
    1922   *The origin and evolution of the human dentition.* Baltimore: Williams and Wilkins.
    1927a   The origin of man from the anthropoid stem—when and where? *Proceedings of the American Philosophical Society* **66**:439–463.
    1927b   How near is the relationship of man to the chimpanzee—gorilla stock? *Quarterly Review of Biology* **2**:549–560.
    1928a   Were the ancestors of man primitive brachiators? *Proceedings of the American Philosophical Society* **67**:129–150.
    1928b   The upright posture of man: a review of its origin and evolution. *Proceedings of the American Philosophical Society* **67**:339–377.
    1929   Is the pre-dawn man a myth? *Human Biology* **1**:153–165.

1930   A critique of Professor Frederic Wood-Jones's paper: "Some landmarks in the phylogeny of the primates." *Human Biology* **2**:99–108.
1934   *Man's place among the anthropoids.* Oxford: Clarendon.
1938   Man's place among the primates. *Palaeobiologica* **6**:208–213.
1949   The bearing of the Australopithecinae upon the problem of man's place in nature. *American Journal of Physical Anthropology* **7**:485–512.
1951   *Evolution emerging* (2 vols.). New York: Macmillan.
Gregory, W. K., M. Hellman, and G. E. Lewis
1938   Fossil anthropoids of the Yale–Cambridge India expedition of 1935. *Carnegie Institute of Washington Publication* **495**:1–27.

Heberer, G.
1956   Die Fossilgeschichte der Hominoidea. *Primatologia* **1**:379–560.
1962   The subhuman evolutionary history of man. In *Ideas on human evolution,* edited by W. W. Howells. Cambridge, Massachusetts: Harvard University Press. Pp. 203–241. (Originally published, 1959.)

Hennig, W.
1966   *Phylogenetic Systematics.* Chicago: University of Illinois Press.
Hershkovitz, P.
1977   *Living New World monkeys (Platyrrhini) 1.* Chicago: University of Chicago Press.
Hoffstetter, R.
1972   Relationships, origins, and history of the ceboid monkeys and caviomorph rodents: a modern reinterpretation. In *Evolutionary biology,* edited by T. Dobzhansky, M. K. Hecht, and W. C. Steere. New York: Appleton. Pp. 323–347.
1974   Phylogeny and geographical deployment of the primates. *Journal of Human Evolution* **3**:327–350.

Hooton, E. A.
1931   *Up from the ape* (first edition). New York: Macmillan.
1946   *Up from the ape* (second edition). New York: Macmillan.
Howells, W. W.
1951   Origin of the Human stock, concluding remarks of the chairman. *Cold Spring Harbor Symposia on Quantitative Biology* **15**:79–86.
1959   *Mankind in the making.* New York: Doubleday.
1967   *Mankind in the making* (second edition). New York: Doubleday.
Hrdlička, A.
1922   The Piltdown jaw. *American Journal of Physical Anthropology* **5**:337–347.
Hürzeler, J.
1949   Neubeschreibung von *Oreopithecus bambolii* Gervais. *Schweizerische Paleontologische Abhandlungen* **66**:1–20.
1958   *Oreopithecus bambolii* Gervais, a preliminary report. *Verhandlungen der Naturforschenden Gesellschaft in Basel* **69**:1–47.
1960   The significance of *Oreopithecus* in the genealogy of man. *Triangle* **4**:164–175.
Huxley, T. H.
1863   *Evidence as to man's place in nature.* London: Williams and Norgate.
Jacobs, L. L., and D. Pilbeam
1980   Of mice and men: Fossil-based divergence dates and molecular "clocks." *Journal of Human Evolution* **9**:551–555.
Jenkins, F. A. Jr., and J. G. Fleagle
1975   Knuckle-walking and the functional anatomy of the wrists in living apes. In *Primate functional morphology and evolution,* edited by R. H. Tuttle. The Hague: Mouton. Pp. 213–227.
Johnson, S. C.
1981   Bonobos: generalized hominid prototypes or specialized insular dwarfs? *Current Anthropology* **22**:363–375.
Kalin, J.
1955   Zur Systematik und evolutiven Deutung der höheren Primaten. *Experientia* **11**:1–17.

Kay, R. F
  1977   The evolution of molar occlusion in the Cercopithecidae and early Catarrhines. *American Journal of Physical Anthropology* **46**:327–352.
Kay, R. F., J. G. Fleagle, and E. L. Simons
  1981   A revision of the Oligocene apes of the Fayum Province, Egypt. *American Journal of Physical Anthropology* **55**:293–322.
Keith, A.
  1902   The extent to which the posterior segments of the body have been transmuted and suppressed in the evolution of man and allied primates. *Journal of Anatomy* **37**:18–40.
  1911   Klaatsch's theory of the descent of man. *Nature (London)* **85**:509–510.
  1912   Certain phases in the evolution of man. *British Medical Journal* **1**:734–736, 788–790.
  1915   *The antiquity of man.* London: Williams and Norgate.
  1920   *The engines of the human body.* Philadelphia: Lippincott.
  1923   Man's posture: its evolution and disorders. *British Medical Journal* **1**:451–454, 499–502, 545–548, 587–590, 624–626, 699–672.
  1934   *The construction of man's family tree.* London: Watts.
  1940   Fifty years ago. *American Journal of Physical Anthropology* **26**:251–267.
Leakey, L. S. B.
  1967   An early Miocene member of Hominidae. *Nature (London)* **213**:155–163.
Le Gros Clark, W. E.
  1934   *Early forerunners of man.* London: Baillière.
  1935   Man's place among the primates. *Man* **35**:1–6.
  1936   Evolutionary parallelism and human phylogeny. *Man* **36**:4–8.
  1939   The scope and limitations of physical anthropology. *British Association for the Advancement of Science, Report* **1939**(Section H):1–24.
  1940   Paleontological evidence bearing on human evolution. *Biological Reviews of the Cambridge Philosophical Society* **15**:202–230.
  1947   The British-Kenya Miocene expedition, 1947. *Nature (London)* **160**:891–892.
  1950   Fossil apes and men. *The Spectator* **January 13**:38–39.
  1955   Reason and fallacy in the study of fossil man. *Discovery* **1955**(1):6–15.
  1959   *The antecedents of man.* Edinburgh: Edinburgh University Press.
  1962   *The antecedents of man* (second edition). Edinburgh: Edinburgh University Press.
Le Gros Clark, W. E., and L. S. B. Leakey
  1950   Diagnoses of East African Miocene Hominoidea. *Quarterly Journal of the Geological Society of London* **105**:260–262.
  1951   The Miocene Hominoidea of East Africa. *Fossil Mammals of Africa.* **1**:1–117.
Le Gros Clark, W. E., and T. P. Thomas
  1951   Associated jaws and limb bones of *Limnopithecus macinnesi. Fossil Mammals of Africa.* **3**:1–27.
Lewis, G. E.
  1934   Preliminary notice of new man-like apes from India. *American Journal of Science* **27**:161–179.
Lewis, O. J.
  1972a Evolution of the hominoid wrist. In *The functional and evolutionary biology of primates,* edited by R. H. Tuttle. Chicago: Aldine. Pp. 207–272.
  1972b Osteological features characterizing the wrists of monkeys and apes, with a reconsideration of this region in *Dryopithecus (Proconsul) africanus. American Journal of Physical Anthropology* **36**:45–58.
  1980a The joints of the evolving foot. Part I. The ankle joint. *Journal of Anatomy* **130**:527–543.
  1980b The joints of the evolving foot. Part II. The intrinsic joints. *Journal of Anatomy* **130**:833–857.
  1980c The joints of the evolving foot. Part III. The fossil evidence. *Journal of Anatomy* **131**:275–298.
Lovejoy, C. O., and R. S. Meindle
  1973   Eukaryote mutation and the protein clock. *Yearbook of Physical Anthropology* **16**:18–30.
Lovejoy, C. O., A. H. Burstein, and K. G. Heiple
  1972   Primate phylogeny and immunological distance. *Science* **176**:803–805.

Luckett, W. P.
   1974   Comparative development and evolution of the placenta in primates. *Contributions to Primatology* **3**:142–234.
   1975   Ontogeny of the fetal membranes and placenta: their bearing on primate phylogeny. In *Phylogeny of the primates: a multidisciplinary approach*, edited by W. P. Luckett and F. S. Szalay. New York: Plenum. Pp. 157–182.
   1976   Cladistic relationships among primate higher categories: evidence of the fetal membranes and placenta. *Folia Primatologica* **25**:245–276.

Miller, G. S.
   1918   The Piltdown jaw. *American Journal of Physical Anthropology* **1**:25–52.
   1920   Conflicting views on the problem of man's ancestry. *American Journal of Physical Anthropology* **3**:213–245.
   1929   The controversy over human "missing links." *Smithsonian Institute, Annual Report* Pp. 413–465.

Morbeck, M. E.
   1975   *Dryopithecus africanus* forelimb. *Journal of Human Evolution* **4**:39–46.
   1977   The use of casts and other problems in reconstructing the *Dryopithecus (Proconsul) africanus* wrist complex. *Journal of Human Evolution* **6**:65–78.

Morton, D. J.
   1922   Evolution of the human foot. Part I. *American Journal of Physical Anthropology* **5**:305–336.
   1924a   Evolution of the human foot. Part II. *American Journal of Physical Anthropology* **7**:1–52.
   1924b   Evolution of the longitudinal arch of the human foot. *Journal of Bone and Joint Surgery* **6**:56–90.
   1926   Evolution of man's erect posture. *Journal of Morphology and Physiology* **43**:147–179.
   1927   Human origin, correlation of previous studies of primate feet and posture with other morphologic evidence. *American Journal of Physical Anthropology* **10**:173–203.

Napier, J. R., and P. R. Davis
   1959   The forelimb skeleton and associated remains of *Proconsul africanus*. *Fossil Mammals of Africa.* **16**:1–69.

Napier, J. R., and P. H. Napier
   1967   *A handbook of living primates.* New York: Academic Press.

O'Connor, B. L.
   1976   *Dryopithecus (Proconsul) africanus*: Quadruped or non-quadruped? *Journal of Human Evolution* **5**:279–283.

Osborn, H. F.
   1923   Why Mongolia may be the home of primitive man. Address before the Wen Yu Hui ("Friends of Literature"), Oct. 8, 1923. Cited in Gregory (1929).
   1924   Where did man originate? *Asia* **24**:427.
   1926   Why Central Asia? *Natural History* **26**:263–269.
   1927a   Recent discoveries relating to the origin and antiquity of man. *Science* **65**:481–488.
   1927b   *Man rises to Parnassus. Critical epochs in the prehistory of man.* New Jersey: Princeton University Press.
   1929   Is the ape–man a myth? *Human Biology* **1**:4–9.

Oxnard, C. E.
   1979   The morphological–behavioral interface in extant primates: some implications for systematics and evolution. In *Environment, behavior and morphology: dynamic interactions in primates*, edited by M. E. Morbeck, H. Preuschoft, and N. Gomberg. Stuttgart: Fischer. Pp. 209–237.

Patterson, B.
   1954   The geologic history of non-hominid primates in the Old World. *Human Biology* **26**:191–209.

Pilbeam, D. R.
    1967   Man's earliest ancestors. *Science* **3**:47–53.
    1968   Human origins. *Advancement of Science* **March 1968**:368–378.
    1969   Tertiary Pongidae of East Africa: evolutionary relationships and taxonomy. *Peabody Museum of Natural History Bulletin* **31**:1–185.
    1970   *The evolution of man.* New York: Funk and Wagnalls.
    1972   *The ascent of man.* New York: Macmillan.
    1978   Rethinking human origins. *Discovery* **13**(1):2–9.
    1979   Recent finds and interpretations of Miocene hominoids. *Annual Review of Anthropology* **8**:333–352.
    1980   Major trends in human evolution. In *Current argument on early man,* edited by L. K. Konigsson. Oxford: Pergamon. Pp. 261–285.
Pilbeam, D. R., and A. Walker
    1968   Fossil monkeys from the Micoene of Napak, northeast Uganda. *Nature (London)* **220**:657–660.
Pilbeam, D. R., G. E. Meyer, C. Badgely, M. D. Rose, M. H. L. Pickford, A. K. Behrensmeyer, and S. M. Ibrahim Shah
    1977   New hominoid primates from the Siwaliks of Pakistan and their bearing on hominoid evolution. *Nature (London)* **270**:689–695.
Piveteau, J.
    1957   *Traite de palé*ontologie (Vol. 7). Paris: Masson.
Radinsky, L.
    1978   Do albumin clocks run on time? *Science* **200**:1182–1183.
Read, D. W., and P. E. Lestrel
    1970   Hominid phylogeny and immunology: a critical appraisal. *Science* **168**:578–580.
Remane, A.
    1952   Methodische Probleme der Hominiden—Phylogenie. I. *Zeitschrift fuer Morphologie und Anthropologie* **44**:188–200.
    1956   Paläontologie und Evolution der Primaten, besonders der Nicht—Hominoiden. *Primatologia* **1**:267–378.
Robinson, J. T.
    1956   The dentition of the Australopithecinae. *Transvaal Museum Memoirs No.* **9**.
Rosenberger, A. L.
    1980   Gradistic views and adaptive radiation of platyrrhine primates. *Zietschrift fuer Morphologie und Anthropologie* **71**:157–163.
Sarich, V. M.
    1968   The origin of the hominids: an immunological approach. In *Perspectives on human evolution I,* edited by S. L. Washburn and P. C. Jay. New York: Holt. Pp. 94–121.
Sarich, V. M., and A. C. Wilson
    1966   Quantitative immunochemistry and the evolution of primate albumins. *Science* **154**:1563–1566.
    1967   Rates of albumin evolution in primates. *Proceedings of the National Academy of Sciences of the United States of America* **58**:142–148.
    1968   Immunological time scale for hominid evolution. *Science* **158**:1200.
Schlosser, M.
    1887   Die Affen, Lemuren, Chiropteren usw. des europaischen Tertiärs. *Beitrage zur Paläontologischen u Geologie Oesterreich—Ungarns u des Orients* **6**:1–227.
Schultz, A. H.
    1927   Studies on the growth of gorilla and other higher primates with special reference to a fetus of gorilla, preserved in the Carnegie Museum. *Memoirs of the Carnegie Museum* **11**:1–88.
    1930   The skeleton of the trunk and limbs of higher primates. *Human Biology* **2**:303–438.
    1936   Characters common to higher primates and characters specific for man. *Quarterly Review of Biology* **2**:259–283, 425–455.

1951   Origin of the human stock: the specializations of man and his place among the catarrhine primates. *Cold Spring Harbor Symposia on Quantitative Biology* **15**:37–54.

Schwalbe, G.
1915   Über den fossilen Affen *Oreopithecus* bambolii: Zugleich ein Beitrag zur Morphologie der Zähne der Primaten. *Zeitschrift fuer Morphologie und Anthropologie* **19**:149–254.

Schwartz, J. H., I. Tattersall, and N. Eldredge
1978   Phylogeny and classification of the primates revisited. *Yearbook of Physical Anthropology* **21**:95–133.

Simons, E. L.
1960a   New fossil primates: a review of the past decade. *American Scientist* **48**:179–192.
1960b   *Apidium* and *Oreopithecus*. *Nature (London)* **186**:824–826.
1961   The phyletic position of *Ramapithecus*. *Postilla* **57**:1–9.
1962   Two new primate species from the African Oligocene. *Postilla* **64**:1–12.
1964   On the mandible of *Ramapithecus*. *Proceedings of the National Academy of Sciences of the United States of America* **51**:528–535.
1965   New fossil apes from Egypt and the initial differentiation of Hominoidea. *Nature (London)* **205**:135–139.
1967a   The earliest apes. *Scientific American* **217**:28–35.
1967b   Review of the phyletic interrelationships of Oligocene and Miocene Old World Anthropoidea. *Colloques Internationaux de Centre National de la Recherche Scientifique* **163**:597–602.
1968   A source for dental comparison of *Ramapithecus* with *Australopithecus* and *Homo*. *South African Journal of Science* **64**:92–112.
1969a   The late Miocene hominid from Fort Ternan, Kenya. *Nature (London)* **221**:448–451.
1969b   The origin and radiation of the primates. *Annals of the New York Academy of Sciences* **167**:319–331.
1970   The deployment and history of Old World monkeys (Cercopithecidae, Primates). In *Old World monkeys: evolution, systematics, and behavior*, edited by J. R. Napier and P. H. Napier New York: Academic Press. Pp. 92–147.
1972   *Primate evolution*. New York: Macmillan.
1976a   The fossil record of primate phylogeny. In *Molecular anthropology*, edited by M. Goodman and R. E. Tashian. New York: Plenum. Pp. 35–62.
1976b   The nature of the transition in the dental mechanism from pongids to hominids. *Journal of Human Evolution* **5**:500–528.
1977   *Ramapithecus*. *Scientific American* **236**:28–35.

Simons, E. L., and E. Delson
1978   Cercopithecidae and Parapithecidae. In *Evolution of African mammals*, edited by V. J. Maglio and H. B. S. Cooke. Cambridge, Massachusetts: Harvard University Press. Pp. 100–119.

Simons, E. L., and J. G. Fleagle
1973   The history of extinct gibbon-like primates. *Gibbon Siamang* **2**:121–148.

Simons, E. L., and D. R. Pilbeam
1972   Hominoid paleoprimatology. In *The functional and evolutionary biology of primates*, edited by R. Tuttle. Chicago: Aldine. Pp. 36–62.
1978   *Ramapithecus* (Hominidae, Hominoidea). In *Evolution of African mammals*, edited by V. J. Maglio and H. B. S. Cooke. Cambridge, Massachusetts: Harvard University Press. Pp. 147–153.

Simpson, G. G.
1949   *The meaning of evolution*. New Haven, Connecticut: Yale University Press.
1951   Some principles of historical biology bearing on human origins. *Cold Spring Harbor Symposia on Quantitative Biology* **15**:55–66.
1963   The meaning of taxonomic statements. In *Classification and human evolution*, edited by S. L. Washburn. Chicago: Aldine. Pp. 1–31.

1966   The biological nature of man. *Science* **152**:472–478.

Stern, J. T., Jr.
1976   Before bipedality. *Yearbook of Physical Anthropology* **19**:59–68.

Stirton, R. A., and D. E. Savage
1951   A new monkey from the La Venta Miocene of Columbia. *Compilacion de los Estudios Geologicos Oficiales en Columbia* **7**:345–356.

Straus, W. L., Jr.
1940   The posture of the great ape hand in locomotion, and its phylogenetic implications. *American Journal of Physical Anthropology* **27**:199–207.
1941   The phylogeny of the human forearm extensors. *Human Biology* **13**:23–50, 203–238.
1949   The riddle of man's ancestry. *Quarterly Review of Biology* **24**:200–223.
1954   Primates. In *Anthropology Today*, edited by A. L. Kroeber. Chicago: University of Chicago Press. Pp. 77–92.
1962   The riddle of man's ancestry (with footnotes). In *Ideas on human evolution*, edited by W. W. Howells. Cambridge, Massachusetts: Harvard University Press. Pp. 69–104.
1963   The classification of *Oreopithecus*. In *Classification and human evolution*, edited by S. L. Washburn. Chicago: Aldine. Pp. 146–177.

Szalay, F. S.
1977   Ancestors, descendents, sister-groups, and testing of phylogenetic hypotheses. *Systematic Zoology* **26**:12–18.
1981   Functional analysis and the practice of the phylogenetic method as reflected by some mammalian studies. *American Zoologists* **21**:37–45.

Szalay, F. S., and E. Delson
1979   *Evolutionary history of the primates.* New York: Academic Press.

Tattersall, L, and N. Eldredge
1977   Fact, theory and fantasy in human paleontology. *American Scientist* **65**:204–211.

Tuttle, R. H.
1972   Functional and evolutionary biology of hylobatid hands and feet. *Gibbon Siamang* **1**:136–206.
1974   Darwin's apes, dental apes, and the descent of man: normal science in evolutionary anthropology. *Current Anthropology* **15**:389–426.
1975   Parallelism, brachiation and hominoid phylogeny. In *Phylogeny of the Primates: a multi-disciplinary approach*, edited by W. P. Luckett and F. S. Szalay. New York: Plenum. Pp. 447–480.

Tuttle, R. H., and J. V. Basmajian
1974   Electromyography of forearm musculature in gorilla and problems related to knuckle-walking. In *Primate locomotion*, edited by F. A. Jenkins, Jr. New York: Academic Press. Pp. 293–347.

Tuttle, R. H., G. W. Cortwright, and D. P. Buxhoeveden
1979   Anthropology on the move: progress in experimental studies of nonhuman primate positional behavior. *Yearbook of Physical Anthropology* **22**:187–214.

Uzzell, T., and D. Pilbeam
1971   Phyletic divergence dates of hominoid primates: a comparison of fossil and molecular data. *Evolution* **25**:615–635.

von Koenigswald, G. H. R.
1955   Remarks on *Oreopithecus*. *Rivista di Scienze Preistoriche* **10**:1–3.

Walker, A.
1976   Splitting times among hominoids deduced from the fossil record. In *Molecular anthropology*, edited by M. Goodman, R. E. Tashian, and J. H. Tashian. New York: Plenum. Pp. 63–77.

Walker, A., and P. Andrews
1973   Reconstruction of the dental arcades of *Ramapithecus wickeri*. *Nature (London)* **244**:313–314.

Washburn, S. L.
  1951   The analysis of primate evolution with particular reference to the origin of man. *Cold Spring Harbor Symposia on Quantitative Biology* **15**:67–77.
  1960   Tools and human evolution. *Scientific American* **203**:63–75.
  1963   Behavior and human evolution. In *Classification and human evolution*, edited by S. L. Washburn. Chicago: Aldine. Pp. 190–203.
  1968   *The study of human evolution.* Condon Lectures, Oregon State System of Higher Education, Eugene, Oregon. Pp. 1–48.
Weinert, H.
  1932   *Ursprung der Menschheit.* Stuttgart: Ferdinand Enke.
Wilder, H. H.
  1926   Summary: the phylogenetic tree of the Primates; the pedigree of the human race. *The pedigree of the human race.* New York: Holt. Pp. 264–272.
Wolpoff, M. H.
  1980   *Paleoanthropology.* New York: Knopf.
Wood Jones, F.
  1918   *The problem of man's ancestry.* London: Society for Promoting Christian Knowledge.
  1923   *The ancestry of man.* Brisbane: Gillies and Co.
  1926   *Arboreal man.* London: Arnold.
  1929   *Man's place among the mammals.* New York: Longmans, Green.
  1948   *Hallmarks of mankind.* Baltimore: Williams and Wilkins.
Yerkes, R. M., and A. W. Yerkes
  1929   *The great apes. A study of anthropoid life.* New Haven, Connecticut: Yale University Press.
Zapfe, H.
  1952   Die *Pliopithecus*—Funde aus der Spaltenfullung vor Neudorf a d. March (CSR). *Verhandlungen der Geologischen Bundesanstalt, Sonderheft* C:126–130.
  1958   The skeleton of *Pliopithecus* (*Epipliopithecus*) *vindobonensis* Zapfe and Hürzeler. *American Journal of Physical Anthropology* **16**:441–455.
  1960   Die Primaten funde aus den miozänen Spaltenfüllung von Neudorf on der Maach (Devinská Nová Ves), Tschechoslowakier. *Schweizerische Paläontologische Abhandlungen* **78**:4–293.
Zihlman, A.
  1979   Pygmy chimpanzee morphology and the interpretation of early hominids. *South African Journal of Science* **75**:165–168.
Zihlman, A., J. E. Cronin, D. L. Cramer and V. M. Sarich
  1978   Pygmy chimpanzee as a possible prototype for the common ancestor of humans, chimpanzees and gorillas. *Nature (London)* **275**:744–746.

8

Reflections on Human Paleontology

Ernst Mayr

Historical Comments

When I was a student in the 1920s, I took a course in physical anthropology. The treatment was purely typological; everything was looked at from the point of view of the morphologist, who compared specimens to imaginary types. When the evolutionary synthesis took place in the 1930s and 1940s, anthropology seemed at first to be little affected, and paleoanatomists continued to describe as a new type just about every fossil hominid that was discovered. By the 1950s, the student of fossil man had to cope with 29 generic and more than 100 specific names (Oakley and Campbell 1966), a totally bewildering diversity of types.

I think the change that nevertheless was going on in the minds of many physical anthropologists manifested itself most conspicuously at the Cold Spring Harbor Symposium of 1950. It was on that occasion that the study of fossil man was integrated into the evolutionary snythesis. I still remember one session, chaired by E. A. Hooton, in which Sherwood L. Washburn had discussed certain evolutionary processes using the word *population* in just about every second or third sentence. After Washburn had finished, Hooton got up and said, "I hate the word *population*." I am afraid he fought a losing battle. By 1950, population thinking had established a well-entrenched beachhead in anthropological thought: however, as I shall show, it had not yet achieved a total victory.

My assignment in 1950 had been to try to make some sense of the bewildering diversity of generic and specific names in paleoanthropology (Mayr 1950). Ruthlessly applying Occam's razor, I cut the number of generic names down to two, *Homo* and *Australopithecus*, stating that there were no good morphological

A HISTORY OF AMERICAN
PHYSICAL ANTHROPOLOGY, 1930–1980

characters clearly differentiating even *Australopithecus* from *Homo*. As far as species were concerned, I stated that, allowing for geographic variation and the probability that sexual dimorphism in fossil man was greater than it is in modern man, it was a defensible thesis to interpret the fossil record as representing only a single species at one time, going as far back as the earliest hominid fossils.

It soon became apparent that my working hypothesis was oversimplified. The discovery of *Zinjanthropus* at Olduvai was proof that there was a separate robust line of australopithecines side by side with the more gracile *africanus* lineage. Also, the enormous difference in brain size between the australopithecines and *Homo* made it evident that the two genera occupied such different adaptive zones that generic separation was fully justified in spite of the slightness of the morphological differences (traditionally considered to be necessary for the recognition of genera).

Like most of paleontology, the study of fossil hominids (paleoanthropology) was strongly dominated by the "vertical" tradition (Mayr 1977). There was an unconscious tendency to arrange all fossils in a single linear sequence, from "lower" to "higher," from more primitive to more advanced. The recognition that the robust australopithecines are a separate lineage was a definite break with that tradition, as was the recognition (Howell 1957) that Neandertal is not necessarily the ancestor of *Homo sapiens sapiens*. But, as I shall point out presently, this was only the beginning of a deeper interest in the origin of diversity.

One can well claim that the year 1950 was the threshold of a new period in the study of fossil man. The subsequent developments are reflected in an enormous and ever increasing literature, particularly in symposia papers emanating from conferences sponsored by the Wenner-Gren Foundation for Anthropological Research. There are many factors that have contributed to the advances made in the past 30 years.

Technical Advances

One of the crucial deficiencies in our understanding of hominid phylogeny prior to the 1950s was the absence of accurate dates for most of the fossil finds. Continuous improvements in the technique of dating through radioactive isotopes has led to a remarkably precise chronology in many areas, particularly in East Africa. In other areas where appropriate lava flows or other volcanic deposits are absent, as in South Africa, determining the age of a find by correlating the associated faunas with the same of similar faunas in well-dated regions has been most revealing. Rapidly evolving lines of animals, such as fossil pigs and proboscideans, have been particularly valuable.

New Fossil Finds

Nothing, of course, has shed as much light on the history of the hominids as new fossil discoveries. The Leakey family clearly takes first prize for its discoveries in the Olduvai Gorge, at Laetoli, in the area east of Lake Turkana, and at other localities in East Africa. Additional finds, many of them still insufficiently described, have been made in Europe (e.g., Hungary), the Near East, India, and China, and as for the earlier, mid-Tertiary history, in Egypt (Fayum). These discoveries have shed clarity as well as raised new problems. Excellent fossil material of australopithecines now goes back to about 3.8 million years (Afar), but there is still an almost total absence of evidence from the very time zone (4–8 million years ago) where, according to the most widely held ideas, the hominid and the African ape lines should have separated. Deposits of the right age seem to exist in northern Ethiopia, and one can hope for crucial discoveries in the not-too-distant future. The specimen from Lothagam is of a crucial age (5.5 million years) but too scrappy to be revealing.

Molecular Anthropology

When Emil Zuckerkandl first used the term *Molecular anthropology* in 1962, he began a program for the future. Now molecular anthropology is a full-fledged discipline with its own, numerous publications, including entire books (Goodman and Tashian 1976).

The molecular methods are of limited applicability, but where they can be employed, they are very powerful. They can be used, of course, only where abundant molecular material is available; that is, only for recent species. However, molecules can provide decisive evidence on the degree of difference between recent man and any of the primates. This degree of difference, in turn, permits estimates as to the time when certain lineages split. What is particularly valuable about these methods is the abundance of the evidence. It includes hundreds or thousands of different proteins and various kinds of nucleic acids, including mitochondrial DNA and RNA. Since proteins seem to change during evolution at a fairly even rate, one can postulate a molecular clock (Pauling and Zuckerkandl 1965; Sarich and Wilson 1967) entirely independent of the chronology provided by the fossil record.

At first, the dating of the molecular clock seemed quite clearly refuted by the fossil record, but subsequent refinements have narrowed the gap. Indeed, the extraordinary molecular similarity between man and the African apes (*Pan*) has now convinced most students of fossil primates that *Ramapithecus*, when properly interpreted, does not contradict the molecular model. The date (4–5 million years) of the branching of the hominid line from the ape line, postulated by the proponents of the molecular clock, still seems a bit too recent, but it fits the existing evidence better than a date of more than 10 million years ago, as was at one time inferred from the *Ramapithecus* theory.

Molecular studies have also provided much new evidence on the degree of relationship among man, the chimpanzee, and the gorilla.

Morphological Analysis

The successes of molecular analysis should not make us forget how much the morphological analysis still can contribute. As far as I am concerned, for instance, the analysis of the dentition of *Australopithecus afarensis* by Greenfield (1978) has strengthened my conviction that this is a valid taxon. Not only that, but the morphological analysis has also shown to what extent this taxon is intermediate between *Homo* and the dryopithecines. Tobias (1980) was able to show that even later australopithecines (*africanus*) differ in their occlusion from the earliest *Homo* (*habilis*). In foot structure, likewise, *Australopithecus* is clearly somewhat inter-mediate between *Homo* and the dryopithecines.

I am quite convinced that several of the still controversial questions of paleo-anthropology, like the interpretation of the so-called robust australopithecines of South Africa, will be settled by further morphological analysis.

Conceptual Advances

The past 10 or 15 years have been witnessed a number of conceptual advances that have a direct bearing on the interpretation of hominid evolution. Most important is the rejection of the traditional definition of evolution by geneticists, that is, that evolution is a change of gene frequencies in populations. This reductionist definition has proved insufficient, if not actually misleading. It places the entire emphasis on adaptive changes in single lineages and completely ignores the fact that one major component of evolution consists of changes in diversity, including the origin of new evolutionary lines initiated by new species. The new focus on the origin of diversity leads to the question, "To what extent does the fossil record of the hominids represent more or less gradual changes in continuous lineages, and to what extent does it represent speciational events, owing to a multiplication of species." More specifically, this focus deals with the origin of the robust australopithecines and with the rise of *Homo*, as I shall discuss later.

Even though Le Gros Clark and myself have emphasized the importance of mosaic evolution in the history of mankind for 30 years, nothing has underscored the importance of this process more than the recent findings of molecular anthropology. They have demonstrated that in the same period during which *Homo* acquired the numerous characteristics of body structure and brain capacity that characterize *H. sapiens*, many protein molecules experienced only a minimal change. Alpha- and beta-hemoglobin and several other macromolecules are identical in man and the chimpanzee. By contrast, these same molecules show considerable differences among some other mammals that we consider more closely related to each other than are man and the African apes.

The most staggering evolutionary change in the hominid line, of course, was the precipitous increase in brain size during the last 2 million years. Actually, the change is not quite as inexplicable as I and others have claimed in the past. There was a simultaneous increase in body size between, let us say, *afarensis* (estimated weight:36 kg.) and *H. sapiens* (75 kg.), and some of the increase in brain size is due to allometry (Pilbeam and Gould 1974). But even after one performs the necessary scaling, there is still an impressive increase in relative brain size in a (geologically speaking) exceedingly short period of time.

Population Thinking and Geographic Variation

Population thinking, unfortunately, has not yet fully displaced typological thinking in the minds of some students of fossil hominids. How else could a specimen from Laetoli (Tanzania), from a deposit at least a third of a million years older than *A. afarensis* have been typed as *A. afarensis* (Johanson *et al.* 1978)? A species consists of populations that vary in time and space, and there is every reason to believe that the Afar and Laetoli populations were not identical genetically. If further material should show them to differ also taxonomically, we would face a nomenclatural dilemma. This shows how dangerous it is to select the name and the type of a new taxon from two different populations that widely differ in time and space.

Most existing species of animals are composed of partially isolated populations, showing various degrees of geographic variation, with some peripherally isolated populations representing incipient species. This description is well illustrated by the living African apes. The mountain gorilla of East Africa is appreciably different from the lowland gorilla of West Africa. Even stronger are the differences between the two kinds of allopatric chimpanzees, the widespread *Pan troglodytes* and the so-called pygmy chimpanzee (*Pan paniscus*). Yet even the latter, in spite of certain peculiarities, is clearly a chimpanzee. There is every reason to believe that similar differences, perhaps even more pronounced ones, existed in all or at least some of the species of fossil hominids. This possibility must be kept in mind when dealing with *A. africanus*. This species was surely polytypic and there are many indications that *A. robustus* evolved from one of its isolates and *H. habilis* from another one.

As always in the study of fossil species, the picture is made more complicated by the uncertainty of chronological correlation. Geographic variation is indicated for me in the case of *A. robustus* and *A. boisei*, even though they are presumably not contemporaries. The tendency in much of the hominid literature to treat *A. africanus* typologically as an invariant entity is surely misleading and conceals an interesting intermediate stage in the evolution of those species that descended from *A. africanus* (i.e., both *A. robustus* and *H. habilis*).

The Hominid Series

The sequence of steps leading to modern man is now reasonably clear (Figure 1). The earliest known stage is represented by *A. afarensis*, which, although unquestionably an australopithecine, shows certain similarities with the chimpanzee. The fossil footprints of *A. afarensis* indicate that it moved by bipedal walking, but the study of the foot of australopithecines by Lewis (1980) clearly shows that it represents a somewhat intermediate stage between *Pan* and *Homo*. Body size and brain are very small. The tooth arcade is more similar to the rectangular one of *Pan* than to the rounded outline of *Homo*. It is now being realized that even on morphological grounds, the gap between early *Australopithecus* (i.e., *afarensis*) and *Pan* is much smaller than was at first thought. This realization greatly reduces the assumed discrepancy between the data of morphology and those of molecular anthropology. How much further back than 3.8 million years (the earliest age of *A. afarensis*) one has to go to reach the point at which the African apes branched off is uncertain for two reasons: (*a*) the absence of any fossils that could be considered genuine missing links and (*b*) the degree of uncertainty introduced by mosaic evolution. The next stage in hominid evolution after *A. afarensis* is represented by *A. africanus*, which we must postulate to have been a highly polytypic species or at least a species with some highly divergent peripheral isolates. One of these, as I have stated, seems to have given rise to *Homo*, another, to the robust australopithecines. This, so far as we can tell, was the last major branching of the hominid line, even though the *H. erectus* stage is represented by some rather divergent types in space and time, as is also the *H. sapiens* stage, with its extreme representatives of late Neandertal and Cro-Magnon.

While we wait for further fossil finds to clarify the remaining questions, the emphasis is shifting to the selection pressures that were responsible for the rapid changes in the hominid sequence. What changes in niche utilization (e.g., the hunting of large herbivores), social structure (from family to band to tribe), and systems of communication (evolution of speech) were involved, and how did they

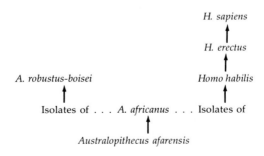

Figure 1   A suggested view of human phylogeny.

interact? Which changes in behavior were pacemakers? What role did the deterioration of climate play in these changes, by increasing certain selection pressures? All of these topics are now actively discussed in the literature, but I shall say no more since this is not my forte. However, it is surely a sign of maturity in physical anthropology that so much emphasis is now placed on the selection forces responsible for, or at least contributory to, the changes in the hominid lineage in contrast to the almost exclusively descriptive morphological approach of former generations.

As one who has observed this field for about 50 years, I do not hesitate to express my extreme satisfaction with the current state of research in hominid evolution and the multiplicity of approaches that have developed toward the solution of the remaining problems.

References

Goodman, M, and R. E. Tashian (editors)
    1976   *Molecular anthropology. Genes and proteins in the evolutionary ascent of the primates.* New York: Plenum.

Greenfield, L. O.
    1978   On the dental arcade reconstructions of *Ramapithecus. Journal of Human Evolution* 7:345–359.

Howell, F. C.
    1957   The evolutionary significance of variation and varieties of "Neanderthal" man. *Quarterly Review of Biology* **32**:330–347.

Johanson, D. C., T. D. White, and Yves Coppens
    1978   A new species of the genus *Australopithecus* (Primates: Hominidae) from the pliocene of Eastern Africa. *Kirtlandia* **28**:3, The Cleveland Museum of Natural History.

Lewis, O. J.
    1980   The joints of the evolving foot. Part III. The fossil evidence. *Journal of Anatomy* **131**(2):275–298.

Mayr, E.
    1950   Taxonomic categories in fossil hominids. *Cold Spring Harbor Symposia on Quantitative Biology* **15**:109–118.
    1977   The study of evolution historically viewed. In *The changing scenes in the natural sciences, 1776–1976,* edited by C. E. Goulden. Pennsylvania: Fulton: Pp. 39–58.

Oakley, K. P., and B. G. Campbell
    1966   *Catalogue of fossil hominids.* London: British Museum (Natural History).

Pilbeam, D., and S. J. Gould
    1974   Size and scaling in human evolution. *Science* **186**:892–901.

Sarich, V. M., and Wilson A.C.
    1967   Immunological time scale for hominoid evolution. *Science* **158**:1200–1203.

Tobias, P. V.
    1980   The natural history of the helicoidal occlusal plane and its evolution in early *Homo. American Journal of Physical Anthropology* **53**:173–188.

Zuckerkandl, E., and L. Pauling
    1965   Evolutionary divergence and convergence in proteins. In *Evolving genes and proteins,* edited by V. Bryson and H. J. Vogel. New York: Academy. Pp. 97–166.

9

American Research on Australopithecines and Early *Homo*, 1925–1980

Noel T. Boaz

Hypotheses prior to 1925 concerning the origin of man posited widely differing times, places, and ancestors for the first hominids. Miller (1920), Straus (1949), Gregory (1949), Kennedy (1960), and McCown and Kennedy (1972) have provided good reviews of the range of these early hypotheses on hominid origins. Although primarily of historical interest now, these ideas have been important in directing paleoanthropological research and in interpreting results, and they have continued to exert their influence, albeit in varying degrees, to the present day.

With the demonstration by Aleš Hrdlička (1912, 1914) that the origin of Hominidae did not lie in the New World, American paleoanthropologists were forced to look to Europe, Asia, or Africa for early hominid remains. Because the European Piltdown find was generally viewed sceptically in America (discussed in a subsequent section of this chapter) and Africa was virtually unknown, Asia, the site of Dubois's *Pithecanthropus* finds (see Trinkaus in the present volume), was favored by many paleontologists and anthropologists as the place of origin of Hominidae. Haeckel (1874) and Wallace (1899) both suggested an Asian birthplace for man, in disagreement with Darwin (1871), who had tended toward an African origin.

In February, 1921, the Central Asiatic Expedition left New York for Peking and Mongolia. Newspapers christened the undertaking the "Missing Link Expedition." Roy Chapman Andrews was to write *On the Trail of Ancient Man* (1926), a chronicle of the expedition's travels and discoveries. Henry Fairfield Osborn, president of the American Museum of Natural History (AMNH), in the forward to Andrews's volume, proclaimed that the Central Asiatic Expedition had discovered the

A HISTORY OF AMERICAN
PHYSICAL ANTHROPOLOGY, 1930–1980

"paleontologic Garden of Eden . . . the Asiatic homeland from which many kinds of reptiles and mammals spread westward and eastward [pp. vii–viii]." Osborn had long considered Asia the birthplace of the primates, including the hominoids (1900, 1918), and his formative influence and subsequent support had been instrumental in Andrew's efforts to launch the expedition to Mongolia (Andrews 1926:xv, 12). This was one of the largest field expeditions in this century devoted wholly or partially to paleoanthropology. It was equipped with 26 scientific personnel, 5 Dodge cars, 2 Fulton trucks, 75 camels, and numerous support personnel. Funded by private donations amounting to $600,000 it was logistically supported by Standard Oil (3000 gallons of gasoline and 50 gallons of oil), Dodge and Fulton Motor Companies, and the United States Rubber Company. Unfortunately, despite the discovery of a Holocene burial and numerous other finds of great paleontological interest (Andrews 1976:306–308), the Central Asiatic Expedition discovered no hominid fossils. One wonders how the history of paleoanthropology would have been affected if the expedition had chosen Africa as its focus.

The Effect of Discoveries
of South African Australopithecines

As the Central Asiatic Expedition was ending its work and about to return to New York, Raymond Dart (1925) published an account of the discovery in South Africa of an ape-like hominid, *Australopithecus africanus*. The response to Dart's (1925) article, particularly in Britain (Broom 1925; Keith 1925; Sollas 1925; and others), had the effect of directing attention towards Africa as an important site of hominoid evolution, if not the actual place of origin of the hominoids. Aleš Hrdlička (1925) early recognized the importance of the Taung skull and in fact was the first foreign anthropologist to visit the site after the discovery (Broom and Schepers 1946:19–20; Dart and Craig 1959). Hrdlička (1925:385) informed the "Science News Service," based in Washington, of the discovery at Taung. The news agency contacted Dart by cable and released a story on the discovery in 1925.

Hrdlička (1925) considered the Taung specimen an anthropoid ape on the basis of molar and craniofacial morphology. He did not attribute any hominid affinities to the specimen largely because of the relatively young age assigned to the site. He attributed importance to the Taung specimen because it demonstrated a more southerly range of apes in Africa than had been known previously (1925:390). But Hrdlička also noted, "Just what relation this fossil form bears, on the one hand, to the human phylum, and on the other to the chimpanzee and gorilla, can only be properly determined after the specimen is well identified, for which are needed additional and adult specimens [1925:390]."

At the 1929 meeting of the British Association for the Advancement of Science in

Johannesburg, during which, parenthetically, Louis Leakey first met Raymond Dart and Robert Broom (L. S. B. Leakey 1974), Alfred S. Romer (then professor of anatomy at the University of Chicago) took the opportunity to study the Taung specimen. His opinion differed from that of Hrdlička. Although unsure of its hominid affinities, Romer stated that Taung could be classified neither as a chimpanzee nor as a gorilla (Romer 1930).

William King Gregory, of the AMNH must be considered the first American worker to endorse *Australopithecus* as a hominid. In the published version of a paper presented at the first meeting of the American Association of Physical Anthropologists (AAPA) in Charlottesville, he stated, "Whatever be the exact age of *Australopithecus*, it is probably not earlier than the late Tertiary and yet it had a progressive anthropoid brain and a primitive human dentition, indicating that it was not far removed from the common source of the two families (Hominidae and Simiidae), as maintained from the first by Dart [1930:138–139]." This paper marks a clear break between Gregory and his superior at the AMNH, Henry Fairfield Osborn, who had continued to support an Asiatic origin of "large-brained Tertiary Man" (1927, 1930:3). His article (1930) entitled "The Discovery of Tertiary Man" does not mention *Australopithecus*.

A major portion of Osborn's argument against an African and hominoid ancestry for Hominidae had to do with locomotor adaptation (see Fleagle and Jungers in the present volume). Invoking Dollo's Law of Irreversibility in evolution, Osborn stated that "the brachiating hand of the ape was used as a hook . . . and the thumb was therefore a grave danger [1927:301]." If man had gone through a long period of brachiating, according to Osborn, he would have lost his thumb. Thus, Osborn believed that "the most welcome gift from anthropology to humanity will be the banishment of the myth and bogie of ape–man ancestry and the substitution of a long line of ancestors of our own at the dividing point that separates the terrestrial from the arboreal lines of primates [1927:301]."

Gregory (1930) did not agree, entitling his paper "A Critique of Professor Osborn's Theory of Human Origin." In addition to discussing the Taung specimen at length, the paper used evidence of titanothere evolution from the early Oligocene of the American West, a project on which Gregory had collaborated with Osborn (Osborn 1929:xix). Gregory (1930) illustrated cases of apparent reversibility in mammalian evolution, noting that a good paleontological record was necessary to document the history of any evolutionary lineage. Along with Broom (1925), Sollas (1925, 1926), and Adloff (1932), Gregory must be considered one of the staunchest early supporters of Dart's claim of hominid status for *Australopithecus*.

Until 1936, there were no additional australopithecines to answer Hrdlička's (1925) reservations. But in that year, Robert Broom "thought [he] would start collecting in the Transvaal limestone caves, in the hope of getting an adult *Australopithecus*, or at least some early human remains [Broom and Schepers 1946:43]." On August 17, 1936, only his third visit to a quarry at Sterkfontein, Broom recovered a fragmentary adult cranium with teeth (TM 1511), which he named *Australopithecus* (later *Plesianthropus*) *transvaalensis* (Broom 1936). This find launched the period of discovery of early hominids in South Africa for which Robert Broom provided the major impetus until his death in 1951.

Americans W. K. Gregory and Milo Hellman visited South Africa in 1938 to study the then-available sample of early hominids. Their conclusions, published in a series of papers (Gregory and Hellman 1938, 1939a, 1939b), confirmed australopithecines as hominids and proposed the subfamily designation, Australopithecinae, that is still generally accepted. Gregory continued work on australopithecines in the following several years, publishing a reconstructed view of the Sterkfontein australopithecine skull (Gregory 1940, 1945).

The Second World War halted investigations in South Africa, but in 1947, Broom resumed work at Sterkfontein despite "active opposition to [his] explosive methods [Terry 1974:13]." An expedition led by P. V. Tobias, then a second-year medical student, in July 1945 to the cave site of Makapansgat prompted renewed interest in the site (Dart 1957), culminating in the discovery in September, 1947 of the MLD 1 cranium by J. Kitching. Dart published the discovery under the new taxonomic name of *Australopithecus prometheus* in the *American Journal of Physical Anthropology* (*AJPA*) (1948).

American interest in South African australopithecines also revived after World War II. Charles Camp, of the Museum of Paleontology at the University of California, Berkeley, led an expedition to South Africa in August 1947, in order "to search for further fossil evidence of the anatomical form, habits, environment, and geological age of the remarkable australopithecine man–apes [Camp 1948:550]." This expedition spent 6 months investigating some 30 sites in the vicinity of Taung. No additional hominid fossils were recovered, although the geology of Taung was clarified and the absence of evidence of fire or stone artifacts was confirmed (Barbour 1949:139; Camp 1948).

From April to July, 1948, the University of California Expedition excavated 26 pits at the site of Bolt's Farm, 1.6 km from Sterkfontein. Camp (1948:551) originally reported that an australopithecine femur was discovered at each of two of these pits, but these have subsequently been identified as belonging to machairodont felids (F. C. Howell, personal communication 1981). Meanwhile, at the nearby Sterkfontein Type Site, where Broom's blasting had yielded, on April 18 1947, the complete cranium of Sts 5, hominid fossils were being consistently recovered during April to July, 1948 (Broom *et al.* 1950; Broom 1951:73–77; Oakley *et al.* 1977), albeit without clear stratigraphical context. The effect of presumed competitiveness between Broom's group and the Berkeley group was likely behind the statement made by E. A. Hooton of Harvard University:

> No American institution should intrude itself into this particular area [South Africa] for purposes of independent explorations, but perhaps some young American anthropologists might be permitted to work under Broom and Dart. The United States should play its usual role of financial assistance (but without occupation). Here we can be assured that the money will not be wasted. The scientific dividends will be huge [1950:504–505].

This dissuasion apparently worked. Although further discoveries and scientific developments in South Africa affected hypotheses by American paleoanthropologists, future American exploration for early hominids along the multidisciplinary lines outlined by Camp (1948) was to be refocused on another part of Africa, the eastern Rift Valley.

By the time of Broom's death in 1951, discoveries in South Africa had wrought a profound change in attitudes toward the australopithecines. Following the studies by Gregory (1930, 1949), Gregory and Hellman (1938), and Le Gros Clark (1947, 1948), most anthropologists accepted *Australopithecus* as hominid. But the acceptance of hominid and possibly ancestral human status for *Australopithecus* created a problem in interpreting other fossil evidence for hominid evolution in the Pliocene—early Pleistocene. For example, *Eoanthropus dawsoni*, of supposed similar age to *A. africanus*, had quite different morphology, and how this specimen fit into the human evolutionary scheme with *Australopithecus* was indeed a difficult question to answer.

The Debunking of a Supposed Pliocene Hominid, *Eoanthropus*

Eoanthropus dawsoni (Smith Woodward 1912) came to light between 1908 and 1915 at Piltdown, Sussex, England. It was the first major find of a fossil hominid of great antiquity since Dubois's discoveries of *Homo erectus* in Java in the 1890s, and it consequently become the focus of intense and worldwide scientific interest. Primary interest in the specimen since the demonstration by Weiner *et al.* (1953) that it was fraudulent has rested in the identity of the hoaxer or hoaxers.

Weiner (1955) made a convincing case against Charles Dawson, the English solicitor and amateur collector, and there is little reason to doubt it. As with many great crimes, however, there are other theories. Millar (1972) indicted G. Elliot Smith, Douglas (Halstead 1978) left a posthumous tape recording pointing to W. J. Sollas as the culprit, and Gould (1980) has suggested Teilhard de Chardin as Dawson's co-conspirator. Apart from the question of the identity of the Piltdown forger, general opinion has held that the Piltdown case is a scientific tragedy: "Piltdown absorbed the professional attention of many fine scientists. It led millions of people astray for forty years. It cast a false light upon the basic processes of human evolution. Careers are too short and time too precious to view so much waste with equanimity [Gould 1980:28]."

In another sense, the demise of Piltdown Man ushers in the modern period of paleoanthropology. The debunking of Piltdown, along with the australopithecine evidence from South Africa, confirmed that bipedalism had occurred prior to the significant cranial vault expansion characteristic of the genus *Homo*. The debates over the association of the cranial and the mandibular fossils focused on general questions that would later go under the rubrics *functional morphology* and *taphonomy*. The fact that the forgery was discovered at all is a testament to the then newly developed chemical dating techniques (Oakley 1955, 1964), an important part of increasing sophistication in the geologic and geochronological under-standing of hominid fossil sites. In a broader sense, the Piltdown case confirmed that although differences in individual interpretations and theoretical predilections can and do affect scientific hypotheses, recourse to empirical results does solve problems. After 1953, no one could use evidence from Piltdown to support a hypothesis of hominid phylogeny.

Piltdown, however, did not have the same effect in America as it had in England and France. In 1915 and again in 1918, Miller had reviewed the available evidence and concluded that the Piltdown mandible and cranium probably were not associated, that the former was probably an ape and the latter was not necessarily particularly primitive in its morphology. Hrdlička (1922) and Gregory (1929) reached essentially the same conclusions. Osborn's hypothesis (1930) of an early, "terrestrial" divergence of hominids, which was hardly recognized as probable by 1953, was compromised by the removal of Piltdown.

The Input of Biological Sciences into Early Hominid Studies

Aleš Hrdlička died in 1943 and the editorship of the *AJPA* passed into the hands of T. Dale Stewart. Stewart initiated the New Series of the *AJPA* with a virtually new editorial board. The format and content of the journal changed. There were no "notes," editorials, or literature notes and there were fewer reviews. The changes in The *AJPA* reflected changes in the *AAPA*: The field had become diversified, with more members spread over a larger number of institutions (Spencer in the present volume). Hominid evolution, perhaps the major component of the Old Series, now shared space in the journal with studies on growth, dermatoglyphics, genetics, and human biology in general (see Lovejoy *et al.* in the present volume). Volume 1 of the New Series of the *AJPA* signals the beginning of a turning away from typology in hominid evolutionary thinking.

An article by R. Ruggles Gates of Woods Hole Marine Biological Laboratory entitled "Phylogeny and Classification of Hominids and Anthropoids" (1944) is illustrative of this change. Discussing the (largely hypothetical) genetic causation of certain morphological features, such as inca bones, Gates called attention to the importance of time and space in hominid evolution. But, at the same time, he speaks of the evolution of human "types."

In a much more influential article, "On Species and Races of Living and Fossil Man" (1944), written by the geneticist Theodosius Dobzhansky, the relations between morphology and genetics, and taxonomy and morphology were outlined from the standpoint of populations of evolving hominids. Dobzhansky was searching for a rapprochement of genetic theory and paleoanthropological data. In reference to Franz Weidenreich's interpretations of *Homo erectus,* he stated, "though made strictly from the point of view of a morphologist, Weidenreich's conclusions deserve careful attention of geneticists interested in the structure and evolution of human populations [1944:251]."

In addition to a switch from typological to populational thinking, another trend in paleoanthropology was the move away from pure description and anthropometric treatment toward an explanatory paradigm. Sherwood L. Washburn and embryologist S. R. Detwiller (1943) collaborated on a study relating the development of the growing eyeball to orbit size in the amphibian *Amblystoma.* They suggested that in like manner, "when description and logic fail to provide an indisputable explanation, anthropologists should avail themselves of experimental methods [1943:174]."

These trends came together at a multidisciplinary conference, "Origin and Evolution of Man," held in Cold Spring Harbor, New York, June 9–17, 1950, which was attended by physical and cultural anthropologists, geneticists, zoologists, and paleontologists. The sessions that have been the most far-reaching in their influence on paleoanthropology were "Origin of the Human Stock" (papers by A. H. Schultz, G. G. Simpson and S. L. Washburn) and "Classification of Fossil Men" (papers by T. D. McCown, T. D. Stewart, and E. Mayr). Mayr (1951) suggested that the australopithecines be classified as *Homo transvaalensis,* a proposition that even shocked Dart (Dart and Craig 1959).

Soon after the Cold Spring Harbor Symposium, Washburn (1951) codified the "new physical anthropology," a term that is still applicable and used (e.g., Birdsell 1981). The "new physical anthropology" was an update on "experimental physical anthropology" and incorporated functional, populational, and behavioral approaches, as distinct from the descriptive and typological "old physical anthropology" (see Hunt 1981).

The Effect of Discoveries of Early Hominids in Eastern Africa

Louis S. B. Leakey first traveled to Olduvai Gorge during the third of his East African Expeditions in 1931, and there he discovered the first Oldowan stone artifacts (Leakey 1937). During the fourth expedition in 1935, he recovered the first australopithecine from East Africa, which consisted of a lower canine (M.18773), from the Laetolil Beds south of Olduvai. This fact has only been recently recognized (White 1981). Ludwig Kohl-Larsen (1943:379–381) found an australopithecine maxillary fragment (Garusi 1) at the same site 4 years later (as well as a single molar, Garusi 2, and an edentulous maxilla, Garusi 3, of unclear age or affinities). It was not until the discovery, in 1959 by M. D. Leakey, of the first robust australopithecine, a cranium, at Olduvai (OH 5; L. S. B. Leakey 1959) that

Americans became involved in early hominid research in eastern Africa. Richard Hay, a geologist from the University of California, Berkeley, began stratigraphic studies at Olduvai in 1962 (Hay 1976:xv). Grommé and Hay (1963) established the paleomagnetic "Olduvai Event" and the Berkeley geophysicists J. F. Evernden and Garniss Curtis (1965) dated Bed I at Olduvai to 1.8 million years B.P. using the potassium–argon method. Funding by the United States National Geographic Society that began in 1960 allowed intensive investigation, which yielded on November 2, 1960, a partial cranial vault, a mandible, and the fragments of a hominid (OH 7) that was to become a holotype of *Homo habilis* (L. S. B. Leakey *et al.* 1964). Thus was established the first clear association of early *Homo* with robust australopithecines.

In 1959, F. Clark Howell, then of the University of Chicago, traveled to the lower Omo Valley of Ethiopia in order to reconnoiter the area for future work. Research was finally arranged during a meeting between L. S. B. Leakey and Emperor Haile Selassie, who gave permission for an expedition to be mounted from Nairobi (L. S. B. Leakey 1974). Geologist F. H. Brown, of the University of California, Berkeley, began stratigraphic work at Omo in 1966, and a full-scale, multidisciplinary, Franco–American–Kenyan expedition began work in 1967. The first early hominid encountered was an australopithecine mandible (Omo 18-67-18), found by the French team 35 years after its director, Camille Arambourg, had first visited Omo (Coppens 1976). The Omo Research Expedition recovered some 238 fossil hominids over a very well-controlled temporal span of 2.5 million years B.P. The scale of the Omo Expedition provided a model for later projects.

Using the expedition's helicopter, Richard Leakey, the leader of the Kenyan team, found fossiliferous sites to the east of Lake Turkana, to which he moved in 1968. Another member of the Omo Expedition, Donald Johanson, through his association with French geologist Maurice Taieb via Yves Coppens, began investigating fossiliferous deposits in the Hadar region of Ethiopia in 1972. Fossils in this area had first been collected by Taieb in 1969 (Coppens 1975).

Discoveries at Hadar broke new ground. The 1973 find of an articulated distal femur and proximal tibia (AL 129-1a, AL 129-1b) became the earliest then known evidence for bipedalism (Johanson and Coppens 1976); a largely intact skeleton (AL 288-1) is the most complete individual specimen from so ancient a time period; and the AL 333 site has provided the oldest sample of fossil hominids who probably lived in a single population (Johanson and White 1979).

The renewed investigations at Laetoli by M. D. Leakey, beginning in 1974, have now revealed 24 hominid fossils, mostly teeth and cranial parts, which have been described by T. D. White (1977, 1980b) of the University of California, Berkeley. Most important are trails of two bipedally progressing hominids, the earliest and most incontrovertible evidence of bipedalism (M. D. Leakey and Hay 1979).

Paleoanthropological research at Olduvai, Laetoli, Omo, East Lake Turkana, and Hadar were to provide fossil hominids, artifacts, chronological data, and paleoenvironmental data to answer questions that had been unclear in South Africa. New questions were also posed, but, for the first time, contextual data were available to begin to test more rigorously hypotheses on evolutionary relationships and behavior of early hominids.

It was clear that *H. habilis* had co-existed with *A. boisei* at Olduvai, Omo, and East Lake Turkana. Stone artifacts found at these and other sites were of uncertain association but were generally attributed to *H. habilis* (M. D. Leakey 1975). The dating of Hadar and Laetoli showed that the hominids from these sites were earlier than, or at the lower range of ages for, the South African gracile australopithecines (Tobias 1980), but their taxonomic and phylogenetic affinities are under debate. Sites around the Baringo area (Lothagam, Lukeino, Ngorora) provided the only fragmentary evidence for the immediate ancestors of the australopithecines (Howell 1978). Interpretations of these data have profoundly affected early hominid research.

Field Methods: Development of Theory and Method for Data Collection

As was noted previously, the collection techniques (i.e., blasting with dynamite) used by Broom in South Africa prompted criticism. This was muted however by Broom's success in discovering hominid fossils. But the contexts, stratigraphic and cultural, in the South African cave sites were in most cases unclear, and stratigraphic control has only been accomplished ex post facto (Butzer 1976; Partridge 1978, 1979). Nevertheless, behavioral questions were posed and answered (e.g., [osteodontokeratic] tool use by *A. africanus* [Dart 1957], fire use at Makapansgat by *A. "prometheus"* [Dart 1948], and interpersonal aggression by *A. africanus* [Dart 1957; Dart and Craig 1959]). A new generation of very able South African researchers (Tobias and Hughes 1969; Brain 1972, 1978; Vrba 1974, 1975) have continued this work and refined earlier interpretations on the basis of more careful excavation and sedimentological and biostratigraphic methods.

Eastern Africa, however, has witnessed the biggest steps in methodological progress in early hominid studies with the formation of multidisciplinary research projects. The idea of involving a number of scientists, each one an expert on a particular faunal group or aspect of a site, evolved at Olduvai as more data and more funding became available (L. S. B. Leakey 1974). But the Omo Research Expedition was the first to put this theory into practice—sending a geologist (F. H. Brown) in the field *prior* to the discovery of fossil hominids was indeed a novel, if logical, step (Howell 1968). Other subsequent research projects at Hadar (Johanson *et al.* 1978a) and Sahabi (Boaz *et al.* 1979) have also followed this procedure. The fact that early rigorous geological and stratigraphic work was not undertaken at Koobi Fora was partially responsible for subsequent dating problems at this site.

Since 1965, when Evernden and Curtis published their potassium–argon data for Olduvai Bed I, geochronological studies have become an important component of fieldwork. The increasing use and reliance on potassium–argon, paleomagnetic and fission-track dating methods was signaled by the publication of the volume, *Calibration of Hominoid Evolution* (Bishop and Miller 1972) in which results from the major early hominid sites were discussed. Absolute dates, in conjunction with biostratigraphic data, have become more important in cross-site comparisons. The controversy over the age of the KBS Tuff at Koobi Fora, with its significant implications for evolution of the genus *Homo* (Boaz 1979b; Cronin *et al.* 1981), was eventually resolved by both absolute and relative (biostratigraphic) methods (Hay 1980).

In addition to accurate geochronology, the multidisciplinary approach allowed total extraction of data from a site, which was necessary for the solution to paleoecological questions (discussed in a later section of this chapter) that were being asked. Sound geology is needed prior to taphonomic studies, which, in turn, are necessary to relate fossil taxa to past environments.

Computer cataloging of fauna was also pioneered by the Omo Research Expedition, particularly by G. G. Eck and F. H. Brown. In addition to greater efficiency in updating information about a fossil collection as well as easier sorting of specimens in selected ways, a computer format allows much easier manipulation of large data sets to obtain solutions to particular problems. Using the Omo computerized data as a base, Shuey *et al.* (1978) employed a statistical method of faunal similarity measures to prove the misdating of the sub-KBS fauna at Koobi Fora, as compared to Omo.

Controlled excavation has been employed by several researchers and accounts for some of the most important findings in Pliocene–Pleistocene hominid studies. Mary D. Leakey (1971) and G. L. Isaac (1976) have discovered artifactual occurrences in association with faunal remains at Olduvai and Koobi Fora. Mary D. Leakey and T. D. White at Laetoli (M. D. Leakey and Hay 1979) and A. K. Behrensmeyer at Koobi Fora (Behrensmeyer and Laporte 1981) excavated early hominid footprints. White (1980b) subsequently calculated stature from the Laetoli tracks, and Charteris *et al.* (1981) deduced the speed of walking ("strolling"). Boaz (1979a) calculated early hominid population densities on the basis of excavations at Omo.

Excavation, geochronology, stratigraphic control, and multidisciplinary field research have allowed approaches to long-standing problems in early hominid studies. As yet, there have been too few of these "modern" research projects. Although they are much more expensive and, therefore, more difficult to fund, they provide the only methodological lines along which future progress will be made.

Development of Hominid Paleoecology as an Outgrowth of the "New Physical Anthropology"

Unlike other fossil hominid taxa, *Australopithecus africanus* was from the first (Dart 1925) connected with an environment distinct from that of the pongids. Dart (1925:199) claimed that the environment at Taung had been an "open veldt," based on the site's closeness to the Kalahari Desert. The environment, and the relationships of hominids to other animals, plants, and natural resources within it (ecology), became of even more importance in the "new physical anthropological" approach to hominid evolution, with its interest in behavior. The beginning of a specialty of hominid paleoecology dates from the publication—by George Bartholomew, an ecologist, and J. B. Birdsell, a physical anthropologist, both of UCLA—of "Ecology and the Protohominids" (1953). This paper provided a theoretical basis for understanding the adaptations of small-bodied, generalized hominid ancestors within a grassland–savanna mosaic environment and has been one of the most widely cited papers in the field.

Empirical assessments of the paleoecology of early hominids have been based on geologic, primarily sedimentological, research (e.g., Brain [1958] and Butzer [1974] in South Africa and Hay [1976] in eastern Africa); associated mammalian microfauna (e.g., Cartmill 1967; Jaeger and Wesselman 1976); associated large mammals (Vrba 1974, 1975); or combinations of these approaches (Behrensmeyer 1975; Boaz 1977). Aspects of hominid paleoecology and behavior have been treated by analogy with extant primates (DeVore and Washburn 1963; McGrew *et al.* 1979) and social carnivores (Schaller and Lowther 1969).

A central concern in early hominid paleoecology has been the resolution of aspects of the so-called dietary hypothesis of J. T. Robinson (1954, 1963), in which is hypothesized that robust *Australopithecus* and coexisting early *Homo* were ecologically separated by dietary differences. The former was hypothesized to be a vegetarian feeder, whereas the latter was an omnivore. This formulation, although now considered overly simplistic, is still a reasonable interpretation of morphological differences between robust australopithecines and *Homo*. Portions of Robinson's hypothesis have been modified and retained. Work by Vrba (1975) and Boaz (1977) indicates that *A. robustus* and *A. boisei* probably lived in relatively open grasslands, rather than in wooded areas, as hypothesized by Robinson. Wallace (1975) failed to see major differences in dental wear between the South African gracile and robust australopithecines, and Weiss (1972) noted the lack of a preponderance of robust hominids in the fossil record, which would be expected if they were herbivorous. These objections to the dietary hypothesis have yet to be adequately answered.

The single species hypothesis, formulated by C. L. Brace (1973) and M. H. Wolpoff (1971) of the University of Michigan was an update of the suggestion by

Mayr (1951) that all fossil hominids at any one time in the past have belonged to a single species. Brace and Wolpoff suggested that because all hominids supposedly occupied a cultural ecological niche and thus were able to adapt to a very broad range of environmental conditions, no two species could coexist; eventually one would exclude the other. The clear demonstration that two hominid species had existed at one time in the past, *A. boisei* (KNM-ER 406) and *H. erectus* (KNM-ER 3733) in the Upper Member of the Koobi Fora Formation (R. E. F. Leakey and Walker 1976), as well as robust australopithecines and *H. habilis* at other sites (Howell 1978), showed that one or more assumptions of the single species hypothesis were incorrect. However, the cultural capabilities of *A. boisei* were probably not as advanced as those of *Homo*.

Diet is one aspect of paleoecological research on hominids that has received much recent attention. Peters (1979) and Peters and O'Brien (1981) reviewed evidence for early hominid diet and provided comparative living primate data. Enamel microwear studies (Walker *et al.* 1978), though promising, have not yet yielded unequivocable results on early hominid diets. Covert and Kay (1981) have pointed out that different diets can produce the same type of dental wear. Ryan (1979) has suggested, on the basis of the incisor wear of AL 400-1a, that vegetation was stripped by being pulled through the mouth.

Taphonomy has taken an important place in the chain of deduction in paleoecology in recent years. Brain's (1972, 1978) work in South Africa has shown that australopithecine bones have accumulated in caves due to collection by carnivores with different prey-size specializations and that the hominids did not live there. Work at Koobi Fora (Behrensmeyer 1975), investigations into the processes of bone deposition in modern environments (Behrensmeyer and Boaz 1980; Shipman and Walker 1980; Shipman and Phillips 1976), and experimental results (Boaz and Behrensmeyer 1976) have drawn attention to the need for caution in drawing paleoecological conclusions. Taphonomic conditions can affect morphological considerations (e.g., interpreting the AL 333 hominids at Hadar as a true biological population [Johanson and White 1979]), or the interpretation of paleodemographic profiles of early hominids (Mann 1975), depending on how the death assemblages (thanatocoenoses) truly represent life assemblages (biocoenoses). Taphonomy is still developing its methodology and theoretical formulations, but, even now, it is an important part of hominid paleoecology.

Importance of Functional Morphology to Early Hominid Studies

The first studies on australopithecine postcranial remains were undertaken by W. L. Straus (1948a, 1948b) of Johns Hopkins University. These studies, from both functional and taxonomic standpoints, have been continued by numerous workers, many of them at American institutions. John T. Robinson, now of the University of Wisconsin, Madison, published *Early Hominid Posture and Locomotion* in 1972, using arguments based on the lower limb morphology of South African australopithecines to deduce that they were more arboreal than had been previously thought. Others contested this view on the basis of damage apparent on certain fossils, which precluded Robinson's morphological interpretation.

The australopithecines were initially looked to for confirmation or refutation of the suggestion of an arboreal, knuckle-walking, or quadrupedal mode of locomotion for the ancestors of the hominids. Oxnard (1975) used multivariate studies on australopithecine postcrania, which indicated affinities with *Pongo*, to argue against gracile australopithecines being ancestral to *Homo*. Others (Lovejoy *et al.* 1973; Zihlman 1978) though not all (Prost 1980), however, have confirmed that australopithecines were fully bipedal.

Napier (1967), in his study of the OH 7 hand attributed to *H. habilis*, suggested that its morphology showed the capability of a "precision grip," consistent with tool making and tool use. Susman and Stern (1979) more recently have restudied this fossil and concluded that on the basis of its strong flexor attachments, it suggests an arboreal adaptation, which could as easily be interpreted as a strong, grasping adaptation relating to stone tool use.

Perhaps the most historically important area of functional morphological studies has been in the interpretation of early hominid endocranial casts (see Falk, in the present volume). Schepers (in Broom and Schepers 1946) attempted functional interpretations of the Taung endocast, concluding that it was hominid-like. Falk (1980) has more recently reviewed and modified Schepers's conclusions, suggesting that *A. africanus* endocasts resemble pongids at a gross level. Ralph Holloway, of Columbia University, has developed methods for accurately obtaining endocranial estimates (e.g., 1975), an important taxonomic feature. Yet, it is clear that there is still much work to be undertaken in the functional interpretations of early hominid endocranial cast morphology.

Relating form to function has been a research focus of American physical anthropology for some time, and it has seen expression, for example, in Washburn's "experimental physical anthropology" (Washburn and Detwiler 1943). Washburn's study of the temporalis muscle (1947) as well as doctoral dissertations written under his direction at the University of Chicago in the 1950s on split-line patterns (by N. Tappen, F. C. Howell and L. Mednik) were directed toward an understanding of the variables in cranial and postcranial morphology. Current work on electromyography (e.g., Tuttle *et al.* 1978), cineradiography (e.g., Jenkins 1972), dental wear and morphology (e.g., Kay 1975), and the relation of morphology to locomotor behavior and environmental substrates (e.g., Morbeck *et al.* 1979) hold promise for future interpretations of early hominid functional morphology. Zihlman *et al.* (1978) have related *Pan paniscus* to early australopithecines on the basis of similar morphology and presumed similar behavior.

Interpretations of Early Hominid Phylogeny

The evolutionary relationships of the australopithecines and early *Homo* have been recently reviewed by Howell (1978), Johanson and White (1979), Boaz (1977, 1982), Cronin *et al.* (1981) and White *et al.* (1981). An earlier bias toward emphasizing the hominid-like features of early, gracile australopithecines (e.g., Le Gros Clark 1947) has given way somewhat in favor of calling attention to aspects of early australopithecine morphology that are pongid-like (Johanson *et al.* 1978b). Problems associated with assessing individual, populational, and specific variation account for disagreements in the phylogenetic placement of early australopithecines. Although Tobias (1978, 1980) and Boaz (1982) consider Laetoli and Hadar samples conspecific with South African *A. africanus* and ancestral to *Homo*, Johanson and White (1979) have erected a new species, *A. afarensis*, that is alone ancestral to *Homo* and have relegated *A. africanus* to a divergent lineage leading to robust autralopithecines (White *et. al.* 1981). Further work in the 2–3-million-year time period will be necessary for resolution of this problem.

The ancestry of the robust australopithecines is unclear. *A. robustus* and *A. boisei* appear in the fossil record at 2 million years B.P in both eastern and southern Africa. Their antecedents are unknown or poorly known. Although Robinson (1963) hypothesized that the robust australopithecine condition was primitive for hominids, further research has disproved this theory. Robust australopithecines must have evolved from hominids similar to *A. africanus* (Rak 1981) or *A. afarensis*.

Although "presapiens" ideas have persisted (e.g., R. E. F. Leakey 1974), morphological continuities and dating support the evolution of early *Homo* from gracile australopithecines. Contrary to suggestions that the appearance of the genus was sudden (Gould and Eldredge 1977), change to the *Homo* condition seems to have been mosaic and graduated over time (Cronin *et al.* 1981).

The gap between estimates of the date of hominid origin proffered by biomolecular anthropologists (Sarich and Cronin 1976) and paleoanthropologists (see Boaz 1982; Cronin and Meikle 1982) is narrowing. A component of this relatively recent change in opinion is the redating of Siwalik *Ramapithecus* and the collection of more complete specimens indicating orangutan-like and not hominid-like morphology (Andrews and Tekkaya 1980).

Conclusions and Future Directions in Early Hominid Research

The search for remains of early hominids has undergone considerable change over the past 50 years. The first fossils were recovered by largely individual efforts and frequently by chance. The development of the multidisciplinary field project as a paleoanthropological research strategy has made the approach to paleobehavioral questions possible, but it has also raised the cost of finding early hominid fossils.

Table 1 estimates the cost per hominid of projects that have successfully recovered fossil hominid remains. Other projects, such as the Central Asiatic Expedition, funded at $600,000 in 1921, found no hominid fossils. Thus, estimates of the cost of recovering hominids in Table 1 are minimum values. Without significant curtailment of scientific goals, funding for future paleoanthropological research projects will have to surpass past levels.

Future work, if funding can be obtained, will be focused on poorly documented portions of the early hominid record—before 4 million years B.P., between 2 and 3 million years B.P., and on other geographic areas outside eastern and southern Africa. Paleoecological and taphonomic studies and functional analyses of early hominids will provide increasingly complete reconstructions of early hominid behavior. The need for intercommunication among earth scientists, paleontologists, and paleoanthropologists on research projects will be solved by the establishment of multidisciplinary institutes, where modern paleoanthropology can be efficiently undertaken. Let us hope that American paleoanthropologists and institutions will play as constructive a role in these future developments in early hominid studies as they have in the past 50 years.

References

Adloff, P.
    1932   Das Gebiss von *Australopithecus africanus. Zeitschrift fuer Anatomie und Entwicklungsgeschichte* **97**:145–156.
Andrews, P., and I. Tekkaya
    1980   A revision of the Turkish Miocene hominoid *Sivapithecus meteai. Paleontology* **23**:85–95.

Table 1   The Comparative Cost of Recovering Hominid Fossils in Africa over the Last Thirty Years[a]

Project	Years funded	Total field budget ($)	Source of funding[b]	Number of hominids recovered	Cost per hominid ($)
Omo[c]	1967–1974	750,000	NSF/WG/LSBL	238	3,151
Koobi Fora	1968–1981	1,442,600	NSF/NGS	120	12,021
Olduvai	1959–1981	850,000	NGS/LSBL	54	15,741
Laetoli	1974–1981	170,000	NGS/LSBL	24	7,083
Hadar[d]	1973–1979	500,000	NGS/NSF/LSBL	150	3,333
Natron	1965	20,000	NGS	1	20,000
Sahabi	1977–1981	143,000	NSF/NGS/LSBL	3	47,667
Totals		3,875,600		590	15,571

[a]Amounts shown are actual award amounts, uncorrected for inflation.
[b]NSF, National Science Foundation; WG, Wenner-Gren Foundation for Anthropological Research; LSBL, L.S.B. Leakey Foundation; NGS, National Geographic Society.
[c]Not including early exploration by Arambourg in 1931–32, H. Mukiri in 1946, and F.C. Howell in 1959.
[d]Not including contributions by the Centre National de la Recherche Scientifique, Paris.

Andrews, R. C.
   1926   *On the trail of ancient man.* New York: Putnam.
Barbour, G. B.
   1949   Ape or man? An incomplete chapter of human ancestry from South Africa. *Ohio Journal of Science* **49**:129–145.
Bartholomew, G. A., and J. B. Birdsell
   1953   Ecology and the protohominids. *American Anthropologist* **55**:481–498.
Behrensmeyer, A. K.
   1975   The taphonomy and paleoecology of Plio–Pleistocene vertebrate assemblages east of Lake Rudolf, Kenya. *Bulletin of the Museum of Comparative Zoology* **146**:473–578.
Behrensmeyer, A. K., and D. Boaz
   1980   The recent bones of Amboseli National Park, Kenya, in relation to East African paleoecology. In *Fossils in the making*, edited by A. K. Behrensmeyer and A. P. Hill. Chicago: University of Chicago Press. Pp. 72–92.
Behrensmeyer, A. K., and L. Laporte
   1981   Footprints of a Pleistocene hominid in northern Kenya. *Nature (London)* **289**:167–169.
Birdsell, J. B.
   1981   *Human evolution: an introduction to the new physical anthropology* (third edition). Boston: Houghton Mifflin.
Bishop, W. W., and J. A. Miller (editors)
   1972   *Calibration of hominoid evolution.* Edinburgh: Scottish Academic Press.
Boaz, N. T.
   1977   Paleoecology of early Hominidae in Africa. *Kroeber Anthropological Society Papers* **50**:37–62.
   1979a   Early hominid population densities: new estimates. *Science* **206**:592–595.
   1979b   Hominid evolution in eastern Africa during the Pliocene and early Pleistocene. *Annual Review of Anthropology* **8**:71–85.
   1982   Morphological trends and phylogenetic relationships from Middle Miocene hominoids to Late Pliocene hominids. In *New interpretations of ape and human ancestry*, edited by R. L. Ciochon and R. S. Corruccini. New York: Plenum, in press.
Boaz, N. T., and A. K. Behrensmeyer
   1976   Hominid taphonomy: transport of skeletal parts in an artificial fluvial environment. *American Journal of Physical Anthropology* **45**:53–60.
Boaz, N. T., A. W. Gaziry, and A. El-Arnauti
   1979   New fossil finds from the Libyan Upper Neogene site of Sahabi. *Nature (London)* **280**:137–140.
Brace, C. L.
   1973   Sexual dimorphism in human evolution. *Yearbook of Physical Anthropology* **16**:31–49.
Brain, C. K.
   1958   Transvaal ape–man-bearing cave deposits. *Transvaal Museum Memoirs* **11**.
   1972   An attempt to reconstruct the behavior of *Australopithecus*: the evidence for interpersonal violence. *South African Museum Association Bulletin* **9**:127–139.
   1978   Some aspects of the South African australopithecine sites and their bone accumulations. In *Early hominids of Africa*, edited by C. Jolly. New York: St. Martin's Press. Pp. 131–161.
Broom, R.
   1925   Some notes on the Taungs skull. *Nature (London)* **115**:569–571.
   1936   A new fossil anthropoid skull from Sterkfontein, near Krugersdorp, South Africa. *Nature (London)* **138**:486–488.
   1951   *Finding the missing link.* London: Watts.
Broom, R., and G. W. H. Schepers
   1946   The South African fossil ape–men. *Transvaal Museum Memoirs* **2**.
Broom, R., J. T. Robinson, and G. W. H. Schepers
   1950   Further evidence of the structure of the Sterkfontein ape–man *Plesianthropus* (I); The brain casts of the recently discovered *Plesianthropus* skulls (II). *Transvaal Museum Memoirs* **4**.

Butzer, K. W.
  1974   Paleoecology of South African australopithecines: Taung revisited. *Current Anthropology*
          15:367–382.
  1976   Lithostratigraphy of the Swartkrans formation. *South African Journal of Science* 72:136–141.
Camp, C. L.
  1948   University of California Expedition—southern section. *Science* 108:550–552.
Cartmill, M.
  1967   The early Pleistocene mammalian micro-faunas of sub-Saharan Africa and their ecological
          significance. *Quaternaria* 9:169–198.
Charteris, J., J. C. Wall, and J. W. Nottrodt
  1981   Functional reconstruction of gait from the Pliocene hominid footprints at Laetoli, northern
          Tanzania. *Nature (London)* 290:496–498.
Coppens, Y.
  1975   L'Éthiopie a l'aube du Quarternaire: Les grands gisements de vertébrés de l'Omo et de
          l'Aouache. *Colloques Internationaux du Centre National de la Recherche Scientifique* 218:887–895.
  1976   Camille Arambourg, 1885–1969. In *Earliest man and environments in the Lake Rudolf Basin*,
          edited by Y. Coppens, F. C. Howell, G. L. Isaac and R. E. F. Leakey. Chicago: University of
          Chicago Press. Pp. v–vi.
Covert, H. H., and R. F. Kay
  1981   Dental microwear and diet: implications for determining the feeding behaviors of extinct
          primates, with a comment on the dietary patterns of *Sivapithecus*. *American Journal of
          Physical Anthropology* 55:331–336.
Cronin, J. E., and W. E. Meikle
  1982   Hominid and gelada baboon evolution: Agreement between molecular and fossil time
          scales. *International Journal of Primatology*, in press.
Cronin, J. E., N. T. Boaz, C. B. Stringer, and Y. Rak
  1981   Tempo and mode in hominid evolution. *Nature (London)* 292:113–122.
Dart, R. A.
  1925   *Australopithecus africanus*, the man–ape of South Africa. *Nature (London)* 115:195–199.
  1948   The Makapansgat proto-human *Australopithecus prometheus*. *American Journal of Physical
          Anthropology* 6:259–284.
  1957   The osteodontokeratic culture of *Australopithecus prometheus*. *Transvaal Museum Memoirs* 10.
Dart, R. A., and D. Craig
  1959   *Adventures with the missing link*. New York: Harper.
Darwin, C. R.
  1871   *The descent of man*. London: Murray.
DeVore, I., and S. L. Washburn
  1963   Baboon ecology and human evolution. In *African ecology and human evolution*, edited by F. C.
          Howell and F. Bourlière. Chicago: Aldine. Pp. 335–367.
Dobzhansky, T.
  1944   On species and races of living and fossil man. *American Journal of Physical Anthropology*
          2:251–265.
Evernden, J. F., and G. H. Curtis
  1965   The potassium–argon dating of late Cenozoic rocks in East Africa and Italy. *Current
          Anthropology* 6:343–364.
Falk, D.
  1980   A reanalysis of the South African australopithecine natural endocasts. *American Journal of
          Physical Anthropology* 53:525–539.
Gates, R. R.
  1944   Phylogeny and classification of hominids and anthropoids. *American Journal of Physical
          Anthropology* 2:279–292.
Gould, S. J.
  1980   The Piltdown controversy. *Natural History* 89(8):8–28.

Gould, S. J., and N. Eldredge
    1977   Punctuated equilibria: the tempo and mode of evolution reconsidered. *Paleobiology* **3**:115–
            151.
Gregory, W. K.
    1929   Is the pre-dawn man a myth? *Human Biology* **1**:153–166.
    1930   A critique of Professor Osborn's theory of human origin. *American Journal of Physical
            Anthropology* **14**:133–164.
    1940   The upper dental arch of *Plesianthropus transvaalensis* Broom, and its relations to other parts
            of the skull. *American Journal of Physical Anthropology* **26**:211–228.
    1945   Revised reconstruction of the skull of *Plesianthropus transvaalensis* Broom. *American Journal
            of Physical Anthropology* **3**:267–275.
    1949   The bearing of the Australopithecinae upon the problem of man's place in nature. *American
            Journal of Physical Anthropology* **7**:485–512.
Gregory, W. K., and M. Hellman
    1938   Evidence of the australopithecine man–apes on the origin of man. *Science* **88**:615–616.
    1939a   Fossil man–apes of South Africa. *Nature (London)* **143**:25.
    1939b   The dentition of the extinct South African man–ape. *Australopithecus (Plesianthropus)
            transvaalensis* Broom. A comparative and phylogenetic study. *Annals of the Transvaal
            Museum* **19**:339–373.
Grommé, C. S., and R. L. Hay
    1963   Magnetization of basalt in Bed I, Olduvai Gorge, Tanganyika. *Nature (London)* **200**:560–561.
Haeckel, E.
    1874   *Anthropogenie oder Entwicklungsgeschichte des Menschen.* Leipzig.
Halstead, L. B.
    1978   New light on the Piltdown hoax. *Nature (London)* **276**:11–13.
Hay, R. L.
    1976   Environmental setting of hominid activities in Bed I, Olduvai Gorge. In *Human Origins,*
            edited by G. L. Isaac and E. R. McCown. Menlo Park, California: Staples. Pp. 209–225.
    1980   The KBS Tuff controversy may be ended. *Nature (London)* **284**:401.
Holloway, R. L.
    1975   *The role of human social behavior in the evolution of the brain. Forty-Third James Arthur Lecture on
            the Evolution of the Human Brain.* New York: American Museum of Natural History.
Hooton, E. A.
    1950   Review of Sterkfontein Ape–man *Plesianthropus* Broom, Robinson and Schepers. *American
            Journal of Physical Anthropology* **8**:502–505.
Howell, F. C.
    1968   Omo Research Expedition. *Nature (London)* **219**:567–572.
    1978   Hominidae. In *Evolution of African mammals,* edited by V. J. Maglio and H. B. S. Cooke.
            Cambridge, Massachusetts: Harvard University Press. Pp. 154–248.
Hrdlička, A.
    1912   Early man in South America. *Bulletin of the Bureau of American Ethnology* **52**.
    1914   The most ancient skeletal remains of man. *Smithsonian Institution, Annual Report* **1913**:429–
            465.
    1922   The Piltdown jaw. *American Journal of Physical Anthropology* **5**:327–347.
    1925   The Taungs ape. *American Journal of Physical Anthropology* **8**:379–392.
Hunt, E. E., Jr.
    1981   The "old" physical anthropology. *American Journal of Physical Anthropology* **56**:339–346.
Isaac, G. L.
    1976   Plio–Pleistocene artifact assemblages from East Rudolf, Kenya. In *Earliest man and environ-
            ments in the Lake Rudolf Basin,* edited by Y. Coppens, F. C. Howell, G. L. Isaac, and R. E. F.
            Leakey. Chicago: University of Chicago Press. Pp. 532–564.
Jaeger, J. J., and H. B. Wesselman
    1976   Fossil remains of micromammals from the Omo Group deposits. In *Earliest man and
            environments in the Lake Rudolf basin,* edited by Y. Coppens, F. C. Howell, G. L. Isaac, and R.
            E. F. Leakey. Chicago: University of Chicago Press. Pp. 351–360.

Jenkins, F. A.
  1972   Chimpanzee bipedalism: Cine-radiographic analysis and implications for the evolution of gait. *Science* **178**:877–879.
Johanson, D. C., and Y. Coppens
  1976   A preliminary diagnosis of the first Plio–Pleistocene hominid discoveries in the central Afar, Ethiopia. *American Journal of Physical Anthropology* **45**:217–234.
Johanson, D. C., and T. D. White
  1979   A systematic assessment of early African hominids. *Science* **203**:321–330.
Johanson, D. C., M. Taieb, B. T. Gray, and Y. Coppens
  1978   Geological framework of the Pliocene Hadar Formation (Afar, Ethiopia) and notes on paleontology including hominids. In *Geological background to fossil man*, edited by W. W. Bishop. Edinburgh: Scottish Academic Press. Pp. 549–564.
Johanson, D. C., T. D. White, and Y. Coppens
  1978b   A new species of the genus *Australopithecus* (Primates: Hominidae) from the Pliocene of eastern Africa. *Kirtlandia* **28**:1–14.
Kay, R.
  1975   The functional adaptations of primate molar teeth. *American Journal of Physical Anthropology* **43**:195–216.
Keith, A.
  1925   The Taungs skull. *Nature (London)* **116**:11.
Kennedy, K. A. R.
  1960   The phylogenetic tree: an analysis of its development in studies of human evolution. *Kroeber Anthropological Society Papers* **21**:7–53.
Kohl-Larsen, L.
  1943   *Auf den Spuren des Vormenschen*, Vol. 2. Stuttgart: Strerker and Schroder.
Leakey, L. S. B.
  1937   *White African*. London: Hodder and Stoughton. (New edition, 1966. Cambridge, Massachusetts: Schenkman.)
  1959   A new fossil skull from Olduvai. *Nature (London)* **184**:491–493.
  1974   *By the evidence*. New York: Harcourt, Brace, Jovanovich.
Leakey, L. S. B., P. V. Tobias, and J. R. Napier
  1964   A new species of the genus *Homo* from Olduvai Gorge. *Nature (London)* **202**:5–7.
Leakey, M. D.
  1971   *Olduvai Gorge. Excavations in Beds I and II, 1960–1963*, Vol. 3. London and New York: Cambridge University Press.
  1975   Cultural patterns in the Olduvai sequence. In *After the Australopithecines*, edited by K. W. Butzer and G. L. Isaac. The Hague: Mouton. Pp. 477–494.
Leakey, M. D., and R. L. Hay
  1979   Pliocene footprints in the Laetolil Beds at Laetoli, northern Tanzania. *Nature (London)* **278**:317–323.
Leakey, R. E. F.
  1974   Further evidence of lower Pleistocene hominids from East Rudolf, North Kenya, 1973. *Nature (London)* **248**:653–656.
Leakey, R. E. F., and A. C. Walker
  1976   *Australopithecus, Homo erectus* and the single species hypothesis. *Nature (London)* **261**:572–574.
Le Gros Clark, W. E.
  1947   Anatomy of the fossil Australopithecinae. *Journal of Anatomy* **81**:300–333.
  1948   Observations on the anatomy of the fossil Australopithecinae. *Yearbook of Physical Anthropology* **3**:143–177.
Lovejoy, C. O., K. G. Heiple, and A. Burstein
  1973   The gait of *Australopithecus*. *American Journal of Physical Anthropology* **38**:757–780.
Mann, A. E.
  1975   Some paleodemographic apsects of the South African australopithecines. *University of Pennsylvania Publication in Anthropology* No. 1.

Mayr, E.
    1951   Taxonomic categories in fossil hominids. *Cold Spring Harbor Symposia on Quantitative Biology*
             15:109–117.
McCown, T. D., and K. A. R. Kennedy
    1972   Climbing man's family tree. Englewood Cliffs, New Jersey: Prentice-Hall.
McGrew, W. C., C. E. G. Tutin, and P. J. Baldwin
    1979   Chimpanzees, tools, and termites: cross-cultural comparisons of Senegal, Tanzania and Rio
             Muni. *Man* **14**:185–214.
McHenry, H. M., and R. S. Corrucini
    1980   Late Tertiary hominids and human origins. *Nature (London)* **285**:397–398.
Millar, R.
    1972   *The Piltdown men.* New York: Ballantine.
Miller, G. S.
    1915   The jaw of Piltdown man. *Smithsonian Miscellaneous Collections* **65**(12):1–31.
    1918   The Piltdown jaw. *American Journal of Physical Anthropology* **1**:25–26.
    1920   Conflicting views on the problems of man's ancestry. *American Journal of Physical
             Anthropology* **3**:213–245.
Morbeck, M. E. H. Preuschoft, and N. Gomberg (editors)
    1979   *Environment, behavior and morphology: dynamic interactions in primates.* New York: Fischer.
Napier, J.
    1967   The evolution of the hand. *Scientific American* **207**:56–62.
Oakley, K. P.
    1955   The composition of the Piltdown hominoid remains. *Bulletin of the British Museum (Natural
             History)* **2**(6):254–261.
    1964   *Frameworks for dating fossil man.* Chicago: Aldine.
Oakley, K. P., B. G. Campbell, and T. Molleson
    1977   *Catalogue of fossil hominids. Part I: Africa* (second edition). London: British Museum (Natural
             History).
Osborn, H. F.
    1900   The geological and faunal relations of Europe and America during the Tertiary Period and
             the theory of the successive invasions of an African fauna. *Science* **11**:561–574.
    1918   *Men of the Old Stone Age: their environment, life and art.* New York: Scribner's.
    1927   Recent discoveries relating to the origin and antiquity of man. *Paleobiologica* **1**:189–202.
             (Reprinted in *Climbing man's family tree*, edited by T. D. McCown and K. A. R. Kennedy,
             Englewood Cliffs, New Jersey: Prentice-Hall. Pp. 285–301.)
    1929   The titanotheres of ancient Wyoming, Dakota, and Nebraska. *U. S. Geological Survey
             Monograph* **55**. Washington, D.C.: U.S. Government Printing Office.
    1930   The discovery of Tertiary man. *Science* **71**:1–7.
Oxnard, C. E.
    1975   The place of the australopithecines in human evolution. Grounds for doubt? *Nature
             (London)* **258**:389–395.
Partridge, T. C.
    1978   Re-appraisal of lithostratigraphy of Sterkfontein hominid site. *Nature (London)* **275**:282–
             287.
    1979   Re-appraisal of lithostratigraphy of Makapansgat limeworks hominid site. *Nature (London)*
             279:484–488.
Peters, C. R.
    1979   Toward an ecological model of African Plio–Pleistocene hominid adaptations. *American
             Anthropologists* **81**:261–278.
Peters, C. R., and E. M. O'Brien
    1981   The early hominid plant-food niche: Insights from an analysis of plant exploitation by
             Homo, Pan, and *Papio* in eastern and southern Africa. *Current Anthropology* **22**:127–
             140.
Prost, J. H.
    1980   Origin of bipedalism. *American Journal of Physical Anthropology* **52**:175–189.

Rak, Y.
1981   *The morphology and architecture of the australopithecine face.* Unpublished Ph.D. dissertation, Department of Anthropology, University of California, Berkeley.

Robinson, J. T.
1954   The genera and species of the Australopithecinae. *American Journal of Physical Anthropology* **12**:181–200.
1963   Adaptive radiation of the australopithecines and the origin of man. In *African ecology and human evolution,* edited by F. C. Howell and F. Bourlière. Chicago: Aldine. Pp. 385–416.
1972   *Early hominid posture and locomotion.* Chicago: University of Chicago Press.

Romer, A. S.
1930   *Australopithecus* not a chimpanzee. *Science* **71**:482–483.

Ryan, A. S.
1979   Scanning electron microscopy of tooth wear of *Australopithecus afarensis. American Journal of Physical Anthropology* **50**:478.

Sarich, V. M., and J. E. Cronin
1976   Molecular systematics of the primates. In *Molecular Anthropology,* edited by M. Goodman and R. Tashian. New York: Plenum. Pp. 141–170.

Schaller, G. B., and G. R. Lowther
1969   The relevance of carnivore behavior to the study of early hominids. *Southwestern Journal of Anthropology* **25**:307–341.

Shipman, P., and J. E. Phillips
1976   Scavenging by hominids and other carnivores. *American Anthropology* **17**:170–172.

Shipman, P., and A. Walker
1980   Bone-collecting in harvesting ants. *Paleobiology* **6**:496–502.

Shuey, R. T., F. H. Brown, G. G. Eck, and F. C. Howell
1978   A statistical approach to temporal biostratigraphy. In *Geological background to fossil man,* edited by W. W. Bishop. Edinburgh: Scottish Academic Press. Pp. 103–124.

Sollas, W. J.
1925   The Taungs skull. *Nature (London)* **115**:908–909.
1926   On a sagittal section of the skull of *Australopithecus africanus. Quarterly Journal of the Geological Society of London* **82**:1–11.

Straus, W. L.
1948a   The limb bones of australopithecines. *American Journal of Physical Anthropology* **6**:237–238.
1948b   The humerus of *Paranthropus robustus. American Journal of Physical Anthropology* **6**:285–311.
1949   The riddle of man's ancestry. *Quarterly Review of Biology* **24**:200–223.

Susman, R. L., and J. T. Stern
1979   Telemetered electromyography of flexor digitorum profundus and flexor digitorum superficialis in *Pan troglodytes* and implications for interpretation of the OH 7 hand. *American Journal of Physical Anthropology* **50**:565–574.

Terry, R.
1974   *Raymond A. Dart, Taung 1924–1974.* Johannesburg: Museum of Man and Science.

Tobias, P. V.
1978   Position et rôle des australopithécinés dans la phylogenèse humaine, avec étude particulière de *Homo habilis* et des thèories controversées avancées à propos des premiers hominidés fossiles de Hadar et de Laetolil. In *Les origines humaines et les époques de l'intelligence,* edited by Y. Coppens. Paris: Foundation Singer–Polignac. Pp. 38–75.
1980   *Australopithecus afarensis* and *A. africanus*: a critique and an alternative hypothesis. *Paleontologia Africana* **23**:1–17.

Tobias, P. V., and A. R. Hughes
1969   The new Witwatersrand University excavation at Sterkfontein. *South African Archaeological Bulletin* **24**:158–169.

Tuttle, R. H., V. H. Basmajian, and H. Ishida
1978   Electromyography of pongid gluteal muscles and hominid evolution. In *Recent advances in primatology,* Vol. 3, edited by D. J. Chivers and K. A. Joysey. New York: Plenum. Pp. 463–468.

Vrba, E. S.
    1974   Chronological and ecological implications of the fossil Bovidae at the Sterkfonteir australopithecine site. *Nature (London)* **250**:19–23.
    1975   Some evidence of chronology and palaeoecology of Sterkfontein, Swartkrans anc Kromdraai from the fossil Bovidae. *Nature (London)* **254**:301–304.
Walker, A., H. N. Hoeck, and L. Perez
    1978   Microwear of mammalian teeth as an indicator of diet. *Science* **201**:908–910.
Wallace, A. R.
    1899   *Darwinism.* New York: Macmillan.
Wallace, J. A.
    1975   Dietary adaptations of *Australopithecus* and early *Homo*. In *Paleoanthropology, morphology and paleoecology,* edited by R. Tuttle. Chicago: Aldine. Pp. 203–224.
Washburn, S. L.
    1947   The relation of the temporal muscle to the form of the skull. *Anatomical Record* **99**:239–248.
    1951   The new physical anthropology. *Transactions of the New York Academy of Science* **13**:298–304.
Washburn, S. L., and S. R. Detwiller
    1943   An experiment bearing on the problems of physical anthropology. *American Journal of Physical Anthropology* **1**:171–190.
Weiner, J. S.
    1955   *The Piltdown forgery.* London and New York: Oxford University Press.
Weiner, J. S., F. P. Oakley, and W. E. Le Gros Clark
    1953   The solution of the Piltdown problem. *Bulletin of the British Museum Natural History, Geology* **2**(3):141–146.
Weiss, K. M.
    1972   A generalized model for competition between hominid populations. *Journal of Human Evolution* **1**:451–456.
White, T. D.
    1977   New fossil hominids from Laetolil, Tanzania. *American Journal of Physical Anthropology* **46**:197–230.
    1980a   Additional fossil hominids from Laetoli, Tanzania, 1976–1979 specimens. *American Journal of Physical Anthropology* **53**:487–504.
    1980b   Evolutionary implications of Pliocene hominid footprints. *Science* **208**:175–176.
    1981   Primitive hominid canine from Tanzania. *Science* **213**:348–349.
White, T. D., D. C. Johanson, and W. H. Kimbel
    1981   *Australopithecus africanus*: its phylogenetic position reconsidered. *South African Journal of Science* **77**:445–470.
Wolpoff, M. H.
    1971   Competitive exclusion among lower Pleistocene hominids: the single species hypothesis. *Man* **6**:601–614.
Zihlman, A.
    1978   Interpretations of early hominid locomotion. In *Early hominids of Africa,* edited by C. J. Jolly. New York: St. Martin's Press. Pp. 361–377.
Zihlman, A., J. E. Cronin, D. L. Cramer, and V. M. Sarich
    1978   Pygmy chimpanzee as a possible prototype for the common ancestor of humans, chimpanzees and gorillas. *Nature (London)* **275**:744–746.

10

A History of *Homo erectus* and *Homo sapiens* Paleontology in America

Erik Trinkaus

A historical review of the past 50 years of our discipline serves two purposes. First, and most obviously, it reminds us of the debt we owe to our predecessors. It was they who formulated the theoretical and empirical basis for much of our current research. Secondly, it should make clear to us that the interpretations of our predecessors, faulty as they may sometimes appear with hindsight, seemed no more flawed when they were written than do ours as we look at them now in the early 1980s. Science has always been limited by the available data and theoretical developments and conditioned by the ongoing intellectual traditions. Perhaps a little retrospection will help us to maintain a healthier perspective on what we are doing today.

Hrdlička, the Neandertals, "Pithecanthropus," and Piltdown

In a review of the history of *Homo erectus* and *Homo sapiens* paleontology in America, it is perhaps best to begin with the classic American work on the subject, *The Skeletal Remains of Early Man*. This study was published, appropriately, by the founder of the American Association of Physical Anthropologists (AAPA) Aleš Hrdlička, just over 50 years ago (Hrdlička 1930). In this volume, Hrdlička summarized his observations and interpretations concerning the then known hominid fossil record. He concluded with a restatement of his Huxley Memorial Lecture of 1927, "The Neanderthal Phase of Man" (Hrdlička 1927).

In *The Skeletal Remains of Early Man,* Hrdlička put forth three interpretations that

A HISTORY OF AMERICAN
PHYSICAL ANTHROPOLOGY, 1930–1980

ran counter to the accepted paleontological wisdom of 1930. He saw a direct lineal relationship between the Neandertals and subsequent populations of modern-appearing humans. He accepted "Pithecanthropus" as representative of a pre-Neandertal stage of human evolution. And he rejected the belief that the Piltdown cranial remains provided evidence of a modern human neurocranium in the Pliocene or lower Pleistocene.

Hrdlička's adherence to a unilineal interpretation of human evolution can probably be traced back to his studies at the Ecole d'Anthropologie in Paris in 1896 (Spencer 1979). It was there that he was introduced to human paleontology by Manouvrier, de Mortillet, and others, all of whom believed in a simple and regular progression of human forms during the Pleistocene (de Mortillet 1883; Manouvrier 1896a; Hammond 1980). Furthermore, Hrdlička's views on the antiquity of man in the New World (Hrdlička 1907; Hrdlička *et al.* 1912) demanded a Neandertal-like stage of human evolution relatively recently in the Pleistocene (Spencer 1979). Hrdlička, who was known for maintaining rather strong views, appears to have adhered to this turn-of-the-century perception of human evolution, whereas, during the second decade of the twentieth century, most other paleontologists came to believe in one version or another of the Pre-Sapiens Theory.[1]

The differences between Hrdlička's interpretations of the Neandertals, "Pithecanthropus," and Piltdown and the paleontological orthodoxy of 1930 illustrate the major issues in human paleontology for much of the twentieth century. In considering these issues, three things should be kept in mind. First, nobody prior to World War II had a very accurate assessment of the length of the Pleistocene (Faul 1978), so that geologic time constraints could be ignored if one chose to do so. Second, none of the human paleontologists, or any other paleontologist, really understood evolutionary processes until the evolutionary synthesis of the 1940s. They all viewed the fossil record from a typological standpoint, and most of them ascribed, usually implicitly, to some form of orthogenesis combined with phyletic gradualism (e.g., Boule 1893, 1911–1913; Keith 1915; Osborn 1922; Weidenreich 1929; see also Holtzman 1973; Mayr 1980; Gould 1980a). Finally, the majority of the human paleontologists prior to World War II, including Hrdlička (1925), excluded the australopithecines from the human lineage (LeGros Clark 1967; Tobias 1980). This had the effect of making "Pithecanthropus," and possibly Piltdown, the oldest known candidates for human ancestry.

The emphasis throughout human paleontology on identifying the direct ancestry for extant humans has placed considerable emphasis on the European Neandertals. As the immediate predecessors of modern appearing humans and as the first-recognized and best-known archaic humans, they have provided a reference

---

[1]The various schemes that have been put forward to characterize Middle and Upper Pleistocene human evolution are here lumped into the Pre-Sapiens, Pre-Neandertal and Neandertal-Phase-of-Man Theories, as defined by Vallois (1958).

sample for the interpretation of earlier and later European and non-European fossil hominids. Hrdlička, for example, was very quick to refer to the Teshik-Tash and even the Chou-Kou-Tien remains as Neandertaloid (Hrdlička 1930, 1939; see also Spencer 1979). Moreover, the Neandertals have become a focus of the primary phylogenetic argument in human paleontology: whether human evolution was characterized by a single lineage or by multiple lineages with resultant extinctions.

By the end of the first decade of the twentieth century, most paleontologists considered the Neandertals to be generally representative of a pre-modern stage of human evolution (e.g., Schwalbe 1904, 1906; Keith, 1911). The Neandertals at that time were represented by the specimens from the Neandertal (Schaafhausen 1858; Klaatsch 1901; Schwalbe 1901), Spy (Fraipont and Lohest 1887), Krapina (Gorjanović-Kramberger 1906), Forbes' Quarry (Broca 1869; Sollas 1907; Sera 1909, 1910), and several other sites. This vaguely unilineal view was challenged at the end of the decade, principally by Marcellin Boule.

Beginning in 1908, there was a series of spectacular discoveries of articulated Neandertal skeletons. These were at the sites of Le Moustier (Hauser 1908, 1909; Klaatsch 1909; Klaatsch and Hauser 1909), La Chapelle-aux-Saints (Bouyssonie et al. 1908a, 1908b), La Ferrassie (Capitan and Peyrony 1909, 1911, 1912, 1921) and La Quina (Martin 1911, 1912a, 1912b, 1912c, 1923), all in southwestern France. The best preserved of the fossils, those from La Chapelle-aux-Saints and La Ferrassie, were turned over to Boule for analysis. In a series of articles (Boule 1908a, 1908b, 1909a, 1909b, 1909c; Boule and Anthony 1910), which culminated in his classic monograph, L'Homme Fossile de La Chapelle-aux-Saints, published during 1911, 1912, and 1913, Boule established the classic description of a Neandertal (Boule 1911–1913). In this monograph, Boule not only described the La Chapelle-aux-Saints partial skeleton but also drew heavily upon information from the La Ferrassie 1 and 2 skeletons and available published information and casts of the Krapina, Neandertal, and Spy fossils to provide what was, for many years to come, the most detailed comparative analysis of a fossil hominid. It was rivaled at the time only by the description of the Krapina fossils by Gorjanović-Kramberger (1906) and was subsequently surpassed only by the studies of the Skhūl and Tabūn remains by McCown and Keith (1939) and of the Chou-Kou-Tien fossils by Black (1931) and Weidenreich (1936, 1937, 1941a, 1943a). Interestingly, Boule never completed his study of the far more intact La Ferrassie remains; they have been described only quite recently by Heim (1968, 1970, 1972, 1974, 1976, 1978).

In addition to his description of the morphology of the La Chapelle-aux-Saints and other Neandertal remains, Boule provided an extensive review of the then-known hominid fossils and a reconstruction of hominid phylogeny. In this he concluded, as is well known, that the Neandertals were a side branch in human evolution, long ago separated from the lineage leading to modern humans (Boule 1911–1913; see also Boule 1921, 1923, Boule and Vallois 1946, 1952, 1957). The effect of Boule's writings was immediate and widespread in the scientific community of western Europe. Even previous unilinealists, such as Keith and Schwalbe, changed rapidly to Boule's view of human phylogeny (compare Keith

[1912a] to Keith [1912b, 1915] and Schwalbe [1904, 1906] to Schwalbe [1914]).

Boule has been criticized in recent years for his stoop-shouldered, bent-kneed reconstruction of the Neandertals (e.g., Arambourg 1955, Straus and Cave 1957; Trinkaus 1975a; Trinkaus and Howells 1979) and for his multilineal interpretations of human phylogeny (e.g., Brace 1964, 1979). Although many of these criticisms are justified in retrospect, it should be pointed out that his views appeared quite reasonable when they were presented.

First, Boule's multilineal interpretation was in agreement with his already-established macroevolutionary views (Boule 1889, 1901, 1911–1913) (see Brace 1966, 1981; Hammon 1982); he did little more than current proponents of punctuated equilibria do when they use the hominid fossil record to support their macroevolutionary views (e.g., Gould and Eldredge 1977).[2]

Second, Boule's reconstruction of the La Chapelle-aux-Saints Neandertal as incompletely erect was based on then current views as to the significance of features—such as tibial retroversion, curved hallucial tarsometatarsal articulations, and long, straight cervical vertebral spines. Boule did choose between alternative explanations for specific features to support his general thesis [e.g., he followed Fraipont (1888) on the significance of tibial retroversion rather than Manouvrier (1893) and Charles (1893)]. However, he was not significantly biased by the relatively minor osteoarthritis on the La Chapelle-aux-Saints remains, as has been claimed (Straus and Cave 1957); in fact, most of the lower limb reconstruction was based on the more complete and largely healthy La Ferrassie 1 and 2 skeletons (Boule 1911–1913).

Even though Boule and his work cannot be rightly considered part of American human paleontology, he has had a profound effect on the ways in which American human paleontologists have viewed the fossil record. Before World War II, most American writers on human evolution followed the interpretations of Boule and other Europeans, such as Keith (1915, 1931) (e.g., Osborn 1915, 1927; Hooton 1931; MacCurdy 1932). Since World War II, reactions to the views of Boule and others (especially Brace 1962a, 1964) have dominated many American assessments of later Pleistocene human evolution.

The multilineal views of Boule, with his prediction of modern-appearing humans prior to the Neandertals, coalesced with the ideas of Elliot Smith (1910, 1912) and others on the preeminence of the brain in human evolution and set the stage for the acceptance of the Piltdown remains in 1913 and thereafter (Dawson and Woodward 1913, 1914; Elliot Smith 1913, 1914; Woodward 1917). By 1913, most human paleontologists had come to accept the idea of a great antiquity for modern human cerebral and neurocranial morphology, and the Piltdown fragments seemed only to confirm the expected.

---

[2]There has been considerable confusion of the microevolutionary views of Boule and his contemporaries with their macroevolutionary interpretations (e.g., Brace 1964, 1966, 1973; Bordes 1966; Vallois 1966; Holtzman 1973). Even though there is usually a correlation between one's microevolutionary and macroevolutionary views, the form of one does not necessarily follow from the other (Stebbins and Ayala 1981).

Despite this preparation for Piltdown, several individuals questioned the association of the human cranium and pongid mandible, although few doubted the supposed Pliocene or Lower Pleistocene age of the remains (e.g., Boule 1915, 1917, 1920; Miller, 1915, 1918; Gregory 1916; Hrdlička 1914, 1922). Hrdlička was one of the few paleontologists who questioned the antiquity of the calvaria (Hrdlička 1930), even though he accepted the mandible as an early hominid (Hrdlička 1923). It was probably his experience in rejecting the antiquity of supposed Pleistocene Amerindian remains and his firm belief in unilineal gradualism and morphological dating (Spencer 1979) that led him to question the legitimacy of the Piltdown calvaria.

In recent years, the Piltdown forgery has become one of the great scientific "who-done-its." Almost every scientist who was alive and could possibly have been near Sussex in 1912 has been accused of perpetrating the crime (Weiner 1955; Millar 1972; Krogman 1978; Halstead 1978; Gould 1980b). We will probably never know who actually planted the bones and implements at Piltdown, but we can gain a feeling for what is more important; that is, why it was accepted so readily by the majority of the scientific community at the time (Gould 1979; Hammond 1979). The Piltdown "fossils" certainly fulfilled the expectations of many paleontologists.

The intellectual atmosphere that led to the acceptance of Piltdown also contributed to the rejection by many paleontologists of the Trinil "Pithecanthropus" remains from human ancestry. There was an initial enthusiasm in the 1890s for "Pithecanthropus" as an early forebear of recent humans (e.g., Dubois 1894, 1896a, 1896b, 1900; Manouvrier 1895a, 1895b, 1986a, 1896b; Tuner 1895; Schwalbe 1899). However, it was later perceived, like the Neandertals, as too divergent and too recent to hold a place in modern human ancestry (e.g., Boule 1911–1913, 1921; Keith 1912b, 1915; Osborn 1915; Hooton 1931), and even Dubois, by the 1920s, was questioning the status of "Pithecanthropus" as an ancestral human form (Dubois 1924, 1932, 1935; Nyèssen 1943). In retrospect, it must be admitted that the incomplete nature of the original Trinil remains and uncertainties as to the associations of the various pieces (Hrdlička 1930) left considerable room for disagreement on their phylogenetic significance. It was not until the 1930s, with discoveries at Chou-Kou-Tien (Zdansky 1926; Black 1926, 1927, 1931; Weidenreich 1936, 1937, 1941a, 1943a), Ngandong (Oppenoorth 1932; Weidenreich 1951), Sangiran (von Koenigswald 1940), and Modjokerto (von Koenigswald 1936), that a decent appreciation of *Homo erectus* morphology could be obtained.

Thus by 1930, when Hrdlička published *The Skeletal Remains of Early Man*, most human paleontologists felt comfortable with one or another model of human phylogeny, usually a version of the Pre-Sapiens Theory. There was little questioning of basic assumptions or conclusions, and new discoveries during the 1920s and 1930s, such as Zuttiyeh (Keith 1927), Chou-Kou-Tien (Zdansky 1926, Black 1926, 1927, 1931; Weidenreich 1936, 1937, 1941a, 1943a), Saccopastore (Sergi 1929, 1944, 1948; Breuil and Blanc 1935), Skhūl and Tabūn (McCown and

Keith 1939), Steinheim (Berckhemer 1933; Weinert 1936), Swanscombe (Marston 1936, 1937), and Circeo (Sergi 1939, 1954), were merely fitted into existing schemes.

It should be emphasized that during this period nobody in the United States worked directly in human paleontology (Stewart 1954; W. W. Howells, personal communication 1981), and most of the American paleontological writing was in the form of general surveys of human evolution. The majority of these American writers—such as Hrdlička, MacCurdy, and Osborn—were based in museums rather than academic departments of universities. The one exception was E. A. Hooton, who, at Harvard University, trained most of the next generation of American physical anthropologists. Among these students were H. L. Shapiro, C. S. Coon, W. W. Howells, and S. L. Washburn, who in turn have trained much of the current generation of American human paleontologists. Only T. D. McCown and T. D. Stewart stand out as major recent American figures in human paleontology who were not trained by Hooton or by one of his students. Hooton also established a tradition of writing general books on human variation and evolution (Hooton 1931, 1937, 1939, 1940, 1942), a tradition that has been carried on especially by Coon (1939, 1962, 1965; Coon *et al.* 1950) and Howells (1944, 1954, 1959, 1973).

At the end of the period between the world wars, one of the more important figures in human paleontology, Franz Weidenreich, arrived in the United States and began to have a significant effect on the course of human paleontology in America. At that time, he was completing his series of classic publications on the *H. erectus* fossils from Chou-Kou-Tien (Weidenreich 1936, 1937, 1938, 1940a, 1941a, 1943a) and beginning to work on some of the *H. erectus* fossils from Java (Weidenreich 1945, 1951). At the same time, he put forth a series of publications that summarized his views on general trends in human evolution and set out his largely unilineal "trellis" model of human evolution (Weidenreich 1940b, 1941b, 1943b, 1946, 1947a, 1947b, 1949). Even though Weidenreich belongs theoretically to the period between the world wars (Mayr 1980), he has had a profound effect on the subsequent development of human paleontology, especially in the United States.

Evolutionary Theory and the Evolution of the Genus *Homo*

During the 1940s, several developments occurred that significantly altered the direction of human paleontology, particularly in the United States. We are still profiting from this intellectual shift.

The first and most important development was the formulation of a synthetic theory of evolution. This began in the late 1930s and continued into the 1940s (e.g., Dobzhansky 1937; Huxley 1942; Mayr 1942; Simpson 1944; Rensch 1947), culminating in the 1947 Princeton conference on "Genetics, Paleontology and Evolution" (Jepsen *et al.* 1949; see Mayr and Provine 1980). The widespread acceptance of the evolutionary synthesis among biologists spread rapidly over into anthropology and led to the 1950 Cold Spring Harbor Symposium on the "Origin and Evolution of Man" (Warren 1951). This theoretical shift was largely responsible for the appearance of populational and adaptational thinking among students of human variation at this time (e.g., Boyd 1950; Coon *et al.* 1950; Washburn 1951). It also led to a more rational taxonomy for fossil hominids, in which all of the postaustralopithecine hominids were placed into either *H. sapiens* or *H. erectus* (Dobzhansky 1944; Mayr 1951).

The second development was the admission of the australopithecines into the human family (LeGros Clark 1947, 1967). The Neandertals and *H. erectus* appeared, as a result, to be much closer to extant humans than had been believed previously. It was not long thereafter that most of the grosser anatomical misconceptions of the Neandertals were corrected (e.g., Arambourg 1955; Schultz 1955; Straus and Cave 1957; Toerien 1957; Stewart 1962a, 1962b).

These developments coincided with the exposure of the Piltdown fraud (Oakley and Hoskins 1950; Weiner *et al.* 1953, 1955; Weiner 1955). It is probably not coincidental that the Piltdown forgery was exposed at this time, since the ideas responsible for its creation had been largely eclipsed. Some workers, such as Vallois (1949, 1954, 1958, Boule and Vallois 1952, 1957) and Leakey (1966), continued to present versions of the Pre-Sapiens Theory, but most human paleontologists subscribed to some form of the Pre-Neandertal Theory (e.g., Weidenreich 1943b; LeGros Clark 1955; Breitinger 1957; Weiner 1958; Howells 1959).

The fourth development in the late 1940s was a growing appreciation for geologic time and a refinement of relative Pleistocene chronologies (Faul 1978). This was due in part to the development of radiometric dating techniques, such as uranium series and radiocarbon dating.

The first reflection of this shift in emphasis in human paleontology was the attempt by Howell (1951, 1952) to explain patterns of European Upper Pleistocene human variation in populational and adaptational terms. Although he did not specify the exact mechanisms involved, Howell suggested that the distribution of Neandertal features could be the product of climatic adaptation combined with the genetic isolation of some of the Neandertal populations, especially in western Europe. Even though many details of Howell's hypothesis have not stood the test of time, it was a howling success when published, and the general type of questions he posed have become integral to American human paleontology.

Howell's ideas were picked up a decade later by Coon and greatly expanded in his book *The Origin of Races* (1962). In this work, Coon took and slightly modified Weidenreich's (1940b, 1943b, 1947a) "trellis" model of human subspecific evolution and postulated a variety of adaptational models to explain recent and Pleistocene patterns of human variation. It is unfortunate that *The Origin of Races* contained racist overtones in places, because it was the first major attempt to discuss Pleistocene human evolution in terms of changing patterns of biological adaptation rather than merely as a sequence of morphological forms.

During the 1960s and into the early 1970s this approach was pursued in the United States, particularly by Brace (1962b, 1967a) and later by Wolpoff (Brose and Wolpoff 1971). Both of them suggested behavioral explanations for some patterns of Pleistocene human variation. It was not until the middle and late 1970s, however, that several of the anatomical regions that are well represented in the fossil record were examined primarily to discern their behavioral, rather than phylogenetic, implications (e.g., Wolpoff 1975, 1980; Trinkaus 1975a, 1975b, 1976b, 1977, 1978, 1980, 1981; Smith 1978, 1980; Brace 1979; Frayer 1980, 1981; Ryan 1980).

Associated with this resurgence of research into later Pleistocene human evolution was a vigorous reincarnation of Hrdlička's Neandertal-Phase-of-Man Theory, primarily by Brace (1962a, 1964, 1967b) and Wolpoff (Brose and Wolpoff 1971). By this time, *H. erectus* was almost universally considered as generally ancestral to later Pleistocene and modern humans (Howells 1966), and the Neandertals and other Upper Pleistocene hominids of a similar evolutionary grade had been included within the species *H. sapiens* (Campbell 1963, 1965). Although discussions of Upper Pleistocene hominid phylogeny were no longer restricted to the European sequence, largely through the influence of Weidenreich and Coon, the major bone of contention remained the fate of European, or "Classic," Neandertals (e.g., Howells 1974, 1975; Mann and Trinkaus 1974; Brace 1979; Trinkaus and Howells 1979; Wolpoff 1981; Stringer *et al.* 1981).

Recent Developments

In the last few years, the determination of whether all or any of the Neandertal populations might have given rise to populations of anatomically modern humans has become, if anything, more complicated. Although many supposedly distinctive Neandertal traits have been shown to be either within recent human ranges of variation or similar to those seen in early, anatomically modern humans, a number of Neandertal traits have continued to support their morphological distinctiveness vis-à-vis more recent humans (Musgrave 1971; Howells 1975; Trinkaus 1975a, 1976a, 1976b, 1981; Frayer 1978; Hublin 1978; Santa Luca 1978; Smith 1978; Stringer 1978; Brace 1979; Trinkaus and Howells 1979; Lovejoy and Trinkaus 1980; Smith and Ranyard 1980; Wolpoff 1980; Stringer and Trinkaus 1981; Trinkaus and LeMay 1982). In addition, as the Asian and African fossil records have improved, patterns of geographic variation in the Upper Pleistocene have become clearer, highlighting the distinctiveness of the European and Near East Neandertals relative to their contemporaries in Africa and East Asia (Rightmire 1978, 1981; Santa Luca 1978; Trinkaus and Howells 1979; Wolpoff 1980; Thorne and Wolpoff 1981; Wu 1981).

This realization has been combined with a recognition that anatomically modern humans may well have appeared considerably earlier in Africa than in the Near

East and Europe (Beaumont *et al.* 1978; Rightmire 1979). Finally, Hrdlička's definition of the Neandertal as the "man of the Mousterian culture" (Hrdlička, 1927) has been shown to be inaccurate; anatomically modern humans have been found associated with Mousterian industries at Skhūl (McCown and Keith 1939; Howell 1958; Howells 1970; Trinkaus 1976a, 1976b) and Qafzeh (Howell 1958; Vandermeersch 1981) in the Near East, and Neandertals have been found associated with early Upper Paleolithic industries at Saint-Césaire (Lévêque and Vandermeersch 1980, 1981) and possibly Vindija (Wolpoff *et al.* 1981) in Europe.

Associated with these complications has been the realization that the traditional Pre-Sapiens, Pre-Neandertal, and Neandertal-Phase-of-Man theories (Vallois 1958) are probably gross oversimplifications of what actually occurred. If one accepts the Neandertals and their relatives in Africa and East Asia into the species *H. sapiens*, then the transition from archaic *H. sapiens* to anatomically modern humans must have involved all of the known processes that come into play during periods of rapid, within-species evolution. These include some regional populational continuity, some local population replacement, and substantial levels of gene flow. All of these processes were probably involved, whether or not the late archaic *H. sapiens* and anatomically modern human gene pools differed in allele representation or only in allelic frequencies.

If one is willing to accept a relatively complicated model for Pleistocene hominid evolution, it becomes questionable whether the fossil record will ever be sufficiently large and contain the proper kinds of information to allow human paleontologists to confirm one out of many possible phylogenetic models. We may simply have to resign ourselves to a certain level of uncertainty in reconstructions of *H. erectus* and *H. sapiens* phylogeny.

Even if human paleontology may never fully clarify the fate of the Neandertals, it is still possible to pursue a productive line of research. There is little disagreement that hominids experienced significant morphological evolution during the Middle and Upper Pleistocene, some as gradual trends through time and others as rapid morphological shifts between periods of relative stasis. Most, if not all, of these morphological changes should reflect the significant behavioral changes that the Paleolithic archaeological record is increasingly revealing. If we are able to decipher the adaptive significances of these anatomical changes during the Pleistocene, it may be possible to gain a far better understanding of the evolution of human behavior than will ever be possible for the details of human phylogeny.

Acknowledgments

I would like to thank the many individuals who have shared their thoughts on the history of American human paleontology with me. In addition, C. L. Brace, F. Spencer, E. Mayr, M. H. Wolpoff, and especially W. W. Howells have provided helpful comments during the preparation of this paper, and to all of them I am most grateful.

References

Arambourg, C.
    1955   Sur l'attitude, en station verticale, des Néanderthaliens. *Comptes Rendus Hebdomadaire des Séances de l'Académie des Sciences, Série D* **240**:804–806.

Beaumont, P. B., H. de Villiers, and J. C. Vogel
    1978   Modern man in sub-Saharan Africa prior to 49,000 years B.P.: a review and evaluation with particular reference to Border Cave. *South African Journal of Science* **74**:409–419.

Berckhemer, F.
    1933   Ein Menschen-Schädel aus den diluvialen Schottern von Steinheim a. d. Murr. *Anthropologischer Anzeiger* **10**:318–321.

Black, D.
    1926   Tertiary man in Asia: the Chou Kou Tien discovery. *Nature (London)* **118**:733–734.
    1927   On lower molar hominid tooth from the Chou Kou Tien deposit. *Palaeontologia Sinica* **7**:1–28.
    1931   On an adolescent skull of *Sinanthropus pekinensis* in comparison with an adult skull of the same species and with other hominid skulls, recent and fossil. *Paleontologia Sinia, New Series D* **7**:1–144.

Bordes, F.
    1966   More on the fate of the "classic" Neanderthals. *Current Anthropology* **7**:205.

Boule, M.
    1889   Le *Canis megamastoides* du Pliocène moyen de Perrier (Puy-de-Dôme). *Bulletin de la Société Géologique de France, Série 3* **17**:321–331.
    1893   Description de l'*Hyaena brevirostris* du Pliocène de Sainzelles, près Le Puy (Haute-Loire). *Annals des Sciences Naturelles, Zoologie et Paléontologie Série 7* **15**:85–97.
    1901   Révision des espèces européenes de *Machairodus*. *Bulletin de la Société Géologique de France, Série 4* **1**:551–573.
    1908a   L'homme fossile de la Chapelle-aux-Saints (Corrèze). *l'Anthropologie, Paris* **19**:519–525. *Séances de l'Académie des Sciences* **147**:1349–1352.
    1908b   L'homme fossile de la Chapelle-aux-Saints (Corrèze). *L'Anthropologie* **19**:519–525.
    1909a   L'homme fossile de La Chapelle-aux-Saints (Corrèze). *Anthropologie, Paris* **20**:257–271.
    1909b   Sur la capacité crânnienne des Hommes fossiles du type de Néanderthal. *Comptes Rendus Hebdomaires des Séances de l'Académie des Sciences* **148**:1352–1355.
    1909c   Le squelette du tronc et des membres de l'homme fossile de La Chapelle-aux-Saints. *Comptes Rendus Hebdomadaires des Séances de l'Académie des Sciences* **148**:1554–1556.
    1911–   L'homme fossile de La Chapelle-aux-Saints. *Annals de Paléontologie* **6**:111–172; **7**:21–56;
    1913   85–192; **8**:1–70.
    1915   La paléontologie humaine en Angleterre. *Anthropologie, Paris* **26**:1–67.
    1917   The jaw of Piltdown Man. *Anthropologie, Paris* **28**:433–435.
    1920   The Piltdown jaw. *Anthropologie, Paris* **29**:566–568.
    1921   *Les hommes fossiles* (first edition). Paris: Masson.
    1923   *Les hommes fossiles* (second edition). Paris: Masson.

Boule, M., and R. Anthony
    1910   L'encèphale de l'homme fossile de La Chapelle-aux-Saints. *Comptes Rendus Hebdomadaires des Séances de l'Académie des Sciences* **150**:1458–1461.

Boule, M., and H. V. Vallois
    1946   *Les hommes fossiles* (third edition). Paris: Masson.
    1952   *Les hommes fossiles* (fourth edition). Paris: Masson.
    1957   *Les hommes fossiles* (fifth edition). Paris: Masson.

Bouyssonie, A., J. Bouyssonie, and L. Bardon
  1908a   Découverte d'un squelette humain moustérien à La Chapelle-aux-Saints (Corrèze). *Comptes Rendus Hebdomadaires des Séances de l'Académie des Sciences* **147**:1414–1415.
  1908b   Découverte d'un squelette humain moustérien à la bouffia de la Chapelle-aux-Saints (Corrèze). *Anthropologie, Paris* **19**:513–518.
Boyd, W. C.
  1950   *Genetics and the races of man.* Boston: Little, Brown.
Brace, C. L.
  1962a   Refocusing on the Neanderthal problem. *American Anthropologist* **64**:729–741.
  1962b   Cultural factors in the evolution of the human dentition. In *Culture and the evolution of man*, edited by M. F. A. Montagu. London and New York: Oxford University Press. Pp. 343–354.
  1964   The fate of the classic Neandertals: a consideration of hominid catastrophism. *Current Anthropology* **5**:3–43.
  1966   More on the fate of the "classic" neanderthals: reply. *Current Anthropology* **7**:210–214.
  1967a   Environment, tooth form, and size in the Pleistocene. *Journal of Dental Research* **46**:809–816.
  1967b   *The stages of human evolution.* Englewood Cliffs, New Jersey: Prentice-Hall.
  1973   On Brace's notion of "hominid catastrophism": reply. *Current Anthropology* **14**:308–309.
  1979   Krapina, "classic" Neanderthals, and the evolution of the European face. *Journal of Human Evolution* **8**:527–550.
  1981   Tales of the Phylogenetic woods; the evolution and significance of evolutionary trees. *American Journal of Physical Anthropology* **56**:411–439.
Breitinger, E.
  1957   Zur phyletischen Evolution von *Homo sapiens*. *Anthropologischer Anzeiger* **21**:62–83.
Breuil, H., and A. C. Blanc
  1935   Rinvenimento in situ di un nuovo cranio di Homo neanderthalensis nel giacimento di Saccopastore (Roma). *Atti della Accademia Nazionale dei Lincei, Classe di Scienze Fisiche, Matematiche e Naturali, Rendiconti, Séries 6* **22**:166–169.
Broca, P.
  1869   Remarques sur les ossements des cavernes de Gibraltar. *Bulletins et Mémoires de la Société d'Anthropologie de Paris, Série 2* **4**:146–158.
Brose, D. S., and M. H. Wolpoff
  1971   Early Upper Paleolithic man and late Middle Paleolithic tools. *American Anthropologist* **73**:1156–1194.
Campbell, B. G.
  1963   Quantitative taxonomy and human evolution. In *Classification and human evolution*, edited by S. L. Washburn. Chicago: Aldine. Pp. 50–74.
  1965   The nomenclature of the Hominidae. *Occasional Papers—Royal Anthropological Institute* **22**.
Capitan, L., and D. Peyrony
  1909   Deux squelettes au milieu des foyers de l'époque moustérienne. *Compte Rendu de l'Academie d'Inscription des Belles-Lettres.* Pp. 797–806.
  1911   Un nouveau squellette humain fossile. *Revue Anthropologique* **21**:148–150.
  1912   Trois nouveaux squelettes humains fossiles. *Revue Anthropologique* **22**:439–442.
  1921   Découverte d'un sixième squelette moustérien à La Ferrassie (Dordogne). *Revue Anthropologique* **31**:382–388.
Charles, R. H.
  1893   The influence of function, as exemplified in the morphology of the lower extremity of the Punjabi. *Journal of Anatomy* **28**:1–18.
Coon, C. S.
  1939   *The races of Europe.* New York: Macmillan.
  1962   *The origin of races.* New York: Knopf.
  1965   *The living races of man.* New York: Knopf.
Coon, C. S., S. M. Garn, and J. B. Birdsell
  1950   *Races.* Springfield, Illinois: Thomas.

Dawson, C., and A. S., Woodward
  1913   On the discovery of a palaeolithic human skull and mandible in a flint bearing gravel overlying the Wealden (Hastings Beds) at Piltdown, Fletching (Sussex). *Quarterly Journal of the Geological Society of London* **69**:117–144.
  1914   Supplementary note on the discovery of a palaeolithic human skull and mandible at Piltdown (Sussex). *Quarterly Journal of the Geological Society of London* **70**:82–93.
de Mortillet, G.
  1883   *Le Préhistorique.* Paris: C. Reinwald, Librairie-Editeur.
Dobzhansky, T.
  1937   *Genetics and the origin of species.* New York: Columbia University Press.
  1944   On species and races of living and fossil man. *American Journal of Physical Anthropology* **2**:251–265.
Dubois, E.
  1894   Pithecanthropus erectus, *eine Menschenaehnliche Uebergangsform aus Java.* Batavia: Landesdruckerei.
  1896a   On *Pithecanthropus erectus*: a transitional form between man and the apes. *Journal of the Royal Anthropological Institute* **25**:240–255.
  1896b   Le *"Pithecanthropus erectus"* et l'origine de l'homme. *Bulletin de la Société d'Anthropologie de Paris, Série 4* **7**:460–467.
  1900   Pithecanthropus erectus—a form from the ancestral stock of mankind. *Smithsonian Report for 1898.* Pp. 445–459.
  1924   On the principal characters of the cranium and the brain, the mandible and the teeth of Pithecanthropus erectus. *Proceedings of the Koninklijke Nederlandse Akademie van Wetenschappen* **27**:265–278.
  1932   The distinct organization of Pithecanthropus of which the femur bears evidence, now confirmed from other individuals of the described species. *Proceedings of the Koninklijke Nederlandse Akademie van Wetenschappen* **35**:716–722.
  1935   On the gibbon-like appearance of *Pithecanthropus erectus.* *Proceedings of the Koninklijke Nederlandse Akademie van Wetenschappen* **38**:578–585.
Elliot Smith, G.
  1910   Some problems relating to the evolution of the brain. *Lancet* **1**:1–6, 147–154, 221–227.
  1912   The evolution of man. *Nature (London)* **90**:118–126.
  1913   Preliminary report on the cranial cast. *Quarterly Journal of the Geological Society of London* **69**:145–147.
  1914   On the exact determination of the medial plane of the Piltdown skull. *Quarterly Journal of the Geological Society of London* **70**:93–97.
Faul, H.
  1978   A history of geological time. *American Scientist* **66**:159–165.
Fraipont, J.
  1888   Le tibia dans la race de Néanderthal. *Revue Anthropologique, Série 3* **3**:145–158.
Fraipont, J., and M. Lohest
  1887   La race humaine de Néanderthal ou de Canstadt en Belgique: recherches ethnographiques sur des ossements humains, découvertes dans les dépôts quaternaires d'une grotte à Spy et détermination de leur âge géologique. *Archives de Biologie* **7**:587–757.
Frayer, D. W.
  1978   Evolution of the dentition in Upper Paleolithic and Mesolithic Europe. *University of Kansas Publications in Anthropology* **10**:1–201.
  1980   Sexual dimorphism and cultural evolution in the late Pleistocene and holocene of Europe. *Journal of Human Evolution* **9**:399–415.
  1981   Body size, weapon use, and natural selection in the European Upper Paleolithic and Mesolithic. *American Anthropologist* **83**:57–73.
Gorjanović-Kramberger, D.
  1906   *Der diluviale Mensch von Krapina in Kroatien. Ein Beitrag zur Paläoanthropologie.* Wiesbaden: Kreidel's Verlag.

Gould, S. J.
1979 Piltdown revisited. *Natural History* **88**(3):86–97.
1980a G. G. Simpson, paleontology and the modern synthesis. In *The evolutionary synthesis; perspectives on the unification of biology*, edited by E. Mayr and W. B. Provine. Cambridge, Massachusetts: Harvard University Press. Pp. 153–172.
1980b The Piltdown conspiracy. *Natural History* **89**(8):8–28.
Gould, S. J., and N. Eldredge
1977 Punctuated equilibria: the tempo and mode of evolution reconsidered. *Paleobiology* **3**:115–151.
Gregory, W. K.
1916 Note on the molar teeth of the Piltdown mandible. *American Anthropologist* **18**:384–387.
Halstead, L. B.
1978 New light on the Piltdown hoax? *Nature (London)* **276**:11–13.
Hammond, M.
1979 A framework of plausibility for an anthropological forgery: the Piltdown case. *Anthropology* **3**:47–58.
1980 Anthropology as a weapon of social combat in late-nineteenth-century France. *Journal of the History of Behavioral Science* **16**:118–132.
1982 The expulsion of the Neanderthals from human ancestry: Marcellin Boule and the social context of scientific research. *Social Studies of Science*, **12**:1–36.
Hauser, O.
1908 Fouilles scientifiques à La Micoque, à Laugerie-Basse et au Moustier. *L'Homme Prehistorique* **6**:40–48.
1909 Découverte d'un squelette du type de Néandertal sous l'abri inférieur du Moustier, Station No 44, Commune de Saint-Léon (Dordogne). *L'Homme Préhistorique* **7**:1–9.
Heim, J. L.
1968 Les restes néandertaliens de La Ferrassie. Nouvelles données sur la stratigraphie et l'inventaire des squelettes. *Comptes Rendus Hebdomadaires des Séances de l'Académie des Sciences, Série D* **266**:576–578.
1970 L'encéphale néandertalien de l'homme de La Ferrassie. *Anthropologie, Paris* **74**:527–572.
1972 Les Néandertaliens adultes de La Ferrassie (Dordogne). Etudes anthropologique et comparative. Thèse de Doctorat d'État, University de Paris VI.
1974 Les hommes fossiles de La Ferrassie (Dordogne) et le problème de la définition des Néandertaliens classiques. *Anthropologie, Paris* **78**:81–112, 321–378.
1976 Les hommes fossiles de La Ferrassie I. *Archives de l'Institut de Paléontologie Humaine, Mémoire* **35**:1–331.
1978 Contribution du massif facial à la morphogenèse du crâne Néanderthalien. In *Les origines humaines et les époques de l'intelligence*, edited by J. Piveteau. Paris: Masson. Pp. 183–215.
Holtzman, S. F.
1973 On Brace's Notion of "Hominid Catastrophism." *Current Anthropology* **14**:306–308.
Hooton, E. A.
1931 *Up from the ape.* New York: Macmillan.
1937 *Apes, men, and morons.* New York: Putnam's.
1939 *Twilight of man.* New York: Putnam's.
1940 *Why men behave like apes and vice versa.* Princeton, New Jersey: Princeton University Press.
1942 *Man's poor relations.* Garden City, New York: Doubleday.
Howell, F. C.
1951 The place of Neanderthal man in human evolution. *American Journal of Physical Anthropology* **9**:379–416.
1952 Pleistocene glacial ecology and the evolution of "classic Neandertal" man. *Southwestern Journal of Anthropology.* **8**:377–410.
1958 Upper Pleistocene men of the southwestern Asian Mousterian. In *Hundert Jahre Neanderthaler*, edited by G. H. R. von Koenigswald. Utrecht: Kemink en Zoon N.V. Pp. 185–198.

Howells, W. W.
  1944   *Mankind so far.* Garden City; New York: Doubleday.
  1954   *Back of history.* Garden City; New York: Doubleday.
  1959   *Mankind in the making.* Garden City; New York: Doubleday.
  1966   *Homo erectus. Scientific American* **215**(5):46–53.
  1970   Mount Carmel man: morphological relationships. *Proceedings of the Eighth International Congress on Anthropological and Ethnological Sciences* **1**:269–272.
  1973   *Evolution of the Genus* Homo. Reading, Massachusetts: Addison-Wesley.
  1974   Neanderthals: names, hypotheses, and scientific method. *American Anthropologists* **76**:24–38.
  1975   Neanderthal man; facts and figures. In *Paleoanthropology: Morphology and paleoecology*, edited by R. H. Tuttle. Paris: Mouton. Pp. 389–407.

Hrdlička, A.
  1907   Skeletal remains suggesting or attributed to early man in North America. *Bulletin of the Bureau of American Ethnology* **33**:1–113.
  1914   The most ancient skeletal remains of man. *Smithsonian Institution, Annual Report.* Pp. 491–552.
  1922   The Piltdown jaw. *American Journal of Physical Anthropology* **5**:337–347.
  1923   Dimensions of the first and second lower molars, with their bearing on the Piltdown jaw and man's phylogeny. *American Journal of Physical Anthropology* **6**:195–216.
  1925   The Taungs ape. *American Journal of Physical Anthropology* **8**:379–392.
  1927   The Neanderthal phase of man. *Journal of the Royal Anthropological Institute* **57**:249–274.
  1930   The skeletal remains of early man. *Smithsonian Miscellaneous Collections* **83**:1–379.
  1939   Important paleolithic find in Central Asia. *Science* **90**:296–298.

Hrdlička, A., W. H. Holmes, B. Willis, F. E. Wright, and C. N. Fenner
  1912   Early Man in South America. *Bulletin of the Bureau of American Ethnology* **52**:1–405.

Hublin, J. J.
  1978   Le torus occipital transverse et les structures associées: evolution dans le Genre *Homo.* Thèse de Docteur, 3e Cycle, Université de Paris VI.

Huxley, J.
  1942   *Evolution, the modern synthesis.* London: Allen and Unwin.

Jepsen, G. L., E. Mayr, and G. G. Simpson
  1949   *Genetics, paleontology, and evolution.* Princeton, New Jersey: Princenton University Press.

Keith, A.
  1911   *Ancient types of man* (first edition). New York: Harper.
  1912a   *Ancient types of man* (second edition). New York: Harper.
  1912b   The relationship of Neanderthal man and Pithecanthropus to modern man. *Nature (London)* **89**:155–156.
  1915   *The antiquity of man.* London: Williams and Norgate.
  1927   *A report on the Galilee skull.* London: British School of Archaeology in Jerusalem. Pp. 53–106.
  1931   *New discoveries relating to the antiquity of man.* New York: Norton.

Klaatsch, H.
  1901   Das Gliedmassenskelet des Neanderthal-menschen. *Verhandlungen der Anatomischen Gesellschaft* **19**:121–154.
  1909   Preuves que L'Homo Mousteriensis Hauseri appartient au type de Néandertal. *L'Homme Préhistorique* **7**:10–16.

Klaatsch, H., and O. Hauser
  1909   Homo mousteriensis Hauseri. Ein altdiluvialer Skelettfund im Departement Dordogne und seine Zugehörigkeit zum Neandertaltypus. *Archiv für Anthropologie, Braunschweig* **7**:287–297.

Krogman, W. M.
  1978   The planned planting of Piltdown: who? why? In *Human evolution. Biosocial perspectives*, edited by S. L. Washburn and E. R. McCown. Menlo Park, California: Benjamin/Cummings. Pp. 239–252.

Leakey, L. S. B.
  1966 *Homo habilis, Homo erectus* and the Australopithecines. *Nature (London)* **209**:1279–1281.
Le Gros Clark, W. E.
  1947 Observations on the anatomy of the fossil Australopithecinae. *Journal of Anatomy* **81**:300–333.
  1955 *The fossil evidence for human evolution.* Chicago: University of Chicago Press.
  1967 *Man–apes or ape–men?* New York: Holt.
Lévêque, F., and B. Vandermeersch
  1980 Découverte de restes humains dans un niveau castelperronien à Saint-Césaire (Charente-Maritime). *Comptes Rendus Hebdomadaires des Séances de l'Académie des Sciences Série D* **291**:187–189.
  1981 Le néandertalien de Saint-Césaire. *Recherche* **12**:242–244.
Lovejoy, C. O., and E. Trinkaus
  1980 Strength and robusticity of the Neandertal tibia. *American Journal of Physical Anthropology* **53**:465–470.
MacCurdy, G. G.
  1932 *The coming of man.* New York: University Society.
Mann, A. E., and E. Trinkaus
  1974 Neandertal and Neandertal-like fossils from the Upper Pleistocene. *Yearbook of Physical Anthropology* **17**:169–193.
Manouvrier, L.
  1893 Etude sur la rétroversion de la tête du tibia et l'attitude humaine à l'époque quaternaire. *Mémoires de la Société d'Anthropologie de Paris, Série 2* **4**:219–264.
  1895a Discussion du "Pithecanthropus erectus" comme précurseur présumé de l'homme. *Bulletin de la Société d'Anthropologie de Paris, Série 4* **6**:12–47.
  1895b Deuxième étude sur le "Pithecanthropus erectus" comme précurseur présumé de l'homme. *Bulletin de la Société d'Anthropologie de Paris, Série 4* **6**:553–651.
  1896a Le Pithecanthropus erectus et la théorie transformiste. *Revue Scientifique, Série 4* **5**:289–299.
  1896b Le "Pithecanthropus erectus" et l'origine de l'homme. *Bulletin de la Société d'Anthropologie de Paris, Série 4* **7**:467–473.
Marston, A. T.
  1936 Preliminary note on a new fossil human skull from Swanscombe, Kent. *Nature (London)* **138**:200–201.
  1937 The Swanscombe Skull. *Journal of the Royal Anthropological Institute* **67**:339–406.
Martin, H.
  1911 Sur un squelette humain à l'époque moustérienne trouvé en Charente. *Comptes Rendus Hebdomadaires des Séances de l'Académie des Sciences* **153**:728–730.
  1912a L'homme fossile moustérien de La Quina: réconstruction du Crâne. *Bulletin de la Société Préhistorique Franqaise* **9**:389–424.
  1912b Position stratigraphique des ossements humains recueillis dans le Moustérien de La Quina de 1908 et 1912. *Bulletin de la Société Préhistorique Franqaise* **9**:700–709.
  1912c Le crâne de l'homme fossile moustérien de La Quina. *Association Franqaise de l'Advancement de Science* **41**:538–539.
  1923 *Recherches sur l'évolution du Moustérien dans le gisement de La Quina (Charente) III: L'homme fossile.* Paris: Librairie Octave Doin.
Mayr, E.
  1942 *Systematics and the origin of species.* New York: Columbia University Press.
  1951 Taxonomic categories in fossil hominids. *Cold Spring Harbor Symposia on Quantitative Biology* **15**:109–118.
  1980 Prologue: some thoughts on the history of the evolutionary synthesis. In *The evolutionary synthesis: perspectives on the unification of biology,* edited by E. Mayr and W. B. Provine. Cambridge, Massachusetts: Harvard University Press. Pp. 1–48.

Mayr, E., and W. B. Provine (editors)
    1980   *The evolutionary synthesis: perspectives on the unification of biology.* Cambridge, Massachusetts: Harvard University Press.
McCown, T. D., and A. Keith
    1939   *The Stone Age of Mount Carmel II: The fossil human remains from the Levalloiso-Mousterian.* Oxford: Clarendon.
Millar, R.
    1972   *The Piltdown men.* London: Chaucer Press.
Miller, G. S.
    1915   The jaw of the Piltdown man. *Smithsonian Miscellaneous Collections* **65**:1–31.
    1918   The Piltdown jaw. *American Journal of Physical Anthropology* **1**:25–52.
Musgrave, J. H.
    1971   How dextrous was Neanderthal man? *Nature (London)* **233**:538–541.
Nyèssen, D. J. H.
    1943   The evolution of Eug. Dubois' conceptions. *Boletin de la Real Sociedad Española de Historia Natural* **41**:459–464.
Oakley, K. P., and C. R. Hoskins
    1950   New evidence on the antiquity of Piltdown man. *Nature (London)* **165**:379–382.
Oppenoorth, W. F. F.
    1932   Ein neuer diluvialer Urmensch von Java. *Natur und Museum* **62**:271–279.
Osborn, H. F.
    1915   *Men of the old Stone Age.* New York: Scribner's.
    1922   Orthogenesis as observed from paleontological evidence beginning in the year 1889. *American Naturalist* **56**:134–143.
    1927   *Man rises to Parnassus.* Princeton, New Jersey: Princeton University Press.
Rensch, B.
    1947   *Neuere Probleme der Abstammungslehre.* Stuttgart: Enke.
Rightmire, G. P.
    1978   Florisbad and human population succession in southern Africa. *American Journal of Physical Anthropology* **48**:475–486.
    1979   Implications of Border Cave skeletal remains for later Pleistocene human evolution. *Current Anthropology* **20**:23–35.
    1981   Later Pleistocene hominids from eastern and southern Africa. *Anthropologie (Brno)* **19**:15–26.
Ryan, A. S.
    1980   Anterior dental microwear in hominid evolution: comparisons with human and non-human primates. Unpublished Ph.D. thesis, Department of Anthropology, University of Michigan.
Santa Luca, A. P.
    1978   A re-examination of presumed Neandertal-like fossils. *Journal of Human Evolution* **7**:619–636.
Schaafhausen, D.
    1858   Zur Kenntnis der ältesten Rassenschädel. *Archiv fuer Anatomie, Physiologie und Wissenschaftliche Medicin* **25**:453–478.
Schultz, A. H.
    1955   The position of the occipital condyles and of the face relative to the skull base in primates. *American Journal of Physical Anthropology* **13**:97–120.
Schwalbe, G.
    1899   Studien Über *Pithecanthropus erectus* Dubois. *Zeitschrift für Morphologie und Anthropologie* **1**:16–22.
    1901   Der Neanderthalschädel. *Bonner Jahrbuch* **106**:1–72.
    1904   *Die Vorgeschichte des Menschen.* Braunschweig: Druck und Verlag von Friedrich Vieweg und Sohn.

1906   Studien zur Vorgeschichte des Menschen. *Zeitschrift für Morphologie und Anthropologie, Sonderheft* **1**:1–228.

1914   Kritische Besprechung von Boule's Werk: "L'homme fossile de La Chapelle-aux-Saints" mit einigen Untersuchungen. *Zeitschrift für Morphologie und Anthropologie* **16**:527–610.

Sera, G. L.
1909   Nouve osservazioni ed induzioni sul Cranio di Gibraltar. *Archivio per l'Antropologia e la Etnologia* **39**:151–212.

1910   Di alcuni caratteri importanti sinora non rilavati nel cranio di Gibraltar. *Atti della Societa Romana di Antropologia* **15**:197–208.

Sergi, S.
1929   La scoperta di un cranio del tipo di Neandertal presso Roma. *Rivista di Antropologia* **28**:457–462.

1939   Il cranio neandertaliano del Monte Circeo. *Atti della Accademia Nazionale dei Lincei, Classe di Scienze Fisiche, Matematiche e Naturali, Rendiconti Series 6* **29**:672–685.

1944   Craniometria e craniografia del primo paleantropo di Saccopastore. *Ricerche di Morfologia* **20–21**:1–59.

1948   Il cranio del secondo paleantropo di Saccopastore. *Paleontographia Italiana* **42**:25–164.

1954   La mandibola neandertaliana Circeo II. *Rivista di Anthropotogia* **41**:305–344.

Simpson, G. G.
1944   *Tempo and mode in evolution.* New York: Columbia University Press.

Smith, F. H.
1978   Evolutionary significance of the mandibular foramen area in Neandertals. *American Journal of Physical Anthropology* **48**:523–532.

1980   Sexual differences in European Neanderthal crania with special reference to the Krapina remains. *Journal of Human Evolution* **9**:359–375.

Smith, F. H., and G. C. Ranyard
1980   Evolution of the supraorbital region in upper Pleistocene fossil hominids from South–Central Europe. *American Journal of Physical Anthropology* **53**:589–610.

Sollas, W. J.
1907   On the cranial and facial characters of the Neanderthal race. *Philosophical Transactions of the Royal Society of London, Series B* **199**:281–339.

Spencer, F.
1979   Aleš Hrdlička, M.D., 1869–1943: a chronicle of the life and work of an American physical anthropologist. Unpublished Ph.D. thesis, Department of Anthropology, University of Michigan, Ann Arbor.

Stebbins, G. L., and F. J. Ayala
1981   Is a new evolutionary synthesis necessary? *Science* **213**:967–971.

Stewart, T. D.
1954   American Institute of Human Paleontology. *Science* **120**:7A.

1962a   Neanderthal scapulae with special attention to the Shanidar Neanderthals from Iraq. *Anthropos* **57**:779–800.

1962b   Neanderthal cervical vertebrae with special attention to the Shanidar Neanderthals from Iraq. *Bibliotheca Primatologica* **1**:130–154.

Straus, W. L., Jr., and A. J. E. Cave
1957   Pathology and the posture of Neanderthal man. *Quarterly Review of Biology* **32**:348–363.

Stringer, C. B.
1978   Some problems in Middle and Upper Pleistocene hominid relationships. In *Recent advances in primatology,* Vol 3, edited by D. J. Chivers and K. A. Joysey. New York: Academic Press. Pp. 395–418.

Stringer, C. B., and E. Trinkaus
1981   The Shanidar Neanderthal crania. In *Aspects of human evolution,* edited by C. B. Stringer. London: Taylor and Francis. Pp. 129–165.

Stringer, C. B., R. G. Kruszynski, and R. M. Jacobi
  1981   Allez Neanderthal. *Nature (London)* **289**:823–824.
Thorne, A. G., and M. H. Wolpoff
  1982   Regional continuity in Australasian Pleistocene hominid evolution. *American Journal of Physical Anthropology* **55**:337–349.
Tobias, P. V.
  1980   *"Australopithecus afarensis"* and *A. africanus*: critique and an alternative hypothesis. *Palaeontologia Africana* **23**:1–17.
Toerien, M. J.
  1957   Note on the cervical vertebrae of the La Chapelle man. *South African Journal of Science* **53**:447–449.
Trinkaus, E.
  1975a   A functional analysis of the Neandertal foot. Unpublished Ph.D. thesis, Department of Anthropology, University of Pennsylvania, Philadelphia.
  1975b   Squatting among the Neandertals: a problem in the behavioral interpretation of skeletal morphology. *Journal of Archaeological Science* **2**:327–351.
  1976a   The morphology of European and Southwest Asian Neandertal pubic bones. *American Journal of Physical Anthropology* **44**:95–104.
  1976b   The evolution of the hominid femoral diaphysis during the Upper Pleistocene in Europe and the Near East. *Zeitschrift für Morphologie und Anthropologie* **67**:291–319.
  1977   A functional interpretation of the axillary border of the Neandertal scapula. *Journal of Human Evolution* **6**:231–234.
  1978   Functional implications of the Krapina Neandertal lower limb remains. In *Krapinski Pračovjek i Evolucija Hominida*, edited by M. Malez. Zagreb: Jugoslavenska Akademija Znanosti i Umjetnosti. Pp. 155–192.
  1980   Sexual differences in Neanderthal limb bones. *Journal of Human Evolution* **9**:377–397.
  1981   Neanderthal limb proportions and cold adaptation. In *Aspects of human evolution*, edited by C. B. Stringer. London: Taylor and Francis. Pp. 187–224.
Trinkaus, E., and W. W. Howells
  1979   The Neanderthals. *Scientific American* **241**(6):118–133.
Trinkaus, E., and M. LeMay
  1982   Occipital bunning among later Pleistocene hominids. *American Journal of Physical Anthropology* **57**:27–36.
Turner, W.
  1895   On M. Dubois's description of remains recently found in Java, named by him *Pithecanthropus erectus*. *Journal of Anatomy and Physiology* **29**:424–445.
Vallois, H. V.
  1949   L'origine de l'*Homo sapiens*. *Comptes Rendus Hebdomadaires des Séances de l'Académie des Sciences* **228**:949–951.
  1954   Neandertals and praesapiens. *Journal of the Royal Anthropological Institute* **84**:111–130.
  1958   La Grotte de Fontéchevade II: Anthropologie. *Archives de l'Institut de Paléontologie Humaine Mémoire* **29**:1–164.
  1966   More on the fate of the "classic" Neanderthals. *Current Anthropology* **7**:205–208.
Vandermeersch, B.
  1981   *Les hommes fossiles de Qafzeh (Israël)*. Paris: Editions du Centre National de la Recherche Scientifique.
von Koenigswald, G. H. R.
  1936   Erste Mitteilung über einen fossilen Hominiden aus dem Altpleistocän Ostjavas. *Proceedings of the Koninklijke Nederlandse Akademie van Wetenschappen* **39**:1000–1009.
  1940   Neue Pithecanthropus-Funde 1936–1938. *Wetenschappelijke Mededeelingen, Dienst van den Mijnbouw in Nederlandsch-Oost-Indie* **28**:1–232.
Warren, K. B. (editor)
  1951   *Origin and evolution of man*, Vol. 15. Cold Spring Harbor Laboratory, Cold Spring Harbor, New York.

Washburn, S. L.
1951   The new physical anthropology. *Transactions at the New York Academy of Science, Series 2* **13**:298–304.

Weidenreich, F.
1929   Vererbungsexperiment und vergleichende Morphologie. *Paläontologische Zeitschrift* **11**:275–286.

1936   The mandibles of *Sinanthropus pekinensis. Palaeontologia Sinica, New Series D* **7**:1–162.

1937   The dentition of *Sinanthropus pekinensis. Palaeontologia Sinica, New Series D* **1**:1–80.

1938   The ramification of the middle meningeal artery in fossil hominids and its bearing on phylogenetic problems. *Palaeontologia Sinica, New Series D* **3**:1–16.

1940a   The torus occipitalis and related structures and their transformation in the course of human evolution. *Bulletin of the Geological Society of China* **19**:379–558.

1940b   Some problems dealing with ancient man. *American Anthropologist* **42**:375–383.

1941a   The extremity bones of *Sinanthropus pekinensis. Palaeontologia Sinica*, New Series D **5**: 1–82.

1941b   The brain and its rôle in the phylogenetic transformation of the human skull. *Transactions of the American Philosophical Society* **31**:321–442.

1943a   The skull of *Sinanthropus pekinensis. Palaeontologia Sinica, New Series D* **10**:1–298.

1943b   The "Neanderthal Man" and the ancestors of "Homo sapiens." *American Anthropologist* **45**:39–48.

1945   Giant early man from Java and South China. *Anthropological Papers of the American Museum of Natural History* **40**:1–134.

1946   *Apes, giants and man.* Chicago: University of Chicago Press.

1947a   Facts and speculations concerning the origin of *Homo sapiens. American Anthropologist* **49**:187–203.

1947b   The trend of human evolution. *Evolution* **1**:221–236.

1949   Interpretations of the fossil material. *Studies in Physical Anthropology* **1**:149–157.

1951   Morphology of Solo man. *Anthropological Papers of the American Museum of Natural History* **43**:205–290.

Weiner, J. S.
1955   *The Piltdown forgery.* London: Oxford University Press.

1958   The pattern of evolutionary development of the genus *Homo. South African Journal of Medical Science* **23**:111–120.

Weiner, J. S., K. P. Oakley, and W. E. Le Gros Clark
1953   The solution of the Piltdown problem. *Bulletin of the British Museum (Natural History), Geology* **2**:139–146.

Weiner, J. S., *et al.*
1955   Further contributions to the solution of the Piltdown problem. *Bulletin of the British Museum (Natural History), Geology* **2**:225–288.

Weinert, H.
1936   Der Urmenschenschädel von Steinheim. *Zeitschrift für Morphologie und Anthropologie* **35**:463–518.

Wolpoff, M. H.
1975   Some aspects of human mandibular evolution. In *Determinants of mandibular form and growth,* edited by J. A. McNamara, Jr. Ann Arbor, Michigan: Center for Human Growth and Development. Pp. 1–64.

1980   *Paleoanthropology.* New York: Knopf.

1981   Allez Neanderthal. *Nature (London)* **289**:823.

Wolpoff, M. H., F. H. Smith, M. Malez, J. Radovčić, and D. Rukavina
1981   Upper Pleistocene human remains from Vindija Cave, Croatia, Yugoslavia. *American Journal of Physical Anthropology* **54**:499–545.

Woodward, A. S.
1917   Fourth note on the Piltdown gravel, with evidence of a second skull of Eoanthropus dawsoni. *Quarterly Journal of the Geological Society of London* **73**:1–10.

Wu, X.
  1981   A well-preserved cranium of an archaic type of early *Homo sapiens* from Dali, China. *Scientia Sinica (English Edition)* **24**:530–539.
Zdansky, O.
  1926   Preliminary notice of two teeth of a hominid from a cave in Chihi (China). *Bulletin of the Geological Society of China* **5**:281–284.

11

Inquiries into the Peopling of the New World: Development of Ideas and Recent Advances

Albert B. Harper and William S. Laughlin

Today, Native Americans present to human biologists a unique opportunity to study the processes of evolution and adaptation. Their ancestors, the first Americans, originally entered the New World as small bands of migrants coming from restricted sources, entering America via known routes, and adapting to widely diverse ecosystems each with unique stressors. Given the enormous literature on Native Americans and their population biology, this review will necessarily omit many topics that are relevant. Our emphasis shall be primarily on studies of Alaskan populations—the gateway populations.

Early Inquiries

From all appearances, the first scientific inquiry into the population affinities of the Eskimo was made by the Danish anatomist, Jakob B. Winslow, who, in 1722, published a description of a female Eskimo skull from Dog Island off the west coast of Greenland. This description is illustrated with plates of such accuracy and detail that it is possible to recognize the mandibular torus and missing third molar as well as the low ascending ramus, the broad, flat face, and other characteristics of the Aleuts and Eskimos (Pedersen 1949). Shortly thereafter, encouraged by Catherine the Great of Russia, a series of expeditions went to Kamchatka in 1728 and 1739 to study the indigenous peoples and natural history of the region. Among the scientists sent to Kamchatka was Georg Wilhelm Steller, who, in addition to discovering Steller's blue jay and the northern sea cow, also noted the great

A HISTORY OF AMERICAN
PHYSICAL ANTHROPOLOGY, 1930–1980

similarity of Eskimos to northern Asians (Hrdlička 1930). Such studies were part of a growing interest in remote peoples. Indeed, Lewis and Clark's expedition to the Pacific Ocean (1804–1806) was largely an expression of Thomas Jefferson's keen interest in the natural history of the Americas.

Towards the end of the eighteenth century, a number of scholars, most notably Johann F. Blumenbach, began collecting and studying human crania. Based on the observations of the crania in his collection, Blumenbach arrived at the conclusion that the Eskimos were of Asiatic origin. He believed they were most closely related to Mongolians (Blumenbach 1795; see Bendyshe 1865:265–266).

During the second half of the nineteenth century, several score of investigators became interested in the origins of the Eskimos and other Native Americans. But with the exception of Augustus H. Keane (a British ethnologist and geographer), who believed that "these islanders [Aleuts] should possibly be regarded not as [an] abnormal offshoot, but as the original stock from which the Eskimos themselves have diverged [Keane 1886–1887:309]," little serious attention was paid to the important role of the Aleut population in the unraveling of the history of the New World.

By the beginning of the twentieth century, scientific opinion on the origins of the Eskimos was divided essentially into two camps, which can be conviently re-presented by the opposing views of Hrdlička and Boas. Hrdlička supported the view that the Eskimos had originated in Asia (discussed in a subsequent section of this chapter). Boas promoted the notion that they had originated in the Hudson Bay region, where he claimed they retained "their ancient characteristics more than any others [Boas 1907:369]." Thus, according to Boas, "the Eskimos must be considered as . . . new arrivals in Alaska, which they reached coming from the east [Boas 1910:534]."

Interestingly enough, it was a former student of Boas's, Edward Sapir, who correctly found the solution to this dilemma: Had the historical significance of linguistic differentiation been more generally appreciated,

> I doubt if the theory, for example, of distribution of Eskimo tribes from the west coast of Hudson Bay as a centre would have received quite such ready acceptance. . . . The Eskimo linguistic stock is sharply divided into two dialectic groups, Eskimo proper and Aleut. Inasmuch as Aleut is confined to Alaska and as a considerable number of distinct Eskimo dialects are spoken in Alaska besides, it seems very probable to me that the earliest at present ascertainable centre of dispersion of the tribes of Eskimo stock lies in Alaska [Sapir 1916:82–83].

Development of Modern Scientific Inquiry and Theory

The year 1930 provides an ideal starting point to discuss the development of modern scientific inquiry and theory. It was in this year that Hrdlička published his monumental "Anthropological Survey in Alaska" (1930) a summary volume that presented the results of his own initial researches on the Alaskan mainland (1926,

1929, 1930) as well as the work of his aides Moore (1912), Stewart (1927), and Collins (1927, 1929, 1930). During the next decade, Hrdlička worked systematically on Kodiak Island (1931–1935) and the Aleutian and Commander Islands (1936–1938). This pioneer effort yielded information that was fundamental to our present understanding of the anthropology of northwestern America and northeastern Asia (see Spencer 1979). The results of Hrdlička's labors in Beringia were published posthumously in two volumes: *The Anthropology of Kodiak Island* (1944) and *The Aleutian and Commander Islands and Their Inhabitants* (1945).

Aleš Hrdlička's Contribution

The state of the art in 1930 lacked many dimensions that we today take for granted (e.g., Hooton 1930, 1931). A restricted time depth was the generally accepted view, with the possibility that Eskimo prehistory might extend back as far as the time of Christ. The Bering Land Bridge was an ingenious construction, conceptually comparable to the Brooklyn Bridge, and of relevance primarily to paleontologists interested in the migration of early forms of terrestrial animals. As indicated by Hrdlička's 1930 map (Figure 1), there were two probable routes of migration of man into North America. One crossed the Bering Strait in the north, and the other proceeded from Kamchatka to the Commander Islands to the Aleutian Islands. The latter route was not eliminated until Hrdlička's visit to the Commander Islands in 1938. At that time, sea level was viewed as static; erosion of coastal sites was acknowledged, but inundation by rising sea level had not yet been considered. Although Heinbecker and Pauli (1927) had blood-typed the first Eskimos (Polar and Baffin Land) at the same time that Hrdlička was making his survey of Alaska, Hrdlička was somewhat *pre*genetic or *a*genetic in his approach to populations. Neither did he immerse himself in complex statistical analysis, though when the need arose, he displayed his characteristic astuteness by coopting the statistical services of either the Prudential Insurance Company of America or the Chief Statistician of the Bureau of the Census (see Spencer 1979:89–91). Another impediment to Hrdlička's analytical vision in 1930 lay in the somber fact that he had not yet studied the Aleuts although he had presented Keane's (1886–1887) observation, which was that the Eskimos developed from the Aleuts (see Hrdlička 1930:333).

Interestingly, and spectularly in retrospect, Hrdlička recognized the distributional pattern in Eskimo morphological variation, now well established, and he further suggested an extrapolation based on geographic variation in the Eskimo and American Indian populations. This extrapolation viewed the groups evolutionarily or, in other words, as ultimately identical. Hrdlička also anticipated the most recent development in his formulation:

> In general the farther west we proceed the less exceptional on the whole the Eskimo becomes and the more he approximates the Indian, particularly the Indian of Alaska and the northwest coast. As this cannot, in the light of present evidence, be attributed alone to admixture, it is plain that if it

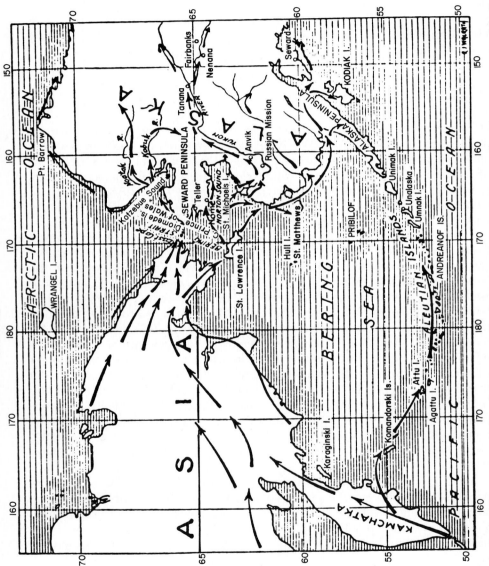

Figure 1 Hrdlička's concept, as of 1930, of population movements from northern Asia to Alaska. From Hrdlička (1930), courtesy of the Smithsonian Institution.

were possible to proceed a few steps farther in this direction the differences between the Eskimo and the Indian would fade out so that a distinction between the two would become difficult if not impossible [Hrdlička 1930:365].

Hrdlička suggested looking for the origin of the Eskimos in the western rather than the northern Arctic or the northeastern area, favoring the area between 160 degrees west and 160 degrees east longitude and from 60 degrees to 75 degrees north latitude as containing the primarily Eskimo-genic center—implying that the larger part of the Eskimo differentiations was probably American.

In discussing the relationship of the American Indian and Eskimo families, Hrdlička frequently resorted to what he called the "double-thumb hypothesis," which was first formally presented in a paper to the American Philosophical Society on April 22, 1932. According to this "hypothesis," the relationship between the two families was represented by a hand with outstretched fingers:

> The diverging fingers proper are the different types of the Indian, the thumb, which should be doubled, representing the Eskimo. The [second] thumb is farther apart, but originates from the same hand, which is the old Asiatic or sometimes called Paleo-Asiatic yellow-brown strain, a strain that, according to the best evidence, gave us the ancestry of all the aboriginal Americans [Hrdlička 1932:402].

As mentioned previously, in 1930 the two competing hypothetical routes for man's entry into the New World were the Bering Strait and the Aleutian Islands. The idea that people may have lived permanently as well as transiently on a former exposed land mass was not formulated until 1963 (Laughlin 1963). The southern route, through the Aleutian Islands, was effectively rejected in 1938. Hrdlička, accompanied by Alan G. May, William Clemes and William S. Laughlin, searched both Medni and Bering islands of the Commander group for signs of pre-Russian habitation. Although their survey was not exhaustive, no evidence of pre-Russian (1741) habitation was found, which was in agreement with Russian researchers, who had a keen interest in the human history of these islands. A few Aleut skeletons had been collected by Grebnitski and others and sent to Leningrad. However, none of these antedated the 1826 relocation of Aleuts to the Commanders.

Because of this survey, Hrdlička was able to exclude migration from Kamchatka to the Commander Islands to the Aleutian Islands, all the while recognizing the unlikely possibility of a longer boat trip from the Kuriles. This was an important step forward in limiting the options for human migration. Hrdlička's research clearly indicated only two possible sources for Aleuts, and these proved relatively simple to discriminate during analysis. The proposition became simply, that Eskimos were derived from Aleuts, or that Aleuts were derived from Eskimos, or that both were derived from a common ancestral population occurring much further back in time than the 2000 years allotted. In brief, the physical, genetic, and cultural evidence effectively ruled out a direct Eskimo paternity, and, therefore, a common ancestry on an earlier Alaskan coastline became the obvious choice.

Several more years were required beyond 1938 to secure high-level proof following the conceptual rigor of Dixon and Massey (1951).

Hrdlička set several wheels in motion with his 1938 investigations. These included the evidence that there had been extensive stylistic change in many artifacts and that the carved stone dishes and pots were associated primarily with the earlier people. Both these kinds of changes had been overlooked by Jochelson (1933) because his excavations were of later period sites than Hrdlička's. The reason for this is that the Nikolski Aleuts were still living on Chaluka when Jochelson was there, but only two households remained on Chaluka in 1938, and it was possible to excavate without disturbing them. The depth of the Chaluka mound itself suggested greater antiquity than 2000 years B.P., but no quantified chronology was possible, and radiocarbon dating was not available for Chaluka until 1950.

Prior to their landing on Umnak Island, May and Laughlin had discovered an abundance of stone cores and unifacial blades on Anangula Island, Hrdlička did not exhibit any particular interest in these stone tools, however; he simply told them to select some nice ones for the Smithsonian and to keep the rest themselves.

This expedition was Hrdlička's last trip to Alaska. Thereafter, he turned his attention to Siberia and, especially, to a meeting with A. P. Okladnikov in 1939. His last book on the Aleutian and Commander islands (Hrdlička 1945) was published posthumously with the expert services of Lucille St. Hoyme. As much as it is a monumental book and one that presented much valuable data that would other- wise have been lost, it also represents his changing opinions about the taxonomic and historical significance of the Aleuts.

Early Post-World War II Developments:
Analysis of Genetic and Discontinuous Variation

The analysis of discontinuous variation with reference to discrete traits of the skeleton, such as Hooton's study of mandibular toris in Greenlandic Eskimos and Icelanders (Hooton 1918), has played a useful role in unraveling the mystery of who peopled the New World. Actually, Hrdlička had studied this torus in many populations, with particular emphasis on the Eskimos and Aleuts. Indeed, in his 1938 field lectures and in the seminars convened about newly exposed skeletons, Hrdlička discussed various traits, including the mandibular torus. Hence, when Laughlin returned to the Aleutians on the Harvard Peabody Museum Expedition in 1948 (at that time, a doctoral candidate at Harvard under Hooton), he was armed with an interest in nonmetric skeletal variations in addition to interests in the anthropometry of the living and their skeletal ancestors and in their blood groups. Among those who accompanied Laughlin to the Aleutians in 1948 were Fred Alexander, Coenraad F. Moorrees, and Stanley M. Garn. Alexander (1949) assembled data on cardiology, hypertension, and general health conditions. Moorrees (1957) studied the dentition in detail, including mandibular toris, while

Garn studied hair and pigmentation, and assembled data on child growth (Garn and Moorrees 1951). It is significant that Moorrees demonstrated the hereditary nature of the mandibular torus by noting (a) its different frequency in two isolate divisions living under the same conditions, (b) its appearance in children too young to respond to masticatory stress, (c) its greater occurrence in males who chewed less than females, and (d) its presence in the few family lines that were available for tracing. This expedition was all the more remarkable because not only was it a multidisciplinary team designed to conduct biomedical research, including infield blood-typing of multiple genes and electrocardiography, it was also truly integrated. Members of the team also excavated, collected linguistic data, and practiced medicine and dentistry, as well as taking scientific measurements.

A valuable impetus to the measurement of biological distance between populations, the utilization of discrete traits of the skeleton, and the use of a test based on historically know relationships was given by J. N. Spuhler (another of Hooton's students) in three of his many insightful studies (Spuhler 1951, 1954, 1979). Spuhler (1951) noted that information on the distribution of eight genetic variations was too scanty to allow proper analysis of the relationships between the native peoples of the Americas. However, he noted that a comparison of the data for American Indians, with that for Caucasoids, Negroids, and Asiatic Mongoloids substantiated the conclusions that American Indians are more closely related to Mongoloids than to Negroids or Caucasoids, based on the rank orders for the distribution of gene or phenotype frequencies. This formal and economical demonstration was, of course, in agreement with the evidence from blood groups and from anthropometric data on both the living and the dead.

Spuhler's prescient observation, contained in a footnote, is especially valuable to the theme of our chapter:

> Here, of course, I am attempting to report rather than to pass an opinion. My opinion is that Boyd's scheme is *strikingly different* from the traditional racial classifications. The important difference lies in their conceptual nature. In Boyd's scheme the difference between races can be expressed in a single concept—change in gene frequency. And we have what appears to be an exhaustive set of rule for changes in gene frequency [1951:178, footnote 1].

The conceptual revolution is obvious in human population genetics and, interestingly, exerted a tangible and beneficial influence on skeletal studies. In his seminal study, "Some Problems in the Physical Anthropology of the American Southwest (1954)," Spuhler dealt with a central problem in physical anthropology and the key problem in understanding peopling of the New World: the determination of the biological relationship of two or more populations. Two points have been unusually influential in subsequent Arctic studies. First, Spuhler determined that the best candidates for traits that can be properly associated with simple modes of inheritance are traits with discontinuous variation, although in many cases they actually prove to be quasicontinuous traits. Second, he called attention to the desirability of testing the results of measuring the degree of biological relationship with a set of historically known relationships. His demonstration of methodology and testing—using the Pueblo of Hano, whose ancestors were known to have migrated from the upper Rio Grande—constitutes the first realistic test of the estimation of biological distance in human populations.

Spuhler's idea of testing in a known situation before venturing into groups for whom alternative classifications are feasible led directly to Laughlin and Jørgensen's (1956) analysis of distance between the cranial isolates of Greenland. Their basis for analysis was simply that the options for migration within Greenland were confined to coastal movements (because of the inland ice) that were in clockwise, counterclockwise, or both directions. Subsequent studies (Ferrell *et al.* 1981; Harper 1980; Laughlin 1963, 1975, 1980; Turner 1967) were all influenced in either minor or a major degree by this concept of defined cases with limited options, which therefore automatically excluded many, most, or all alternative explanations.

Advances in Dating the Past

While Laughlin and Spuhler were independently unraveling the population affinities of Native North American tribes using genetic and skeletal evidence (Laughlin 1951a, 1951b), both metric and nonmetric, the study of prehistory also took on new dimensions with the development of precise dating techniques. Libby's pioneering work in the carbon 14 dating methodology (Libby *et al.* 1949) opened new vistas of prehistory that had previously been closed due to inexact dates. Laughlin began applying radiocarbon dating to the question of human entry into the New World very shortly after the technique was introduced. The discovery that Chaluka was nearly 4000 years old was revolutionary because it meant that nearby Anangula, which Laughlin and Marsh (1951) argued to be the oldest Aleut village, had to be much older. When Anangula Blade site was finally excavated in 1962–1963, the radiocarbon dates indicated an age between 7600 and 8300 years B.P. (Black and Laughlin 1964), making Anangula the oldest site in Alaska until Onion Portage was dated by Anderson (1970).

These studies of prehistory, although significant in themselves, were crucial to the study of the origins and affinities of the first Americans. Finally, an accurate time scale was created, thereby giving investigators some notion of both the sequence of events and, perhaps more importantly, the time available for Native American populations to evolve and adapt to the challenges of their new hemisphere.

Recent Advances

The past decade has marked the beginnings of a new refinement of the theories and investigations of the peopling of the New World. We see four key developments that have particular promise in the reconstruction of the population history of the first Americans, especially of their history on entering the American hemisphere. These developments include

1. the discovery and accurate dating of a score of archaeological sites in Alaska and the continental United States
2. the development and application of sophisticated multivariate distance analyses to increasingly more sophisticated and elaborate genetic marker and morphological data
3. the establishment of the bifurcated migration route model for American Indians and Bering Sea Mongoloids.
4. The integration of archaeological, linguistic, and genetic data to form a calibrated divergence schedule.

These events, in our view, are especially relevant to our understanding of the evolutionary history of the early American populations—not only Alaska natives, but also the entire aboriginal population of the New World. It is not our intention to exhaustively review these topics but rather to try to provide the essential flavor of the arguments as they now stand.

Archaeological Advances

In the absence of human skeletal remains, we must rely on archaeological evidence to attempt to identify the population composition of early New World inhabitants. In contrast to the current view held by many archaeologists that the tools provide diagnostic identity for the people who made the tools (Dumond 1977), we note that people, with a broad gamut of genes, bone, and brains, were responsible for the tools and that their identity can be argued not by the tool typology, but rather by evidence of cultural continuity, ecological constraints, and, in the case of most native Alaskan populations, by the presence of the living descendants of the original tool manufacturer. This view of the continuity of human population provides, then, the analytical ability to make inferences about the nature and rate of evolutionary change (Harper 1980; Neel 1973) for the species as a whole.

After exhaustive attempts to integrate the entire late Pleistocene and early Holocene history have failed, it is now becoming increasingly clear to many physical anthropologists that the early history of Alaska can be divided into two separate and distinct human occupations. The earlier migration into the New World was based on an interior-adapted population that followed the Yukon River, probably from its ancient mouth south of present day St. Lawrence Island, inland. The extensive surveys conducted during the 1970s in response to the Alaskan pipeline and the North Slope Pet IV explorations have revealed many sites that, when considered as a unit, form a large rectangle encompassing much of the upper Yukon drainage east of Mt. McKinley. Bowers (1980), Dumond (1980), and West (1980) have critically reviewed these areas and come to the inescapable conclusion that none of the archaeological sites in the Alaskan interior predate 13,000 years B.P. Bower's synthesis of pre-7000 years B.P. dates include such places as Moose Creek Bluff (11,730 years B.P.), Dry Creek (10,690–11,120 years B.P.), Carlo Creek (8400–10,040 years B.P.), Healy Lake (8210–11,090 years B.P.), Tangle Lakes (8810–10,150 years B.P.), Onion Portage (8070–9857 years B.P.), Gallagher Flint Station (10,540 years B.P.), and Putu (6090–11,470 years B.P.). These industries vary among themselves considerably. Some are either unifacial core and blade traditions or are characterized by microblade production. Others have the early introduction of bifaces, including fluted points, which are at the current time an enigma to most archaeologists. Clark and McFayden Clark (1980) have provided an extremely useful summary of the fluted point dilemma. If Ackerman's (1980) microblade and core industry from Goundhog Bay in southeastern Alaska, which spans 7545 to 10,180 years B.P., is included in the realm of the central Alaskan occupations, the distribution of time available to the early populations spans some 3000 years, with most dates falling in the late 8000- to early 9000-year range. Importantly, however, it is clear that the interior sites have firm dating extending back to pre-Holocene times.

The search for early man in the Aleutian–Alaskan Peninsula–Kodiak Triangle also advanced significantly during the last decade. Major excavations at the Anangula core blade and burin site near the former terminus of the Bering Land Bridge revealed a huge occupation that lasted some 2000 years, (7202–8734 years B.P.) and at least 3,000,000 stone tools (Laughlin 1975). We regard Anangula as the earliest Aleut occupation (a) because of its location and (b) because of the patent continuity between the Anangula blade industry and the successive Anangula Village transition culture and, thence, between Anangula Village and Chaluka, which exists today. Clark's (1979) review of Kodiak Island provides a sequence of events for the origins of the Eskimo that parallels the Aleut development. Kodiak was populated slightly later than the Anangula area, partly because deglaciation proceeded from the west; hence, Dumond's (1977, 1980) Ugashik Narrows and Naknek dates of 7675 to 8995 years B.P. provide evidence for the earliest Eskimo. These traditions are in many ways similar to the Anangula core, blade, and burin industry, except for the occurrence of transverse burins, carved stone dishes, lamps, red ochre, obsidian, and shaft smoothers. These elements are characteristically Aleut because they have persisted in varying degrees from the earliest Anangula levels to modern times and are consistently associated with Aleuts.

The resultant conclusion from the archaeological investigations of the last decade is that an earlier, interior, riverine population crossed the Bering Land Bridge some 12,000 to 13,000 years ago and then followed the Yukon River east through Alaska. These populations were or became the ancestors of the American Indian. At the same time or perhaps slightly later, populations who resided on the southern margin of the Bering Land Bridge were forced, by rapidly receding coastlines, to migrate southward into the Umnak–Kuskokwim–Kodiak Triangle. Those people who followed the land bridge to its terminus, near present day Nikolski Bay, became Aleut. Those who maintained residence near the current

Alaskan coastline can be identified as Eskimo (Laughlin *et al.* 1979b). Certainly, by 9000 years B.P., the division of the Bering Sea Mongoloids into Aleuts and Eskimos had occurred.

Analysis of Morphological and Genetic Systems

Biometric treatment of human biological data had its roots firmly established with the development of the discipline (see Armelagos *et al.* and Weiss and Chakraborty in the present volume). Pearson, Fisher, and Malhanobis were keenly interested in problems describing human variation. The statistical methods devised by these workers, however, were not applied to problems concerning the origins and affinities of the first Americans until the mid-1950s, when Spuhler (1954) and Laughlin and Jørgensen (1956) used genetic or biological distance models to test hypotheses concerning the evolutionary history of Native American tribes in the southwestern United States and Greenlandic Eskimos, respectively. These studies were not generally extended to other northern populations until the 1970s. We shall limit our review of the application of biometrics to problems concerning the origins of American populations to those investigators who, in our minds, have extensively sampled entire population systems or who have developed well-founded models that are amenable to critical review.

Zegura (1978) reviewed the concordance between population affinity and linguistic grouping (as determined by present-day linguistic boundaries) in 12 series of Aleut, Yupik, and Inupiaq crania, which effectively sampled the Alaskan Aleut–Eskimo population. The results of the discriminant function assignment of crania to linguistic groups showed a surprisingly high concordance or correct assignment of 88% in male crania and 95% in female crania. These results strongly imply that "biological differentiation parallels linguistic differentiation (Zegura 1978:24)." The high concordance is further demonstrated by cluster analysis of Mahalanobis D^2, which shows high concordance with linguistic groups, both at the dialect (i.e., Siberian Yupik versus Central Yupik) and at the larger contour of true language grouping (Aleut versus Eskimo). With the exception of Koniag and Aleut females, which cluster rather closely, Zegura's results are remarkable for the high fidelity of the various population systems. Later, we shall discuss the concordance of genetic marker systems and linguistics. They too show this fidelity.

More recently, Turner (1981) has considered the origins of Native Americans based on evidence for dental traits that may be under reasonably strict genetic control. This analysis involved the examination of some 20 dental crown and root traits from over 4000 North and South American precontact crania. Judged from the teeth, all New World populations share in common a complex of dental characteristics, including incisor shoveling, double shoveling, one-rooted upper first premolars, and three-rooted lower first molars, with populations of northern Asia. However, when the contour interval is focused more closely, early American dental variation can be partitioned into three distinct clusters of Aleut–Eskimo, Na-Dene–Athabascan, and other American Indians. Turner interprets this sequence as indicating three separate migrations of Siberians into the New Worlds. First, some 15,000 to 16,000 years B.P., a group of big-game hunters bearing Clovis culture crossed Alaska and spread southward into the continental United States. Their movement permitted the ancestral Na-Dene speakers to occupy central Alaskan rivers and newly developed boreal forests. The third wave consisted of the ancestral Aleut–Eskimo, who resided on the southern margin of the now sub-merged Bering Land Bridge. Turner suggests that this group may have originated near the Amur Basin. Despite the three-cluster partition of native American dental variation, Turner reminds us that there is much less intergroup variation than in East Asia (Palomino *et al.* 1977). The reduced variation is consistent with the hypothesis of the recent entry (less than 15,000 years) of small numbers of immigrants who crossed the land bridge at different times and over different routes.

Szathmary and Ossenberg (1978) should be credited for their insightful and nearly overwhelming attempt to examine both the nonmetric morphological and blood-group data on a large number of Native American tribes. The genetic distances are, at times, quite confusing, such as when the distance between East and West Greenland is as large as the distance between West Greenland and the Navaho. Similarly, the morphological data ignore many key traits that are known to strictly segregate between Aleut–Eskimo and American Indians (Harper 1979). For example, the mandibular torus is distributed throughout the entire Aleut–Eskimo population system in extremely high frequencies (Fröhlich 1979), but it is not included in Szathmary and Ossenberg's battery of traits. Part of the solution to the dilemma Szathmary and Ossenberg propose is contained in an early paper (Szathmary 1979), in which Szathmary uses larger contour or hierarchical intervals that, for the type of population systems she is considering, are more appropriate. Here she was able to demonstrate that:

> Eskimos and North American Indians are more similar to each other in blood group charac-teristics than to any other populations. Both measures (E and D genetic distances) agree that Eskimos are more similar to Mongoloids than are North American Indians [Szathmary 1979:196].

This view is entirely consistent with our observations that the time available for evolutionary differentiation of New World populations is short, hence all Native American populations are vastly more similar than dissimilar. Had they been separated for a longer period of time, greater differences would necessarily have developed.

Another approach to the problems of classifying the variation in Native North Americans is given by Spuhler (1979). He uses stepwise discriminate function analysis to estimate the probabilities of multiple genetic affinities so that branching descent and admixture are reflected. In practice, it is convenient to examine the percentage of each language phylum or each cultural area that have the highest probability of being classified with their own group. Spuhler finds that, in terms of concordance with language, 83% of Arctic populations are correctly classified, whereas 67% of Na-Dene speaking tribes have the highest probability of being classified as Na-Dene. Other values of linguistic concordance include Macro-Algonquian, 33%; Macro-Siouan, 50%; Hokan, 67%; Penutian, 50%; and Aztec–Tanoan, 62%. The concordance with culture area (based ultimately on Kroeber 1939) reveals that Arctic groups are most often classified as Arctic, whereas the American Indian groups are distributed thusly: sub-Arctic, 44%; Northwest Coast, 50%; Plateau, 50%; California, 50%; Plains, 62%; and Southwest, 43%. Spuhler notes that

> Among North American Indian tribes there is significant, but not high, correlation among biology, language and culture. The association is not perfect, even for the Eskimo language family and culture area; the association is weakest for the Algonquian languages and the Southwest culture area. In general, gene frequency affinities are a little stronger by language family than by culture area; overall, genetic distances classify tribes into their present culture area in only 58.5 percent of the 53 cases and languages into their families in 64.7 percent [1979:176].

We would consider this a truly high degree of success, given the complex and intertwined history of many of the Native American tribes, and the lack of geographic patterning and their isolation from each other.

It is almost axiomatic that many additional isolates of the Native Americans should be studied for the first time (and many older studies should be repeated) using a greatly extended battery of genetic marker determinations. Special attention should be given to those populations who, by the nature of their evolutionary history, occupy critical positions, such as linguistic boundaries or ecological transition zones.

Ferrell et al. (1981) have, for the first time, provided a complete and accurate analysis of polymorphic red cell antigens and serum proteins in the St. Lawrence Eskimos, who occupy a place near the transition of Yupik Eskimos and Inupiaq Eskimos.

The studies of Ferrell and his co-workers have revealed three private polymorphisms at the 2,3-diphosphoglycerate mutase, peptidase B, and purine nucleoside phosphorylase loci. Recalling Lampl and Blumberg's (1979) discussions we feel that these new loci may be very useful in future studies of the genetic relationships between Eskimos and other circumpolar populations. The genetic distance analysis based on Nei's (1972) method reveals a close relationship between the St. Lawrence Island Eskimos and other Eskimo populations (Figure 2). The Eskimo populations also form a distinct cluster from American Indian populations. In this respect, the St. Lawrence Island Eskimos are most closely related to Asiatic Eskimos, a point that was anticipated on the historical return of Yupik Eskimos from Siberia to St. Lawrence Island after the widespread population demise in the late 1870s. The estimates of the maximum number of recent Caucasian genes give admixture estimates of 6.6% for the total population, 6.0% for Savoonga, and 13.5% for Gambell.

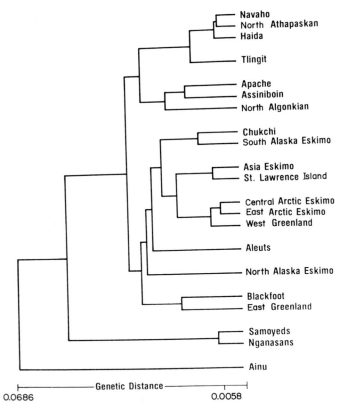

Figure 2   Genetic distance map of Asian and North American populations. From Ferrell *et al.*, (1981) courtesy of Alan Liss, New York.

Origins and Migrations of the First Americans

It is an indisputable fact that all Native American populations trace their ultimate origins to Northeast Asia. Furthermore, all Native American populations must have, at some time, crossed some portion of Beringia to enter the North American continent. The essential questions concern when and where these migrations took place. Because the Bering Land Bridge is now submerged, we must infer routes based upon analysis of the current population and coastal configurations on both sides of the Bering Sea.

The Bering Land Bridge was a large, primarily sub-Arctic corridor that provided two distinct kinds of ecosystems, and hence, migration routes into North America. One route was clearly interior, characterized by the river drainages of the Anadyr and Yukon rivers, which served as corridors for the passage of small groups of Siberians who may or may not have been megafauna hunters. The alternate route

was along the southern margins of the land bridge coast. Here, resident populations adapted to the marine–coastal ecosystem, and, thus, were geographically
separated from the interior migrants. Only as sea level began to rise some 13,000
years ago (Hopkins 1979) did these populations begin to move in response to
rising waters. These coastal populations formed the nucleus of Bering Sea
Mongoloids, whereas the interior base populations evolved into American Indians
(Figure 3).

It is indeed fortunate that both migration routes were sub-Arctic because had the
land bridge been positioned more northerly, it is highly likely that the migrations
would not have occurred at all. In fact, it took some 10,000 years to develop the
necessary sustaining population, complete with cultural sophistication sufficient to
explore the Arctic, and then another 4000 years to develop a permanent occupation of the true Arctic from Alaska to Greenland. Thus, in relation to the early
occupation of interior Alaska, we note that the early sites are typically sub-Arctic
with rare intrusions, such as Onion Portage and the Gallagher Flint Station, which
just border on the "true Arctic." The remainder are decidedly sub-Arctic and

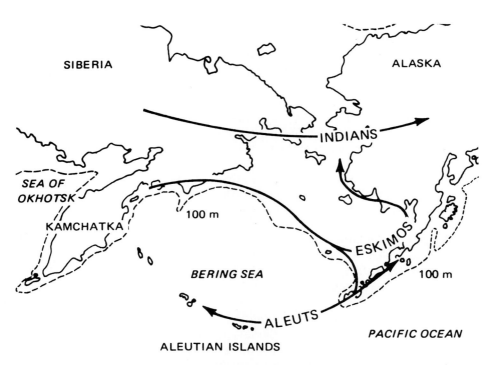

Figure 3   Migration routes across Beringia. The ancestral Native Americans crossed the interior of the
land bridge approximately 15,000 B.P. The ancestral Bering Sea Mongoloids followed the southern
coast before bifurcating near the Alaska Peninsula. From Laughlin *et al.* (1979b) courtesy of the Wenner-
Gren Foundation for Anthropological Research, Incorporated, New York.

closely associated with the Yukon drainage system, which provided a natural highway complete with easily accessible food supplies. Today, the interior of Alaska is inhospitable; however, 15,000 years B.P., when temperatures were somewhat colder and the climate dryer, the interior winters would have been significantly more adverse. Therefore, we cannot envision large, stable populations attempting to colonize this wilderness. Instead, we suspect that most of the early migrants who chose the interior route departed for warmer climes as quickly as possible.

The contrasting route along the Bering Sea coast was more amenable to human occupation. In addition to more moderate temperatures ameliorated by both the marine climate and the more southern location, the ecosystem available to the early migrants was in most part similar to the abundant marine coast of western Alaska south of the Seward Peninsula. It is easy to envision stable resident populations living much the same way as current resident Eskimo populations do. Rising sea levels due to deglaciation forced these populations south and east, to the area around Bristol Bay, whereupon they divided and hence differentiated into Aleuts, who continued to follow the Bering Land Bridge to its southwestern extent, and Eskimos, who followed the coastline eastward into Bristol Bay and eventually Kodiak Island.

The development of the unique Aleut culture, language, and biology must have required considerable isolation, which was provided by the small population sizes of the early inhabitants and by the great distance (800 km) between Aleut and Eskimo seminal populations. Only when both groups had developed sufficiently large populations did they expand: Aleuts moved simultaneously east and west from the Umnak Island region. The eastern migration of Aleuts encountered Eskimos moving west along the Alaska Peninsula. Having been separated for thousands of years, they established a sharp boundary zone at Port Moller on the peninsula about 3000 years B.P. (Laughlin *et al.* 1979a).

At the same time that the distinctive Aleut language, culture, and biology was developing in the Umnak region of the Aleutian Islands, a similar development among the Eskimos was occurring between the area south of the Kuskokwim River and Kodiak Island. We would follow Clark (1979) in his hypothesis that the origins of Eskimos are in southern Alaska. These populations developed and evolved in the marine–coastal–riverine habitat of the Alaskan sub-Arctic before migrating northward. Today, the boundary of Yupik and Inupiaq occurs at Unalakleet, which, interestingly, is just south of the Denbigh coastal complex, dated 4500–5000 years B.P. (Giddings 1964). From this base, we see the progressive colonization of the high Arctic. There were several attempts to occupy Greenland. In each case, populations from northwestern Alaska spread rapidly to the east, eventually terminating in Greenland. These migrations were unsuccessful. It has been only in the last thousand years that man has succeeded in establishing permanent colonies north of the Arctic Circle that span from the Seward Peninsula in the west across north Alaska, north Canada, and on to Greenland (Maxwell 1980). Thus, Eskimo bearing the Thule culture arrived in Greenland about 1000 years B.P. and spread in both directions around Greenland. It is possible that without the timely "rediscovery" of the most northerly Thule Eskimos that this group, too, would have become extinct.

This unique evolutionary history also has had an effect on the processes of aging and the skeletal biology of these populations as they made the latitudinal ascension from the sub-Arctic into the high Arctic. The variation in cortical thickness is directly proportional to the history of these groups (Figure 4). Likewise, the shortest length of life, the lowest bone mineral content, and the most rapid rate of secondary osteon formation is found in the most recent Inupiaq Arctic division; whereas a longer length of life, higher bone mineral, and a slower rate of osteon formation is found in the older Aleut sub-Arctic division (Laughlin *et al.* 1979a). Other features, such as the frequency and severity of vertebral or neural tube defects, varies on the same axis. Moreover, these differences are temporally patterned. The analysis of continuity within each major division of Bering Sea Mongoloids reveals the existence of these major differences prior to the influences of European contact. They most likely extend as far back as the origins of each subdivision.

Calibrating the Successive Divergence Schedule

The configuration of Native American populations can only be described as bipartite. Aleuts and Eskimos are markedly different from other American Indians

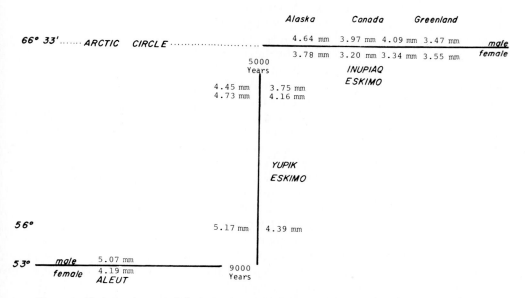

Figure 4   Variation in cortical thickness (femoral) among Bering Sea Mongoloid populations.

in their serological markers, their dentition, their mandible, their vertebral column, their crania, and their anthropometry. The linguistic differentiation is also un-equivocal. Bergsland summarizes the totality of the linguistic differentiation: "the extremely clear-cut border between Eskimo–Aleut and the Amerindian languages must be recognized as a socio-linguistic fact [1979:14]."

In order to understand the evolutionary history of the Native Americans, it is important to recall the geographic sequence that these populations have assumed. The Aleuts are contiguous with Yupik Eskimos only. Yupik Eskimos share a common border with Inupiaq Eskimos and with Athabascan Indians. In addition to the boundary with Yupik Eskimos, Inupiaq Eskimos share boundaries with both Athabascan- and Algonquin-speaking Indians. By carefully measuring the diversity within and between these groups—Aleuts, Yupik Eskimos, Inupiaq Eskimos, and Athabascan Indians—it is possible to reconstruct the successive origins and divergences of each group. When a verifiable time marker is inserted into the divergence matrix, we then may calibrate the timing of these events.

The prerequisite for this developmental schedule is genetic data that ex-haustively sample the component populations. Such data that demonstrat the major difference between Athabascan Indians and Aleut and Eskimo are found in a comprehensive investigation by Scott (1979), which studied seven serum loci in every major linguistic group in Alaska. We (Harper 1980) have simply reclassified the various tribal and dialectical units into successively larger population ag-gregates and calculated the average mean difference in gene frequencies for the seven loci studies.

The results of this manipulation reveal an amazing natural order in the sequence of these groups. First, the eight Athabascan tribes (Koyukon, Tanaina, Ahtna, Kutchin, Ingalik, Upper Tanana, Upper Kuskokwim, and Tanana) are most diver-gent from all Bering Sea Mongoloids (Aleuts, the three Yupik dialects, and Inupiaq) ($d = 0.328 \pm 0.013$). Additionally, each of the five Bering Sea Mongoloid groups is approximately equidistant from the combined Athabascan group. In succession, the distance between the Aleut and the other Bering Sea Mongoloids (Yupiks and Inupiaq) is 0.197 ± 0.036 units, and the distance between Yupik and Inupaiq dialects is the smallest at 0.113 ± 0.023 units. The within-group differences also show this orderly progression from the largest population unit of North American natives (all Aleuts, Eskimos, and Athabascans, $d = 0.309 \pm 0.012$) to the smallest unit (Eskimo, $d = 0.147 \pm 0.021$).

For many loci, the evolutionary forces operating at that loci are effectively neutral; hence, the ratio of the between-group distances is proportional to the time since the bifurcation of each group. Likewise, the ratio of within-group genetic distances is a proportional measure of the time each population isolate has had to organize its unique gene pool. In this scheme, the between-group distances are a measure of the time of origin. If the systems are selectively neutral or if the nature of the evolutionary force operating at any loci is approximately equal for all groups, then the ratios of divergence may be converted into years of time since each event took place if (*a*) the degree of admixture is small and (*b*) an accurate date on any bifurcation point can be determined. We have previously argued (here and elsewhere, Laughlin 1975, 1980) that by 8700 years B.P., ancestral Aleuts were living at Anangula, and that the artifact assemblages dated to approximately 8500 years B.P. from the Alaska Peninsula are ancestral Eskimos (Clark 1979).

Applying a scale factor of 9000 years for the divergence of Aleut and Eskimo, we find that the divergence between Athabascan and Bering Sea Mongoloids is some 14,985 years. In the same way, the divergence of Yupik and Inupiaq is proportionally smaller and should occur at 5162 years B.P. The origins of the populations can be calculated in this same manner, provided we assume that the early Bering Sea Mongoloids were highly organized into subunits as they approached the area west of Bristol Bay. We infer that in this case, but not in all cases, the divergence of Bering Sea Mongoloids into Aleut and Eskimo was simultaneously the point of origin for each population. We believe that Eskimos, as a recognizable population unit, have existed some 9000 years. Given that this value is the origin point, then the common origin of Bering Sea Mongoloids (Aleuts and Eskimos) is proportional to the diversity within all Eskimos compared to the diversity within all Bering Sea Mongoloids, or 10,224 years. The origins of the populations that gave rise to the first Americans is dated as the ratio of diversity within all Eskimo populations to the diversity within all Alaskan populations, or approximately 18,918 years B.P.

The picture that emerges is one of gestation and subsequent bifurcation (Figure 5). Approximately 19,000 years ago the gene pool that spawned the entire early American population began to organize. At 15,000 years, the Athabascans and likely all other American Indian tribes diverged. Later, about 10,000 years B.P., the Bering Sea Mongoloid gene pool formed and quickly bifurcated into Aleuts and Eskimos. The Eskimo population gestated some 4000 years in southern Alaska, then moved north along the coast until Inupiaq was split off some 5000 years ago. The final Inupiaq migrations did not end until approximately 1000 years ago when Greenland was finally permanently colonized.

Summary

The study of the origins, affinities, and adaptations of the first Americans has a history extending as far back as the first scientific description of a human cranium and mandible by Winslow in 1722. Early studies, however, were not systematic and concentrated on typological comparisons of isolated specimens with little regard to temporal or spatial provienience. Furthermore, early investigators were unprepared for the concept of any appreciable time to allow for the evolution of the Native Americans. Even by the early 1900s, the possibility of a European origin for American populations was considered plausible.

Although there are several notable exceptions (e.g., Heinbecker and Pauli 1927; Sapir 1916), systematic study of the origins of Americans was lacking. Hrdlička

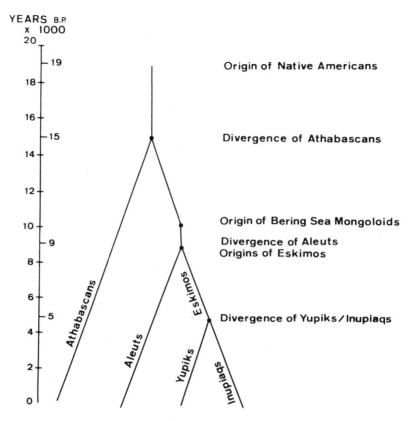

Figure 5 Proposed model of origins and divergence of Aleuts, Eskimos, and Native Americans. From Harper (1980) courtesy of Taylor and Francis Ltd, London.

began the study of origins, believing that the Americans had entered the New World via two routes: Aleuts following the Aleutian Islands from the west and American Indians following the Bering Land Bridge. Later, on actually exploring the physical anthropology of the Koniag Eskimo and the Aleut, he reversed his position and concluded that the Aleuts too entered their domain from the east.

Hrdlička's studies were carried on primarily by Laughlin who demonstrated (*a*) that Aleuts evolved within the Aleut ecosystem, (*b*) that a great time depth existed in the Aleutians, and (*c*) that the population variation between the Aleut isolates was as great as the variation between many Indian tribes. These points lead to the conclusion that the Aleut population system was ancient and had evolved independently as the terminal isolate in a much larger Aleut–Eskimo population system the other terminus of which, Greenland, was also an independent evolutionary sample of the genetic variation of Bering Sea Mongoloids.

The work of the past decade has largely been stimulated by Laughlin and his co-workers. We find that four developments promise to provide working hypotheses to continue the search for the origins of the first Americans. Scanning such widely distant fields as archaeology, linguistics, genetics, skeletal biology, and statistics, we now see an emerging pattern that suggests that the early American populations were truly Americans in the sense that their emergence took place so recently as to preclude more than an ultimate Siberian component.

Acknowledgments

We are deeply appreciative of Maria Acayan's assistance in preparing this manuscript. This work was supported, in part, by a National Institute on Aging grant (AG 01299). The University of Connecticut Research Foundation and the University of Connecticut Computer Center also provided support.

References

Ackerman, R. E.
    1980   Microblades and prehistory: technological and cultural considerations for the north Pacific coast. In *Early native Americans*, edited by D. L. Browman. The Hague: Mouton Publishers. Pp. 189–197.
Alexander, F.
    1949   A medical survey of the Aleutian Islands. *New England Journal of Medicine,* **240**:1035–1040.
Anderson, D. D.
    1970   *Akmak: an early archaeological assemblage from Onion Portage, Northwestern Alaska.* Copenhagen: Acta Arctica.
Bendyshe, T.
    1865   *The anthropological treatises of Johann Friedrich Blumenbach.* London: Longman's, Green.
Bergsland, K.
    1979   The comparison of Eskimo–Aleut and Uralic. *Fenno-Ugrica Suecana* **2**:7–18.
Black, R. F., and W. S. Laughlin
    1964   Anangula—a geological interpretation of the oldest archaeological site in Alaska. *Science* **143**:1321–1322.
Blumenbach, J. F.
    1795   *De Generis Humani Varietate Nativa [On the natural variety of mankind].* Goettingen: Rosenbusch.
Boas, F.
    1907   Eskimos of Baffin Land and Hudson Bay. *Bulletin of the American Museum of Natural History* **15**:371–570.
    1910   Ethnological problems in Canada. *Journal of the Royal Anthropological Institute* **40**:529–539.
Bowers, P. M.
    1980   *The Carlo Creek site: geological and archeology of an early Holocene site in the central Alaska range. Occasional Paper No.* **27**. Anthropology and Historic Preservation Cooperative Park Studies Unit, University of Alaska, Fairbanks.
Clark, D. W.
    1979   *Ocean Bay: an early north pacific maritime culture.* Ottawa, Canada: National Museum of Man.

Clark, D. W., and A. McFayden Clark
    1980   Fluted points at the Eatza Tena obsidian source, northwestern interior Alaska. In *Early Native Americans*, edited by D. L. Brownman. The Hague: Mouton Publishers. Pp. 141–159.
Dixon, W. J., and F. J. Massey
    1951   *Introduction to statistical analysis*. New York: McGraw-Hill.
Dumond, D. E.
    1977   *The Eskimos and Aleuts*. London: Thames and Hudson.
    1980   The archeology of Alaska and the peopling of Alaska. *Science* **209**:984–991.
Ferrell, R. D., R. Chakraborty, H. Gershowitz, W. S. Laughlin, and W. J. Schull
    1981   The St. Lawrence Island Eskimos: genetic variation and genetic distance. *American Journal of Physical Anthropology* **55**:351–358.
Frøhlich, B.
    1979   The Aleut–Eskimo mandible. Unpublished Ph.D. thesis, Department of Anthropology, University of Connecticut, Storrs.
Garn, S. M., and C. F. A. Moorrees
    1951   Stature, body-build and tooth emergence in Aleutian Aleut children. *Child Development* **22**:261–270.
Giddings, J. L.
    1964   *The archaeology of Cape Denbigh*. Providence, Rhode Island: Brown University Press.
Harper, A. B.
    1979   Comment on "Are the biological differences between North American Indians and Eskimos truly profound." *Current Anthropology* **19**:688.
    1980   Origin and divergence of Aleuts, Eskimos and American Indians. *Annals of Human Biology* **7**:547–554.
Heinbecker, P., and R. H. Pauli
    1927   Blood grouping of the Polar Eskimo. *Journal of Immunology* **13**:279–283.
Hooton, E. A.
    1918   On certain Eskimoid characters in Icelandic skulls. *American Journal of Physical Anthropology* **1**(OS):53–76.
    1930   *The indians of Pecos Pueblo*. New Haven, Connecticut: Yale University Press.
    1931   *Up from the ape*. New York: Macmillan.
Hopkins, D. M.
    1979   Landscape and climate of Beringia during late Pleistocene and Holocene time. In *The first Americans: origins, affinities and adaptations*, edited by W. S. Laughlin and A. B. Harper. New York: Fischer.
Hrdlička, A.
    1930   Anthropological survey in Alaska. In *The forty-sixth annual report of the Bureau of American Ethnology*. Washington, D. C.: U.S. Government Printing Office.
    1932   The coming of man from Asia in the light of recent discoveries. *Proceedings of the American Philosophical Society* **71**:393–402.
    1944   *The anthropology of Kodiak Island*. Philadelphia: Wistar Press.
    1945   *The Aleutian and Commander Islands and their inhabitants*. Philadelphia: Wistar Press.
Jochelson, W.
    1933   *History, ethnology and anthropology of the Aleut*. Washington, D.C.: Carnegie Institute.
Keane, A. H.
    1886–   The Eskimos: a commentary. *Nature (London)* **35**:309–310.
    1887
Kroeber, A. L.
    1939   *Cultural and natural areas of native north America*. Berkeley: University of California Press.
Lampl, M., and B. S. Blumberg
    1979   Blood polymorphisms and the origins of New World populations. In *The first Americans: origins, affinities and adaptations*, edited by W. S. Laughlin and A. B. Harper. New York: Fischer. Pp. 107–123.

Laughlin, W. S.
   1951a   Blood groups, morphology and population size of the Eskimos. *Cold Spring Harbor Symposia on Quantitative Biology* **15**:165–173.
   1951b   The Alaska gateway viewed from the Aleutian Islands. In *The physical anthropology of the American Indian*, edited by W. S. Laughlin. New York: Viking Fund. Pp. 98–126.
   1963   Eskimos and Aleuts: their origins and evolution. *Science* **142**:633–645.
   1975   Aleuts: ecosystem, Holocene history and Siberian origin. *Science* **189**:507–515.
   1980   *Aleuts: survivors of the Bering Land Bridge.* New York: Holt.
Laughlin, W. S., and J. B. Jørgensen
   1956   Isolate variation in Greenlandic Eskimo crania. *Acta Genetica et Statistica Medica* **6**:3–12.
Laughlin, W. S., and G. H. Marsh
   1951   A new view of the history of the Aleutians. *Arctic* **4**:75–88.
Laughlin, W. S., A. B. Harper, and D. D. Thompson
   1979a   New approaches to the pre and post contact history of Arctic peoples. *American Journal of Physical Anthropology* **51**:579–587.
Laughlin, W. S., J. B. Jørgensen, and B. Frøhlich
   1979b   Aleuts and Eskimos: Survivors of the Bering Land Bridge coast. In *The first Americans: Origins, affinities and adaptations*, edited by W. S. Laughlin and A. B. Harper. New York: Fischer. Pp. 91–104.
Libby, W. P., E. C. Anderson, and J. R. Arnold
   1949   Age determination by radiocarbon content: world wide assay of natural radiocarbon. *Science* **109**:227–228.
Maxwell, M. S.
   1980   Archaeology of the Arctic and subarctic zones. *Annual Review of Anthropology* **9**:161–185.
Moorrees, C. F. A.
   1957   *The Aleut dentition.* Cambridge Massachusetts: Harvard University Press.
Neel, J. V.
   1973   Diversity within and between South American Indian tribes. *Israel Journal of Medical Sciences* **9**:1216–1224.
Nei, M.
   1972   Genetic distance between populations. *American Naturalist* **106**:283–292.
Palomino, H., R. Chakraborty, and F. Rothhammer
   1977   Dental morphology and population diversity. *Human Biology* **49**:61–70.
Pedersen, P. O.
   1949   The East Greenland Eskimo dentition: numerical variation and anatomy. *Meddelelser Om Grønland* **142**:1–256.
Sapir, E.
   1916   Time perspective in aboriginal American culture, a study in method. *Canada Department of Mines, Geological Survey, Memoir* **90**.
Scott, E. M.
   1979   Genetic diversity of Athabascan Indians. *Annals of Human Biology* **6**:241–247.
Spencer, F.
   1979   Aleš Hrdlička, M. D. 1869–1943: a chronicle of the life and work of an American physical anthropologist. Unpublished Ph.D. thesis, Department of Anthropology, University of Michigan, Ann Arbor.
Spuhler, J. N.
   1951   Some genetic variations in American Indians. In *The physical anthropology of the American Indian*, edited by W. S. Laughlin. New York: Viking Fund. Pp. 177–202.
   1954   Some problems in the physical anthropology of the American southwest. *American Anthropologist* **56**:604–625.
   1979   Genetic distances, trees and maps of North American Indians. In *The first Americans: Origins, affinities and adaptations*, edited by W. S. Laughlin and A. B. Harper. New York: Fischer. Pp. 135–183.

Szathmary, E. J. E.
    1979   Blood groups of Siberians, Eskimos, sub-arctic and northwest coast Indians: the problem of origins and genetic relationships. In *The first Americans: origins, affinities, and adaptations,* edited by W. S. Laughlin and A. B. Harper. New York: Fischer. Pp. 185–209.
Szathmary, E. J. E., and N. S. Ossenberg
    1978   Are the biological differences between North American Indians and Eskimos truly profound? *Current Anthropology* **19**:673–701.
Turner, C. G., II
    1967   The dentition of arctic peoples. Unpublished Ph.D. thesis, Department of Anthropology, University of Wisconsin, Madison.
    1981   Dental evidence for the peopling of the Americas. Paper presented at the 46th Annul Meeting of the Society for American Archaeology, San Diego, California.
West, F. H.
    1980   Late Paleolithic cultures in Alaska. In *Early Native Americans,* edited by David L. Browman. The Hague: Mouton Publishers. Pp. 161–187.
Winslow, J. B.
    1722   Conformation particulière de crane d'un sauvage de l'Amerique. *Memoires de l'Academie Royale des Sciences.* Pp. 322–324.
Zegura, S. L.
    1978   The Eskimo population system: linguistic framework and skeletal remains. In *Eskimos of northwestern Alaska,* edited by P. L. Jamison, S. L. Zegura, and F. A. Milan. Stroudsburg, Pennsylvania: Dowden, Hutchinson and Ross. Pp. 8–30.

12

The Theoretical Foundations and Development of Skeletal Biology

George J. Armelagos, David S. Carlson, and Dennis P. Van Gerven

> Some people think that the philosophy a scientist accepts is not of very much importance; his job is to observe the phenomena. This is a gross oversimplification and it involves the subsidiary hypothesis that all scientists are fully equipped with serendipity. A sensible philosophy controlled by a relevant set of concepts saves so much research time that it can nearly act as a substitute for genius. . . . A scientist can have no more valuable skill than the ability to see whether the problem he is investigating exists and whether the concepts he is using are applicable.
>
> N.W. Pirie 1952

Skeletal analysis has played a significant role in the development of physical anthropology. Indeed, physical anthropology in its preoccupation with qualitative and quantitative evaluations of human skeletal morphology, has an origin as a subdiscipline that is distinct from those of anatomy and anthropology. Interest in morphological analysis was generated, initially, by a concern for explaining variation among extant human populations or racial groups. It received added stimulation during the mid-nineteenth century by efforts to establish the natural position of modern *Homo sapiens* relative to earlier fossil forms and to the rest of the primate order. Blumenbach's (1795) reliance on his extensive collection of crania to establish his racial classification and Huxley's (1863) use of skeletal remains to interpret the Neanderthal fossil were only the beginnings of the discipline's use of osteological material.

There have been major technical advances in skeletal analysis since Petrus Camper first proposed the facial angle as a comparative measure of facial form in 1792. For example, the development and use of roentgenography, multivariate statistics, high-speed computers, and atomic absorption spectrometers for trace element analysis have greatly influenced skeletal biology. Unfortunately, however, theoretical perspectives have failed to keep pace with the development of new

A HISTORY OF AMERICAN
PHYSICAL ANTHROPOLOGY, 1930–1980

techniques. Reliance on a descriptive–historical model utilizing racial typologies has proved a major deterent to other theoretical approaches. The application of a population model that stresses functional interpretation of morphological features can provide an alternative to the descriptive–historical approach as well as a basis for determining the evolution and adaptation of prehistoric populations through time.

In this chapter, we will discuss (*a*) the impact of racial typology in assessing historical relationships between populations, (*b*) the rise of anthropometry in interpreting biological relationships, and (*c*) the development of a functional approach in skeletal biology.

Race, Type, and Historical Reconstructions

Traditionally, human biologists have maintained a conceptional framework characterized by the extensive utilization of historically oriented typological models as explanatory devices. This approach was developed in the late eighteenth and early nineteenth centuries and, although criticized by many physical anthropologists, continues to be used today. Lasker (1970), in a review of the literature, noted that physical anthropologists, despite statements to the contrary, are still largely concerned with historical, rather than processual, problems. Although theoretical aspects are often discussed, physical anthropologists have tended to focus on the description of events rather than on an explanation of the processes that have brought about these events.

Traditional emphasis on description in skeletal biology stems from pre-Darwinian ideals of biological discreteness. Anthropometric data was normally described within a framework that emphasized morphological differences and thus, reinforced the ideas that certain human populations (e.g., racial groups) were discrete biological units. Any similarity of morphological features among populations was attributed to the exchange of genes. Even when arranged within a temporal framework, populations tended to be described as a temporal sequence of unique events, each with its own coordinates in space and time and with no obvious connection with its morphologically distinct predecessor or successor. The roots of this orientation are not unique to skeletal analysis. They can be found entrenched in broader scientific and cultural conditions.

> With the rise of Christianity a sense of time totally unlike that entertained by the historically shallow primitive or the endless cycles over which Greco–Roman thought brooded in antiquity took possession of the European mind. The Christian saw time, wordly time, as essentially the divine medium in which a great play—the drama of the human Fall and Redemption—was being played out upon the stage of the world. . . . Older pagan notions of eternal recurrent cycles were blasphemous to the Christian mind. "God forbid," protested St. Augustine, "that we should believe this. For Christ died once for our sins, and rising again dies no more" [Eiseley 1961:60].

According to Lynn White, "the axiom of the uniqueness of the Incarnation required a belief that history is a straight line guided by God. . . . No more radical revolution has ever taken place in the world outlook of a larger area [1942:147]."

With the growth of taxonomy as an observational science even Linnaeus, whose system of classification was a bastion of static morphological analysis, could not resist the historical implications. In the later editions of *Systema Naturae* Linnaeus, himself, referred to species as "daughters of time [Greene 1959]." This "evolutionary vacillation", notwithstanding, it was not until 1859, 124 years after the first edition of *Systema Naturae*, that the full impact of the descriptive elegance of Linnean taxonomy became apparent. Prior to *The Origin of Species*, the morphological configurations of life forms were believed to represent a static gradation resulting from the single act of creation. In this context, taxonomic categories were conceived of as empirically verifiable, static, morphological units. However, the meaning of Linnean taxa became radically extended when viewed in light of Darwinian evolution. Subspecies, species, genera, and families came to stand, inferentially, as observable effects of prior evolutionary causes.

The extension of meaning from Linnean taxonomy to post-Darwinian phylogeny has been tremendously important to the development of physical anthropology, although not for the reasons traditionally given. Whereas the theoretical concept of evolution became synonomous with gradual dynamic change in organic structure through time, the impact of Darwinian evolution on scientific method remained quite different. Evolutionism, rather than shifting the focus of scientific attention away from an essentially static Linnean taxonomy toward the mechanisms of evolution *via* functionally oriented explanatory models, served to reinforce a broad scientific commitment to accelerated taxonomic description and definition. Thus, taxonomic description, as an inherently static, preevolutionary concept, did not give way to evolutionism after 1859; rather, evolutionism became cast in the form of traditional descriptive historicism.

The mechanisms of evolution have remained essentially theoretical, having broad definitions but little contextual meaning. Logically, this is to be expected. The meaning of the mechanisms of evolution must be derived from the context of specific evolutionary processes. Phylogenetic models, by assuming evolutionary change, beg the question of evolutionary process entirely. Change is asserted, rather than approached directly as an area of empirical analysis. The mechanisms of evolution are invoked to justify that assertion. In this sense, the greatest impact of *The Origin of Species* on physical anthropology has not been the concept of gradual dynamic change in complex organic systems; it has been the methodological entrenchment of taxonomy as a descriptive historical approach.

The historical paradigm is most clearly reflected in the extensive use of cranial material since the beginnings of physical anthropology. The skull is an extremely complex structure the morphology of which often varies widely between even closely related species. Intraspecies variation is extensive, particularly in *Homo sapiens*. Because of this factor, among others, the human skull has been most extensively studied by physical anthropologists seeking to establish taxonomies at the subspecific level. The human skull has been thought of not only as an indicator of individual identity, which it certainly is, but also as an indicator of racial identity. In his classic treatise *On the Natural Varieties of Mankind* (published initially in 1775) and *Contribution to Natural History* Johann Friedrich Blumenbach relied extensively on the analysis of cranial remains (a total of 82 skulls), to formulate his views on human variation. In 1795, Blumenbach stated,

> But it might have been expected that a more careful anatomical investigation of genuine skulls of different nations would throw a good deal of light upon the study of the variety of mankind; because when stripped of the soft parts and changeable parts they exhibit the firm and stable foundation of the head, and can be conveniently handled and examined, and considered under different aspects and compared together. It is clear from a comparison of this kind that from the forms of skulls take all sorts of license in individuals, just as color of skin and other varieties, of the same kind, one running as it were into the other by all sorts of shapes, gradually and insensibly: But that still, in general there is in them a constancy of characteristics which cannot be denied, and is indeed remarkable, which has a great deal to do with the racial habit and which answers most accurately to the nations and their peculiar physiogonomy [1795/1969:234–235].

There were, however, a number of criticisms of the use of cranial material even in the early post-Darwinian era. In 1896, Rudolf Virchow, an extremely influential scientist, supported the typological concept while being extremely critical of the use of crania for assessing biological affinity. As to the relationship of cranial morphology and racial type, Virchow stated that,

> Here we must come to clear understanding as to whether we wish to lay greater weight upon skull form or on pigmentation of eyes and skin with its appurtenance, hair or, expressed otherwise, whether we wish to divide mankind more from the standpoint of the osteologist or from that of the dermatologist, the answer seems to admit of no doubt. The attempt of Anders Retzius to select a few categories of skull type as a basic principle for classifying man—though to be sure he mitigated it by adding in prognathism and orthoganthism—has had no thoroughgoing success. Even the corrections which have been undertaken in the course of the years, have not made it possible for even a practiced craniologist to tell for certain without knowing anything of the provenience of the skull, to which race, let alone stock, it belonged [1950:191].

Physical anthropologists not only failed to heed Virchow's warnings about the use of similarities in cranial morphology for establishing the history of a population but devoted even greater energy in the late 1800s and early 1900s toward the development and standardization of measurements and indexes that would hopefully give the clearest indication of biological affinity. Hrdlička describes (see Stewart 1947) many attempts to standardize anthropometric technique, for example, meetings were convened in Monaco (1906) and Geneva (1929) to resolve the disagreements over the methods and measurements used by various countries. This concern for standardization underscores the importance of measurement and of craniometry for physical anthropology.

Even when researchers did question the validity of certain anthropometric practices, there was little evidence that it diminished the significance of anthropometry. For example, the cranial index remains one of the most frequently used measures of racial affinity. Yet, as early as 1910, Franz Boas discussed the instability of the cephalic index and its inappropriate use in racial analysis. The differences in the cephalic index of Jewish and Sicilian immigrants raised in the United States compared with relatives in their homeland suggested the instability of this feature. The change in cephalic index should have indicated the problems that the skeletal biologist faced in using crania for the analysis of the biological relationship between populations. Instead, Boas's research was attacked on a number of different points. Radosavljevich (1911) argued that Boas failed to demonstrate the instability of the cephalic index because: he did not consider evidence for the inheritance of the head form; he made countless mathematical, technical, and methodological errors that invalidate his conclusions; he was uncritical in the collection of data; and his measurements of the cephalic index lacked the necessary scientific exactness. Radosavljevich's criticisms, however, were largely unsubstantiated. For example, he stated that Boas's sample of nearly 6,000 was inadequate and that comparisons were invalid since Boas did not measure all individuals in the study. Shapiro (1959:377), in evaluating the impact of Boas's study on the stability of cranial typology, states that the older concepts of a relative fixity of physical type were shattered. As will be seen in the following, Shapiro's assessment was not warranted in light of the subsequent history of skeletal studies.

Earnest A. Hooton developed a method of typological analysis that greatly influenced the study of skeletal biology from 1925 until the late 1940s. Like his scientific predecessors, Hooton argued that an individual could be racially typed and that this racial typology would provide information on the biological history of the population. Hooton's (1930) study, *The Indians of Pecos Pueblo*, was a key to his methodology, and he used the typology of the Pecos Pueblo population to interpret their racial history. Exemplary of the extent to which the racial–typological approach could be extended, Hooton ascertained a "pseudo-Negroid" type within the Pecos Pueblo population. Hooton was careful and states that an "undiluted" Negro type would be different than the "Full African Negro type" and that there need not necessarily be a biological relationship between these types. Nevertheless, these similarities existed and required an explanation. He reverted to the obvious interpretation by stating that "pseudo-Negroids" could be explained by "earlier invaders who worked their way up Northeast Asia across the Bering Straits down the New World, and carried with them a minor infusion of Negroid blood which had trickled in from the tropical parts of the Old World [Hooton 1930:356]."

During the early 1950s, there were significant changes in the race concept as physical anthropology incorporated the population orientation. One would have expected concomitant shifts in methodology in which population and mechanisms for altering its structure (natural selection, mutation, gene flow and drift) would gradually become the focus of physical anthropological studies. However, just as human biologists maintained their traditional focus on taxonomy following the Darwinian revolution, the development of population biology did not drastically alter the approach of the physical anthropologist (see Weiss and Chakraborty, in the present volume). Instead, the taxonomists incorporated genetic traits into their classificatory systems.

The analysis of skeletal material in the 1950s showed traces of the Hootonian influence. Typological analysis of skeletons utilizing a racial model remained a major perspective of the skeletal biologist. There was, however, a devastating attack on skeletal biology presented by William C. Boyd in *Genetics and the Races of Man* (1950). Boyd, in one of the most influential studies of the period, attempted to develop a genetic perspective for race. He emphasized the importance of using traits of known inheritance, such as blood group, in racial classification. He stated that although bones may have been useful in racial classification during physical anthropology's infancy, there was no longer a necessity to rely on such imprecise material. Specifically, Boyd discussed four major reasons for the unacceptability of skeletal analysis in racial classification: (*a*) it is difficult to determine skeletal morphology in the living, (*b*) the skeleton adapts rapidly to its environment, (*c*) skeletal features are polygenetic, and (*d*) anthropometry and craniometry are passé since metric studies were never logically conceived.

It is obvious that Boyd's obituary of skeletal biology was premature. As Shapiro has noted, anthropologists are still willing to measure skulls at the drop of a hat. Furthermore, it is interesting to note that Boyd's criticisms of skeletal biology were not theoretical or conceptual but entirely *methodological*. The basic goals of his research were identical to those of the traditional anthropological approach—the definition and delineation of racial groups. Indeed, even the racial groups defined by Boyd on the basis of blood types were the same as those most often defined by traditional anthropometry. Thus, it is apparent that whereas Boyd's analysis may have initiated a change in many of the methods of racial analysis, the major questions asked by those methods had not changed; they remained racially and typologically oriented.

Major problems with the genetic approach to the analysis of human racial history were more recently discussed in more detail by Weiss and Maruyama (1976). These authors present the major views in the analysis of racial history and the methodology used to generate this information, which includes the traditional anthropometric approach and the population genetics approach. According to Weiss and Maruyama, the genetic approach to reconstructing racial history is certainly no less ambiguous and problematical than the anthropometric approach. Weiss and Maruyama state that

> Not only is the classification into major races a tenuous pursuit, but . . . there really may have been no effective separation between populations taken to represent the major races. What then is the meaning of genetic separation times? They really are nothing other than simple transformations of genetic distance, and add no definitive empirical support to any position regarding human evolution [1976:47].

There can be little doubt that human osteology has been and continues to be dominated by an overriding concern for the description of biological differences between populations, the result of which has been an ever-growing number of taxonomic definitions. However, because no attempts have been made to analyze systematically the nature of human variation within human populations, such definitions have served only to generate a series of broad typological categories in the absence of any understanding of the lower order processes that such categories assume.

The analyses of the racial history of Amerindian populations by such workers as Neumann (1952), Bass (1964), and Long (1966) provide graphic examples of the limitations of this approach. Neumann developed a model to explain the peopling of the New World in which he placed all Amerindian populations within what has been referred to as the "Mongoloid subspecies." With a temporal framework, he proposed that all Amerindian populations can be dealt with as "1) earlier phylogenetically more primitive Paleoamerind, 2) more recent derived or modified Mesoamerind, and 3) most recent immigrant Cenoamerind series [Neumann 1959a:66]."

Beyond the temporal configuration, Neumann classified the Amerindian populations into eight races based on their geography, cultural association, and morphological similarity. By applying both racial and temporal classifications simultaneously, Neumann was able to generate a descriptive typology of interpopulational variation.

Each of Neumann's varietal series of races was defined by a series of qualitative and metric cranial features that he believed ideally separated each race from the other. For instance, Neumann asserted:

> In cranial vault form the Lenid variety tends toward exhibiting more elliptical contours, while the Walcolid variety tends toward exhibiting broader ovoid and spherical forms. Development of more medial frontal cresting, greater anterior projection of the zygomatic bones, a more elevated nasal bridge, a somewhat larger face, and greater chin prominence, distinguish the Walcolid from Lenid variety [1959b:72].

In the racial approach, no attempt is made to determine the relationship of one feature to another, or to determine the extent of intrapopulational variation. Anatomical features are defined as racial because they distinguish populations. Such a definition provides no explanation of the traits themselves. Furthermore, once a morphological feature becomes defined as "belonging" to a specific racial type, the only possible explanation of its occurrence in other populations is admixture resulting from migration. Such a view incorrectly portrays human populations as internally static units that only change as a function of gene flow.

Criticism of the racial–typological model has had little impact on its use. Although the use of the preconceived racial types was criticized at the turn of the century (Myers 1905, 1908, for example), they were never taken seriously. However, in 1959, Edward E. Hunt, Jr., a former student of Hooton, presented an extremely critical evaluation of Hooton's methods of typological analysis that had a significant impact on the use of typology in skeletal biology. Hunt saw no genetic reason "why . . . 'ancestral' morphological types would persist in an ancestral population more than one might expect by chance [Hunt 1959:81]." Hunt was especially critical of the use of morphological types to establish relationships between populations that were geographically distant.

However, Hunt was willing to accept regional typological analysis in those cases where chronology and cultural affiliation were well established (Hunt 1959:74). Specifically, he was impressed with Neumann's classification of North American cranial material that, he states, was based on Neumann's study of over 10,000 skulls. Because Neumann's study was based on archaeological samples in context, rather than on individual crania, Hunt considered the analysis "provisionally convincing" (Hunt 1959:74). However, Neumann's analysis actually utilized only a small number of the total 10,000 crania in the formulation of his classification. Two types, for example, are based on 15 and 18 specimens each!

Other skeletal biologists have attempted to extend the Neumann classification with more elaborate statistical procedures and analysis (e.g., Bass 1964; Long 1966; Wilkinson 1971; Robbins and Neumann 1972). Bass (1964) reanalyzed the biological relationship between the Plains Indian populations originally described by Georg Neumann. Although Bass criticized Neumann for his small sample size and sampling technique and was concerned with the limitations of Neumann's racial categories, Bass brought no new theoretical insight to the problem.

Similarly, Long (1966), in an attempt to understand cranial changes in Amerindian populations within a microevolutionary context, tested Neumann's methodology and approach. He used a series of discriminant function analyses and rejected much of Neumann's earlier typology but, at the same time, introducing a new Iroquoian type. As an alternative, Long proposed that:

> All relations discovered in this study can be explained by micro-evolution, occasionally involving genetic drift but more frequently involving the mixing of groups. ... Multiple discriminant analysis can probably best be used to define major groups based on the degree of "fit" of individuals from closely related cultures. Such groups would be homogeneous for 1) a limited geographic area, 2) a limited time period, and/or 3) a limited cultural or linguistic affiliation [1966:464].

This focus on interpopulational variation does not provide us with any greater understanding of the nature of human variation than Neumann's original classification. Neumann, Bass, and Long do not consider the relationship of variables used in their analysis. In order to understand microevolutionary change, this information is essential. Although Long notes that some variables were weighted on the basis of their interpopulational variation, he makes no systematic attempt to determine the source or nature of the observed variation.

Hardy and Van Gerven (1976) have shown that Neumann's (1952) classification of the Indian Knoll variety as Iswanid and the Fort Ancient folk as Muskogid (Robbins and Neumann 1972) did not consider size relationship in their racial assessments. Robbins and Neumann believed that these two groups were racially distinct since 16 of 19 t tests were significantly different at the 0.05 probability level. Using principal components analysis and analysis of covariation, Hardy and Van Gerven showed that when size was held constant, only four of the variables were significantly different. In this sense, two groups originally thought to be distinct were found to be more closely related after size factors had been removed.

High-speed computers and a series of multivariate statistical packages have recently become available to the physical anthropologist. However, the theoretical and methodological commitment toward the analysis of interpopulational variation has remained. Old measurements and taxonomies continue to be reanalyzed with little new insight gained into the nature of human variation (e.g., Birkby 1966; Crichton 1966; Rightmire 1970a, 1970b).

Multivariate analysis has not eliminated typological thinking. Analyses of skeletal remains that use racial categories in the context of multivariate methodology frequently resort to typological analysis. When we discuss the origins of the "Asian component" of the American Indian, or the "Negro component" of an African population, we are especially prone to slip into typological thinking. The classification of contemporary groups using genetic traits does insure nontypological thinking. Most racial classifications that use genetic features remain typological. In the same way, skeletal biologists remain typological thinkers even though they speak of variation and use multivariate techniques.

Because it shows promise as a way to escape this dilemma, there has been an increased interest in the use of discrete traits, which are thought to represent features under genetic control. Berry and Berry (1967, 1972) and Finnegan and Faust (1974) have suggested that noncontinuous variants of the teeth and bony skeleton can be used to establish biological distances between skeletal populations. There are many problems in defining even the most common discrete traits, in understanding the nature of discontinuous variation, and in understanding the inheritance of these traits. For example, the influence of development upon the appearance of discrete traits may be intimately related to nongenetically determined (canalized) development (Howe and Parsons 1968). Thus, the appearance of discrete skeletal traits may be as much a function of nongenetic factors as genetic factors. For this reason, the use of discrete traits to obtain genetic differences or similarities may not be as useful as many researchers believe.

Anthropometry, Statistics, and Biological Processes

Our inability to break away from historical–descriptive approaches in the light of more sophisticated statistical procedure needs to be examined in more detail. The paradox of typological analysis undertaken with complex procedures, such as multivariate analysis, was noted by Blackith and Reyment (1971). Their discussion of the development of multivariate techniques in life science confirms many of our observations that evolutionary theory had little impact on the development of processual models. Despite the evolutionary concepts of change, adaptation, and variation, the typological approach continued. According to Blackith and Reyment, "this fact in itself is witness to the superficial nature of biology at the classificatory level [1971:5]."

Relatively advanced statistical techniques were developed quite early to describe variation and compare attributes among large samples. Pearson, in 1896, first applied his regression analysis to cranial material in an investigation of the correlation between cranial width and length in different racial groups. Subsequently, Lee (1901), Fawcett (1901–1902), and MacDonnell (1901) also published correlation analyses using craniometric variables.

Correlation analyses of craniometric variables continued throughout the 1920s. In 1924, Pearson and Davin published an analysis that differed significantly from earlier studies and has since become a classic in both anthropology and biostatistics. Using a sample of 1600 ancient Egyptian crania, Pearson and Davin attempted to determine the major factors accounting for particular *patterns* of correlations in the human skull. In doing so, they delineated two broad types of correlations that can be found in anatomical data: "spurious" and "organic." Spurious correlations generally occur between two variables spanning the same anatomical region, and thus, for this reason alone, a strongly positive correlation is to be expected. Organic correlations, on the other hand, occur between two measures covering different, and often distinct, anatomical regions. More importantly, Pearson and Davin (1924) stressed that it is the *pattern* of organic correlations that is most likely to reveal meaningful biological relationships. Indeed, as Solow has noted,

> although the required calculations were too comprehensive to be carried out at that time, Pearson and Davin predicted the development of the factor analysis technique and its use in the study of the determinants of the growth and development of cranial bones [Solow 1966:16].

Pearson and his co-workers continued to study cranial variation with similar approaches, often focusing upon specific areas of the human skull in the hopes of understanding particular relationships (Woo 1931, 1937; Elderton and Woo 1932; Pearson and Woo 1935).

Early biostatistical analysis of crania tended to focus on the mathematics of a particular statistical procedure rather than on the biological aspects of craniofacial morphology. Often the primary objective of craniological studies was a demonstration and substantiation of statistical procedures on large, multivariate samples. As a result of this overriding concern, very little attempt was made at a biological explanation of observed statistical phenomena, Pearson and Davin's work being the most notable exception. In fact the development of distance measures and related techniques merely reinforced the typological and taxonomic concerns of physical anthropology at this time, especially in relation to the concept of race (Fisher 1936a, 1936b).

Prior to World War II biostatistical research clearly reflected the interest in problems of historical reconstruction and racial origins. For example, Pearson's (1926) "coefficient of racial likeness" (CRL) utilized mean, standard deviation, and sample size to determine a measure that was essentially an additive assessment of the critical ratio. As a consequence, the CRL is biased toward separating samples when the units of measure are correlated; it emphasizes differences when more kinds of measurements are introduced (Hunt 1959:75).

Although other distance statistics have been developed to overcome the limitations of Pearson's CRL, the problem of interpreting the meaning of the differences remains. Take, for example, Mahalanobis D^2, which, as Hunt (1959) notes, is a more appropriate measure of distance because it can correct for correlation of variables and differences in sample size as well as test the impact of additional variables to the D^2 score. There are procedures for measuring the significance of D^2 differences between populations. According to Hunt, however, Roberts (1954) has ascertained that differences in D^2 depend on the measurements taken.

The role that size and shape play in the distance between populations was investigated by Penrose (1954). Although this represents an attempt at uncovering the "meaning" of biological distance in terms of size and shape, it provides interpretation at the broadest level. As Hunt observed,

> When any multivariate distance function is used, similar distances in two comparisons are no guarantee that the pattern or divergence of the separate variables are alike. What we measure, then, is at the heart of using anthropometry for racial studies [1959:76].

Unfortunately, neither the anthropologist nor the biostatistician of the pre-war period understood the biology of the skeleton well enough to question whether the observed differences have biological significance. Both undertook their analyses with the express purpose of establishing racial, typological distinctions between skeletal samples (e.g., Morant 1925, 1935; Stoessiger 1927; Collett 1933; Fawcett 1901–02; Elliot Smith and Wood Jones 1910).

The fact that this orientation has continued until the present is evidenced by a more recent discussion by Weiner and Huizinga:

> Human biologists have a variety of reasons for making comparisons between populations, or rather between appropriate populations samples. The oldest established object of inter-group comparisons still continues to be of interest to many, namely the tracing of historic or prehistoric relationships amongst human populations. These may reflect actual genetic relationships, the derivation of one group from another of two groups from a common ancestry or again a group may be the result of actual mixing between two parental communities [1972:v].

Similarly, Howells, in a symposium on craniofacial growth and development, reflected concern for historical analysis by stating that: "my purpose is not the study of growth but of taxonomy, of the variation between existing recent populations in the dry skull, for obvious reasons relating to the study of human evolution [1971:210]."

This is confounded by his observation that, although the primary goal of multivariate craniometrics is to determine racial and taxonomic affiliations, "we do not actually know whether . . . variation is of taxonomical, functional or genetic importance, relative to other known or unknown features of the skull [Howells, 1973:3]."

Questions relating to such processual concerns as adaptation, structural–functional relationships, and more general biological phenomena that might *explain* cranial variation and evolution are rarely considered in the dry skull. Instead, gene flow or admixture are usually implemented to explain cranial variation in both ancient and extant human populations. With some notable exceptions (Bieleki and Weton 1964; Tattersall 1968; Suzuki 1969), the same research strategy is generally followed even when cranial materials are arranged within a temporal framework and evolutionary mechanisms other than gene flow might be investigated more readily (Jantz 1973; Wiercinski 1966).

Specific criticism of anthropological craniology has recently been provided by craniologists who take a more dynamic approach to the study of the human skull. Horowitz and Osborne for example, stated,

> The historical beginnings of anthropometric interest in the dentition and cranial and facial characteristics implanted a conceptual orientation which is seriously in need of re-evaluation in respect to their adaptive significance in human evolution [1971:189].

Only by injecting a notion of process into the theoretical foundation for craniometric studies can we consider broad evolutionary problems in both the fossil record and more recent remains. Without this, anthropometric studies will continue to be typologically and historically oriented and will provide no real understanding of human evolution in general.

This criticism of the analysis of cranial material also applies to the use of postcranial remains. Often, postcranial remains were not deemed of sufficient biological interest to be retained. Vast numbers of long bones, vertebral columns, pelvises, etc. were reburied or discarded in the backdirt of excavation. When postcranial material *was* collected, it was used only to determine the age and sex of the individual (e.g., Dwight 1904–1905; Holtby 1918; Pearson and Bell 1919).

Analysis of Form and Function

Alternatives to the historical–descriptive studies in osteology were available, beginning in the early 1900s. The analysis of form and function from a growth and development perspective could have provided a method for interpreting morphological features.

The theoretical foundation for the dynamic study of form was provided by D'Arcy Thompson's classic work *On Growth and Form* (1917/1942). Thompson recognized that form, growth, and function are all intimately related. In terms of form as it relates to growth, for example, he stated,

> The form of an object is defined when we know its magnitude, actual or relative, in various directions; and growth involves the same concepts of magnitude and direction, related to the further concept, or "dimension," of time [1971:15].

Similarly, Thompson showed that the degree of dependence of form on function is quite extensive. Mechanical relationships between two or more structures act both to limit and stimulate growth. Form, therefore, is the result of the forces placed on anatomical components and their associated structures throughout ontogeny, or the growth process.

> It is clear, I think, that we may account for many ordinary biological processes of development or *transformations of form* by the existence of trammels or lines of constraint, which limit and determine the action of the expansive forces of growth that would otherwise be uniform and symmetrical [Thompson 1971:287 (emphasis added)].

Thompson's interpretation of form and function utilized a descriptive analysis of structure based on the "statics" of the civil engineer. In this model, the body is viewed as a machine that must accommodate the "stress" and "strains" placed on it in the course of activity.

Thus, Thompson outlined what has become a basis for functional anatomy and biomechanics—that form is linked causally and temporally to function as the latter influences growth. Studies of form and function have also been concerned with broad questions of biological process as they relate to human origins and evolution. The most recent research has emphasized functional interpretation of postcranial remains since this material forms the basis for the comparison of prehistoric populations. There is some question as to the value of the functional interpretation of cranial material. Russell H. Tuttle, for example (1972:viii), suggests that except for certain features of the masticatory apparatus, orbital dimensions, and neurocranium, the skull provides few functional correlates.

Tuttle's interpretation is consistent with the traditional view of craniometrics discussed in the previous section. In fact, Howells (1972) concurred with Tuttle's conclusions, suggesting that functional considerations are of little value in the analysis of human crania. Although Howells (1957) and others (e.g., Landauer 1962) have been concerned with variation of human skull form (Howells 1957, 1968, 1972), these studies have tended to minimize biological causes of variation in form other than direct genetic response. For example, Howells stated that studies of the interrelationships of growth factors, function, and related compensatory factors have offered little to anthropologists dealing with the dry skull,

> because (a) these are secondary explanations, and (b) the broad range of differences *between* major populations still faces us. We must still find the various local growth determinants which, combining with one another, produce both the continuing differences in head form between racial types, and the range of variation within such a type [Howells 1957:20].

Thus, Howells has remained concerned with only the validity of specific craniometric variables for "taxonomic purposes."

The analysis of crania for taxonomic purpose alone has been rejected by a number of researchers who believe that a functional approach to craniology is possible. Functional craniology, as a holistic approach to the study of the skull, was introduced by Moss and Young (1960). In discussions of functional craniology,

Moss (1968a, 1968b, 1971, 1972; Moss and Young 1960) expanded on several points conceived by van der Klaauw (1945, 1952) and proposed additional concepts for analysis of function in the skull. He extended van der Klaauw's original concept of "functional cranial components" from the consideration of bony elements only to include the soft tissues and spaces within the head. Each "functional component," such as mastication, protection for the brain, and housing and structural support for the sense organs, subsumed two additional operational units: a "functional matrix" corresponding to all the soft tissues and spaces necessary for a given function, and a "skeletal unit" including all the skeletal tissues necessary to carry out a given function (Moss 1968a).

Operationally, functional craniology rests on the assumption "that cranial skeletal growth is [a] secondary, compensatory, and mechanically obligatory response to temporally and morphologically prior growth changes in specially related tissues [Moss 1972:481]." In other words, there are significant developmental and environmental processes that affect cranial growth and, consequently, cranial form. In order to understand these processes, we must first understand the functional relationships *within* the human skull and the degree to which they can affect change in both a phylogenetic and ontogenetic sense. Merely to ascribe variation and the processes that bring about variation to genetic ("racial") differences or simply to suggest that cranial change through time resulted from genetic mutation provides no real explanation of cranial morphology in either modern or fossil hominids. Such explanations, which are so common in traditional craniometric studies, only beg the more important processual questions of how and why variation and change came about.

The approach of functional craniology is clearly appealing to anthropological investigation of craniofacial variation and evolution. Because of its emphasis on the skull as a complex of "functioning" areas, each maintaining a degree of dependence as well as independence from the other, functional craniology provides a framework for viewing processes operating within the skull. In terms of anthropological considerations, investigation of the interaction of functional cranial components will make clearer the meaning and causes of human craniofacial change and variation.

The relatively minor interest, in physical anthropology, in the analysis of postcranial remains can also be attributed to an overriding concern for racial diagnosis. Whereas bones such as the femur were an early subject of description for racial assessment (Parsons 1913–1914, 1914–1915b; Pearson and Bell 1919; Ingalls 1924) and its use has continued through the application of multivariate techniques (Thieme 1957; Thieme and Schull 1957), the racial assessment of postcranial remains never captured the interest of physical anthropologists to the degree that cranial studies had. As a result, the common pattern was to exclude postcranial remains from detailed analysis.

Only when it was realized that information about sex and age could be ascertained from the skeletons were postcranial remains finally retained for further study. Although a methodology for interpreting the functional significance of sexual dimorphism could have been developed, it was not. Physical anthropologists instead created statistical techniques for determining sex without concern for the functional factors that lead to these differences.

Recently, however, there has been an attempt to assess the evolutionary significance of sexual dimorphism. In a series of papers edited by David Frayer (see the *Journal of Human Evolution* Vol. 9, 1980), the importance of sexual dimorphism in making taxonomic decisions, determining phylogenetic relationships and interpreting evolutionary trends was discussed. Yet, as these researchers note, there is much disagreement about the approach and methods that should be used to answer the questions asked (see Armelagos and Van Gervan 1980).

The functional interpretation of postcranial remains received its greatest impetus from comparative studies of primate locomotion. Functional anatomical studies of human and nonhuman primates were carried out by Sir Arthur Keith as early as 1899. These, and subsequent studies, attempted to establish a relationship between certain anatomical and behavioral features. The focus of these studies was a correlation between gross body form and locomotor activity. Even later researchers (Oxnard 1963; Ashton and Oxnard 1964), utilizing a more sophisticated statistical methodology, did not move beyond the descriptive level. Often, intensive multivariate descriptions were developed in the hope that a comprehensive description would uncover the function inherent in the shape (Corruccini 1975; Day 1967; McHenry 1973; Oxnard and Lisowski 1980). In many instances, a single bone was analyzed, and the locomotor potential of the organism was interpreted from that specimen alone. According to Gomberg 1981, a multivariate analysis that merely describes an anatomical structure, or points out correlations between the form of a structure and a broad spectrum classification of behavior, without demonstrating causal relationships between specific forms and specific locomotor or postural behavior is, in the last analysis, still typological in terms of orientation, interpretation and goals.

Thus, we encounter a basic theoretical problem in the application and interpretation of multivariate statistical methods that is clearly similar to the one we discussed previously for the genetic approach. The methods of analysis may have changed, but the basic orientation toward explanation via typologically oriented descriptive models remains essentially unaltered. This certainly does not imply that multivariate statistical procedures have been unfruitful in the analysis of morphological form, or that they do not have great potential for investigating problems relating to form and function. However, such potential can only be realized by the knowledgable and thoughtful application and interpretation of these methods within a conceptual framework that allows for explanation within a nontypological, nonclassificatory framework. Addressing himself to a similar problem within an entirely different context, Einstein, at the beginning of the century, stated,

> Even scholars of audacious spirit and fine instinct can be obstructed in the interpretation of the facts by philosophical prejudices. The prejudice—which has be no means died out in the meantime—consists in the faith that facts by themselves can and should yield scientific knowledge without free conceptual construction [as cited in Clark 1971:90].

More recently, Ripley (1967), Grand (1972), Stern and Oxnard (1973), and Morbeck (1975) have been critical of the descriptive nature of earlier functional studies and have suggested alternatives based on an analysis of functional features of the anatomy and behavior with the environment.

Biomechanical analysis utilizing a static approach has been implemented by Preuschoft (1970, 1973) in the analysis of the feet and lower extremities of selected nonhuman primate species, looking primarily at the the locomotion capabilities of Dryopithecines and early pleistocene hominids. Lovejoy et al. (1973) and Hieple and Lovejoy (1971) have applied biomechanical analysis to the reconstruction of australopithecine gait.

In addition, biomechanical analysis of motion (Prost 1965a, 1967, 1970; Grand 1972; Jenkins 1971, 1972; Wells 1974, Wells and Tebbets 1975) has developed, which applies kinematic and kinetic analysis to locomotor problems. The methodology for motion analysis was stimulated by Manter (1938), who analyzed the quadrepedal movement of the cat, by the analysis of sport movement (Carlsoo 1967; Hay 1978; Plagenhoef 1971) and by the analysis of the development of prosthetic devises by orthopedists (Elftman 1954; Denham 1959). It is not surprising that the origin and development of the biomechanical analysis came outside the discipline, which continued its philosophical commitment to description and taxonomy rather than explanation and process (Gomberg 1981).

The many difficulties encountered in establishing the relationships between behavior and anatomy in contemporary primates are only compounded when fossil materials are considered. The completeness of the fossils and the amount of environmental reconstruction possible vary, making interpretations difficult. Although methods of taphonomy are becoming quite sophisticated, there are still problems in understanding the relationship between anatomy, behavior and, the environment. For example, the joint complexes for some of the Dryopithecines have been reconstructed, yet there are still difficulties in interpreting the postural capabilities of these forms. A great deal of information is needed to establish the population parameters for the mophology of these joint systems. We are now beginning to interpret the behavior–anatomy–environment interactions in fossil primates, and the development of a methodology for undertaking such studies should place them on a more sound foundation.

The application of the functional approach is beginning to have a major impact on the analysis of the skeletal biology of archaeological populations. It has been used to establish the relationships between populations, to interpret the interrelationship of biology and behavior and to elucidate process in skeletal development.

We have been critical of the use of racial typology in establishing historical relationships. However, there have been a number of attempts to apply a functional approach to the study of the morphology of archaeological populations. Even in the Sudan, where the racial approach (Strouhal 1971) has been the major focus, functional studies have been applied to the interpretation of postmesolithic facial development. Carlson (1976), Carlson and Van Gerven (1977, 1979), and Van Gerven et al. (1977) have used an evolutionary model to interpret the reduction in facial morphology. They suggest that conversion to an agricultural subsistence pattern was a primary cause of the changes in facial morphology. Working in a very different part of the world, Hylander (1975) has provided a functional model for understanding the craniofacial development of the Eskimo. These studies suggest that in assessing biological affinities, one must understand the extent of the intrapopulation variation before interpreting interpopulation variation. In addition, the function of features must be determined prior to their use to establish the relationship between groups. For example, the extent and function of cranial indexes must be determined before they can be used to establish relationship between groups.

The problems of analyzing fossil hominids have improved somewhat with the increase in the size of samples and better methods for reconstructing the culture and environment of a group. The latter provides a basis for interpreting the functional complexes from a population perspective.

The relationship of changes in morphology to alterations in the subsistence pattern suggests that the biocultural approach can be applied in other areas. For example, Angel (1969) has demonstrated how changes in the ecology of classical Greece resulted in population changes in stature, morbidity, and mortality. Similarly, Buikstra (1977) has used a regional approach to study prehistoric biocultural changes in the lower Illinois River valley. At the Dickson Mounds (near Lewiston, Illinois), changes in the pattern of pathology were associated with changes in subsistence: Lallo and co-workers found a fourfold increase in iron deficiency anemia, a threefold increase in infectious disease, and a significant increase in mortality with the intensification of maize agriculture (1978).

The study of process in skeletal biology is often overlooked in archaeological samples, although these samples represent a major untapped resource for understanding response to environmental conditions. Problems, such as growth and development (Armelagos et al. 1972; Johnston 1962; Merchant and Ubelaker 1977), and specific conditions, such as osteoporosis (Dewey et al. 1969) and function features of long bones (Lovejoy et al. 1976), can be studied using skeletal material from archaeological populations.

The functional approach provides the skeletal biologist with one of the most important useful concepts. The analysis of the morphology is enhanced by the functional interpretation of adaptive complexes. It is the key to understanding the significance of *intra*populational and *inter*populational variation in extant and extinct primate and hominid populations.

References

Angel, J. L.
    1969   Paleodemography and evolution. *American Journal of Physical Anthropology* **31**:343–354.
Armelagos, G. J., and D. P. Van Gerven
    1980   Sexual dimorphism and human evolution: an overview. *Journal of Human Evolution* **9**:437–446.

Armelagos, G. J. et al.
    1972   Bone growth and development in prehistoric populations from Sudanese Nubia. *Journal of Human Evolution* **1**:89–119.
Ashton, E. H., and G. E. Oxnard
    1964   Functional adaptations in the primate shoulder girdle. *Proceedings of the Zoological Society of London* **142**:49–66.
Bass, W. M.
    1964   The variation in physical types of the prehistoric Plains Indians. *Plains Anthropology* **9**:65–145.
Berry, A. C., and R. J. Berry
    1967   Epigenetic variation in the human cranium. *Journal of Anatomy* **101**:361–379.
    1972   Origins and relationships of the ancient Egyptians based on a study of non-metric variation in the skull. *Journal of Human Evolution* **1**:199–208.
Berry, A. C., R. J. Berry, and P. J. Ucko
    1967   Genetical change in ancient Egypt. *Man* **2**:551–568.
Bieleki, T., and Z. Weton
    1964   The operation of natural selection on human head form in an East European population. *Homo* **15**:22–30.
Birkby, W. H.
    1966   An evaluation of race and sex identification from cranial measurements. *American Journal of Physical Anthropology* **24**:21–28.
Blackith, R. E., and R. A. Reyment
    1971   *Multivariate morphometrics.* New York: Academic Press.
Blumenbach, J. F.
    1969   *On the natural varieties of mankind.* New York: Bergmann. Third edition Goettingen, 1795. (Translated by T. Bendyshe and originally published for the Anthropological Society of London, 1865.)
Boyd, W. C.
    1950   *Genetics and the races of man.* Boston: Heath.
Buikstra, J. E.
    1977   Biocultural dimensions of archeological study: A regional perspective. In *Biocultural adaptation in prehistoric America,* edited by R. L. Blakely. Athens: University of Georgia Press. Pp. 67–84.
Carlson, D. S.
    1976   Temporal variation in prehistoric Nubian crania. *American Journal of Physical Anthropology* **45**:467–484.
Carlson, D. S., and D. P. Van Gerven
    1977   Masticatory function and post-Pleistocene evolution in Nubia. *American Journal of Physical Anthropology* **46**:495–506.
    1979   Diffusion, biological determinism and biocultural adaptation in the Nubian corridor. *American Anthropologist* **81**:561–580.
Carlsoo, S.
    1967   A kinetic analysis of the golf swing. *Journal of Sports Medicine and Physical Fitness* **7**:76–82.
Clark, R. W.
    1971   *Einstein: the life and times.* New York: Crowell-Collier.
Collett, M. A.
    1933   A study of twelfth and thirteenth dynasty skulls from Kerma (Nubia). *Biometrik* **25**:254–284.
Corruccini, R. S.
    1975   Multivariate analysis in biological anthropology: some considerations. *Journal of Human Evolution* **4**:1–19.
Crichton, J. M.
    1966   A multiple discriminant analysis of Egyptian and African Negro crania. *Papers of the Peabody Museum of Archaeology and Ethnology* **57**:43–67.

Robbins, L., and G. K. Neumann
    1972   *Prehistoric people of the Fort Ancient culture of the central Ohio valley.* Anthropological Papers of
            the Museum of Anthropology. Ann Arbor: University of Michigan.
Roberts, D. F.
    1954   The Cretins: a geographical analysis of some aspects of the physical anthropology. *Journal
            of the Royal Anthropological Institute* **84**:1–13.
Shapiro, H. L.
    1959   The history and development of physical anthropology. *American Anthropologist* **61**:371.
Solow, B.
    1966   The pattern of cranio-facial associations. A morphological and methodological correlation
            and factor analysis study on young male adults. *Acta Odontologica Scandinavica* **24**(Suppl.
            46).
Stern, J. T., and C. E. Oxnard
    1973   Primate locomotions: some links with evolution and morphology. *Primatologia* **4**:1–93.
Stewart, T. D. (editor)
    1947   *Hrdlička's practical anthropometry.* Philadelphia: Wistar Press.
Stoessiger, B. N.
    1927   A study of the Badarian crania recently excavated by the British School of Archaeology in
            Egypt. *Biometrika* **19**:110–150.
Strouhal, E.
    1971   Evidence of the early penetration of Negroes into prehistoric Egypt. *Journal of African
            History* **12**:1–9.
Suzuki, H.
    1969   Microevolutionary changes in Japanese population; from prehistoric age to the present.
            Journal of the Faculty of Science, University of Tokyo, Section 5 **3**(4):279–309.
Tattersall, I.
    1968   Multivariate analysis of some medieval British cranial series. *Man* **3**:284–292.
Thieme, F. P.
    1957   Sex in the Negro skeleton. *Journal of Forensic Medicine* **4**:72–81.
Thieme, F. P., and W. J. Schull
    1957   Sex determination of the skeleton. *Human Biology* **29**:242–273.
Thompson, D.
    1942   *On growth and form.* London and New York: Cambridge University Press. (Originally
            published in 1917).
    1971   *On growth and form* (abridged). London and New York: Cambridge University Press.
Tuttle, R. H. (editor)
    1972   *The functional and evolution biology of primates.* Chicago: Aldine.
van der Klaauw, C. J.
    1945   *Cerebral skull and facial skull. Archives Neerlandaises de Zoologie* **7**:16–38.
    1952   *Functional components of the skull.* Long Island, New York: E. J. Brill.
Van Gerven, D. P., G. J. Armelagos, and A. Rohr
    1977   Continuity and change in cranial morphology of three Nubian archaeological populations.
            Man **12**:270–277.
Virchow, R.
    1950   Heredity and the formation of race. In *This is race,* edited by E. W. Count. New York:
            Schuman. Pp. 178–193.
Weiner, J. S., and J. Huizinga
    1972   *The assessment of the population affinities in man.* Oxford: Clarendon.
Weiss, K. M., and T. Maruyama
    1976   Archeology, population genetics and studies of human racial ancestry. *American Journal of
            Physical Anthropology* **44**:31–49.
Wells, J. P.
    1974   Positional behavior of *Cercopithecus aethiops sabaeus,* a functional mechanical analysis.

Unpublished Ph.D. thesis, Department of Anthropology, University of Massachusetts, Amherst.

Wells, J. P., and G. Tebbets
1975   Positional behavior: a quantitative view of primate posture and locomotion. *Yearbook of Physical Anthropology* **10**:53–58.

Wiercinski, A.
1966   Some microevolutionary changes in the population of Wisica in the last millenary. *Acta Facultatis Rerum Naturalium Universitatis Comenianae, X, Anthropologia* **11**:43–57.

Wilkinson, R. G.
1971   Prehistoric biological relationships in the Great Lakes region. *Anthropological Papers. Museum of Anthropology No.* **43**. *University of Michigan,* Ann Arbor.

Woo, T. L.
1931   On the assymetry of the human skull. *Biometrika* **22**:324–352.
1937   Biometric study of the human malar bone. *Biometrika* **29**:113–123.

White, L.
1942   Christian myth and Christian history, *Journal of the History of Ideas.* **3**:147.

13

Five Decades of Skeletal Biology as Reflected in the *American Journal of Physical Anthropology*

C. Owen Lovejoy, Robert P. Mensforth, and George J. Armelagos

About a decade and a half ago, John Platt reviewed the general processes of scientific advancement and pointed out the great inequalities in the success achieved by different natural and physical disciplines. He characterized some fields as "rapidly moving," and others as approaching stagnation. He concluded that "rapidly moving" sciences were characterized by what he called "strong inference":

> In its separate elements, strong inference is just the simple and old-fashioned method of inductive inference that goes back to Francis Bacon. The steps are familiar to every college student and are practiced, off and on, by every scientist. The difference comes in their systematic application [Platt 1965:347].

Platt points out that deductive inference is far less efficient than is simple induction:

> It is clear why this makes for rapid and powerful progress. For exploring the unknown, there is no faster method: this is the minimum sequence of steps. Any conclusion that is not an exclusion is insecure and must be rechecked. Any delay in recycling to the next set of hypotheses is only a delay . . . "But what is so novel about this" someone will say. "That is *the* method of science and always has been; why give it a special name?" The reason is that many of us have almost forgotten it. Science is now an everyday business. Equipment, calculations, lectures become ends in themselves . . . We become "method oriented" rather than "problem oriented." We say we prefer to "feel our way" toward generalizations [Platt 1965:347–348; present chapter author's emphasis].

Platt's generalization clearly characterizes skeletal biology as a subdiscipline of physical anthropology. This conclusion is clearly documented by material

A HISTORY OF AMERICAN
PHYSICAL ANTHROPOLOGY, 1930–1980

published in the *American Journal of Physical Anthropology* (*AJPA*) during the past 50 years. Science is not just data collection, nor is it simply whatever scientists do. Science is first and foremost explanation, and therefore requires systematic statement and continual restatement of objectives, rather than endless collection of data or methods. In order to examine the presence of "strong inference" in anthropological skeletal biology, we have carried out a content analysis of the *AJPA* for the past 50 years (1930–1980). Since the *AJPA* is the official publication of the American Association of Physical Anthropologists (AAPA), it should be representative of the field. However, we are well aware of the possibility that it may reflect a more conservative aspect of the discipline and may contain a disproportionate number of data-oriented articles.

Content Analysis

We classified all papers published into two broad categories: skeletal biology and non-skeletal biology. Ignoring the latter, we then subdivided the former into two further categories: human skeletal biology and nonhuman skeletal biology (see Table 1). We will discuss these groups separately.

An analysis of the frequency of osteological studies published in the *AJPA* shows that skeletal studies have risen from 36% (1930–1939) to over 50% (1970–1980) (Table 1). Although descriptive studies have always dominated osteological research, there has been an increase in *analytical* reports (reports that propose and test specific hypotheses) in comparison to *descriptive* reports (reports that present simple description, sorting procedures, identification methods, or pure data) (Table 2).

A further breakdown by subtopics (see Table 3) indicates that anatomical studies have dominated skeletal biology. Paleontology and pathology have fluctuated. The former is clearly dependent on new discoveries, whereas the latter has increased in recent years because of the publication of organized symposia. Studies dealing with descriptive and problem-oriented aspects of skeletal growth were very

Table 1 The Frequency of Osteological Articles Published in the *AJPA* by Decade

Period	Total	Osteology	
		Number	Percentage
1930–1939	261	96	36.8
1940–1949	282	95	33.7
1950–1959	345	145	42.0
1960–1969	479	212	44.3
1970–1980	872	447	51.3
Total	2239	995	44.4

Table 2   The Frequency of Descriptive versus Analytical Articles Published in the *AJPA* by Decade

Period	Total	Descriptive		Analytical	
		Number	Percentage	Number	Percentage
1930–1939	96	83	86.5	13	13.5
1940–1949	95	75	78.9	20	21.1
1950–1959	145	102	70.3	43	29.7
1960–1969	212	137	64.6	75	35.4
1970–1980	447	250	55.9	197	44.1
Total	995	647	65.0	348	35.0

prevalent during the 1950s and 1960s, as were methodological studies concerned with skeletal aging, sexing, stature reconstruction, and demography. Osteological site reports, more frequent in the earlier years, became virtually extinct by the 1970s. Experimental biology, histochemistry, and the biomechanics of the skeleton have always been rare.

For all subtopics combined over the past five decades, approximately two thirds have been primarily descriptive (see Table 4). Reports on experimental biology and studies of skeletal maturation, although infrequent, have been most commonly analytical. Reports on general growth and pathology have been primarily descriptive. Only about 13% of all osteological reports were concerned with primate studies (see Table 5). Craniofacial and dental anatomy were the most frequent topics for every decade except the 1960s. About one fifth of the studies published in the *AJPA* have been devoted to methodology, demography, or genetics as related to the human or primate skeleton.

Trends in Skeletal Biology by Decade

1930–1939

This period was dominated by quantitative and qualitative descriptive anatomical studies. Cranial metric and nonmetric studies were most frequent. Pathology reports were much less common but were likewise primarily descriptive. Almost all studies were nonanalytical.

1940–1949

The early 1940s were again dominated by descriptive anatomical reports. Those focusing upon the incidence of metric and nonmetric traits in diverse human skeletal samples were common. The late 1940s saw a slight rise in the number of

Table 3   Frequency of Subject Matter in Osteological Articles Published in the *AJPA* by Decade[a]

Period	Total	Anatomy		Paleontology		Pathology	
		Number	Percentage	Number	Percentage	Number	Percentage
1930–1939	96	66	68.8	2	2.1	11	11.5
1940–1949	95	55	57.9	14	14.7	7	7.4
1950–1959	145	58	40.0	29	20.0	6	4.1
1960–1969	212	87	41.0	13	6.1	23	10.8
1970–1980	447	190	42.5	68	15.2	54	12.1
Total	995	456	45.8	126	12.7	101	10.2

[a]Skeletal maturation studies are represented separately from growth because they deal almost exclusively with various aspects of hand–wrist ossification.

Table 4   The Frequency of descriptive versus Analytical Articles by Subject Matter Published in the *AJPA*[a]

Topic	Total	Descriptive		Analytical	
		Number	Percentage	Number	Percentage
Anatomy	450	317	70.4	133	29.6
Paleontology	126	88	69.8	38	30.2
Pathology	101	84	83.2	17	16.8
Growth	71	59	83.1	12	16.9
Age, sex, stature, demography	93	57	61.3	36	38.7
Experimental biology, histochemistry, biomechanics	77	24	31.2	53	68.8
Skeletal maturation	57	23	40.4	34	59.6
Total	975	652	66.9	323	33.1

[a]Site reports have been omitted since all entries were purely descriptive.

Growth		Age, sex, stature demography		Site report		Skeletal maturation		Histochemistry, Biomechanics, experimental biology	
Number	Percentage	Number	Percentage	Number	Percentage	Number	Percentage	Number	Percentage
2	2.1	3	3.1	6	6.3	2	2.1	4	4.2
0	0.0	7	7.4	10	10.5	2	2.1	6	6.3
11	7.6	19	13.1	2	1.4	4	2.8	16	11.0
31	14.6	22	10.4	1	0.5	15	7.1	20	9.4
27	6.0	42	9.4	1	0.2	34	7.6	31	6.9
71	7.1	93	9.3	20	2.0	57	5.7	77	7.7

human paleontological reports that were primarily descriptive, but a few studies were devoted to evolutionary adaptation. There was an increase in skeletal identification studies, including aging, sexing, and race determination. Experimental biology, genetics, and histochemistry were still rare.

1950–1959

Anatomical studies were still primarily descriptive during this decade. Reports on the South African australopithecines became more common subsequent to new

Table 5   Differential Emphasis of Human versus Nonhuman Osteological Studies Published in the *AJPA*.

Topic	Total	Primate		Human	
		Number	Percentage	Number	Percentage
Anatomy	450	73	16.2	377	83.8
Paleontology	126	14	11.1	112	88.9
Pathology	101	8	7.9	93	92.1
Growth	71	9	12.7	62	87.3
Age, sex, stature, demography	93	8	8.6	85	91.4
Experimental biology, histochemistry, biomechanics	77	9	11.7	68	88.3
Skeletal maturation	57	2	3.5	55	96.5
Total	975	123	12.6	852	87.4

discoveries. Studies on skeletal growth, development, and maturation were also more frequent. The major trends during the 1950s were a continued metric and nonmetric focus on human skeletal variation and a shift toward more attention to patterns of growth, development, maturation, and aging.

1960–1969

This period was characterized by several major shifts. Although anatomical studies still dominated, reports rather than being purely descriptive began to reflect a more functional orientation. Paleontological reports were not as prevalent as they had been and the focus on paleopathology increased. Reports on the growth, stature, demography, and health status of skeletal populations were more common. Likewise, the qualitative methods of skeletal aging and sexing began to give way to multivariate approaches. The discriminant function was routinely applied to any bone that could offer no resistance to the Helios dial caliper. Experimental skeletal biology and biochemistry remained very sparsely represented in the literature. During the late 1960s, a number of organized symposia covering such topics as primate locomotion, general primate studies, in vivo bone-growth markers, paleodemography and paleopathology, and skeletal population studies set the stage for research in the succeeding decade. Generally, the 1960s were characterized by an increased interest in skeletal populations and in multivariate statistical techniques.

1970–1980

The major trend in the 1970s was the further application of multivariate statistical techniques. Simple metric and nonmetric studies gave way to the morphometric multivariate profile. The amount of biological distance (using both metric and nonmetric data) studies increased. New fossil discoveries generated new primary descriptions of the remains and more multivariate descriptions. While new fossils were being cleaned, older ones were being reanalyzed using morphometric techniques. Aging and sexing were taken up as topics for multivariate analysis. Experimental biology, biochemistry, histochemistry, and heritability were still rare. Paleopathology became a more frequent topic with the resurgence of 1930s-type case reports. Additional symposia on human adaptation and skeletal maturation were published.

Discussion

The content analysis provided here makes several important features of anthropological skeletal biology clear. It is a popular subdiscipline of physical anthropology. It accounts for half of the publications in the *AJPA*. If this figure is representative, this implies that it is the largest subdiscipline of physical anthropology. It certainly has grown steadily during the 50-year history just documented.

Table 6 Cranial versus Postcranial Osteological Articles Published in the *AJPA* by Decade

Decade	Total	Cranial		Postcranial		Both	
		Number	Percentage	Number	Percentage	Number	Percentage
1930–1939	96	56	58.3	28	29.2	12	12.5
1940–1949	95	47	49.5	28	29.5	20	21.1
1950–1959	145	81	55.9	38	26.2	26	17.9
1960–1969	212	98	46.2	104	49.1	10	4.7
1970–1980	447	252	56.4	150	33.6	45	10.1
Total	995	534	53.7	348	35.0	113	11.4

The number of papers published doubled between 1930 and 1960 and then doubled again in the past decade (see Table 6). Interest in archaeological skeletal biology and forensics is clearly strong, since about two-fifths of the papers published have been devoted to identification methodology (see Table 7). Paleontology has become a major subarea primarily during the past decade.

There is a favorable trend toward an increase in the number of analytical papers (see Table 2) in the 1970s. However, the scope of these analyses has tended to be highly specific, with greatest attention given to the solution of specific, rather than general, problem areas. Essentially, skeletal biology has remained primarily a descriptive science during the 50-year history documented here. To a certain extent, this is to be expected because the topical area of the science is historical. Clearly, areas such as paleontology and paleopathology require an extensive descriptive data base before analysis can proceed. Yet, the proportion of description documented here seems excessive, especially when compared to the virtual dearth of papers in which the "strong inference" of Platt can be documented. Even major shifts in the field fall short of true analysis.

Table 7 Subtopical Osteological Issues Published in the *AJPA*

Topic	Number	Percentage[a]
Age determination	39	3.9
Sex determination	38	3.8
Stature reconstruction	14	1.4
Demography	15	1.5
Genetics	24	2.4
Biomechanics	35	3.5
Histochemical techniques	27	2.7
Experimental skeletal biology	43	4.3
Total	235	23.6

[a]total number of articles is 995.

A clear trend in the past two decades was the replacement of simple metric description with multivariate morphometrics; the end product, however, generally remained the same—identification and sorting. In general, there has been a continual shift in the *Type* of description, rather than a true influx of analytical approaches. One of the most dangerous aspects of this historical record is the tendency for this subfield to be data directed, rather than problem directed. Age, sex, race, maturational status, stature, pathological changes, and allometric relationships are all primary data. Unless such data are used for more general conclusions, they are of little significance.

Predominantly theoretical papers have clearly been lacking in the pages of the *AJPA* in the past 50 years,. In order to use the data that we have and are collecting, we need the organizational and motivational influences of general theory, something that the field seems to have failed to generate. Clearly, we do not lack general theoretical issues requiring solution: What are the major environmental determiners of skeletal form, and what proportions do heredity and environment play in determining skeletal morphology? Are infrequent high-stress episodes more important than more continuous "positional behavior" in skeletal remodeling? What have been the effects on health of the major demographic transitions during the past 10,000 years? What primary theoretical positions do we hold on these topics? Can they be tested with our data? If not, what data are required, and are these data available? Why are the skeletal elements of earlier human ancestors so much more robust than anatomically modern man? These are but a few of the questions for which skeletal biology, as a discipline, should propose theoretical positions; yet such positions seem to be lacking—at least in the pages of the *AJPA*.

Attributed to Niels Bohr, the Danish physicist, was the comment that "the opposite of an ordinary truth is a falsehood; the opposite of a profound truth is another profound truth." Such a statement is, perhaps, a little overly dramatic for the field of skeletal biology, but the inference that can be drawn from it is not. We need to take new and more general theoretical positions. The ones we take may be totally wrong, but science learns a great deal from the process of disproof. Strong inference may lead to erroneous conclusions, but it invariably leads to new knowledge, new problems, and new theoretical positions. It would seem that as a discipline, skeletal biology has, as of the past decade, completed its first phase as a descriptive enterprise, and it is clearly time for the analysis and construction of general theory to begin.

Reference

Platt, J. R.
    1965   The step to man. *Science* **149**:607–613.

14

The Development of American Paleopathology

Douglas H. Ubelaker

In 1774, Johann Friedrich Esper reported on pathological conditions he observed on the femur of a paleontological cave bear from France, thereby quietly inaugurating the scientific discipline that would later be called *paleopathology*. Subsequently, the field has grown dramatically into a complex explanatory science that involves high technology and incorporates expertise in many fields.

Several scholars (Armelagos *et al.* 1971; Roney 1959) follow Pales (1930) in recognizing four chronological periods in the development of the discipline:

1. 1774–1870 focus—diseases of Quaternary fauna
2. 1870–1900 focus—traumatic lesions and syphilis in human remains
3. 1900–1930 focus—infectious disease and evidence for medical treatment in prehistory
4. 1930 to present focus—the paleoepidemiological approach, viewing disease with an ecological perspective

Each of the above periods loosely marks the beginning of new interest rather than the cessation of the old. The divisions are necessarily arbitary since interest continues today in most of the problems addressed during the discipline's 200-year history, and some aspects of at least the last three periods can be detected well before the dates suggested.

A HISTORY OF AMERICAN
PHYSICAL ANTHROPOLOGY, 1930–1980

Early History of the Discipline

Study of Disease in Quaternary Fauna

Esper's (1774) observations on the French cave bear initiate this period even though his diagnosis of osteosarcoma has been challenged (Moodie 1923a:4). Other notable works include Goldfuss's (1810) description of healed trauma in a fossil hyena occipital; Schmerling's 1835 study of the pathological remains of Quarternary vertebrates found in caves at Lìège, Belgium; and Mayer's (1854) summary of pathological conditions observed on fossil vertebrates. Moodie (1917) and Pales (1930) summarize additional research of this type.

Study of Disease in Ancient Human Bone

In the beginning, Americans were spectators rather than participants in the field of paleopathology. Interest among American scholars in the "abnormal" in prehistoric human samples is first marked by reference to evidence of intentional flattening of the cranium by Warren (1822, 1838) and Morton (1839, 1844). The omission of a discussion of any pathology present is noteworthy in these publications since both Warren and Morton had medical training and demonstrated intense interest in human remains. However, at that time, comparative human anatomy was a relatively new field that found investigators such as Warren and Morton rigorously following the example of Blumenbach in featuring measurements and beautiful illustrations of crania in their publications. These reports did not include discussions of the postcranial skeleton or evidence of disease. Nor were skeletal samples differentiated chronologically, which was perhaps because of the lack of adequate archaeological interpretation but also because the field was so new that the primary goal was an overview of worldwide variability.

Later, in 1857, Meigs published a list of the human crania in the Philadelphia Academy of Natural Sciences collection and noted that a Hindu soldier's cranium in the collection displayed "cicatrised fracture and depression of the right frontal, malar and superior maxillary bones [1857:45]," whereas another Hindu from Calcutta showed "syphilitic perforating ulcers of the cranium [1857:45]."

In 1868, Wyman published observations on Polynesian skulls that included discussion of periosteal inflammation, artificial deformation, "bony nodules" in the auditory meatus, "punched out" incisors and other dental anomalies (1868:19–20). The beginnings of a comparative population approach can be found in Wyman's discussion of the auditory nodules (presumably auditory exostoses) that he found to be "most common in the ancient Peruvians and the inhabitants of the Pacific Islands [1868:19]." Wyman also devotes several pages of discussion to "synostotic crania," noting even earlier work in Europe on this subject by Virchow, Lucae, and Welcker in Germany and by Minchin, Turner, Thurnham, Davis, and Huxley in England.

Joseph Jones's 1876 publication on disease in human remains recovered archaeologically in the eastern United States represents the first major discussion of disease in American archaeological samples. This publication inaugurates Pale's (1930) second period with its emphasis on discussion of skeletal evidence for syphilis and trauma. Again, archaeological controls of chronology were lacking in the study, but Jones presented detailed descriptions of skeletal lesions that showed his knowledge of the biology of disease and skeletal tissue. Jones also introduced histological techniques in the analysis of paleopathological samples noting "when thin sections of these bones were carefully examined with the naked eye, and by the aid of magnifying glasses, portions were found resembling cancellous tissue from the enlargement and irregular erosions of the Haversian canals, and increase in the number and size of the lacunae [Jones 1876:66]." Six years later, Broesike (1882) followed Jones's example in describing the microstructure of a 200-year-old human tibia, using a ground section to demonstrate that no organic material remained.

Jarcho (1966:8) has speculated that Jones's interest in paleopathology was due to the influence of his anatomy teacher at the University of Pennsylvania, Joseph Leidy. Although best known for his work in vertebrate and invertebrate anatomy, paleontology, and helminthology, Leidy also had a research interest in anthropology and pathology. Among his most notable contributions to human pathology were the discovery in 1846 of *Trichinella spiralis* in pork and the demonstration of the existence of bacterial flora in the intestine in 1849. He also pioneered a method of transplanting tumors in pathological research (see Ruschenberger 1892). In addition to the influence he had on Jones, it appears Leidy was also responsible for Harrison Allen's brief but significant excursion into anthropology and the field of human pathology. Allen's work represents the continuing interest in craniology in Philadelphian medical circles (Allen 1898) and also indicates a subtle shift from Morton's earlier static treatment of cranial anatomy to the recognition that the human skeleton was the product of dynamic biological processes—of which disease was an important factor (see Allen 1870, 1893, 1895).

Interest in paleopathology continued to grow with key publications by Putnam (1878, 1884), Langdon (1881), and Whitney (1883, 1886). These papers focused strongly on the syphylis debate but also identified much of the range of pathological lesions present in American archaeological samples. In particular, Langdon's (1881) report emphasizes pathology in his sample of 662 skeletons by presenting frequency data on ankylosis, fractures, arthritic conditions, and evidence of infectious disease. The descriptions are remarkably thorough for the time, and many are illustrated. Whitney's (1886) survey of pathological material in Harvard's Peabody Museum shows strong attention to detail and notes "the necessity of preserving the bones of the skeleton as well as the skull [Whitney 1886:448]."

The development of paleopathology was augumented considerably from 1897 to 1941 by the research of Hrdlička, Ruffer, Moodie, Williams and others. Hrdlička's major contribution to paleopathology was indirect and consisted of his continued strong emphasis on building large collections of archaeologically controlled skeletal samples, developing objectively defined procedures for researching human materials, and training qualified personnel to gather and interpret the data. His own broad research interests and publications only occasionally focused on general interpretations of paleopathology, but the skeletal collections he assembled and the professionalism he fostered stimulated much of the research of the twentieth century in paleopathology.

Hrdlička's own interest in paleopathology concentrated mostly in the areas of the cultural effects on the skeleton and developmental anomalies. His interest in the former was expressed as early as 1897 in an article with Lumholtz on trephining in Mexico (Lumholtz and Hrdlička 1897) and continued with solo articles on deformed and trephined skulls from Peru (1911), (1914), Alaska (1941a), and the Americas in general (1939) and on ritual ablation of the teeth in Siberia and America (1940a).

Hrdlička's interest in skeletal "anomalies" is a direct outgrowth of his career interest in documenting human variation. Since he sometimes regarded "disease" as a possible cause, anomalies can be included in this discussion of paleopathology. This interest is manifested early in his career in an article (1899a, published in Spanish in 1900) describing various anomalies on a skeleton from the Valley of Mexico and also presenting model descriptions and measurements of the post-cranial skeleton. The same year (1899b) he described an anomalous ulna from a burial cave in Chihuahua, Mexico. Subsequent articles devoted to anomalous conditions appeared in 1935 on ear exostoses, in 1940 on mandibular and maxillary hyperostoses (1940b) and in 1941 on mandibular double condyles (1941b). These last three articles are exemplary because in them, Hrdlička provides comparative data from large, diverse skeletal samples, incorporates information from a variety of sources (clinical data, histology, etc.), and attempts to interpret these data.

Observations by Hrdlička on general pathology in early skeletal samples are occasionally featured in articles (1899c, 1927) but are usually scattered within general skeletal reports, such as those on remains from Missouri mounds (1910), Peru (1914) and eastern United States Indians (1916).

Hrdlička's possible bias toward cultural effects on skeletal materials can best be seen in his 1941 article, "Diseases of and Artifacts on Skulls and Bones from Kodiak Island" (1941a). In this article he comments that disease is "rare" and then, without presenting descriptions and frequencies, passes directly to detailed discussion of cultural modifications of the bones. Hrdlička provided large samples and encouraged the objective, detailed description so important in paleopathology, but he left major synthesis on the subject to others.

The writings of Hrdlička as well as those of his predecessors indicate only occasional interest in pathology and then mostly as an interesting anomaly rather than as a field of investigation that can provide general interpretative data. This general disinterest was not due to a lack of familiarity with the disease process since most investigators of that time held medical degrees. Rather, it reflected a preoccupation with anthropometry and craniology. The goal of the discipline was to document human variation and use cranial measurements to assess biological affinities. To some extent, disease processes and cultural modifications presented unwanted "noise" in the system.

Paleopathology as a Distinct Discipline

Although he is European, Marc Armand Ruffer's writings are relevant here in that they inaugurate the beginning of detailed analysis of mummified soft tissue (1914), the diagnosis of specific disease from soft-tissue analysis (1910), an emphasis on the potential of teeth for paleopathological analysis (1920), and the dawn of the specialist in "paleopathology." In contrast to Hrdlička, Ruffer emphasized pathology over anthropometry, commenting in 1914, "I made no attempt to measure the skeletons, as this will be done by a competent anthropologist. . . . All the pathological specimens were set aside and sent off to Alexandria, where they were examined at leisure [1914:453]."

Paleopathology advanced considerably with Ruffer's work, particularly in the use of medical technology to investigate disease in mummified soft tissue. As early as 1910, Ruffer applied histological technique to identify "bilharzia haematobia" in Egyptian mummies dating before Christ by locating calcified eggs among the straight tubules of the kidneys. Ruffer also was one of the first to utilize the x-ray in paleopathological research (preceded by Eaton in 1916) and is usually credited with inaugurating the term paleopathology, although Moodie (1923a:21) pointed out that it appeared as early as 1895 in *Funk and Wagnall's Standard Dictionary*.

In the United States, paleopathology was advanced primarily through the efforts of Roy L. Moodie, a contemporary of Hrdlička. Like Ruffer, Moodie emphasized pathology over anthropometry in his writing and can be credited with the first major American syntheses of vertebrate (including human) paleopathology (1917, 1923a, 1923b, 1931). Moodie's summary volumes offer good discussions of the history of paleopathology as well as critical evaluations of research results for human as well as nonhuman vertebrate samples. By that time, most of the types of bone afflictions known today from archaeological material had been discovered and were ably summarized by Moodie.

The next major summary (Williams 1929) reflected the growth of the field by focusing on just *human* paleopathology. Williams recognized the increasing need for sound chronological dating by archaeologists and the difficulties involved: "The amateur archeologist may easily make mistakes, while professional archeologists may sometimes hold diverse opinions [1929:4]." Williams's work shows considerable sophistication not only in the use of the technology of the time but also in careful interpretation of skeletal evidence of disease. His thorough discussion of various disease conditions demonstrates an appreciation for the complex factors that must be considered in interpretation. His summary largely traces the evidence for the antiquity of individual diseases.

Hooton: The Epidemiological Approach

Hooton's 1930 study of the Pecos Pueblo material brought a new dimension to paleopathological research by presenting detailed frequency data on disease in a large, well-documented archaeological sample. Hooton presented percentage occurrences for arthritic changes, inflammatory lesions, cranial lesions, evidence of trauma, and "osteoporosis symmetrica." The publication is important not only for systematically presenting new data but also for presenting them in a broad ecological perspective that considers the influence of diet and culture on the expression of disease. To a large extent, Hooton's work marks the beginning of the epidemiological approach that has flourished in recent years. In contrast to earlier works that view samples merely as pre- or post-Columbian, Hooton relied on archaeological information to differentiate the sample into temporal subunits, thus enabling a study of temporal change in disease frequency. Again, this approach shows the antecedence of modern epidemiological studies of documented samples and allowed Hooton to conclude that health declined during the closing periods of the settlement.

Following the pioneer work of Hrdlička, Moodie, Williams, and Hooton, momentum has been maintained in America by Stewart and Angel at the Smithsonian and by a variety of other workers. Stewart's research follows the pattern set by Hrdlička in emphasizing cultural effects on the skeleton, particularly dental modifications (Holder and Stewart 1958; Stewart 1942, 1944; Stewart and Groome 1968; Stewart and Titterington 1946), anomalies (Stewart 1935), careful, detailed reporting of diseased tissue (Stewart 1931, 1974, 1976; Stewart and Quade 1969; Stewart and Spoehr 1952), and observations of pathology in the reporting of samples recovered archaeologically. Stewart's work shows his customary great attention to detail and thoughtful caution in interpretation (Stewart 1966, 1976).

Angel's contributions follow Hooton's approach in using disease as one component in a broad biocultural study of one geographic area. Concentrating primarily in the Near East, Angel has worked closely with archaeologists to study human remains from a wide range of sites, not only documenting the frequency of many disease entities but also suggesting how disease factors may be related to other biocultural variables such as mortality, age structure, population size, morphology, and culture (Angel 1948, 1957, 1963, 1964, 1966a, 1966b, 1967, 1971, 1973, 1974, 1975).

Other contributions to paleopathology since Hooton are too numerous to be mentioned here individually. Goldstein's 1932 article on dental problems among Eskimo samples, his 1957 publication on the "skeletal pathology of early Indians in Texas," and Roney's 1959 article, "Palaeopathology of a California archaeological site," document the approach of that time—detailed reporting of disease in archaeological samples that have increasing temporal and cultural documentation.

Means (1932) emphasized the use of radiographs in paleopathological analysis. Various summary articles and volumes are available from 1961 to the present that offer overviews of method and theory in paleopathology as well as accumulated knowledge. Brothwell's *Dental Anthropology* (1963) contains several articles by Americans that summarize knowledge of dental pathology at that time, whereas his earlier (1961) essay focused on general problems of diagnosis in paleopathology. European books by Wells in 1964, Ackerknecht in 1965, and Janssens in 1970 presented information on paleopathology to a wide American audience through their easy-to-read writing styles. The 1966 publication of the proceedings of a 1965 symposium on human paleopathology brought together many of the researchers of that time. Organizer–editor Jarcho expressed disappointment that more progress had not been made but also eloquently displayed optimism that interest and the quality of research seemed to be on the increase.

The next year (1967), Brothwell and Sandison published their edited volume, *Diseases in Antiquity*, that made available several "classic" older papers as well as new innovative articles that especially offered insights to American paleopathologists into differential diagnosis of individual diseases. That same year, Kerley and Bass (1967) brought the discipline of paleopathology to the attention of readers of *Science*, noting that the field needed input and collaboration from orthopedists, radiologists, epidemiologists, obstetricians, dental researchers, nutritionists, geneticists, historians, archaeologists, ethnologists, paleontologists, zoologists, and, of course, physical anthropologists. Armelagos's article 2 years later in the same journal showed how such interdisciplinary research had been conducted in ancient Nubia (Armelagos 1969), whereas Morse's (1969) volume summarized interpretations from the midwestern United States.

In 1971, Armelagos *et al.* published a bibliography of human paleopathology. This volume notes 1788 individual contributions and remains an important reference work for anyone working in the field. More recently, Steinbock (1976) published a text, *Paleopathological Diagnosis and Interpretation*, that is frequently cited for practicality in researching disease in skeletal samples. Ubelaker (1978) has summarized the history of interest in microscopic analysis, emphasizing the use of microscopic bone structure in age determination as well as past and potential histological contributions to disease interpretation. Our considerable progress in mummy analysis has been reported by Allison (1976), Allison and Gerszten (1975), and Cockburn and Cockburn (1980).

Buikstra and Cook (1980) have summarized recent developments in paleopathology, calling attention to areas of differential diagnosis, the interpretation of disease in a biocultural context, general skeletal indicators of stress (lines of increased density, dental defects, variance in growth patterns), bone remodeling dynamics, paleodemography, paleonutrition, and communication among scientists on this subject. Buikstra (1981) also has edited a volume on prehistoric tuberculosis in the Americas that focuses expertise from many areas on this one historically important topic. Finally, a new Smithsonian volume by Ortner and Putschar (1982) promises to augment Steinbock's work in proving greater coverage of the range of disease processes that affect bone, examples from museum collections around the world, and important diagnostic criteria from an experienced pathologist (Putschar).

Paleopathology Today

Present research in paleopathology continues on most of the traditional areas of interest as well as many new ones. The recent review by Buikstra and Cook (1980) includes research in long-bone growth, bone remodeling, demography, nutrition, diet, and disease diagnosis from skeletal structure. Although all research in these areas is not paleopathology, data generated from that research is very relevant to inferences about ancient disease process, the impact of disease on populations, and some of the complex factors involved. Aside from this diversity of research interest within the general field of paleopathology, there are two factors that characterize current work: (*a*) increased accuracy in diagnosis and (*b*) research design directed toward an understanding of the disease process and the assessment of its causal factors and biocultural impact.

Increased Accuracy in Disease Diagnosis

"Increased accuracy in diagnosis" takes two forms: (*a*) an increase in the precision of diagnosis, resulting from technological advances or more sophisticated, problem-oriented research design and (*b*) more realistic classification of disease categories that accepts the limitations of diagnosis but still provides useful information.

Almost since its inception, the field of paleopathology has been clouded by the difficulty of diagnosing disease from skeletal or mummified tissue alone. Nevertheless, as mentioned previously, Ruffer (1910) was able to diagnose schistosomiasis from the presence of calcified eggs in the kidneys of Egyptian mummies. Others working as far back as the nineteenth century recognized the more obvious conditions, such as fractures, arthritic change, dental caries, general evidence of infectious disease, and some cultural effects on the skeleton. In more recent years, Allison *et al.* (1973) were able to diagnosis pre-Columbian tuberculosis in a Peruvian mummy, through the presence of expected morphological changes in bone and soft tissue, as well as the discovery of acid-fast bacilli in sections taken from the lung, liver, and kidney.

Radiography, histochemical procedures, and other relevant techniques are now used routinely in individual disease diagnosis (Zimmerman 1979), and we can surely look forward to some additional progress in our ability to diagnose specific disease. However, prospects for progress in this area are outweighed by the realization that many diseases produce similar skeletal changes and that the skeletal manifestation of one disease process may be affected by another. In the absence of clinical history and data from the seldom-present soft tissue, diagnosis of specific disease frequently is not possible. Reaching an understanding of this situation is progress in itself, as we look back at the futile, inconclusive debates regarding the diagnosis of syphilis and other infectious disease. The accuracy of modern diagnosis of disease from archaeological specimens is increased dramatically by the use of general categories of disease that avoid the problem of unrealistic diagnosis (Johnson 1966; Putschar 1966; Stothers and Metress 1976).

Disease in a Biocultural Context

The use of the categories of disease just mentioned, rather than unrealistic diagnoses of specific diseases, correlates with a modern shift of research interest from "What is the history of a particular disease?" to "What are the frequencies of the disease categories in a population, and how do they relate to other biocultural data?" This latter approach can be traced back through the work of Angel and others to Hooton, but it certainly flourishes in current research (Cook 1979). The approach has been encouraged not only by the difficulty in diagnosing specific disease but also by revolutions in archaeological dating and research design, the increase in large skeletal samples with temporal–spatial documentation, increased communication among paleopathologists and specialists in other disciplines, increased availability of computer technology, and increased appreciation for the application of methodological approaches in demography, epidemiology, nutrition, and social anthropology.

Close collaboration with archaeologists or actual excavation by paleopathologists–physical anthropologists has allowed such research as Saul's (1972) "osteobiographic" analysis of the remains from Altar de Sacrificios in Guatemala, Buikstra's (1976) biocultural study of the lower Illinois Valley, Rathbun et al.'s (1980) examination of disease patterns in prehistoric South Carolina, and my own work in Ecuador (Ubelaker 1980a, 1980b, 1981). This research allows correlations of disease and other variables at both the individual and population levels, primarily because well-preserved samples of skeletons have been collected and can be correlated with archaeological dates and information. For example, Cybulski (1974) was able to examine the dental effects of wearing stone labrets in prehistoric British Columbia because of the archaeological discovery of human skeletons with associated labrets. Blakely's (1980) study of pathological human skeletons from Etowah, Georgia, suggested sociocultural distinctions between populations represented in the village area versus those in a burial mound.

Evidence of temporal changes in disease frequencies and their correlation with change in subsistence (e.g., Larsen 1980a, 1980b; Ubelaker 1980a, 1980b) is possible only because of the archaeological controls of the samples. Similarly, Lallo *et al.* (1977) suggested correlations between disease frequencies and subsistence in four prehistoric Illinois populations. This research was possible only because skeletal samples had been excavated and preserved and because archaeological interpretations had been made regarding the subsistence and settlement patterns of the groups they represent.

Ancient disease in a biocultural, epidemiological perspective represents an exciting area for research, but one with many methodological problems. The problems center on the incomplete evidence for disease and the need for more accurate chronological controls and more exact indicators of subsistence and other cultural variables. Some aspects of subsistence can be reconstructed directly from analysis of faunal material or copralites recovered at the site. In most areas, such materials recovered archaeologically are limited to bone and shell, with no direct evidence of more perishable or more completely consumed foodstuffs.

Several recent research developments in the area of trace-element analysis of bone offer new hope for increased accuracy in this area. One such development involves the analysis of ^{12}C–^{13}C ratios. This approach is based on the fact that carbon in the human body ultimately comes from carbon dioxide in the atmosphere that has been metabolized by plants and passed on to man via the food chain. Three isotopes of carbon appear in the human body: the stable isotope ^{12}C (the most common form), the stable isotope ^{13}C and the relatively uncommon radioactive ^{14}C isotope that is useful for dating. It is known that not all plants carry the same levels of ^{13}C. Several types of plants, including sorghum and maize, have a carbon molecular structure that allows a higher ^{13}C level. This higher ^{13}C level is passed on to humans if these plants are consumed in the food chain. The ratio of ^{12}C to ^{13}C in humans ultimately reflects the types of foods consumed during the life of the individual.

Analysis of human bones for ratios of carbon isotopes should detect if those plants that have high ^{13}C ratios were relied on extensively for subsistence, although by itself the method cannot determine exactly which ^{13}C plants were involved. Published works by Vogel and Van de Merwe (1977), Van der Merwe (1978), and Burleigh and Brothwell (1978) show how the approach can be applied to a variety of problems in prehistory but also point out many of the uncertainties involved.

Trace-mineral analysis (particularly strontium) has emerged as another potential data source for diet reconstruction (Brown 1973; Burleigh and Brothwell 1978; Geidel 1981; Kavanagh 1979; Schoeninger 1979; Sillen 1981; Van der Merwe 1978; Vogel and Van der Merwe 1977). This approach measures small quantities of minerals in the skeleton on the assumption that variability revealed by comparison reflects the dietary differences of the individuals examined. Strontium levels in particular vary considerably, depending largely on diet, and can potentially offer valuable information if variables can be controlled.

Strontium enters the land-based food chain from the soil and ground water through the roots of plants, and concentrations gradually decrease with the move up the food chain. Thus, humans and other animals who consume mostly plants will have higher concentrations of strontium than those who consume mostly other animals. The measurement of strontium levels has obvious application in determining general subsistence, but some of the problems involved appear to be substantial. Much more work needs to be done to determine (*a*) the variability in strontium available to plants in different areas and in different seasons within the same area; (*b*) the variability in plants' capacity to absorb strontium; (*c*) the variability in the amount transmitted along the food chain; (*d*) the extent to which human strontium levels are affected by ingestion of a variety of food sources from several levels along the food chain; (*e*) the extent to which trace-element levels in buried bone are altered by the soil environment; and (*f*) the reliability of our ability to measure accurately and consistently strontium variance (due to the age, sex, type of bone, condition of bone, procedure of measurement, quality of equipment, and experience of equipment operator).

Even if many of these variables can be worked out, major problems in research design may remain. It will be difficult to distinguish high strontium levels caused by the consumption of domesticated grains from those produced by root crops or marine sources. The use of other methods (e.g., $^{12}C-^{13}C$ ratios) or other trace elements (Geidel 1981; Gilbert 1977) may be useful in this regard, but clearly much more research is required before reasonably exact statements can be made.

Evidence for "disease" in ancient human bone is now being generated from a variety of new sources other than the specific disease diagnoses or even disease categories mentioned earlier. Skeletal evidence for various kinds of metabolic stress has been suggested for lines of increased density in long bones (Garn and Schwager 1967; Garn et al. 1968; McHenry 1968; McHenry and Schulz 1976), dental abnormalities (Cook and Buikstra 1979; El-Najjar et al. 1978; Goodman et al. 1980; Molnar and Ward 1975; Rose 1977, 1979; Rose et al. 1978; Sciulli 1978), dental asymmetry (DiBennardo and Bailit 1978; Doyle and Johnston 1977; Perzigian 1977), cortical bone loss (Carlson et al. 1976; Dewey et al. 1969;Ericksen 1976), and histochemical variance in microscopic structure (Gunness-Hay 1980; Martin and Armelagos 1979; Richman et al. 1979; Stout and Simmons 1979; Thompson 1978, 1980; Weinstein et al. 1981). Like so many other aspects of paleopathology, these indicators reflect a variety of causal factors, comprise an incomplete record of disease, and often present seemingly conflicting evidence.

Death represents the ultimate effect of the disease process. Although cause of death can rarely be determined from skeletal evidence alone, the distribution of ages at death, especially in the form of the life table, can offer useful information. The frequencies of individuals dying in particular age groups may offer some insights into the kinds and intensities of the disease processes acting on the population, especially when they can be correlated with skeletal evidence of disease (Clarke 1977, 1980; Elmendorf 1979; Owsley and Bass 1979). Palkovich (1981) used multivariate statistics and computer technology to relate frequencies of disease categories to peaks in age-specific mortality. The Palkovich approach recognizes that the population frequency of a disease probably was greater than the frequency of skeletal lesions and that the disease process may have caused mortality directly or in combination with other factors.

Summary and Concluding Remarks

The range of research being conducted today offers exciting possibilities for an explanation of the nature of the disease process and its biocultural impact in past populations. Naturally, in such complex research, caution and logic are mandatory. The need for accurate, detailed description of pathological specimens is greater than ever. Meaningful comparison and more elaborate research designs are simply not possible unless data are presented in full in the literature and can be trusted.

Basic frequency information on the majority of pathological categories is still lacking from most geographic areas and temporal periods. Differential diagnosis of specific diseases or even disease categories must ask not only if the suspected entity could produce the observed lesions but also which of the other disease processes have similar effects and how these can be differentiated. The need for large samples of well-documented skeletons is greater than ever, calling for increased collaboration between paleopathologists and archaeologists, including fieldwork by the former. Existing collections should be researched critically for documentation and for evidence of sampling problems.

Archaeological interpretations of subsistence, settlement patterns, and the like should be utilized in innovative research designs, but the evidence for such interpretation should be examined fully and critically. Just because an archaeologist believes that a prehistoric population relied primarily on maize agriculture for subsistence does not mean that meat, fish, or other plant materials were not included in the diet. Research designs must determine what suspected variables correlate (e.g., increased use of maize and increased frequency of caries) and what other variables may be involved (e.g., introduction of other food products, change in cooking habits). Pathological data should be correlated as much as possible with the age and sex of the individual, but the error involved in estimating age and sex must be considered as well.

Research needs to be intensified on our existing methodology in paleopathology. Additional chemical data are needed on how most diseases affect bone and how the evidence can be interpreted after years in the soil or in a museum drawer. How do these soil contaminants affect trace-element studies and carbon isotope ratios? Samples for trace-element analysis should be taken from the soil and from appropriate fauna and flora of the area to distinguish differences due to subsistence from those caused by normal variation and soil contaminants. The error of technology involved in generating these data must be firmly established and considered in interpretation. Lines of arrested growth and dental indicators offer promising data, but major questions remain on how different indicators correlate with each other and how accurately they can detect metabolic disorders.

In 1966, Stewart discussed a trephined Peruvian skull on exhibit at the United States National Museum, "Hrdlička always told me that the scarred area surrounding the trephine hole represented the scraping away of the bone by the surgeon in the process of trephination. One accepts such a statement when the master has spoken [1966:45]." "You don't question the views of a great man like

Hrdlička. Those of you who have heard him speak in this building know how impressive he was [1966:43]." Stewart goes on to describe how he later realized that the modified tissue represented infection of the bone in the area exposed through the opening of the scalp. The message here for all of us is that we should critically examine the presented evidence, logic, and interpretations—no matter how impressive the credentials of the investigator. This caution is also directed toward the trust we tend to place in sophisticated models, machines, and computer programs. Paleopathology is at a point of development where complex procedures are required, but they must be scrutinized by qualified personnel and objectively applied.

Paleopathology has evolved from a sporadic interest in the ancient, medically unusual specimen to a complex discipline that encompasses many fields. Growth has been augmented tremendously by the acquisition of numerous, large, documented samples of human skeletons and technological advances in radiography, histology, the chemistry of bone and mummified soft tissue, and trace-element analysis. Although advances have been numerous, many of the present needs are the same as in the past. Still relevant is Hooton's plea in 1930, "We shall never be able to acquire any satisfactory basis for study of palaeopathology until clinical pathologists and anatomists cooperate in the preservation of skeletal material of known clinical history [Hooton 1930:306]."

The need also remains for increased cooperation among human skeletal biologists, radiologists, pathologists, and other related professionals. Individuals specializing in paleopathology should acquire training in all of these areas and gain an understanding of the applications and limitations of high technology. Communication among individuals within the field of paleopathology has increased dramatically with the formation of the Paleopathology Association and the Paleopathology Club in 1973 but should be strengthened with scholars in other disciplines, particularly those in pathology, epidemiology, and nutrition.

The future of paleopathology appears brighter now than at any point in the past, especially in the areas of analysis of mummified soft tissue and correlations of disease with diet and demography. Once newly introduced methodology is perfected, exciting results should flow from holistic studies of large skeletal collections that can resolve important problems not only in the history of disease but in general studies of biocultural evolution. Paleopathology appears poised to evolve from Kerley and Bass's "meeting ground for many disciplines" (1967) to a discipline of its own that can make a profound statement on the history of the human condition.

References

Ackerknecht, E. H.
    1965   *History and geography of the most important diseases.* New York: Hafner.
Allen, H.
    1870   Localization of disease action in the osseous system. *American Journal of the Medical Sciences* **XVI**: 401–405.

1893   Remarks on congenital defect of face, with exhibition of a rare form of cleft palate. *New York Medical Journal* **LVIII**: 759–760.

1895   Demonstration of skulls showing the effects of cretinism on the shape of the nasal chambers. *New York Medical Journal* **LXI**: 139–140.

1898   The study of skulls from the Hawaiian Islands, with an introduction by D. G. Brinton, Wagner Institute of Science, Philadelphia. *Proceedings, Academy of Natural Sciences, Philadelphia* **V**: 1–55.

Allison, M. J. (Editor)

1976   Paleopathology. *Medical College of Virginia Quarterly* **12**(2).

Allison, M. J., and E. Gerszten

1975   *Paleopathology in Peruvian mummies.* Richmond: Virginia Commonweath University.

Allison, M. J., D. Mendosa, and A. Pezzia

1973   Documentation of a case of tuberculosis in pre-Columbian America. *American Review of Respiratory Disease* **107**:985–991.

Angel, J. L.

1948   Health and the course of civilization as seen in ancient Greece. Part 1. *The Interne* **January**: 15–17, 45–48.

1957   Human biological changes in ancient Greece, with special reference to Lerna. *Yearbook of the American Philosophical Society*:266–270.

1963   Physical anthropology and medicine. *Journal of the National Medical Association* **55**(2):107–116.

1964   Osteoporosis: Thalassemia? *American Journal of Physical Anthropology* **22**:369–374.

1966a   Porotic hyperostosis, anemias, malarias, and marshes in the prehistoric Eastern Mediterranean. *Science* **153**:760–763.

1966b   *Early skeletons from Tranquillity, California. Smithsonian Contributions to Anthropology* **2**(1).

1967   Porotic hyperostosis or osteoporosis symmetrica. In *Diseases in antiquity*, edited by D. Brothwell and A. T. Sandison. Springfield, Illinois: Thomas. Pp. 378–389.

1971   *The people of Lerna.* Washington, D. C.: Smithsonian Institution Press.

1973   Early Neolithic people of Nea Nikomedeia. *Fundamenta Monographien zur Urgeschichte, B* **3**:103–112.

1974   Patterns of fractures from Neolithic to modern times. *Anthropological Közlemények* **18**:9–18.

1975   Paleoecology, paleodemography, and health. In *Ninth international congress of anthropological and ethnological sciences*, edited by S. Polgar. The Hague: Mouton. Pp. 167–190.

Armelagos, G. J.

1969   Disease in ancient Nubia. *Science* **163**:255–259.

Armelagos, G. J., J. H. Mielke and J. Winter

1971   *Bibliography of human paleopathology. Research Reports No.* **8**. Amherst: University of Massachusetts Press.

Blakely, R. L.

1980   Sociocultural implications of pathology between the village area and Mound C skeletal remains from Etowah, Georgia. *Tennessee Anthropological Association, Miscellaneous Paper* **5**:28–38.

Broesike, G.

1882   Ueber die feinere Structur des Normalen Knochengewebes. *Archivfuer Mikroskopische Anatomie* **21**:695–765.

Brothwell, D. R.

1961   The palaeopathology of early British Man: An essay on the problems of diagnosis and analysis. *Journal of the Royal Anthropological Institute of Great Britain and Ireland* **91**:318–344.

Brothwell, D. R. (Editor)

1963   *Dental Anthropology.* Oxford: Pergamon.

Brothwell, D. R. and A. T. Sandison (Editors)

1967   *Diseases in antiquity.* Springfield, Illinois: Thomas.

Brown, A. B.

1973   Bone strontium as a dietary indicator in human skeletal populations. Unpublished Ph.D. dissertation, Department of Anthropology, University of Michigan, Ann Arbor.

Buikstra, J. E.

1976   Hopewell in the lower Illinois Valley. *Northwestern University Archeological Program, Scientific Papers* 2.

1981   Editor. *Prehistoric tuberculosis in the Americas.* Evanston, Illinois: Northwestern University Archeological Program.

Buikstra, J. E. and D. C. Cook

1980   Palaeopathology: an American account. *Annual Review of Anthropology* 9:433–470.

Burleigh, R., and D. Brothwell

1978   Studies on Amerindian dogs, carbon isotopes in relation to maize in the diet of domestic dogs from early Peru and Ecuador. *Journal of Archaeological Science* 5:355–362.

Carlson, D. S., G. J. Armelagos, and D. P. Van Gerven

1976   Patterns of age-related cortical bone loss (osteoporosis) within the femoral diaphysis. *Human Biology* 48(2):295–314.

Clarke, S. K.

1977   Mortality trends in prehistoric populations. *Human Biology* 49(2):181–186.

1980   Early childhood morbidity trends in prehistoric populations. *Human Biology* 52(1):79–85.

Cockburn, A., and E. Cockburn (Editors)

1980   *Mummies, disease, and ancient cultures.* London and New York: Cambridge University Press.

Cook, D. C.

1979   Subsistence base and health in prehistoric Illinois Valley: evidence from the human skeleton. *Medical Anthropology* 3:109–124.

Cook, D. C., and J. E. Buikstra

1979   Health and differential survival in prehistoric populations: Prenatal dental defects. *American Journal of Physical Anthropology* 51:649–664.

Cybulski, J. S.

1974   Tooth wear and material culture: pre-contact patterns in the Tsimshian area, British Columbia. *Syesis* 7:31–35.

Dewey, J. R., G. J. Armelagos, and M. H. Bartley

1969   Femoral cortical involution in three Nubian archaeological populations. *Human Biology* 41(1):13–28.

DiBennardo, R., and L. Bailit

1978   Stress and dental asymmetry in a population of Japanese children. *American Journal of Physical Anthropology* 48:89–94.

Doyle, W. J., and O. Johnston

1977   On the meaning of increased fluctuating dental asymmetry: A cross populational study. *American Journal of Physical Anthropology* 46:127–134.

Eaton, G. F.

1916   The collection of osteological material from Machu Picchu. *Memoirs of the Connecticut Academy of Arts and Sciences* 5:1–96.

Elmendorf, J.

1979   The skeletal pathology of the Nanjemoy II ossuary. Unpublished M.A. thesis, Department of Anthropology, Catholic University, Washington, D. C.

El-Najjar, M. Y., M. V. Desanti, and L. Ozebek

1978   Prevelance and possible etiology of dental enamel hypoplasia. *American Journal of Physical Anthropology* 48:185–192.

Ericksen, M. F.

1976   Cortical bone loss with age in three native American populations. *American Journal of Physical Anthropology* 45:443–452.

Esper, J. E.

1774   *Aüsfurliche Nachrichten von neuentdeckten Zoolithen unbekannter vierfussiger thiere.* Nuremberg.

Garn, S. M., and P. M. Schwager

1967   Age dynamics of persistent transverse lines in the tibia. *American Journal of Physical Anthropology* **27**:375–378.

Garn, S. M., F. N. Silverman, K. P. Hertzog, and C. G. Rohmann
1968   Lines and bands of increased density. *Medical Radiography and Photography* **44**:58–89.

Geidel, R. A.
1981   Paleonutrition and social stratification: a study of trace elements in human skeletons from the Dallas archaeological culture of eastern Tennessee. Unpublished M.A. thesis, Department of Anthropology, Pennsylvania State University, University Park.

Gilbert, R. I.
1977   Applications of trace element research to problems in archeology. In *Biolcultural adaptation in prehistoric America*, edited by R. L. Blakely. Athens: University of Georgia Press. Pp. 85–100.

Goldfuss, A.
1810   *Die Umgebringen von muggendorf.* Erlangen. P. 276.

Goldstein, M. S.
1932   Caries and attrition in the molar teeth of the Eskimo mandible. *American Journal of Physical Anthropology* **16**:421–430.
1957   Skeletal pathology of early Indians in Texas. *American Journal of Physical Anthropology* **15**:299–311.

Goodman, A. H., G. J. Armelagos, and J. C. Rose
1980   Enamel hypoplasias as indicators of stress in three prehistoric populations from Illinois. *Human Biology* **52**(3):381–391.

Gunness-Hay, M. E.
1980   Bone mineral and histological variation with age and vertebral pathology in two human skeletal populations. Unpublished Ph.D. thesis, Department of Biobehavioral Sciences, University of Connecticut, Storrs.

Holder, P., and T. D. Stewart
1958   A complete find of filed teeth from Cahokia Mounds in Illinois. *Journal of the Washington Academy of Sciences* **48**:349–357.

Hooton, E. A.
1930   *The Indians of Pecos Pueblo, a study of their skeletal remains. Papers of the Southwestern Expedition,* **4**. New Haven, Connecticut: Yale University Press.

Hrdlička, A.
1899a   Description of an ancient anomalous skeleton from the Valley of Mexico; with special reference to supernumerary and bicipital ribs in man. *Bulletin of the American Museum of History* **12**:81–107.
1899b   An anomalous ulna-supra-capitol foramen, a new joint formation. *American Anthropologist* **1**:248–250.
1899c   A new joint formation. *American anthropologist* **1**:550–551.
1900   *Description de un antiquo esqueleto humano anormal del Valle de Mexico,* Vol. VII. Mexico: Anales del Museo Nacional.
1910   Report on skeletal material from Missouri mounds, collected in 1906–1907 by Mr. Gerand Fowke. *Smithsonian Institution Bureau of American Ethnology Bulletin* **37**:103–319.
1911   *Some results of recent anthropological exploration in Peru. Smithsonian Miscellaneous Collections* **56**(16).
1914   Anthropological work in Peru in 1913, with notes on the pathology of the ancient Peruvians. *Smithsonian Miscellaneous Collections* **61**(18):54–61.
1916   Physical anthropology of the Lenape or Delawares, and of the eastern Indians in general. *Smithsonian Institution Bureau of American Ethnology Bulletin* **62**.
1927   Anthropology and medicine. *American Journal of Physical Anthropology* **10**:1–9.
1935   *Ear exostoses. Smithsonian Miscellaneous Collections* **93**(6).
1939   Trepanation among prehistoric people, especially in America. *Ciba Symposia* **1**:170–200.
1940a   Ritual ablation of front teeth in Siberia and America. *Smithsonian Miscellaneous Collections* **99**(3).

1940b   Mandibular and maxillary hyperostoses. *American Journal of Physical Anthropology* **27**(1):1–67.

1941a   Diseases of and artifacts on skulls and bones from Kodiak Island. *Smithsonian Miscellaneous Collections* **101**(4).

1941b   Lower jaw: Double condyles. *American Journal of Physical Anthropology* **28**(1):75–89.

Janssens, P. A.

1970   *Palaeopathology: diseases and injuries of prehistoric man.* London: John Baker, Ltd.

Jarcho, S. (editor)

1966   *Human palaeopathology.* New Haven, Connecticut: Yale University Press.

Johnson, L. C.

1966   The principles of structural analysis. In *Human palaeopathology*, edited by S. Jarcho. New Haven, Connecticut: Yale University Press. Pp. 68–81.

Jones, J.

1876   Explorations of the aboriginal remains of Tennessee. *Smithsonian Contributions to Knowledge* **22**(259):1–171.

Kavanagh, M.

1979   Strontium in bone as a dietary indicator. Unpublished M.A. thesis, Department of Anthropology, University of Wisconsin, Madison.

Kerley, E. R., and W. M. Bass

1967   Paleopathology: meeting ground for many disciplines. *Science* **157**:638–644.

Lallo, J. W., G. J. Armelagos, and R. P. Mensforth

1977   The role of diet, disease, and physiology in the origin of porotic hyperostosis. *Human Biology* **49**(3):471–483.

Langdon, F. W.

1881   The Madisonville prehistoric cemetery: anthropological notes. *Journal of the Cincinati Society of Natural History* **4**:237–257.

Larsen, C. S.

1980a   Dental caries experimental and biocultural evidence. *Tennessee Anthropological Association, Miscellaneous Papers* **5**:75–80.

1980b   Prehistoric human biological adaptation: case study from the Georgia coast. Unpublished Ph.D. thesis, Department of Anthropology, University of Michigan, Ann Arbor.

Lumholtz, C., and A. Hrdlička

1897   Trephining in Mexico. *American Anthropologist* **1 0**:389–396.

Martin, D. L., and G. J. Armelagos

1979   Morphometrics of compact bone: an example from Sudanese Nubia. *American Journal of Physical Anthropology* **51**:571–578.

Mayer, D.

1854   Ueber Krankhafter knochen vorweltlicher Thiere. *Nova Acta Leopoldina* **24**(2):673–689.

McHenry, H. M.

1968   Transverse lines in long bones of prehistoric California Indians. *American Journal of Physical Anthropology* **29**:1–18.

McHenry, H. M., and P. D. Schulz

1976   The association between Harris lines and enamel hypoplasia in prehistoric California Indians. *American Journal of Physical Anthropology* **44**:477–488.

Means, J. H.

1932   A roentgenological study of the skeletal remains of the prehistoric mound builder Indians of Ohio. *American Journal of Roentgenology* **13**:359–367.

Meigs, J. A.

1857   *Catalogue of human crania in the collection of the Academy of Natural Sciences of Philadelphia.* Philadelphia: Lippincott.

Molnar, S., and S. C. Ward

1975   Mineral metabolism and microstructural defects in primate teeth. *American Journal of Physical Anthropology* **43**:3–18.

Moodie, R. L.

1917   Studies in paleopathology. 1, General consideration of the evidences of pathological conditions found among fossil animals. *Annals of Medical History* **1**:374–393.

1923a   *The antiquity of disease.* Chicago: University of Chicago Press.

1923b   *Paleopathology: an introduction to the study of ancient evidences of disease.* Urbana: University of Illinois Press.

1931   *Roentgenologic studies of Egyptian and Peruvian Mummies. Anthropological Memoirs* **3**. Chicago: Field Museum of Natural History.

Morse, D.
1969   Ancient Disease in the Midwest. *Report of Investigations. Illinois State Museum of Natural History* **15**.

Morton, S. G.
1839   *Crania Americana; or a comparative view of the skulls of various aboriginal nations of North and South America, to which is prefixed an essay on the varieties of the human species.* Philadelphia: Dobson.

1844   *An inquiry into the distinctive characteristics of the aboriginal race of America* (second edition). Philadelphia: John Penington.

Ortner, D. J., and W. G. J. Putschar
1982   *Identification of pathological conditions in human skeletal remains. Smithsonian Contributions to Anthropology* **28**.

Owsley, D. W., and W. M. Bass
1979   A demographic analysis of skeletons from the Larson Site (39WW2) Walworth County, South Dakota: vital statistics. *American Journal of Physical Anthropology* **51**:145–154.

Pales, L.
1930   *Paléopathologie et pathologie comparative.* Paris: Masson.

Palkovich, A. M.
1981   Tuberculosis epidemiology in two Arikara skeletal samples: A study of disease impact. in *Prehistoric tuberculosis in the Americas,* edited by J. Buikstra. Evanston, Illinois: Northwestern University Archeological Program. Pp. 161–175.

Perzigian, A. J.
1977   Fluctuating dental asymmetry: Variation among skeletal populations. *American Journal of Physical Anthropology* **47**:81–88.

Putnam, F. W.
1878   Archaeological explorations in Tennessee. *Report of the Peabody Museum* **2**:305–360.

1884   Abnormal human skull from stone graves in Tennessee. *Proceedings of the American Association for the Advancement of Science* **32**:390–392.

Putschar, W. G. J.
1966   Problems in the pathology and palaeopathology of bone. In *Human paleopathology,* edited by S. Jarcho. New Haven, Connecticut: Yale University Press. Pp. 57–65.

Rathbun, T. A., J. Sexton, and J. Michie
1980   Disease patterns in a formative period South Carolina coastal population. *Tennessee Anthropological Association, Miscellaneous Papers* **5**:52–74.

Richman, E. A., D. J. Ortner, and F. P. Schulter-Ellis
1979   Differences in intracortical bone remodeling in three aboriginal American populations: Possible dietary factors. *Calcified Tissue International* **28**:209–214.

Roney, J. G.
1959   Palaeopathology of a California archaeological site. *Bulletin of the History of Medicine* **33**(2):97–109.

Rose, J. C.
1977   Defective enamel histology of prehistoric teeth from Illinois. *American Journal of Physical Anthropology* **46**:439–446.

1979   Morphological variations of enamel prisms within abnormal striae of Retzius. *Human Biology* **51**:139–151.

Rose, J. C., G. J. Armelagos, and J. W. Lallo

1978   Histological enamel indicator of childhood stress in prehistoric skeletal samples. *American Journal of Physical Anthropology* **49**:511–516.

Ruffer, M. A.
1910   Note on the presence of "Bilharzia haematobia" in Egyptian mummies of the twentieth dynasty. *British Medical Journal* **1**:16.
1914   Studies in palaeopathology, note on the diseases of the Sudan and Nubia in ancient times. *Mitteillungen zur Geschichte der Medizin und der Naturwissenschaften* **13**:453–460.
1920   Study of Abnormalities and pathology of ancient Egyptian teeth. *American Journal of Physical Anthropology* **3**:335–382.

Ruschenberger, W. S. W.
1892   A sketch of the life of Joseph Leidy, M.D., L.L.D. *Proceedings, American Philosophical Society* **XXX**:135–184.

Saul, F. B.
1972   *The human skeletal remains of Altar de Sacrificios, an osteobiographic analysis. Papers of the Peabody Museum* **63**.

Schmerling, P. C.
1835   Description des ossemens fossiles, a l'état pathologique, provenant des cavernes de la province de Liège. *Bulletin de la Societe Geologique de France* **7**:51–61.

Schoeninger, M. J.
1979   *Dietary reconstruction at Chalcatzingo, a formative period site in Morelos, Mexico. Technical Report* **9**. Museum of Anthropology, University of Michigan, Ann Arbor.

Sciulli, P. W.
1978   Developmental abnormalities of the permanent dentition in prehistoric Ohio Valley Amerindians. *American Journal of Physical Anthropology* **48**:193–198.

Sillen, A.
1981   Strontium and diet at Hayonim Cave, Israel, an evaluation of the strontium/calcium technique for investigating prehistoric diets. Unpublished Ph.D. thesis, Department of Anthropology, University of Pennsylvania, Philadelphia.

Steinbock, R. T.
1976   *Paleopathological diagnosis and interpretation.* Springfield, Illinois: Thomas.

Stewart, T. D.
1931   Dental caries in Peruvian skulls. *American Journal of Physical Anthropology* **15**:315–326.
1935   Spondylolisthesis without separate neural arch (Pseudospondylolisthesis of Junghanns). *Journal of Bone and Joint Surgery* **17**(3):640–648.
1942   Persistence of the African type of tooth pointing in Panama. *American Anthropologist* **44**(2):328–330.
1944   Filed Indian teeth from Illinois. *Journal of the Washington Academy of Sciences* **34**(10):317–321.
1966   Some problems in human palaeopathology. In *Human palaeopathology*, edited by S. Jarcho. New Haven, Connecticut: Yale University Press. Pp. 43–55.
1974   Nonunion of fractures in antiquity, with descriptions of five cases from the New World involving the forearm. *Bulletin of the New York Academy of Medicine* **50**(8):875–891.
1976   Are supra-inion depressions evidence of prophylactic trephination? *Bulletin of the History of Medicine* **50**:414–434.

Stewart, T. D., and J. R. Groome
1968   The African custom of tooth mutilation in America. *American Journal of Physical Anthropology* **28**(1):31–41.

Stewart, T. D., and L. G. Quade
1969   Lesions of the frontal bone in American Indians. *American Journal of Physical Anthropology* **30**:89–110.

Stewart, T. D., and A. Spoehr
1952   Evidence on the paleopathology of yaws. *Bulletin of the History of Medicine* **26**(6):538–553.

Stewart, T. D., and P. F. Titterington

1946   More filed Indian teeth from the United States. *Journal of the Washington Academy of Sciences* **36**(8):259–261.

Stothers, D. M., and J. F. Metress
1976   A system for the description and analysis of pathological changes in prehistoric skeletons. *Ossa* **2**(1):3–10.

Stout, S., and D. J. Simmons
1979   Use of histology in ancient bone research. *Yearbook of Physical Anthropology* **22**:228–249.

Thompson, D. D.
1978   Age related changes in osteon remodeling and bone mineralization. Unpublished Ph.D. thesis, Department of Anthropology, University of Connecticut, Storrs.
1980   Age changes in bone mineralization, cortical thickness, and Haversion canal area. *Calcified Tissue International* **31**:5–11.

Ubelaker, D. H.
1978   Microscopic analysis of archaeological bone. *Report of Investigations. Illinois State Museum of Natural History* **15**:66–72.
1980a   Human remains from site OGSE-80, a preceramic site on the Sta. Elena Peninsula, coastal Ecuador. *Journal of the Washington Academy of Sciences* **70**(1):3–24.
1980b   Prehistoric human remains from the Cotocollao Site, Pichincha Province, Ecuador. *Journal of the Washington Academy of Sciences* **70**(2):59–74.
1981   *The Ayalán Cemetery: a late Integration period burial site on the south coast of Ecuador. Smithsonian Contributions to Anthropology* **29**.

Van der Merwe, N. J.
1978   Carbon 12 vs Carbon 13. *Early Man* **2**:11–13.

Vogel, J. C., and N. J. Van der Merwe
1977   Isotopic evidence for early Maize cultivation in New York State. *American Antiquity* **42**:238–242.

Warren, J. C.
1822   Account of the crania of some of the aborigines of the United States. In: *A comparative view of the sensorial and nervous systems in men and animals.* Boston: Ingraham, Pp. 129–144.
1838   North American antiquities. *American Journal of Science and Arts* **34**:47–49.

Weinstein, R. S., D. J. Simmons, and C. O. Lovejoy
1981   Ancient bone disease in a Peruvian mummy revealed by quantitative skeletal histomorphometry. *American Journal of Physical Anthropology* **54**:321–326.

Wells, C.
1964   *Bones, bodies and disease, evidence of disease and abnormality in early man.* London: Thames and Hudson.

Whitney, W. F.
1883   On the existence of syphilis in America before the discovery by Columbus. *Boston Medical and Surgical Journal* **108**:365–366.
1886   Notes on the anomalies, injuries, and diseases of the bones of the native peoples of North America contained in the osteological collection of the museum. *Annual Report of the Peabody Museum* **3**:433–448.

Williams, H. U.
1929   Human paleopathology, with some original observations on symmetrical osteoporosis of the skull. *Archives of Pathology* **7**:839–902.

Wyman, J.
1868   *Observations on crania.* Boston: A. A. Kingman.

Zimmerman, M. R.
1979   Paleopathologic diagnosis based on experimental mummification. *American Journal of Physical Anthropology* **51**:235–254.

15

Forensic Anthropology

David D. Thompson

> Forensic anthropology is that branch of physical anthropology
> which, for forensic purposes deals with the identification of more or
> less skeletonized remains known to be, or suspected of being,
> human.
>
> T. D. Stewart 1979

Forensic anthropology has its roots in the medical sciences, principally anatomical sciences. Methods used in the identification of human skeletal remains
were derived largely from the analysis of anatomy school cadavers whose age, sex,
race, and morbidity are known. If we use 1930 as a starting point for the historical
treatment of forensic anthropology, we place it within the period of time when
anatomy departments were (a) the principal contributors to methodology and (b)
the major training centers for the study of human skeletal variation, using skeletal
series with documented ages, sex, and race. Exceptions to this were the individual
departments of anthropology at Harvard University (the Peabody Museum), the
Smithsonian Insitution, and the American Museum of Natural History (AMNH)
where Earnest A. Hooton, Aleš Hrdlička, and Harry L. Shapiro, respectively, were
interested in applied forensic aspects of physical anthropology but were rarely
called on for assistance in medicolegal identification of human skeletal remains.

Three periods can be delineated within the time span of 1930–1980: (a) pre-
1939, (b) 1939–1972, and (c) 1972–1980.

The publication in 1939 of the "Guide to the Identification of Human Skeletal
Material" by W. M. Krogman in the *FBI Law Enforcement Bulletin* signified the first
contribution to forensic anthropology by a trained anthropologist on the topic of
the identification of human skeletal remains with medicolegal objectives. Prior to
this publication, two of the most prominent American physical anthropologists,
Hrdlička of the Smithsonian and Hooton of Harvard University, involved themselves in a small number of forensic cases, but only Hooton (1934) published an
article documenting the role of physical anthropology in the identification of

skeletal remains. Therein, he described his limited role and the future prospects for physical anthropologists in the forensic field:

> The present writer, who has been in charge of a well equipped laboratory of physical anthropology for nearly thirty years, has not been called upon to assist the police in personal identification problems more than a dozen times. Since the experience of other physical anthropologists is probably similar, it can be seen that there has been little practical incentive for the developing of new methods of approach [Hooton 1943:1619].

Later, Hooton (1946) in his book *Up from the Ape* provided an appendix documenting methods used in determining age, sex, race, and stature, but he did not describe this system as having direct medicolegal implications.

Pre-1939

Contributions of Anatomy Departments

The principal contributors to the field of forensic anthropology during this period were not anthropologists, but anatomists. The goal of anatomical research during this time was not the identification of human skeletal remains, but rather the documentation and description of basic age, sex, and racial skeletal differences.[1] It was with Krogman's (1939) "Guide" that the methods of determining age, sex, and race could be practically applied to human identification. The significance of the contributions of the anatomists in documenting age, sex, and race differences is attested to by the fact that the data, the methodologies, and the skeletons used for training students and conducting research are still used today for identification and are standards by which to compare new methods and techniques.

Two centers of anatomy in the United States can be identified as leaders in basic research on human skeletal differences that has resulted in methods used in human identification: Case Western Reserve University in Cleveland, Ohio, and Washington University in St. Louis, Missouri. At Case Western Reserve University, research on skeletal differences was initiated by Carl August Hamann, a physician who arrived in Cleveland in 1893 and assumed the position of Professor of Anatomy. From the outset of his appointment at Case Western, Hamann was involved in establishing skeletal collections from dissecting room populations. This collection of skeletons of known age, sex, and race grew to more than 100 skeletons before Hamann's promotion to Dean of the Medical School in 1912. The successor

---

[1]One of the first such collections in the United States was made by George S. Huntington at the College of Physicians and Surgeons, Columbia University, New York. This collection was initially cataloged and organized by Aleš Hrdlička at the turn of the century (e.g., Hrdlička 1937). Hrdlička (1900) had rather specific ideas on the arrangement and preservation of osteological material. His system of organization later became the model for a number of osteological collections, such as those at Case Western Reserve and Washington (St. Louis) universities.

to Hamann in the Chair of Anatomy was T. Wingate Todd, who continued the collection of cadaveral skeletons and initiated basic research on all aspects of skeletal biology. With each skeleton included in Todd's collection, a detailed file was assembled, including photographs of the undissected cadaver, anthroposcopic observations, 86 anthropometric measurements, hair samples, skin samples, and personal data on each cadaver including age, sex, race, place of birth, occupation, and cause of death (Cobb 1959). During Todd's tenure at Case Western, he assembled a collection of skeletons greater than 3300 individuals. From this collection alone, numerous reports were published describing age, sex, and racial differences and formulae for the reconstruction of stature. Todd's standards for the determination of age at death by the degree of remodeling on the faces of the pubic symphyses (Todd 1920, 1921) are still widely used by forensic anthropologists. Furthermore, the standards for the determination of age at death by the degree of cranial suture closure (Todd and Lyon 1925) also are used as general age indicators by contemporary anthropologists.

Individuals who were trained by, worked with, or succeeded Todd at Case Western and who were to become major figures in the field of human identification include Wilton M. Krogman, W. W. Graves, W. Montague Cobb, C. C. Francis, S. I. Pyle, and W. W. Greulich. Todd's association and interest in physical anthropology is further demonstrated by his active participation in the affairs of the newly formed American Association of Physical Anthropologists (AAPA). Besides being a charter member, he also served briefly as the association's president (in 1938). Unfortunately, eight months after assuming this office he died, at 53 years of age. The Todd collection of skeletons, now housed in the Cleveland Museum of Natural History, continues to serve as a basic resource for teaching and research in the field of forensic anthropology and the study of human skeletal variation in general.

As mentioned, the second anatomy center in the United States to have a significant impact on the development of forensic anthropology over the past 50 years was the Department of Anatomy at Washington University in St. Louis headed by Robert J. Terry (from 1900–1941) and later by Mildred Trotter. During the period 1914–1965, 1636 skeletons with documented age, sex, and race were assembled by Terry and his colleagues. Figuring prominently in the collection of these skeletons and carrying out research in forensic aspects of them was Mildred Trotter. The collection of skeletons, how housed at the United States National Museum (USNM) of Natural History, Smithsonian Institution, continues to be a primary training and research collection for forensic anthropologists. Like Todd, Terry was a charter member and an active participant in the AAPA, serving as president from 1939 to 1941.

Methodological Advances

The basic research conducted on the Terry and Todd collections was in the area of age changes and sex and race differences. Additionally, an important aspect of these researches was the delineation of the limitations of the methods applied in skeletal identification and the inherent variability of human skeletal morphology.

Krogman (1935), working in Todd's laboratory, describes in detail procedures used in the identification of two human skeletons found buried in "Indian mounds" but associated with nails and wood fragments, which suggested to Krogman the existence of coffins. Although not of immediate interest to law enforcement authorities, the report does illustrate one approach used by forensic anthropologists in identifying human skeletal remains. The methods used by Krogman to reconstruct the age, sex, and race of the two skeletons provide an excellent synthesis of the field of forensic anthropology in 1935.

The radiographic study of bones in the living was also used to generate standards of growth, sexing, and racial identification to supplement the research performed on the cadaveral skeletons. The representation of young adults and children is low in cadaveral populations: thus, the utilization of x-ray standards for age changes and sex and race differences in this end of the age range provided standards for the entire age range. As Krogman stated:

> It is a fact to be noted that much of the data we use for age, for sex, for race in the bone were collected without medico-legal objectives firmly in view. For the most part, we must rely upon the studies of extensive dissecting-room populations which are notoriously biased samples of the total population [Krogman 1962:4].

Studies utilizing x-rays for the purposes of assessing patterns of epiphyseal appearance and closure—without medicolegal objectives in mind, but having applications in identification—included Davies and Parsons (1927); Flecker (1932–1933); Pryor (1925, 1928); and Stevenson (1924). Hodges (1933) published a comprehensive chart on epiphyseal appearance and closure based on x-rays. Todd (1930a, 1930b) was aware of the importance of radiography and used it to expand his knowledge of skeletal development and aging and to identify sex and race differences in the skeleton. Francis and Werle (1939) and Francis (1940) published a definitive work on the appearance of ossification centers from birth to 5 years of age and from 6 to 15 years of age, respectively. These standards are still used today in the identification of skeletal remains. Hill (1939), working in Todd's laboratory, described the sequence of the appearance of ossification centers in fetuses.

1939–1972

In 1939, when W. M. Krogman's "Guide" was published in the *FBI Law Enforcement Bulletin*, it was the first publication to synthesize the many sources of data on the determination of age at death, sex, race, stature, and other features useful in identifying a skeleton. It is with the publication of this paper that forensic anthropology became associated with the medicolegal identification of human skeletal remains.

World War II

With the close of World War II and the need to identify the war dead, physical anthropologists with training in identification methods were called into action. Krogman's "Guide" became a working manual for anthropologists involved in the identification process. European forensic scientists were responsible for the identification of the war dead in Europe (Simonin 1948). Shapiro, of the AMNH, acted as consultant for this program. The Pacific identification or repartriation program directly involved American physical anthropologists in the identification of the war dead.

A central identification laboratory was established in 1947 in Hawaii to facilitate identification of the American war dead with Charles C. Snow of the University of Kentucky as the chief physical anthropologist. In 1948, Mildred Trotter of the Department of Anatomy, Washington University, succeeded Snow in the Hawiian laboratory. While working there, Trotter secured long-bone measurements from the war dead skeletons that resulted in new regression equations for the estimation of stature (Trotter and Gleser 1952). These new equations promptly replaced the equations generated by Pearson (1899), based on Rollet's measurements on 100 French cadavers.

In 1948, a symposium on applied physical anthropology was held as part of the program of the annual meeting of the AAPA; F. E. Randall served as chairman, and E. A. Hooton as the discussion leader. The first four papers read at this symposium concerned medicolegal applications (see *Proceedings of the American Association of Physical Anthropologists*, Vol. 6, No. 2, 1948, pp. 227–258): T. D. Stewart, "Medico-Legal Aspects of the Skeleton: I. Sex, Age, Race and Stature"; W. M. Krogman, "Medico-Legal Aspects of the Skeleton: II. Related Factors, as a Condition of Interment, Action of Fire, Reconstruction, etc."; H. L. Shapiro, "Anthropology in the U.S. Army Reburial Program"; and Charles C. Snow, "The Processing of the Pacific Unknown War Dead."

Krogman (1943) published a second report in the *FBI Law Enforcement Bulletin* in which he described the procedures used in identifying two forensic skeletons. This report is an extension of his 1939 report in the same publication, in that the two reports are to be used together: the first as a description of the methodology, and the second as, an application of the methodology.

Korean Conflict

The Korean conflict, ending in July, 1953, marked the second major anthropological involvement in the identification of war dead. The Memorial Division of the Office of the Quartermaster General enlisted the cooperation of Stewart of the Smithsonian Institution to undertake an investigation of skeletal age changes in the American war dead. Working on the actual identification of the dead in the laboratories in Kokura, Japan were two additional physical anthropologists, Ellis R.

Kerley and Charles C. Warren. Stewart's involvement with identification of skeletal remains for the FBI and the United States Government had begun in 1942 (Stewart 1979). During the 5 months he spent in Japan, Stewart analyzed 450 skeletons, 375 of which were positively identified. Changes in several skeletal features were noted, including cranial suture closure, eruption of third molars, epiphyseal closure, metamorphosis of the pubic symphses, and osteophytosis of the joints. Publications derived from this investigation appeared under the authorship of McKern and Stewart (1957).

The noteworthy importance of this work in the development of forensic anthropology is well known. The precise quantification of age changes in skeletons with known age, sex, race, and stature was performed by a single physical anthropologist. Unlike studies that utilized cadavers from aged individuals, and individuals who suffered from nutritional deprivation and disease conditions, the sample of war dead represented a healthy, well-fed population meeting sudden death. One of the features of the final report was a new method of estimating age at death from pubic symphyseal face changes. This method of age estimation divides the face of the pubic symphysis into three components, the combined score from which yields the estimated age at death. Finally, a most important outcome of this research was the documentation of variability of age changes in various parts of the skeletons and between individuals of the same age. The range of variation in patterns of aging between age-matched individuals provided the limitations and probable errors of the methods used by forensic anthropologists.

Textbooks in forensic medicine and forensic scientists in general acknowledged the importance of forensic anthropology in the identification of human remains. Gradwohl's 1954 edition of *Legal Medicine* included a chapter written by Stewart, "Identification of the Skeletal Structures."

Krogman, one of the leading forensic anthropologists, wrote the first major textbook in the field of forensic anthropology. The book, *The Human Skeleton in Forensic Medicine* (1962), was "The result of some 30 years experience, not only with human skeletal material, but with the identification of unknown bones. The theme of intrinsic variability and its range has been a major concern during all this time [Krogman 1962:vii]." Krogman's text is a compilation of methods, techniques, and case examples used in the medicolegal identification of human skeletal remains. The text summarizes methods for the determination of age, sex, race, stature, individuating characteristics, and restoration of facial features from the skull.

In 1955, the Wenner-Gren Foundation for Anthropological Research sponsored a seminar on "The Role of Physical Anthropology in the Field of Human Identification," which brought together experts in the field of forensic anthropology. A summary of the seminar has been reported by Stewart and Trotter (1955). The seminar was organized around five topics, with each topic receiving a half-day of discussion. The topics and chairpersons included in the seminar were (a) "Qualifications for Identification Specialists," W. M. Krogman; (b) "Identification of Small Remnants of the Human Body," W. S. Laughlin; (c) "Sex and age," J.

L. Angel and T. D. Stewart; (*d*) Stature, Body Build, and Facial Features," Mildred Trotter; and (*e*) "Educational and Administrative Aspects," T. D. McCown.

Vietnam Conflict

The Vietnam conflict of the 1960s and early 1970s again required the services of forensic anthropologists for the identification of skeletal remains. The United States Army maintained the Mortuary Central Identification Laboratory in Saigon, the purpose of which was the identification of the war dead. As part of its need to maintain an up-to-date knowledge of the identification procedures used by forensic anthropologists, the United States Army funded a symposium that was organized by Stewart at the Smithsonian in December, 1968, to bring together experts in the field of identification (Stewart 1970). Forensic anthropologists participating as faculty members in the symposium included Thomas McKern, "Estimation of Skeletal Age: From Puberty to about 30 Years of Age"; Ellis R. Kerley, "Estimation of Skeletal Age: After about 30"; Mildred Trotter, "Estimation of Stature from Intact Long Limb Bones"; D. Gentry Steele, "Estimation of Stature from Fragments of Long Limb Bones"; E. Giles, "Discriminant Function Sexing of the Human Skeleton; W. W. Howells, "Multivariate Analysis for the Identification of Race from Crania"; and T. D. Stewart, "Identification of Scars of Parturition in the Skeletal Remains of Females". Stewart described the role of the United States Army in the development of forensic anthropology: "The remarkable developments since 1939 outlined in the foregoing were stimulated and made possible mainly by the U.S. Army through its repatriation and reburial programs abroad [1979:17]."

Methodological Advances

The standards of cranial suture closure developed by Todd and Lyons (1925), and summarized by Krogman (1939), were deemed by Singer (1953) to be inappropriate for accurate age estimation for medicolegal purposes. Brooks (1955) arrived at the same conclusion. She also tested the accuracy of the Todd system of age estimation by morphological changes in the pubic symphyseal face. Her results from the analysis of male pubic symphyseal faces showed a high correlation with known age in males, whereas her analysis of females showed a lower coefficient of correlation. Brooks's sample was, in part, the cadaveral skeletons collected by Todd.

Trotter and Gleser (1952) generated regression equations for stature reconstruction of skeletal remains based on Trotter's measurements, which were taken from the skeletons of World War II American soldiers killed in the Pacific. They next generated stature-estimating regression equations based on the long-bone measurements obtained in the laboratory in Japan on the Korean war dead (Trotter and Gleser 1958). This study also included stature-reconstruction regression equations for Mexicans and Mongoloids, in addition to the recalculation of equations for Blacks and Whites.

The accurate determination of sex in human skeletal material was the objective of much research during this period. Stewart (1948, 1951) reported that he could achieve an accuracy of 90–95% when an entire skeleton was present. Krogman (1962) reported a sexing accuracy of 100% with a complete, dissecting-room skeleton and 95% if only the pelvis was used. Thieme and Schull (1957; Thieme 1957) reported an accuracy in excess of 95% using measurements on the femur, humerus, clavicle, and innominate from skeletons contained in the Terry collection. The study by Thieme and Schull (1957) applied discriminant function analysis to certain anthropometric data to ascertain the sex of the skeleton. With the application of discriminant function analysis to the determination of sex based on equations generated in a series of known sex, the probability of correct sex assignment in an unknown skeleton from the same population could be determined. Hanihara (1958, 1959), Howells (1970), Giles and Elliot (1963), and Giles (1970) expanded the application of discriminant function analysis to include race determination as well. Phenice (1969) described a method for sexing skeletal material based on nonmetric differences in the pubic bone.

The use of multivariate statistics became an important tool for the determination of age, sex, race, and stature. Giles and Elliot (1963), Hanihara (1958, 1959), and Hanihara *et al.* (1964) have provided discriminant function equations for the determination of sex from long bones, crania, mandibles, and innominates. The reliability of the sex determinations for these equations is generally in the 80–90% range. The accuracy of the results, however, may depend upon the population from which the skeleton was obtained. On this point, Giles and Elliot stated,

> Estimates of the reliability of the technique have been calculated, and tests made on chimpanzee, early Irish, and American Indian crania to determine the possibility of extending the results to other groups. It was found that the discriminatory power held up, but the male–female point in some cases may need to be adjusted to the population at hand [1963:67].

Howells (1970) provided discriminant function equations for the determination of race from skeletons, and Trotter and Gleser (1958) generated multiple regression equations for stature reconstruction in skeletons. Kerley (1965) generated multiple regression equations for the determination of age in skeletons.

Kerley's (1965) method for estimating age at death in skeletons from the quantification of cortical bone microstructure permitted age determination for skeletal remains that were fragmentary or incomplete, conditions often encountered in forensic identification of skeletal remains. Kerley's method used thin sections of cortical bone from the midshaft of the femur, tibia, or fibula. Standard error ranged from 3.66 to 14.62 years, depending on the variable used for age estimation (Kerley and Ubelaker 1978). The four cortical bone microstructural variables quantified by Kerley were (*a*) secondary osteons, (*b*) osteon fragments, (*c*) primary osteons, and (*d*) circumferential lamellar bone. Ahlqvist and Damsten

(1969) modified the Kerley method by using a grid system for the quantification of cortical bone microstructures. Later, Thompson (1978, 1979) proposed a revised method of cortical bone microstructures age estimation by using a core of bone taken from the anterior midshaft of the femur or tibia and employing stereological methods of microscopic quantification. Complete cross sections of bone were required for age estimations by Kerley's and Ahlqvist and Damsten's methods, whereas Thompson's method required only a small core of bone, thus leaving the bone itself intact. Gustafson (1966) and Moorrees *et al.* (1963) proposed methods of determining age at death using teeth. Significant improvements in reconstructing facial features from skulls have been made by Snow *et al.* (1970).

1972–1980

American Academy of Forensic Sciences

As the country's leading body of forensic scientists, the American Academy of Forensic Sciences is subdivided into various sections, including Criminalistics, Jurisprudence, Pathology–Biology, Psychiatry, Questioned Documents, Toxicology, and Odontology. Prior to 1972, forensic anthropologists were members of the Pathology–Biology section. The official publication of the American Academy of Forensic Sciences, the *Journal of Forensic Sciences*, was first published in 1956 and since, numerous articles on forensic anthropology have appeared in it. In 1972, with a roster of 14 members, the Forensic Anthropology Section was established. The formal recognition of this section within the Academy of Forensic Sciences has increased awareness within the field of forensics of the role of forensic anthropologists in the identification of skeletal remains. The membership of the Forensic Anthropology section has grown from 14 members in 1972 to 37 members in 1980.[2]

In 1978 the American Board of Forensic Anthropology was created to certify forensic anthropologists. As of 1980, 19 members of the American Academy of Forensic Sciences were certified as Diplomates of the American Board of Forensic Anthropology.[3]

The number of textbooks in forensic anthropology increased in the 1970s: W. M. Krogman's (1962 [reprinted in 1973 and 1978]); T. D. Stewart's *Essentials of Forensic Anthropology: Especially as Developed in the United States* (1979); and M. Y. El-Najjar and K. R. McWilliams's *Forensic Anthropology: The Structure, Morphology and Variation of Human Bone and Dentition* (1978). Stewart (1979) was the first to include a chapter describing the legal and courtroom procedures associated with giving expert witness testimony.

[2]See the *American Academy of Forensic Sciences Membership Directory,* 1979–1980.

[3]See the *American Academy of Forensic Sciences Membership Directory,* 1979–1980.

Methodological Advances

Methodological advances made during this period have been summarized by Bass (1979). Gilbert and McKern (1973) have described standards for the estimation of age at death in females by pubic symphyseal face remodeling. The problems and limitations of the Gilbert–McKern system of age determination have been defined by Suchey *et al.* (1980). There have also been improvements in the methods for determination of age at death by tooth morphology and composition (Burns and Maples 1976) and by cortical bone microstructures (Thompson 1979). Methods for removing forensic skeletons from sites of discovery were reported by Morse *et al.* (1976).

The United States National Museum of Natural History, the Smithsonian Institution has continued its role as the principal center for forensic anthropology, identifying human remains for local, state, and federal governmental agencies, most notably the FBI. This work was initiated by Hrdlička, continued, but in an expanded capacity by T. D. Stewart, and maintained at this level by J. Lawrence Angel and D. H. Ubelaker.

With the recognition accompanying forensic anthropology's membership in the Academy of Forensic Sciences and improved methods in accurate identification of skeletal remains came cooperative research with other disciplines in the forensic sciences—medical examiners and odontologists. Rhine and Campbell (1980), Suchey *et al.* (1979, 1980), and Thompson and Galvin (1981) show the benefit of mutual research ventures between forensic anthropologists and other forensic scientists and the improved methods that have resulted. The need for establishing new improved methods for identification requires validation in a skeletal series of known age, sex, race, and morbidity. This fact has been recognized, because the work of Todd and Terry continues today with the cooperation of medical examiners and pathologists in joint research.

References

Ahlqvist, A. R, and O. Damsten
   1969   A modification of Kerley's method for microscopic determination of age in human bone. *Journal of Forensic Science* **14**:205–212.
Bass, W. M.
   1979   Developments in the identification of human skeletal material (1968–1978). *American Journal of Physical Anthropology* **51**:555–562.
Brooks, S. T.
   1955   Skeletal age at death: the reliability of cranial and pubic age indicators. *American Journal of Physical Anthropology* **13**:567–597.
Burns, K. R., and W. R. Maples
   1976   Estimation of age from individual adult teeth. *Journal of Forensic Science* **21**:343–356.
Cobb, W. M.
   1959   Thomas Wingate Todd. *Journal of the National Medical Association* **51**:233–246.
Davies, D. A., and F. G. Parsons

1927   The age order of the appearance and union of normal epiphyses as seen by x-rays. *Journal of Anatomy* **62**:58–71.

El-Najjar, M. Y., and K. R. McWilliams
1978   *Forensic anthropology: The structure, morphology, and variation of human bone and dentition.* Springfield, Illinois: Thomas.

Flecker, H.
1932–   Roentgenographic observations of the times of appearance of epiphyses and their fusion
1933   with diaphyses. *Journal of Anatomy* **67**:118–164.

Francis, C. C.
1940   The appearance of centers of ossification from 6 to 15 years. *American Journal of Physical Anthropology* **21**:127–138.

Francis, C. C., P. P. Werle, and R. Behm
1939   The appearance of centers of ossification from birth to five years. *American Journal of Physical Anthropology* **24**:273–299.

Gilbert, B. M., and T. W. McKern
1973   A method for aging the female *os pubis*. *American Journal of Physical Anthropology* **38**:31–38.

Giles, E.
1970   Discriminant function sexing of the human skeleton. In *Personal identification in mass disasters*, edited by T. D. Stewart. Washington, D.C.: National Museum of Natural History, Smithsonian Institution. Pp. 99–109.

Giles, E., and O. Elliot
1963   Sex determination by discriminant function analysis of crania. *American Journal of Physical Anthropology* **21**:53–68.

Gradwohl, R. H. B.
1954   *Legal medicine.* St. Louis, Missouri: Mosby.

Gustafson, G.
1966   *Forensic odontology.* New York: American Elsevier.

Hanihara, K.
1958   Sexual diagnosis of Japanese long bones by means of discriminant function. *Journal of the Anthropological Society of Nippon* **66**:187–196 (In Japanese, with English summary).

1959   Sex diagnosis of Japanese skulls and scapular by means of discriminant functions. *Journal of the Anthropological Society of Nippon* **67**:191–197 (in Japanese, with English summary).

Hanihara, K., K. Kimura, and T. Minamidate
1964   The sexing of Japanese skeletons by means of discriminant function. *Japanese Journal of Legal Medicine* **18**:107–114 (in Japanese, with English summary).

Hill, A. H.
1939   Fetal age assessment by centers of ossification. *American Journal of Physical Anthropology* **24**:251–272.

Hodges, P. C.
1933   An epiphyseal chart. *American Journal of Roentgenology and Radium Therapy* **30**:809–810.

Hooton, E. A.
1943   Medico-legal aspects of physical anthropology. *Clinics* **1**:1612–1624.
1946   *Up from the ape.* New York: Macmillan.

Howells, W. W.
1970   Multivariate analysis for the identification of race from crania. In *Personal identification in mass disasters*, edited by T. D. Stewart. Washington, D.C.: National Museum of Natural History, Smithsonian Institution. Pp. 111–122.

Hrdlička, A.
1900   Arrangement and preservation of large collections of human bones for purposes of investigation. *American Naturalist* **24**:9–15.

Hrdlička, A.
1937   Biographical memoir of George Sumner Huntington, 1861–1927. Biographical Memoirs. National Academy of Sciences. **18**:245–284.

Kerley, F. R.
    1965   The microscopic determination of age in human bone. *American Journal of Physical Anthropology* **23**:149–163.
Kerley, E. R., and D. H. Ubelaker
    1978   Revisions in the microscopic method of estimating age at death in human cortical bone. *American Journal of Physical Anthropology* **49**:545–546.
Krogman, W. M.
    1935   Life histories recorded in skeletons. *American Anthropologist* **37**:92–103.
    1939   A guide to the identification of human skeletal material. *FBI Law Enforcement Bulletin* **3**:3–31.
    1943   Role of the physical anthropologist in the identification of human skeletal remains. *FBI Law Enforcement Bulletin* **12**(4–5):17–40, 12–28.
    1962   *The human skeleton in forensic medicine.* Springfield, Illinois: Thomas.
McKern, T. W., and T. D. Stewart
    1957   Skeletal age changes in young American males, analyzed from the standpoint of identification (Technical Report EP-45). Headquarters Quartermaster Research and Development Command, United States Army, Natick, Massachusetts.
Moorrees, C. F. A., E. A. Fanning, and E. E. Hunt, Jr.
    1963   Formation and resorption of three deciduous teeth in children. *American Journal of Physical Anthropology* **21**:205–213.
Morse, D., D. Crusoe, and N. G. Smith
    1976   Forensic archaeology. *Journal of Forensic Science* **21**:323–332.
Pearson, K.
    1899   Mathematical contributions to the theory of evolution: on the reconstruction of the structure of prehistoric races. *Philosophical Transactions of the Royal Society of London, Series A* **192**:169–244.
Phenice, T. W.
    1969   A newly developed visual method of sexing the *os pubis. American Journal of Physical Anthropology* **30**:297–301.
Pryor, J. W.
    1925   Time of ossification of the bones of the hand of the male and female and union of epiphyses with the diaphyses. *American Journal of Physical Anthropology* **8**:401–410.
    1928   Differences in the ossification of the male and female skeleton. *Journal of Anatomy* **62**:499–506.
Rhine, J. S., and H. R. Campbell
    1980   Thickness of facial tissues in American Blacks. *Journal of Forensic Science* **25**:847–858.
Simonin, C.
    1948   Identification des corps des soldats Americains inconnus. *Acta Medicinae Legalis et Socialis* **1**:382–386.
Singer, R.
    1953   Estimation of age from cranial suture closure. *Journal of Forensic Medicine* **1**:52–59.
Snow, C. C., B. P. Gatliff, and K. R. McWilliams
    1970   Reconstruction of facial features from the skull: an evaluation of its usefulness in forensic anthropology. *American Journal of Physical Anthropology* **33**:221–227.
Stevenson, P. H.
    1934   Age order of epiphyseal union in man. *American Journal of Physical Anthropology* **7**:53–93.
Stewart, T. D.
    1948   Medico-legal aspects of the skeleton. I. Sex, age, race and stature. *American Journal of Physical Anthropology* **6**:315–322.
    1951   What the bones tell. *FBI Law Enforcement Bulletin* **20**:2–5,19.
Stewart, T. D. (editor)
    1970   *Personal identification in mass disasters.* Washington, D.C.: National Museum of Natural History, Smithsonian Institution.
Stewart, T. D.

1979   *Essentials of forensic anthropology, especially as developed in the United States.* Springfield, Illinois: Thomas.

Stewart, T. D., and M. Trotter
1955   The role of physical anthropology in the field of human identification. *Science* **122**:883–884.

Suchey, J. M., D. V. Wiseley, R. F. Green, and T. T. Noguchi
1979   Analysis of dorsal pitting in the *os pubis* in an extensive sample of modern American females. *American Journal of Physical Anthropology* **51**:517–540.

Suchey, J. M., D. V. Wisely, and T. T. Noguchi
1980   Aging the male *os pubis.* Paper presented to the 32nd Annual Meeting of the American Academy of Forensic Sciences, New Orleans, February.

Thieme, F. P.
1957   Sex in Negro skeletons. *Journal of Forensic Medicine* **4**:72–81.

Thieme, F. P., and W. J. Schull
1957   Sex determination from the skeleton. *Human Biology* **29**:242–273.

Thompson, D. D.
1973   Age-related changes in osteon remodeling and bone mineralization., Unpublished Ph.D. dissertation, Department of Biobehavioral Sciences, University of Connecticut, Storrs.
1979   The core technique in the determination of age at death in skeletons. *Journal of Forensic Science* **24**:902–915.

Thompson, D. D., and C. Galvin
1981   Osteon remodeling in a forensic autopsy series. Paper presented at the 33rd Annual Meeting of the American Academy of Forensic Sciences, Los Angeles, February.

Todd, T. W.
1920   Age changes in the pubic bone. I. The male White pubis. *American Journal of Physical Anthropology* **3**:285–334.
1921   Age changes in the pubic bone. II–IV. *American Journal of Physical Anthropology* **4**:1–70.
1930a   The roentgenographic record of differentiation of the pubic bone. *American Journal of Physical Anthropology* **14**:255–271.
1930b   The anatomical features of epiphyseal union. *Child Development* **1**:186–194.

Todd, T. W., and D. W. Lyon
1925   Cranial suture closure: its progress and age relationship. II. Ectocranial closure in adult males of White stock. *American Journal of Anthropology* **8**:23–45.

Trotter, M., and G. C. Gleser
1952   Estimation of stature from long bones of American Whites and Negroes. *American Journal of Physical Anthropology* **9**:427–440.
1958   A re-evaluation of estimation of stature based on measurements of stature taken during life and of long bones after death. *American Journal of Physical Anthropology* **16**:79–123.

16

Genes, Populations, and Disease, 1930–1980: A Problem-Oriented Review

Kenneth M. Weiss and Ranajit Chakraborty

Although the theory of evolution by adaptation and natural selection was propounded by Darwin and Wallace in 1859 and applied in depth by Darwin to humans in 1871, its material foundation, genetics, was not yet developed at the beginnings of the twentieth century. In fact, there was such considerable doubt at that time about the origin of new variation and the nature of its inheritance that Darwinism was itself in danger. Darwin had long been troubled by this problem. He thought that parental hereditary elements (of unknown physical nature) were blended in the offspring, and that new variation was acquired only very gradually by modification of these hereditary elements, possibly through the habits of an individual's life in some basically Lamarckian process. Hence, he felt that morphological traits evolved slowly and *continuously*, by slight changes in each generation.

Essentially, this view of evolution was developed quantitatively by Francis Galton and Karl Pearson, who called it a *biometrical* approach because it dealt with changes in measurements of quantitative traits. Blending inheritance would reduce variation quite rapidly. The source of new variants still was not known. Furthermore, August Weismann, during the last decades of the nineteenth century, showed that there was a physical separation of somatic from germinal elements, which made Lamarckian transmission impossible. At about the same time, Wilhelm Johannsen's experiments with purebred lines of bean plants showed that even if a generation was formed from parents chosen at the extreme of the trait distribution (e.g., bean size), the offspring generation they produced had the same mean and variance in trait value as did the parental generation, which is not compatible with the blending theory.

A HISTORY OF AMERICAN
PHYSICAL ANTHROPOLOGY, 1930–1980

At this juncture Gregor Mendel's laws of particulate inheritance were re-discovered, and several workers—including Hugo DeVries, William Bateson, and T. H. Morgan—began to document the occurrence of spontaneous Mendelizing mutations. The *mutational*, or Mendelian, view of evolution became a long-standing major competitor with the Galton-Pearson biometrical school. To the mutational school, mutations seemed to produce large and *discrete* changes. In addition, they could produce traits de novo, that is, without the need for a long period of gradual evolution of an incipient (and hence functionless) trait, which seemed to be required by the Darwinian explanation. Mutational changes could produce new biological species, something that had never been observed (and still has not) in regard to small changes in quantitative characters. Morgan and others showed that mutations are not all large or freakish as had generally been thought, but that many, if not most, mutations produce very small changes in existing traits (Morgan 1913, 1918).

In 1918, R. A. Fisher resolved these seemingly irreconcilable positions by showing that the additive action of many Mendelizing loci could produce quantitative traits with characteristics and correlations between relatives like those observed (e.g., height). Thus, the inheritance of particulate, Mendelian elements could serve as the universal basis for inheritance and provide a single set of predictive principles. The quantitative formal theory of evolutionary population genetics was developed over the following 20 years, largely by R. A. Fisher, J. B. S. Haldane, and Sewall Wright. Fisher's book, *The Genetical Theory of Natural Selection*, published in 1930, was an important contribution to this synthesis. In that work, he showed that polymorphisms could not be regarded as merely the result of the pressure of recurrent mutations under blending inheritance because that would require too high a mutation rate. He expressed fitness in terms of *reproductive value*, a demographic concept using age-specific birth and death rates—an approach that was later to have some biomedical importance.

Such was the state of evolutionary genetics in 1930. From a medical point of view, of course, there were limits to progress until the basic nature of inheritance and genetic change was worked out. However, medical genetics was by no means silent during this period. At the turn of the century, Garrod (1902, 1908) had developed the concept of "inborn errors of metabolism." His work began with the study of alkaptonuria and the documentation of the Mendelian nature of such diseases, and, where recessive, their excess occurrence in the offspring of con-sanguineous marriages. At the same time, Bateson in support of the mutational school had amassed a catalogue of Mendelizing human traits (including diseases), which he subsequently published as *Mendel's Principles of Heredity* (1902). By 1929, enough such traits had been identified to fill a large volume (e.g., Gates 1929). Nonetheless, catalogues of rare genetic diseases were at that time mainly of clinical rather than population or evolutionary interest.

In 1900, Karl Landsteiner discovered the ABO system in studies of blood transfusion reactions; this was the first documentation of a widespread genetic polymorphism. Not until 1919, when the Hirschfelds demonstrated that racial and ethnic groups differ in their ABO blood type frequencies, did the utility of Landsteiner's discovery to physical anthropology became apparent, as collections of data from populations around the world quickly appeared. Only in 1925, however, was it shown clearly that the ABO system was a single locus. By the late 1920s, this system had become a useful tool in comparing populations, for which purpose Snyder (1926, 1929) devised simple indexes.

Notwithstanding these developments, Darwinism at discrete Mendelian loci was not universally accepted as the means of human evolution. Indeed, in 1929, many still considered the issue to be unsettled and Bolk (1929) argued that racial differences were due to different hormonally caused degrees of neoteny. Clearly, when the physical anthropologists held their inaugural meeting in Charlottesville, Virginia in 1930, there was not a consensus among workers as to the issue's importance. And it is in this intellectual context that we may begin our review of the subsequent developments of several lines of research involving populations, disease, and genes.

The Age and Origin of Racial Diversity

During the late 1920s and early 1930s physical anthropologists were greatly influenced by the thinking of E. A. Hooton, who considered that human races could best be understood if they were *defined* in terms of traits that were selectively nonadaptive (Hooton 1926). The ABO blood group system seemed to be an ideal nonadaptive character. Besides being discrete and easily classifiable, it was stable and concealed from environmental selective influences. It also varied in allele frequency among the major races. However, before such a trait could be used to classify races, it first had to be determined if it was an ancient or recent polymorphism. Its similar polymorphism in primates had not been clearly demonstrated in the late 1920s. Snyder (1926) noted that such variation appeared to occur rarely, "if at all" in lower animals. Thus, since the different blood types clearly had worldwide distribution, it seemed that they must have arisen in separate races by mutation, later spreading to other groups by admixture. In fact, ABO gene frequencies in known admixed groups approximated the expected intermediate values. The great age of the ABO polymorphisms, in regard to human beings at least, was shown by the work of Boyd (see Wyman and Boyd 1937) and Candela (1936) through the examination of skeletal and mummified material for ABO blood types. As a consequence of this work, race reconstruction, using ABO blood types, was placed on what appeared to be firm ground.

Given the ABO system as a valuable race-history tool and the fact that no adaptive explanation was thought necessary for its frequency distribution, the problem then was to explain the origin of the various alleles and the geographic history of their rise in frequency to current values. Two major views on this issue existed in the 1930s. One was that mutation provided the initial allele characteristic of each major racial group, which then spread by population expansion and intermixture; the history of that allele could therefore be reconstructed from the current frequency distribution. Because the same alleles are found in different populations, it was believed that the original mutation probably antedated the races. This was the view held by Boyd, who postulated some original frequency patterns and explained modern ones by known (and inferred) historical patterns. He argued for example that the peculiar distribution of Amerindian ABO types, in relation to their putative East Asian ancestors (low frequency of A and lower of B), could be explained by a low frequency of such genes arriving with the first settlers (Boyd 1939, 1940). Since his work on Pueblo mummies provided evidence of early bearers of A and B alleles in North America (Wyman and Boyd 1937), there was no need to postulate new mutations for these alleles in the New World.

The second proposed explanations for ABO patterns was recurrent mutations, the chief proponent of which was the former botanist, R. R. Gates. Gates had begun his career working with mutations in the primrose (*Oenothera*) and was predisposed to view polymorphisms of nonadaptive alleles as due to the pressure of recurrent mutations. He argued that races (which he characterized as separate species having risen by parallel evolution, a view similar to that later adopted by Coon [1963]) were subject to recurrent mutation pressure that was race-specific for different alleles at the ABO locus. Over a long period of time, which he estimated through the mutation rates (Gates 1936, 1939), mutations of this sort would accumulate (he did not acknowledge an important role for stochastic loss) until an appreciable frequency had been attained. Subsequently, population expansion and intermixture would lead to the mixed, geographic clinal patterns that we observe today. Recurrent mutation would explain the high frequency of the B allele in East Asia and the new, small frequency of the A allele in the New World.

The recurrent mutation view was opposed by both Boyd (see Wyman and Boyd 1935) and Haldane (1940). According to them, mutation rates were not sufficient to explain the very high polymorphic frequencies observed in the central areas of the major races, a point noted earlier by Fisher (1930). Indeed, as Boyd (1940) pointed out, after a great many tests, mutation had never been directly observed in the ABO system (and probably still has not). Both Boyd (1940) and Haldane (1940) reached a similar reconstruction of gene frequencies in Europe, explaining among other things (*a*) the frequency of the B allele as a derivative from Asia (see Candela 1942) and (*b*) the pecularities of the distribution of the A allele (e.g., in Basques).

Much later, Boyd (e.g., 1955) abandoned the view that a locus must be selectively neutral to be useful in race classification. Hooton himself arrived at this conclusion (1946), apparently under the influence of Boyd (G. W. Lasker, personal communication 1980). Although generally critical of physical anthropologists for their ignorance of genetic principles, and especially for their reluctance to use blood groups to classify the races when blood group frequencies did not coincide with preconceived notions of racial categories and relationships (see Boyd 1950),

Boyd nevertheless worked tirelessly to forge a stronger connection between genetics and physical anthropology.

Since the discovery of the ABO system, there have been many blood group systems classified in the populations of the world. Most of this work was done in the 1940s and 1950s (Crawford 1973). With Smithies's (1955) development of gel electrophoresis, the mass screening of many enzyme loci became practical, and it was quickly found that there was an unexpected amount of genetic variability in man (and in other species). Much of the work on enzyme polymorphism was done by Harry Harris (1970) and has recently been catalogued in Mourant *et al.* (1978a). It is now thought that basically every locus is variable. Furthermore, the recurrent mutation concept has been generally abandoned in favor of an "infinite" allele, unique mutation model, which is more consistent with DNA structure (e.g., see Nei 1975). Genetic drift on a species and racial evolutionary scale has become a tenable explanation for patterns of polymorphism, and the selection-drift controversy is the central problem in evolutionary population genetics today (e.g., Lewontin 1974; Livingstone 1980a; Nei 1975). This is largely because there is no adequate selection model to explain the maintainence of the vast amount of polymorphism that has been found. Selection by disease, as will be seen, is tenable in principle but not yet sufficiently demonstrated by the available evidence.

As new loci were added and surveyed around the world, it became increasingly clear that no consistent racial or clinal pattern existed, but, rather, that the loci had their own individual distributions. This has been seen by Livingstone as evidence of selection at these loci (1980a). However, the distribution may also be due to stochastic factors, as the developers of the *neutral* theory of evolution argue (e.g., Nei 1975). If this is true, or if selection has been slow and systematic over large geographic areas, the patterns of genetic diversity between groups can still be used to reflect historical ancestry, provided many loci are considered at once.

The study of racial diversity and arguments over interpretation of gene frequency differences tie in directly with the study of diseases, which warrants the attention we have given to it. However, before this could become a serious tie, other matters had to be developed. This development occurred contemporaneously with much of the work we have just surveyed, and it is to this material that we now turn.

Mutations, Eugenics, and Genetic Load

As we have seen, in the early 1900s there were many single-locus diseases documented in man. These were clearly of a deleterious nature, were generally quite rare, and it seemed likely that they were maintained by recurrent mutations, for only this could explain the persistence of selectively deleterious alleles. In 1921, Charles H. Danforth suggested that over time, a balance would be reached between the rate of new occurrences by mutation, and loss through selection, of such disease genes. Subsequently, Haldane (1927) showed that a mutation–selection balance would occur, with equilibrium gene frequencies dependent on the mutation and selection rates, and on the degree of dominance. For this and other reasons, it was clearly important to estimate the spontaneous mutation rate in man. The first attempts to do this were based on the diseases achondroplasia (Mørch 1941) hemophilia (Haldane 1947), epiloia (Gunther and Penrose 1935), and others (see Vogel and Rathenburg 1975). All of these studies found rates of about 10^{-5} per gamete, which is consistent with later estimates.

One important assertion of evolutionary population genetics, supported by work in Drosophila and other species, was the expectation that wild-type alleles should evolve dominance over new mutations: A gene that could suppress the effect of new mutants would generally have a selective advantage (Fisher 1930; Provine 1971). However, Levit (1936) noted that many hereditary *diseases* in man seemed in fact to be dominant in that they produced serious pathology in the heterozygote (often homozygotes were too rare to occur or were thought to be lethal). Such loci might be in the process of evolving the expected dominance of the normal allele over the deleterious mutant. Under the protective umbrella of civilization, many heterozygotes with slight effects could survive and reproduce normally, thus relaxing selection in regard to the mutants. Degenerative disease, striking with delayed age of onset, may be the result of this kind of incompletely evolved dominance. New mutants occurring in civilized societies might persist with only moderate deleterious effect before dominance could evolve (see also Haldane 1937).

This topic became very important during the middle of the century due to the increasing importance placed on analyzing the means by which deleteriousness arises and is eliminated or tolerated by the species. In 1937, Haldane quantified the amount of reproduction needed in a population to sustain natural selection among alleles segregating at a locus—which he later called the "cost" of natural selection (Haldane 1957)—components of which have been identified and quantified (Crow and Kimura 1970; Kimura 1961). Haldane (1937) also showed that the amount of cost depended on the mutation *rate* but not on the severity of its effect on the individual.

In the early 1900s, a long search was begun to find the causes of mutations, which, at that time, seemed to arise "spontaneously." The search was fruitless until 1927, when H. J. Muller clearly proved (in Drosophila) what others had been suggesting, namely, that mutations could be induced by radiation. Other workers in radiation biology showed the carcinogenic potential of radiation. The impact of radiation mutagenesis and carcinogenesis on subsequent work in genetics cannot be overstated, especially after the use of nuclear weapons to end World War II and the subsequent proliferation in the use of nuclear energy in industry and medicine.

Closely associated with these issues was the eugenics movement, the intellectual roots of which can be traced to the nineteenth century and Francis Galton in England. The growth of this movement in America, which was initially fostered by such men as Charles B. Davenport and Henry Fairfield Osborn, has been examined by Chase (1977). Many social and political events in the first decades of this century led to a growing concern that deleteriousness in the human gene pool might be increasing and should be controlled. It seemed clear to Galton, and later to Fisher (1917, 1930) and others, that civilization protected those who, in earlier times, would have been eliminated by natural selection. More recently, Richard H. Post spent many years attempting to document the effects of relaxed selection in the accumulation of mildly deleterious traits, such as defects in vision and hearing (e.g., Post 1971).

Negative eugenics, or social control over reproduction, was advocated by many who were alarmed at the rise in the numbers of the lower social classes (see Chase 1977) After the Nazi movement and World War II, such harsh concepts were clearly untenable, although a more positive eugenics has still seemed in order, such as providing reproductive counseling for individuals suspected of being carriers of deleterious mutations. The eugenics movement, however, was not simply a matter of social politics; it was a natural concern fed by the growing evidence of accumulating mutations. Indeed, the first paper in the *American Journal of Human Genetics*, founded in 1949, was an appraisal by J. V. Neel (who has spent a lifetime working on the mutation problem) of the available means for detecting hetero-zygous carriers of deleterious mutations (1949a).

The signal event, however, in both eugenics and mutation research was H. J. Muller's paper, "Our Load of Mutations", published in 1950, in which the concept of *genetic load* was first clearly articulated. Muller summarized the problems of maintaining deleterious mutations, while pondering the future of a species subject to many new sources of mutation (e.g., man-made radiation, chemicals). In wild populations, and presumably early human populations, local groups were highly inbred. Deleterious mutations (generally recessive) would have been eliminated quickly by appearance in homozygous individuals, giving rise to a mutation–selection balance with small gene frequency. However, Muller argued that in recent times humans have become one very large outbred species. New mutations, natural and man-made, can accumulate for many generations before their frequency will rise to a point at which recessive homozygotes will appear and be subject to natural selection. Eventually, each deleterious mutation will have to be eliminated (being balanced by recurrent new mutants); such elimination Muller termed *genetic death*. This process could take a long time under the conditions of civilization, and, since there is often some harmful effect in heterozygotes (Levit 1936), a very large amount of suffering would ensue before each mutant gene would disappear. In addition, the equilibrium gene frequency would become much larger. Muller (1950) estimated that, on the average, we have a 20% suppression in fitness due to deleterious mutations and that $1/5$–$1/3$ of all prereproductive mortality is due to their elimination. This was the "penalty for relaxed selection." Since it appeared from experiments with Drosophila that most loci act in-dependently (*nonsynergistically*), the load of "lethal equivalents" borne by each of us would rise drastically.

As mentioned already, much of the work by human geneticists, particularly of the generation from 1945 to 1965, was motivated directly by a desire to assess the amount and effect of deleterious mutations in man. Such work might even have been fueled further with the discovery of great amounts of electrophoretic polymorphism, if the neutral evolution theory (Kimura 1968a, 1968b; King and Jukes 1969) had not served to soften views of mutations, variation, and load. Furthermore, working from the same new data, physical anthropologists in the 1970s showed that the concept of an inbred human species in the days before the rise of civilizations, was incorrect, because the degree of genetic heterozygosity within even relatively small traditional local groups is nearly as great as that in the species as a whole. Efforts to estimate the components of the recurrent mutational load on the impact of disease continue, however (Crow and Denniston, 1981).

Population Metrics Using Inbreeding

If, as it was generally thought, only a few genetic traits were at any time undergoing positive adaptive selection, then most genetic differences in fitness would be due to the maintenance either of (a) balanced polymorphism or (b) mutation–selection balance. But to what degree are each of these factors acting? Morton et al. (1956) have argued that in a subset of individuals in whom there is excess homozygosity relative to Hardy-Weinberg expectations, heterosis and mutation–selection balance would appear differently. This is because, for a given selection intensity, the amount of lowered fitness differs under the two types of selection. Morton et al. (1956) devised an index to assess the relative action of the two modes of selection in inbred individuals. There was a shortage of known informative gene loci available for extensive direct mutation tests at that time, but it was thought that fitness suppression should be detectable through anthropometric measurements, abortion rates, and congenital anomalies in the offspring of inbred matings.

For a time this index was widely used (see Vogel and Motulsky 1979, for a summary of this work). Now interest in the use of inbreeding as a measure of genetic load has almost completely disappeared especially since little of significance was found. By and large, results were intermediate between the expectations under heterosis and those under mutation–selection balance. But, more importantly, these studies required assumptions that could not be supported by the empirical data (Morton 1960; Schull and Neel 1965; Vogel and Motulsky 1979).

The impact of this work goes far beyong its direct application. The load question set off a flurry of inbreeding studies in many different populations. Some looked at deleterious effects in offspring (e.g., Schull 1959; Neel and Schull 1968; Cavalli-Sforza and Bodmer 1971; Vogel and Motulsky 1979), while others simply estimated inbreeding with seemingly little underlying motivation other than the hope that it could be related to population genetics in a theoretical way. For example, Crow and Mange (1965) developed a numerical means of using isonymous marriages to partition inbreeding into random (due to small population) and nonrandom components, which has been used in several applications (Cavalli-Sforza and Bodmer 1971; Crow 1980; Lasker 1968; Reid 1973; Vogel and Motulsky 1979). It seems fair to assert that physical anthropologists, as opposed to human geneticists, especially in the 1970s, have done much work on inbreeding and kindred topics with little if any sense of problem and certainly with faint reference to the original driving motivation behind the studies as they were developed.

In an effort to circumscribe the genetic load problem, Crow (1958) devised an "Index of Total Selection." Through the age-specific schedules of birth and death rates, he explored the way in which selection could act and showed, by a version of Fisher's Fundamental Theorem, how the maximum possible amount of natural selection, equal to the total variation in fitness, could be partitioned into segments due to differential mortality and differential fertility. Crow's index was picked up eagerly by anthropologists: Neel and Chagnon (1968) applied it to Amazonia Amerindian data (updated by Neel and Weiss 1975), Morgan applied it to the Ramah Novajo (1973), and Spuhler has applied it to many groups (e.g., 1963, 1977). There have also been other efforts to characterize fitness using vital rate schedules of anthropological populations (Henneberg 1976; Weiss 1972). Since differences in fitness are not all of genetic origin, there seems to be little one can hope to learn from these indexes, except that both mortality and fertility have been potentially important factors throughout most of human history.

However, inbreeding studies have had a separate impetus related to the study of disease, which predates even Garrod's work at the beginning of the century. Inbred families often show diseases that are otherwise very rare. Clearly, a way to find rare recessive diseases is to find them segregating in small, isolated populations with high levels of inbreeding. Isolates also serve to demonstrate the Founder Effect and genetic drift in general, and this often leads to the presence of traits not usually observed in larger populations. This has been the motivation behind the widespread study of various religious sects and other genetic isolates. Here, we can mention studies on albinism in the San Blas Indians (see Gates 1946), McKusick's work on diseases in the Amish (1978), Steinberg and others' work in the Hutterites (e.g., Martin *et al.* 1980; Steinberg *et al.* 1967), studies of the Rh system in Basques (e.g., see Boyd 1950), and Glass's study of the Pennsylvania Dunkers (1956). This latter study showed erratic changes in gene frequencies over generations—as expected under genetic drift but in contrast to the more patterned change expected under natural selection. Gajdusek (1964) stressed the strong effect of drift in human isolates, the conditions under which it is presumed most of human evolution has occurred, and cautioned that selection will be difficult to detect in the midst of stochastic noise in tribal populations. Indeed, studies of individual isolates have done little, other than to document curiosities. However, the focus of the bulk of the work of genetic anthropologists in the early 1970s was *population structure*, that is, the study of genetic differentiation in networks of small populations; and this work served to document the great role played by genetic drift in determining the pattern of human variation, especially at the local level (Harpending 1974).

Mutation Rate Studies

As mentioned above, after World War II there was a dramatic increase in the number of studies investigating the genetic effect of radiation as a source of mutations. Taking advantage of the tragedy in Japan, a huge project was begun to study the long-term genetic effects of single large doses of radiation. This project, sponsored by the Atomic Bomb Casualty Commission, was placed under the direction of J. V. Neel and W. J. Schull. Its first major report was on the effects of radiation on pregnant mothers in Hiroshima and Nagasaki (Neel and Schull 1956). Since the X chromosome is a larger target than the Y, an alteration of the sex ratio was expected, but was not borne out by subsequent studies (Schull 1958; Schull and Neel 1958; Schull et al. 1968).

Indeed, clear-cut, *heritable* (as opposed to disease) radiation damage is difficult to detect in man, and suprisingly little has been found considering the widespread concern that existed at the end of the war (Schull 1958; Newcombe 1972; Vogel and Rathenburg 1975; Neel 1963). Large or chronic doses do seem dangerous to health, however, and doses to gametes or early fetuses are clearly deleterious. The Japanese studies have followed individuals who were irradiated and are now finding, decades later, an increase of cancer at some organ sites (Schull et al. 1980). Although this increase in frequency is slight, there has recently been much concern that the exposure of these populations to neutrons was greatly overestimated so that the dose response pattern for gamma radiation may in fact be higher than first thought.

It was obviously impossible to understand the effects of man-made exposures to radiation in Japan or elsewhere without some clear understanding of the "spontaneous" mutation rate. A number of studies have been undertaken to estimate this — most notably by those workers associated with J. V. Neel, W. J. Schull, and T. E. Reed at the University of Michigan. In these Michigan studies, two basic methods were employed. One was indirect; it compared the frequency of recessive disease bearers against their loss of reproductive fitness. The other was direct; it equated the occurrence of new mutants (affected children of unaffected parents) with the mutation rate. In both, a mutation–selection balance was assumed in relation to certain "sentinel phenotypes" (Neel 1972)—that is, the estimates were of mutation measured at the phenotypic, and not the genotypic level.

The concept of recurrent mutation was central to this work, the results of many studies were a rather consistent estimate of 10^{-5} per generation for a wide range of disorders for which no a priori assumption of equal mutation rate would have been reasonable (e.g., neurofibromatosis, Huntington's disease, aniridia, polyposis coli, retinoblastoma; see Vogel and Motulsky [1979] for a summary). These findings are consistent with those obtained from laboratory experiments using mice and fruit flies. More recently, however, Neel (1973; also Neel and Thompson 1978) has claimed that the Yanomama Indians, presumably living under aboriginal relatively and "pristine" conditions, may have a mutation rate nearly an order of magnitude higher. There are now under way very large-scale *direct* tests of mutation, using parent–offspring blood data in Japan, searching for new electrophoretic and other variants. Hundreds of thousands of tests will be needed, and the mutation rate in man is still an elusive quantity, if indeed it is a single meaningful quantity. Certainly at the DNA level, one less often uses recurrent mutations as a fundamental concept. Mutations are now presumed to be generally unique at this level.

Recognizing that a good understanding of mutation, selection, etc., in mankind required an understanding of the tribal conditions under which man has evolved, physical anthropologists made a general effort after 1960 to collect such data. Unfortunately, by this time there were very few human groups that could be regarded as unacculturated, which gave a certain urgency to the effort (see Neel 1958, 1968, 1975; Neel and Salzano 1966). Nevertheless, between 1965 and 1975, a host of "salvage" studies were executed in Africa, Pacifica, India, Alaska, and Australia. Clearly, the most extensive of these studies was the one by Neel and co-workers in Amazonia, which made the Yanomama a household name and which had important disease-related objectives (Neel 1971a, 1971b). Much, however, was not learned. Time and population were too limited, and, as a consequence, much will remain forever a secret of the jungle.

The Population Genetics of Disease
and the Maintenance of Polymorphism

There are three basic ways for a polymorphism to be maintained in a population: (a) recurrent mutation balanced by selection; (b) genetic drift; and (c) some episodic or heterotic form of selection. As has been mentioned, it was concluded that the genetic polymorphisms in man, as represented by blood groups and serum proteins, could not be due to recurrent mutations because the mutation rate would have to be too high. Today many geneticists would argue that such polymorphisms are in fact due to the random genetic drift of selectively neutral alleles. However, most physical anthropologists have a clearly selectionist viewpoint and therefore, tend to favor the third possibility. This view is also held by many biomedically oriented human geneticists. The problem, and it is a difficult one, is to identify the causes of natural selection. The search for such causes has generally centered on allele-specific disease susceptibility or resistance or on incompatibility problems. Forms of selection not related to clinical entities have less often been entertained, except in regard to racial morphology and a few biochemical traits.

Soon after the ABO system was discovered, speculation arose as to what medical factors might be associated with its specific types. Early attempts to discover disease associations were made by Alexander (1921), Buchanan and Higley (1921), and Hirschfeld and Zborowski (1925) by considering maternal effects on birth-weight, various cancers, and the like. Their findings were negative. Indeed, nothing in this regard had been solidly established prior to the 1960s (Reed 1961; Roberts

1957). Although failure to test for the right disease was a contributing factor, the major impediment to these studies was the small sample size. Still, the ABO locus has a peculiar frequency distribution, which can be interpreted as indirect evidence for the action of natural selection.

Focusing on this fact, Alice Brues wrote a paper in 1954 entitled: "Selection and Polymorphism in the ABO Blood Groups," which is now regarded as a classic in physical anthropology. Among closely related populations, such as Amerindian groups, allele frequencies have an erratic distribution such as would be produced by genetic drift. But, if one looks at the worldwide distribution of frequencies, they are clustered in a restricted part of their possible range (e.g., the O allele is always the most common). For a polymorphism as ancient as the ABO system, this would not be expected under drift. Therefore, Brues concluded that some form of selection must be occurring to restrict gene frequencies. She later (Brues 1963) simulated the ABO distribution and found it to be consistent, under her simplified assumptions, with heterotic selection (including maternal-fetal incompatibility). Yet, if this inference is valid, there is still little in the frequency distribution of the ABO, or most other loci, to give a clear clue as to what kinds of selective factors are involved. Even though specific factors were not identified, it was the opinion of some leading geneticists that balanced polymorphisms would be found to be the explanation for the blood group polymorphisms (Ford 1942, 1945). Haldane (1949a, 1949b) suggested that diseases might be the selective forces involved.

In the early 1900s, two forms of severe anemia were described in the United States. One was thalassemia (Cooley and Lee 1925), found in Mediterranean-derived people, and the other was sickle-cell anemia, found in blacks (Herrick 1910). That these diseases were common but only found in racial subgroups, and that they seemed to be familial, led to the suspicion that they might be genetic and raised the question of how they might have reached their high frequency. In 1949, Linus C. Pauling and co-workers showed that sickle-cell anemia is due to a hemoglobin biochemical variant, and Neel (1949b) demonstrated that the variant was inherited as an allele at a single locus. Likewise, thalassemia was shown to segregate as a single locus (Valentine and Neel 1944). Also, there seemed to be a dose effect in operation, that is, a degree of impairment in heterozygotes, the origin and maintenance of which was then difficult to explain, especially given the prevailing intellectual preoccupation with the concept of genetic load. The mutation rate needed to balance depressed fitness would have to be as high as 10^{-2}, which clearly was excessive. Some dismissed the sickle-cell anemia locus as an important evolutionary problem because it had not yet been clearly demonstrated that anemia of this type existed in Africa. It was considered plausible that the locus had its deleterious effect only because American Blacks were admixed with Europeans (Raper 1950). The extent of the allele's expression, if any, in "pure" African populations was not known.

In two reviews, Neel (1951, 1953) attempted to construct explanations for the observed frequency of these blood disorders, including small heterozygote fertility advantages, such as by reproductive compensation (as Glass had argued in regard to Rh incompatibility). Neel argued that the admixture argument was weak and predicted that sickle-cell anemia would be found in Africa when a search was made to find homozygous recessive children before they died of the disease (thereby explaining its absence in adult Africans). This prediction turned out to be true. It is quite interesting to view the filling in of this important puzzle from our perspective a quarter-century later. Just after Neel's speculations on the causes of high Hb S frequency, Allison (1954a, 1954b) showed convincingly that sickle-cell hetero-zygotes enjoyed an advantage in resistance to malaria. He did this by finding a geographic relationship between the frequency of Hb S and the distribution of malaria and by testing several Ugandan tribesmen by direct exposure to the parasite. Many studies were undertaken to verify Allison's assertion, and most skeptics were satisfied: hospitalized sickle-cell heterozygote patients showed not only less severe malaria but also a quicker recovery rate. That sickle-cell anemia is a case of balanced polymorphism has, of course, been proved in great biochemical detail in the past 25 years.

For anthropology, the sickle-cell story did not end with the discovery of malarial heterosis. In 1958, Livingstone published what is now undoubtedly the most widely read paper in physical anthropology: "Anthropological implications of the Sickle Cell Gene Distribution in West Africa." In this paper, he argued that the frequency of Hb S in West Africa varied locally in a pattern that was best understood in terms of the distribution and historical duration of malaria, and that this itself was determined by the history of the spread of agriculture. Agriculture (initially of slash-and-burn type) required cleared land and thus produced suffi-cient standing water for the breeding of the malarial mosquito. That is, *human culture itself* was responsible for establishing the selective coefficients required to maintain the Hb S polymorphism. From the sickle-cell frequency distribution, Livingstone attempted to reconstruct some of the migrational and cultural history of West Africa, which he expanded to include other hemoglobinopathies and other geographic areas in later work (1964a, 1964b, 1967, 1971). The major thrust of Livingstone's synthesis, namely, the *ongoing* effect of culture in molding human evolution, is a point still largely misunderstood or ignored by many researchers without anthropological training.

Many other hemoglobinopathies have since been shown to be selectively involved with malarial resistance (e.g., Motulsky 1975), and they remain the single best-documented cases of heterosis in man. This story is continually updated, but several loose ends remain. For example, we do not know whether these anomalies arose once or repeatedly by mutation. If only once, then we should be able to reconstruct culture history in a relatively direct way. On the other hand, if there were many foci of origin for the same mutation, then clearly such a reconstruction would not be possible. Some recent indications using restriction enzyme sites linked to hemoglobin locus show polymorphism between the African and Indian sickle-cell genes (Kan and Dozy 1978), which not only suggests multiple origins, but also alerts us to the probability that more soon-to-be-discovered variability remains.

Livingstone has carried his original work forward in many ways over the past 25 years. He has given attention to the problem of competition among the different malaria-resistance variants—the various hemoglobins, the thalassemias, G6PD deficiency—and has concluded that Hb S is a "predatory" mutant that outcompetes others, in West Africa at least (1971, 1980a, 1980b). Because the G6PD deficiency is sex linked, it has its own dynamics; individuals can be affected by both a hemoglobin variant and G6PD deficiency, which presents additional complications in reconstructing the selection coefficients maintaining the polymorphisms (Livingstone 1971; Motulsky 1975).

The malaria-based balanced polymorphisms are the textbook cases of this kind of selection in man. They are certainly a success story in genetics and are an important contribution to human health. They have become the model for many other disease–genetics studies, but whether we will soon document the balancing forces in other diseases in a convincing way is an open question. Nonetheless, it is largely because of the hemoglobinopathies that heterosis is a major viable competitor to selective neutrality in explaining the enzyme variability in living organisms. For physical anthropology, this story put on a genetic basis the importance of culture as the human niche. Subsequent work on lactose tolerance, PTC tasting, diabetes, and other conditions have augmented our knowledge of the effects of culture on genes. But culture changes and evolution can be painfully slow relative to our historical and archaeological knowledge, making proof very hard to obtain.

Disease Associations: Infectious Diseases

The spectacular success of the abnormal hemoglobin story helped to stimulate a large amount of work to uncover any disease selection of a similar nature in relation to other loci. We have referred to the earliest studies of the ABO system and disease. Immediately after the sickle-cell story unfolded, speculation rose that heterosis occured at other loci (Allison 1955, 1964; Livingstone 1960; Reed 1961), and, although little has been found to support this speculation, it is still a position favored by Livingstone (1980a) and doubtlessly many others.

These authors did not argue that heterozygote selection was important simply because of the discovery of malarial heterosis but because of the realization that mutation rates for specific alleles are not sufficient to explain high frequencies. Also, they felt that though drift, transient selection, and migration might explain some polymorphism, there is too much such variation for this to be the likely overall explanation. The cataloging of many electrophoretic polymorphisms during the 1960s made this abundantly clear, and we now must acknowledge that species are far more variable than evolutionary theory had predicted based on substitutional, or adaptive selection.

Livingstone has speculated that malaria may have killed more human beings than any other disease (1971). If this is true, part of its truth relates to the fact that it has affected the species reasonably recently, since the advent of larger agricultural populations. Throughout most of our history, there has probably been a limit on the extent to which transmissable diseases of a life-threatening type can affect preagricultural bands (Black 1966, 1975; Black *et al.* 1970; Neel 1971a, 1971b; Neel *et al.* 1970). Although parasites of all sorts are a major and holoendemic problem in tropical rainforest settings, it is hard to assess the degree to which they have affected reproductive fitness in the past. The same can be said for chronic infectious diseases.

Acute communicable diseases possibly were not a major factor until recently. The a priori constraints that must be placed on the interpretation of poly-morphisms are thus unclear. For the interpretation of ABO-related associations, this can be a particular problem because the polymorphism is old. Hence, efforts to associate gene frequencies with *recent* balancing types of disease events (e.g., Allison 1964; Livingstone 1960; Penrose 1955) might be correct but unrelated to the previous history of selection. Not enough work has been done on animal sources of disease and vectors or on disease dynamics in small populations for this problem to be realistically addressed in this context.

Several workers have, however, taken advantage of diseases whose patterns may be related to recent historical–cultural patterns and–or known history (Motulsky 1960). It is natural to ask whether there may be genetic host-resistance factors in relation to disease, and this has been done for influenza, poliomyelitis, syphillis, tuberculosis, leprosy, hepatitis, and smallpox in relation to the ABO system (e.g., Vogel 1975; Vogel and Motulsky 1979). Many associations have been found (though few have been confirmed), usually implicating the A or O alleles as the most susceptible. In fact, Pettenkofer (1962) and others have shown an apparent antigenic similarity between the A substance and substances associated with smallpox and plague pathogens.

This discovery could explain the association existing between smallpox and the frequency of the A allele that was found by Vogel and colleagues in India (Vogel 1975; Vogel and Chakravartti 1966). Although the immunology of this work has been questioned, this does not diminish the *logic* prompting the investigation to look for antigenic reasons for host-resistance factors. In fact, Otten (1967) has suggested that the antigenic similarity between ABO substances and those found in pathogens, and even in foods, may help to explain ABO heterogeneity and the secretor locus that produces ABO substances in saliva. It is noteworthy that many of the ABO associations that have been suggested involved diseases of the gastrointestinal tract.

The associations of ABO with infectious diseases are not yet universally accepted. In any case, they provide no means for establishing the forces for a balanced polymorphism, especially because maternal–fetal incompatibility may select mildly *against* heterozygotes at this locus (there may be a protection afforded by the Rh system). If there is a balance, the balancing forces are clearly complex and as yet, not at all clear. It is for this reason that we are presently unable to explain the polymorphism simply by looking at the single-disease "marginals," one by one, in relation to the ABO alleles (Livingstone 1980a, 1980b). In addition to the likelihood that selection has been complex over a long time period, there are well-known difficulties in detecting small selection coefficients (Boyd 1955; Neel and Schull 1968; Roberts 1957; Schull 1965), especially if one needs to take into account genotype-specific schedules of birth and death in order to estimate fitness (Bodmer 1968; Cavalli-Sforza and Bodmer 1971).

Even the basic methodology for detecting selection, the use of odds ratios developed by Woolf (1955) for genetic tests, can have statistical difficulties if the conditions are rare or samples are small (Weiss *et al.* 1982). Reed (1975) has shown that if anthropometric, fertility, and neonatal health statistics are used to assess selection in relation to blood-group genotypes, selection as high as 28% might go undetected. Samples sizes might need, in fact, to be bigger than the populations themselves if one wants to detect selection in "anthropological" population settings (Livingstone 1980a), which is clearly a prohibitive problem.

We should briefly mention the HLA system, which was discovered, like the ABO system, in relation to clinical, as opposed to "natural," disease problems. From all appearances, the HLA system is related to many diseases, from infective to autoimmune and degenerative. What one is to make of this, and how many of the associations are due to linkage vis-à-vis direct biochemical immunological effects of the HLA system itself, are still mysteries at present. Recent complications and discussion of the associations, including their statistical basis, are described in (McMichael and Dewitt 1977) Bodmer and Bodmer (1978), Mourant *et al.* (1978b), Schanfield (1980), or Vogel and Motulsky (1979). The anthropological and evolutionary implications of this system and its great variability have been discussed by Bodmer and Bodmer (1978).

Important loci were discovered through serious diseases that occur mainly in certain restricted populations. The most extensively studied of these are cystic fibrosis (in Europeans) and Tay–Sachs disease (in Ashkenazi Jews). In both cases, the severity of the homozygous disease is well known, but the forces maintaining the gene frequency at appreciable levels remain cryptic. In both cases, there is the possibility that genetic drift is the only factor (Livingstone 1980a; Neel 1979; Wagener *et al.* 1978).

There is some evidence for heterozygous advantage manifested by fertility excess as well as resistance to typhus and tuberculosis in cystic fibrosis (Knudson 1979 *et al.* 1967). Heterozygote fertility excess and tuberculosis resistance have also been suggested for Tay–Sachs (Myrianthopoulous and Aronson 1966), based on gene frequency and tuberculosis rates in Europe. By indirect theoretical inference concerning the unlikeliness that the high gene frequency is due only to genetic drift, a selective argument has been advocated (Chakravarti and Chakraborty 1978; Livingstone 1980b). This issue is open and an example of diametric hypotheses advocated on the same data by over-powerful theory (Ewens 1978). It has also been suggested that Tay–Sachs heterozygotes' resistance may have lowered the overall transmission probabilities and, hence, the endemicity of tuberculosis (Myrianthopoulos 1972) a suggestion made also in relation to sickle cell and malaria (Wiesenfeld 1967). However, the frequency of the genotypes seems far too low to affect the epidemiology of such prevalent diseases in a serious way (Livingstone 1980b).

We should not leave the subject of genes and infectious disease without mentioning several other cases that clearly have been of anthropological relevance, even though they turned out *not* to be genetic. These are kuru (Gajdusek 1977), the Australia antigen associated with hepatitis B (Blumberg 1977), and the neurological degenerations (Parkinsonism dementia and amyotrophic lateral sclerosis) found in high frequency among the Chamorro of Guam (Gajdusek 1964; Rossmann 1978 and references therein). These three disorders appear to be familial and were first thought to be genetic. Kuru has been shown to be due to a slow virus transmitted by familial ritual cannibalism. Hepatitis is also viral. The Guam dementia case is still unsolved.

There is an ever-increasing number of slow viral diseases being defined, and it seems from recent work that these diseases may often require other factors in order to become clinically manifest. Poliomyelitis, Hodgkins disease, and infectious mononucleosis are examples in which the age and duration of infection affect the expression and severity of the disease, and in which host factors cannot be ruled out. This is true for Herpes virus also. The Epstein—Barr virus, found associated with Burkitt's lymphoma in Africa, seems to require host specificity as well as malarial infection to produce lymphoma. The same virus has also been found associated in unclear ways with nasopharyngeal carcinoma, a common cancer in Asians and certain other ethnic groups. Some of the tumors associated with these viruses, and certainly such diseases as mononucleosis and polio, strike severely and early enough that they may have selective effects on gene frequency. These are recent findings, and little is known definitely; they remain almost totally uninvestigated in regard to tribal or human historical ecology. How long such diseases, or their vectors, have been around remains to be determined.

Disease Associations: Noninfectious Diseases

There remains the problem of inferring selection of a more subtle kind than the major infectious diseases. Many noninfectious diseases are statistically associated with the blood groups (Clarke 1961; Mourant et al. 1978b), although the results are variable and rarely conclusive. The earliest attempts looked at diseases such as cancer and failed, on the grounds of sample size and other problems. Progress in this area of inquiry has also been retarded by uncertainty as to whether or not diseases might, themselves, alter the ABO substances expressed (Roberts 1957). Efforts in the early 1950s, based on stomach cancer–gene frequency correlations (of the A allele) in the United Kingdom (Aird et al. 1953) succeeded in finding a statistically significant association which was based not on geography, but rather on individual relative odds. The apparent association of peptic ulcer with type O, first suspected in the 1920s also was established (Aird et al. 1954). Many other associations quickly followed (Roberts 1957). From these, it is possible to hypothesize all sorts of balances because some of the associations are with the A and some with the O allele. However, explaining the high frequency of the B allele anywhere, especially in Asia, is more difficult and has not been done successfully. Most of these associations are with degenerative diseases of presumably very low selective effect (e.g., Mourant *et al.* 1978; Ramot 1974; Roberts 1959; Vogel and Motulsky 1979).

Bodmer (1968) attempted to estimate fitness by use of age-specific birth and death rates in relation to schizophrenia. This has also been attempted for Huntington's chorea (Reed and Chandler 1958; Reed and Neel 1959) and for the ulcer–ABO association (Cavalli-Sforza and Bodmer 1971). Sample sizes and data on the relevant rates have been inadequate to demonstrate much beyond the nature of the method. Although ABO associations with digestive disorders might be related to long-standing needs to react to environmental toxins and infectious agents (Otten 1967), it is difficult to make much evolutionary sense of late-age-of-onset diseases as important factors in relation to gene frequency. Whether we can ever get off the horns of sample-size problems is uncertain. Thus, although there is every probability that we may in the future document many associations at the individual and clinical–biochemical levels, to show an evolutionary relationship to gene frequency may remain a fundamental and intractable problem. Furthermore, the ecological and evolutionary nature of noninfectious disease may be quite complex and long standing, and our understanding of disease in preindustrial times is still very rudimentary (Neel 1958, 1971b, 1975; Neel and Salzano 1966; Weiss 1976, 1981).

We may take adult-onset diabetes mellitus as an example of ecological complexity. The disease is currently regarded as degenerative, but it has been suggested that alleles for diabetes may in the past have had selective advantage in a "boom-or-bust" dietary environment (Neel 1962). This hypothesis might explain the high frequency of this condition in certain Amerinidan groups of the American Southwest, such as the Pima and Papago (Neel 1971a), however, it may be just a secondary effect of reservation existence. The fact that its *present* expression is as a degenerative disease does not imply that its selective effect, in the past, was expressed only late in life.

For some loci, it is not the locus but the disease that was discovered first, and this makes the a priori search for balancing selection—when the condition, discovered to be genetic, is at all common—quite reasonable. There are several examples of this. One early case was erythroblastosis fetalis and maternal–fetal incompatibility in the Rh, and later in the ABO systems. First described by Levine and co-workers (1941), this system was more than the archetype of selection against heterozygotes. It presented a problem in regard to (*a*) the high frequency of the Rh phenotype in populations like the Basques, whose unusual gene frequencies have been the subject of much debate since the 1930s about the early European aboriginese (e.g., Boyd 1950; Haldane 1940), and (*b*) the fact that this selection against heterozygotes mandates a counterbalancing selective force in order to maintain the polymorphism. This may in part be due to interaction between the ABO and Rh systems (Levine 1958), or as Glass (1950) argued, there may be reproductive compensation at the locus, a subject that has been debated on several occasions since.

The history of thought about the human polymorphisms, especially the blood groups, has been oscillatory, varying from anthropologists' early assumption that such hidden traits are selectively neutral, to the hyperselectionism of some who feel that neutrality is extremely unlikely (Reed 1975). Boyd switched completely on this between the 1930s and 1950s. Currently genetics is split over the subject. One fact, however, is important, and that is that much of the theory used to make inference from gene frequency data is equilibrium theory, and equilibrium is certainly not likely in many, if indeed any, current human populations, given our active recent cultural history (Livingstone 1980a, 1980b). The effect of historical "noise" in relation even to very large sample sizes impedes long-term inference while at the same time facilitating short-term inference (Harpending 1974). Livingstone argues that we rediscovered selection in the 1950s (1980a). If this is true, then we rediscovered neutrality in the 1970s. Nevertheless, far too much polymorphism remains to be explained on the basis of simple disease hypotheses. Selection and neutrality are probably concepts that are largely dependent on the scale of resolution used. The new restriction-enzyme methods of dividing up the genome surely portend to disclose a great amount of thus-far-undetected polymorphism (e.g., Botstein *et al.* 1980), adding to our explanatory "load," being even one step further removed from any reasonably suggestable selection hypotheses at the moment. In this context, it is interesting that the evolutionary rate of intervening sequences in eukaryote DNA seems to be very different in speed and type of mutation from that in the coded sequences of the same genes, even at codons in those genes which are thought to be selectively neutral (van Ooyen *et al.* 1979). Probably, there is some purifying selection occurring in the exons that does not occur in the introns (Li *et al.* 1981). Perhaps we should think of different kinds of neutrality as we do of selection.

Disease Associations: Other Means of Indirect Inference

It is clear that even for the more acute kinds of disease, associations with blood group loci are difficult to establish. Competing explanations, such as drift versus balancing selection, run head-to-head against each other in different interpretations of the same data, as in the case of Tay-Sachs. Indeed, except for ABO and Rh, few associations leading to fitness differences have been demonstrated in relation to blood groups (Mourant *et al.* 1978). One approach to the problem of detection is the use of computer simulation to see whether or not various hypotheses are at least tenable. After his first early efforts to explain gene frequency patterns at the hemoglobin loci and ABO locus in terms of the history of disease and culture, Livingstone turned to such simulation. In a series of papers over the past 20 years, he has described many of these efforts in relation to hemoglobins (1969b), skin pigmentation (1969a), and the general problem of polymorphism in rapidly growing populations (1980b). Characterizing himself as an "old Darwinian" (1980b), he argues that genetic equilibrium has not been reached in most human populations (and, hence, has not annihilated history) and that current patterns of polymorphism are consistent with his strongly selectionist viewpoint, one held by many anthropologists but opposed by a host of neutralists.

If the aboriginal gene frequencies and population admixture rates can be accurately estimated, it is in principal possible to detect the effects of selection from the gene frequencies of a hybrid population, such as American Blacks. Such attempts have been made (e.g., Workman *et al.* 1963), but they have been criticized on the grounds of inadequate knowledge of the required data and their assumptions (Reed 1969; Adams and Ward 1973; Mandarino and Cadien 1974), so that conclusions of major importance have not resulted from this strategy.

Neither of the approaches just discussed is designed to determine what factors may be involved in genetic selection but merely to document its existence; that more cannot be done reflects the inadequacy of the data available. The work discussed thus far also assumes that the genetics of a disease under selection is known. But a major problem is *detecting* the existence and nature of genetic factors in disease causation.

In the first decades of this century, work by Weinberg Haldane, Snyder, and others led to the development of various indexes and ratios to describe the expected occurrence of disease in nuclear families under specific genetic hypotheses (e.g., dominant, recessive, sex-linked). This is called *segregation analysis* and seeks to document Mendelian segregation of genes in families, taking into account the way in which the data were ascertained. It is a very complex problem, especially if there is ascertainment bias and incomplete gene penetrance, and for this reason its use was restricted until the advent of high-speed computers to do some of the tedious computations (Morton 1958, 1959).

In spite of this advance, investigations were restricted to the study of nuclear families only until 1971, when Elston and Stewart produced a more general likelihood approach for pedigrees of arbitrary size. This method was further improved by Cannings *et al.* (1976, 1978, 1980) to include pedigrees with any number of independent ancestors, inbreeding, and complex genetic hypotheses. These models have become quite general and powerful (e.g., Elston 1980), and include corrections for ascertainment. They do require sizable computer costs and effort, and the interpretation of results can be quite difficult. But, at least it is now possible to make general searches through pedigree data looking for genetic patterns and, more importantly, for linkage to genetic markers where blood samples are available, so that diseases may be mapped onto chromosomes. These programs, however, are still very much in their infancy and have yet to be fully evaluated.

For some quantitative diseases (e.g., hypertension), qualitative Mendelian models are not adequate, and the strategy of quantitative genetics, which dates back to the biometrical school of evolution, has been used. In some cases, many genes act to produce the disease, but it may only occur if a genetic threshold has been reached. Falconer (1965) has provided a means for estimating the heritabillity of the trait from data on relatives of the affected; this method has been applied to show the possibility of this kind of inheritance in diabetes risk. In recent years, Morton, Rao, and others have advocated the use of Sewall Wright's method of path analysis for the study of quantitative inheritance when the possibility of complex environmental factors is believed to be important. These researchers introduced a significance testing method so that competing hypotheses of genetic control could be tested on pedigree data (Morton 1974; Morton and Rao 1978, 1980). Ward and co-workers (1980) have applied this method to the study of acculturation effects on blood pressure in Tokelauan migrants to New Zealand. However, what contribution path analysis can make to our understanding of the genetics of important diseases is as yet undetermined.

Attention has clearly turned to the study of common degenerative diseases— such as cancer, diabetes, and heart disease—and many workers who were involved in more standard anthropology have become interested in these problems. These are the major diseases of modern life, and they are quite commonly familial, and probably genetic (Carter 1969; Knudson 1979). However, interest in this area is not new. In 1932, Macklin outlined the different ways in which genetically caused disease could be recognized in terms of severity, age-of-onset patterns, and so on (1932a), and argued that all cancer was probably genetic on these criteria (1932b). Although the latter conclusion is incorrect, the strategy employed is quite modern. Age-of-onset and pathological details are still major ways to distinguish genetic from other kinds of causation for complex disorders.

Using methods originally developed by Karl Pearson, Edwards (1960, 1969) has shown that a polygenic trait can appear to segregate in families much as would a Mendelian trait. This is an ironic twist in light of the Mendelian–biometry controversy of the early 1900s. This "simulation" of Mendelism illustrates the major problem with contemporary genetic epidemiology, namely, distinguishing between competing genetic hypotheses with pedigree data. Pedigrees may be large or small, but when there are some nongenetic cases in the population and genes are either not fully penetrant or are characterized merely by different onset-age curves, it is difficult to be definitive about genetic details.

Penrose (1953) developed an index of relative risk among relatives of an affected person when there is incomplete penetrance and under several genetic modes of inheritance. Similarly, Newcombe (1964) examined the observed relative risk in siblings for a wide array of diseases. The critical facts are the gene frequency, mode of inheritance, and overall disease incidence or prevalence rates. Whereas many diseases appear to occur in a manner consistent with single-locus etiology, most seem to be multifactorial with varying degrees of heritability—that is, most, although familial, are of uncertain nature. Pedigree error can only compound the problem further (Chakraborty et al. 1980). The test for genetic linkage using marker loci is probably the most hopeful aspect of this new work, but at present, no simple conclusions have arisen in the study of the genetics of chronic disease. There are several collections available that summarize what is known or what analytic problems are involved (Mielke and Crawford 1980; Morton and Chung 1978; Sing and Skolnick 1979; Schull and Weiss 1980).

Aging and Life Span:
The Biology of Human Life History

Many important diseases strike at different ages in different people and, hence, can only fully be understood in the context of their age-of-onset patterns. The diseases that have become important since the conquest of the major communicable diseases are mostly of this type, and determining their genetics is a major contemporary challenge, as we have just seen. Interestingly, analagous diseases seem to strike other mammals with age-of-onset curves that are very similar to those of humans if calibrated on the animal's life span. Since these are species-specific differences, there must be a genetic basis for them. This conclusion leads one to question what the genetic factors that affect the aging rate (since these diseases are part of the aging process) in humans are. This is an area almost totally ignored by physical anthropologists until very recently.

Early work on the inheritance of longevity—the crudest way to look at aging—was done in England with data on British peers (Beeton and Pearson 1899). First-degree relatives are correlated as to age at death. After this study, little was done for several decades until an extensive effort was made by Raymond Pearl in Baltimore in the late 1920s and early 1930s (Pearl 1924, 1931; Pearl and Pearl 1934). From this work, it seemed that there was some heritability to length of life (Cohen 1964a). However, because there were many problems with the data, new studies of familial longevity were begun in Baltimore in the 1960s (Cohen 1964b; Abbott et al. 1978). These are, as yet, incompletely reported, but indications are that there is a small familial component to longevity that is not due to obvious socioeconomic factors (Abbott et al. 1978; Murphy 1978). Similar findings have come from a study on French Canadians (Philippe 1976). Mortality is due to many factors, most of which appear to be random, at least with regard to genotype (e.g., Weiss 1981). Hence, if there are specific genetic susceptibilities, there is also considerable "noise" in longevity data. Longevity, therefore, is too vague to use as a measure of aging processes.

Is the genetic basis for life span a simple or complex one? Studies of its change over the time of mammalian evolution, and the more recent period of human evolution from a pongid stock, suggest that only a few mutations were required to transform the aging scale from that of ape-like ancestors to that of humans. Age-related biological changes seem to be too numerous and different to be under separate evolutionary control, given the short time available. Something relatively simple, such as the genetics of basic metabolism, is probably at the root of the life span of a species (Cutler 1975, 1976, 1980; Sacher 1975, 1976). It is also unlikely that individual age curves for degenerative disease risks are totally local in their etiology: There must be some systemic foundation. Yet, specific diseases with idiosyncratic histopathology are often familial, and since one mark of the familial case is an altered age of onset (usually younger), there must be some local genetic factors as well as systemic ones. There is no reason to doubt the existence of genetic heritability or familial variation in genes relating to the length of life generally, but what proportion of risk-variant alleles is systemic and what porportion is local is, as yet, totally unknown. Burnet (1974) has argued that aging and its concomitant diseases reflect the breakdown of the immune and error-repair systems, due perhaps to the accumulation of stochastic errors in cells. Recent evidence in relation to carcinogenesis, however, does not support this. Rather, it suggests that duration of time of exposure to risk factors, and not age *per se*, determine the onset time of disease (Peto *et al.* 1975).

In all probability, diseases of older age have little relationship to natural selection, and in any case, human beings are *not* unusually longevous for a mammal of their size and body temperature (see Sacher 1978). Thus, there is no reason to expect genes to exist that specifically preserve us into old age. On the other hand, stochastic probablity models are quite able to fit disease-onset curves closely (e.g., Cook *et al.* 1969), indicating that positive regulation of life span by life-shortening genes are not needed to rid the species of its elderly so as to accommodate the young.

From an evolutionary point of view, then, there seems to be no reason to expect any active genes to be involved with the expression of disease at older ages, other than simply the genes that calibrate our metabolic physiology (Weiss 1981). The genetics and evolution of human life history are, however, important in the study of the diseases that now affect most of us, and they are relatively untouched subjects in which physical anthropologists can be expected to take a more active interest in the future.

Conclusion

In this review, we have restricted our attention as much as possible to the major work accomplished in the United States between 1930 and 1980 that was carried out by or would be of interest to physical anthropologists. However, this has been an international and mostly medical history, a trend that shows no evidence of changing. Also, because it is such a large area of work, we are painfully aware of the inadequacy of our bibliography and have had to cite secondary and tertiary sources to provide an adequate survey of the existing literature.

Anthropologists have been mainly interested in variation from an evolutionary viewpoint, questioning its amount, racial and geographic patterns, and origins.

Medical researchers have stressed the clinical, diagnostic, and etiological aspects of disease. However, the thread of evolutionary inquiry has often been woven closely with the medical issues, largely because of the need, even from a medical viewpoint, to explain the source of disease and the reasons for its frequency. Genetic epidemiology thus keeps these two facets interwined, although as medical technology and capability grow, specialization will undoubtedly force some separation.

The recent explosion in genetic knowledge comes at a time when we have not adequately explained the pattern and origin of the first clearly recognized genetic polymorphism, the ABO system, and its kindred marker loci, and we continue to discover new racially patterned variation in a growing member of identifiable genes. Similarly, the relationship of the major diseases to known genes, and their role, if any, in the maintenance of genetic polymorphisms are questions as open today as they have ever been.

The persistence of the same questions for more than a half-century does not indicate lack of progress because there has been a *wealth* of progress. It means that we are asking very deep questions, and that there is still very much to learn. The next 50 years promise to be as exciting as the past 50 years.

Acknowledgments

We would like to thank W. J. Schull and J. V. Neel for their discussions with us in regard to this paper. We have received financial assistance from the National Cancer Institute, grant CA 19311, the National Institute of Aging, grant AG 01028, and the National Institute of General Medical Sciences, grant KO4 GM 00230, for which we are grateful. This is Demographic Epidemiology of Aging and Disease, Paper No. 11.

References

Abbott, M., H. Abbey, D. Polling, and E. A. Murphy
      1978   The familial component in longevity—a study of offspring of nonagenarians: intrafamilial studies. *American Journal of Medical Genetics* 2:105–120.
Adams, J., and R. H. Ward
      1973   Admixture studies and the detection of selection. *Science* 180:1137–1143.
Aird, L., H. Bendall, and J. A. E. Roberts
      1953   A relationship between cancer of the stomach and the ABO groups. *British Medical Journal* 1:799–801.
Aird, I., H. Bendall, J. A. Mehigan, and J. A. F. Roberts
      1954   The blood groups in relation to peptic ulceration and carcinoma of the colon, rectum, breast, and bronchus: an association between the ABO groups and peptic ulceration. *British Medical Journal* 2:315–321.
Alexander, W.
      1921   An inquiry into the distribution of the blood groups in patients suffering from 'malignant disease.' *British Journal of Experimental Pathology* 2:66–69.

Allison, A. C.
    1954a   Protection afforded by sickle-cell trait against subtertian malarial infection. *British Medical Journal* **1**:290–294.
    1954b   The distribution of the sickle-cell trait in East Africa and elsewhere, and its apparent relationship to the incidence of subtertian malaria. *Transactions of the Royal Society of Tropical Medicine* **48**:312–318.
    1955   Aspects of polymorphism in man. *Cold Spring Harbor Symposia on Quantitative Biology* **20**:239–255.
    1964   Polymorphism and natural selection in human populations. *Cold Spring Harbor Symposia on Quantitative Biology* **29**:137–149.
Bateson, W.
    1902   *Mendel's principles of heredity*. London and New York: Cambridge University Press.
Beeton, M., and K. Pearson
    1899   Data for the problem of evolution in man. II. A first study of the inheritance of longevity and selective death rate in man. *Proceedings of the Royal Society of London* **65**:290–305.
Black, F. L.
    1966   Measles endemicity in insular populations: critical community size and its evolutionary implications. *Journal of Theoretical Biology* **11**:207–211.
    1975   Infectious diseases in primitive societies. *Science* **187**:515–518.
Black, F. L., J. Boodall, A. Evans, H. Liebhaber, and G. Henle
    1970   Prevalence of antibody against viruses in the Tiriyo, an isolated Amazon tribe. *American Journal of Epidemiology* **91**:430.
Blumberg, B. S.
    1977   Australia antigen and the biology of hepatitis B. *Science* **197**:17–25.
Bodmer, W. F.
    1968   Demographic approaches to the measurement of differential selection in human populations. *Proceedings of the National Academy of Sciences of the United States of America* **59**:41–50.
Bodmer, W. F., and J. G. Bodmer
    1978   Evolution and function of the HLA system. *British Medical Bulletin* **34**:390–316.
Bolk, L.
    1929   Origin of racial characteristics in man. *American Journal Physical Anthropology* **13**:1–28.
Botstein, D., R. White, M. Skolnick and R. Davis
    1980   Construction of a genetic linkage map in man using restriction fragment length polymorphism. *American Journal of Human Genetics* **32**:314–331.
Boyd, W. C.
    1939   Blood groups of American Indians. *American Journal of Physical Anthropology* **25**:215–235.
    1940   Critique of methods of classifying mankind. *American Journal of Physical Anthropology* **27**:333–364.
    1950   *Genetics and the races of man*. Boston: Heath.
    1955   Detection of selective advantages of the heterozygotes in man. *American Journal of Physical Anthropology* **13**:37–52.
Brues, A. M.
    1954   Selection and polymorphism in the ABO blood groups. *American Journal of Physical Anthropology* **12**:559–597.
    1963   Stochastic tests of selection in the ABO blood groups. *American Journal of Physical Anthropology* **21**:287–299.
Buchanan, J. A., and E. Higley
    1921   The relationship of blood groups to disease. *British Journal of Experimental Pathology* **2**:247–255.
Burnet, M. E.
    1974   *Intrinsic mutagenesis*. Lancaster, England: Medical and Technical Publ.
Candela, P. B.
    1936   Blood-group reactions in ancient human skeletons. *American Journal of Physical Anthropology* **21**:429–432.

1942   The introduction of blood group B into Europe. *Human Biology* **14**:413–433.

Cannings, C., E. Thompson, and M. Skolnick
1976   Recursive derivation of likelihoods on pedigrees of arbitrary complexity. *Advances in Applied Probability* **8**:622–625.
1978   Probability functions on complex pedigrees. *Advances in Applied Probability* **10**:26–61.
1980   Pedigree analysis of complex models. In *Current developments in anthropological genetics. I. Theory and methods*, edited by J. Mielke and M. Crawford. New York: Plenum. Pp. 251–298.

Carter, C. O.
1969   Genetics of common disorders. *British Medical Bulletin* **25**:52–57.

Cavalli-Sforza, L. L., and W. F. Bodmer
1971   *The genetics of human populations*. San Francisco: Freeman.

Chakraborty, R., K. M. Weiss, and R. H. Ward
1980   Evaluation of relative risks from the correlation between relatives: a theoretical approach. *Medical Anthropology* **4**:397–414.

Chakravarti, A., and R. Chakraborty
1978   Elevated frequency of Tay–Sachs disease among Ashkenazic Jews unlikely by genetic drift alone. *American Journal of Human Genetics* **30**: 256–261.

Chase, A.
1977   *The legacy of Malthus: the social costs of the new scientific racism*. New York: Knopf.

Clarke, C. A.
1961   Blood groups and disease. *Progress in Medical Genetics* **1**: 81–119.

Cohen, B. H.
1964a   Familial patterns of mortality and lifespan. *Quarterly Review of Biology* **39**:130–181.
1964b   Family patterns of longevity and mortality. In *Genetics and the epidemiology of chronic diseases*, edited by J. V. Neel, M. W. Shaw, and W. J. Schull. *United States Public Health Service Publication* **1**163:237–263.

Cook, P., R. Doll, and S. Fellingham
1969   A mathematical model for the age distribution of cancer in man. *International Journal of Cancer* **4**:93–112.

Cooley, T. B., and P. Lee
1925   Series of cases of splenomegaly in children with anemia and peculiar bone changes. *Transaction of the American Pediatric Society* **37**:29–30.

Coon, C. S.
1963   *The origin of races*. New York: Knopf.

Crawford, M. H.
1973   The use of genetic markers of the blood in the study of the evolution of human populations. In *Methods and theories of anthropological genetics*, edited by M. Crawford and P. Workman. Albuquerque: University of New Mexico Press. Pp. 19–38.

Crow, J. F.
1958   Some possibilities for measuring selection intensities in man. *Human Biology* **30**:1–13.
1980   The estimation of inbreeding from isonymy. *Human Biology* **52**:1–14.

Crow, J. F., and C. Denniston
1981   The mutation component of genetic damage. *Science* **212**:888–892.

Crow, J. F., and M. Kimura
1970   *An introduction to population genetics theory*. New York: Harper and Row.

Crow, J. F., and A. P. Mange
1965   Measurement of inbreeding from the frequency of marriages between persons of the same surname. *Eugenics Quarterly* **12**:199–203.

Cutler, R. G.
1975   Evolution of human longevity and the genetic complexity governing aging rate. *Proceedings of the National Academy of Sciences of the United States of America* **72**:4664–4668.
1976   Evolution of longevity in primates. *Journal of Human Evolution* **5**:169–202.
1980   Evolution of human longevity. In *Aging, cancer, and cell membranes*, edited by C. Borek, C. Fenoglio, and D. King. Stuttgart: Thieme. Pp. 43–79.

Danforth, C. H.
  1921   The frequency of mutation and the incidence of hereditary traits in man. *Eugenics, Genetics and the Family: Scientific Papers of the Second International Congress on Eugenics* 1:120–128.
Edwards, J. H.
  1960   The simulation of mendelism. *Acta Genetica Statistica Medica* 10:63–70.
  1969   The familial predisposition in man. *British Medical Bulletin* 25:58–63.
Elston, R. C.
  1980   Segregation analysis. In *Current developments in anthropological genetics. I. Theory and methods*, edited by J. Mielke and M. Crawford. New York: Plenum. Pp. 327–354.
Elston, R. C., and J. Stewart
  1971   A general model for the genetic analysis of pedigree data. *Human Heredity* 21:523–542.
Ewens, W.
  1978   Tay–Sachs disease and theoretical population genetics. *American Journal of Human Genetics* 30:328–329.
Falconer, D. S.
  1965   The inheritance of liability to certain diseases estimated from the incidence among relatives. *Annals of Human Genetics* 29:51–76.
Fisher, R. A.
  1917   Positive eugenics. *Eugenics Review* 9:206–212.
  1918   The correlation between relatives on the supposition of Mendelian inheritance. *Transactions of the Royal Society* (Edinburgh) 52:399–433.
  1930   *The genetical theory of natural selection.* London and New York: Oxford University Press.
Ford, E. B.
  1942   *Genetics for medical students.* London: Methuen.
  1945   Polymorphism. *Biological Reviews of the Cambridge Philosophical Society* 20:73–88.
Gajdusek, D. C.
  1964   Factors governing the genetics of primitive human populations. *Cold Spring Harbor Symposia on Quantitative Biology* 29:121–135.
  1977   Unconventional viruses and the origin and disappearance of kuru. *Science* 197:943–960.
Garrod, A. E.
  1902   The incidence of alkaptonuria: a study in chemical individuality. *Lancet* 2:1616–1620.
  1908   The Croonian lectures on inborn errors of metabolism. *Lancet* 2:1–7, 73–79, 142–148, 214–220.
Gates, R. R.
  1929   *Heredity in man.* London: Constable.
  1936   Recent progress in blood group investigations. *Genetica* 18:47–65.
  1939   Blood groupings and racial classification. *American Journal of Physical Anthropology* 24:385–390.
  1946   *Human genetics* (2 vols.) New York: Macmillan.
Glass, B.
  1950   The action of selection on the principle Rh alleles. *American Journal of Human Genetics* 2:269–278.
  1956   On the evidence of random genetic drift in human populations. *American Journal of Physical Anthropology* 14:541–555.
Gunther, M., and L. S. Penrose
  1935   The genetics of epiloia. *Journal of Genetics* 31:413–430.
Haldane, J. B. S.
  1927   A mathematical theory of natural and artificial selection. Part V. Selection and mutation. *Proceedings of the Cambridge Philosophical Society* 28:838–844.
  1937   The effect of variation on fitness. *American Naturalist* 71:337–349.
  1940   The blood-group frequencies of the European peoples, and racial origins. *Human Biology* 12:457–480.
  1947   The mutation rate of the gene for haemophilia and its segregation ratios in males and females. *Annals of Eugenics* (London) 13:262–271.

1949a   The rate of mutation of human genes. *Hereditas* **Supplement:**267–273.
1949b   Disease and evolution. *Ricerca Scientifica Supplemento* **19:**3–10.
1957   The cost of natural selection. *Journal of Genetics* **55:**511–524.

Harpending, H.
1974   Genetic structure of small populations. *Annual Review of Anthropology* **3:**229–243.

Harris, H.
1970   *The principles of human biochemical genetics.* Amsterdam: North-Holland.

Henneberg, M.
1976   On the estimation of demographic variables from prehistoric populations. In *The demographic evolution of human populations,* edited by R. H. Ward and K. M. Weiss. New York: Academic Press. Pp. 41–48.

Herrick, J. B.
1910   Peculiar elongated and sickle-shaped red blood corpuscles in a case of severe anemia. *Archives of Internal Medicine* **6:**517.

Hirschfeld, L., and H. Hirschfeld
1919   Serological differences between the blood of different races. *Lancet* **2:**675–679.

Hirschfeld, L., and H. Zborowski
1925   Gruppenspezifische Beziehungen zwischen Mutter und Frucht und elektive Durchlässigkeit der Placenta. *Klinische Wochenschrift* **4:**1152–1157.

Hooton, E. A.
1926   Significance of the term race. *Science* **63:**75–81.
1946   *Up from the ape.* New York: Macmillan.

Kan, Y. W., and A. M. Dozy
1978   Polymorphisms of DNA sequence adjacent to the human β globin structural gene in its relation to the sickle mutation. *Proceedings of the National Academy of Sciences of the United States of America* **75:**5631–5635.

Kimura, M.
1961   Some calculations on the mutational load. *Japanese Journal of Genetics* **36**(suppl.):179–190.
1968a   Evolutionary rate at the molecular level. *Nature (London)* **217:**624–626.
1968b   Genetic variability maintained in a finite population due to mutational production of neutral and nearly neutral isoalleles. *Genetic Research* **11:**247–269.

King, J. L., and T. H. Jukes
1969   Non-Darwinian evolution. *Science* **164:**788–798.

Knudson, A. G.
1979   Our load of mutation and its burden of disease. *American Journal of Human Genetics* **31:**401–413.

Knudson, A. G., L. Wayne, and W. Hallett
1967   On the selective advantages of cystic fibrosis heterozygotes. *American Journal of Human Genetics* **19:**388–392.

Landsteiner, K.
1900   Zur Kenntnis der antifermentativen, lytischen und agglutinierenden Wirkungen des Blutserums und der Lymphe. *Zentralblatt fuer Bakteriologie, Parasitekunde und Infektionskrankheiten, Abteilung 1* **27:**357–362.

Lasker, G. W.
1968   The occurrence of identical (isonymous) surnames in various relationships in pedigrees: a preliminary analysis of the relation of surname combinations to inbreeding. *American Journal of Human Genetics* **20:**250–257.

Levine, P.
1958   The influence of the ABO system on Rh hemolytic disease. *Human Biology* **30:**14–28.

Levine, P., L. Burnham, E. Katzin, and P. Vogel
1941   The role of isoimmunization in the pathogenesis of erythroblastosis fetalis. *American Journal of Obstetrics and Gynecology* **42:**925–937.

Levit, S. G.
1936   The problem of dominance in man. *Journal of Genetics* **33:**411–434.

Lewontin, R. C.
  1974   *The genetic basis of evolutionary change.* New York: Columbia University Press.
Li, W-H., T. Gojobori, and M. Nei
  1981   Pseudogenes as a paradigm of neutral evolution. *Nature* **292**:237–239.
Livingstone, F. B.
  1958   Anthropological implications of the sickle cell gene distribution in West Africa. *American Anthropologist* **60**:533–562.
  1960   Natural selection, disease, and ongoing human evolution, as illustrated by the ABO blood groups. *Human Biology* **32**:17–27.
  1964a   Aspects of the population dynamics of the abnormal hemoglobin and glucose-6-phosphate dehydrogenase deficiency genes. *American Journal of Human Genetics* **16**:435–450.
  1964b   The distribution of the abnormal hemoglobin genes and their significance for human evolution. *Evolution* **18**:685–699.
  1967   *Abnormal hemoglobins in human populations.* Chicago: Aldine.
  1969a   Gene frequency clines of the β hemoglobin locus in various human populations and their simulation by models involving differential selection. *Human Biology* **41**:223–236.
  1969b   Polygenic models for the evolution of skin color differences. *Human Biology* **41**:480–493.
  1971   Malaria and human polymorphisms. *Annual Review of Genetics* **5**:33–64.
  1980a   Natural selection and the origin and maintenance of standard genetic marker systems. *Yearbook of Physical Anthropology* **23**:25–42.
  1980b   Natural selection and random variation in human evolution. In *Current developments in anthropological genetics. I. Theory and methods,* edited by J. Mielke and M. Crawford. New York: Plenum. Pp. 87–109.
Macklin, M. T.
  1932a   The relation of the mode of inheritance to the severity of an inherited disease. *Human Biology* **4**:69–79.
  1932b   The hereditary factor in human neoplasm. *Quarterly Review of Biology* **7**:255–281.
Mandarino, L., and J. Cadien
  1974   Use of ranked migration estimate for detecting natural selection. *American Journal of Genetics* **26**:108–110.
Martin, A. O., *et al.*
  1980   Genetics of neoplasia in a human isolate. In *Genetic and environmental factors in experimental and human cancer,* edited by H. Gelboin *et al.* Tokyo: Japan Science Society Press. Pp. 291–302.
McKusick, V. M.
  1978   *Medical genetic studies of the Amish.* Baltimore: Johns Hopkins University Press.
McMichael, A., and H. Dewitt
  1977   The association between the HLA system and disease. *Progress in Medical Genetics* **2**:39–100.
Mielke, J., and M. Crawford (editors)
  1980   *Current developments in anthropological genetics. I. Theory and methods.* New York: Plenum.
Mørch, E. T.
  1941   Chondrodystrophic dwarfs in Denmark. *Opera ex Domo Biologiae Hereditariae Humanae* **3**.
Morgan, K.
  1973   Historical demography of a Navajo community. In *Methods and theories in anthropological genetics,* edited by M. Crawford and P. Workman. Albuquerque: University of New Mexico Press. Pp. 263–314.
Morgan, T. H.
  1913   Factors and unit characters in Mendelian heredity. *American Naturalist* **47**:5–16.
  1918   Concerning the mutation theory. *Scientific Monthly* **25**:385–405.
Morton, N. E.
  1958   Segregation analysis in human genetics. *Science* **127**:79–80.
  1959   Genetic tests under incomplete ascertainment. *American Journal of Human Genetics* **11**:1–16.
  1960   The mutational load due to detrimental genes in man. *American Journal of Human Genetics* **12**:348–364.

1974   Analysis of family resemblance. I. Introduction. *American Journal of Human Genetics* **26**:318–330.

Morton, N. E., and C. S. Chung
1978   *Genetic epidemiology.* New York: Academic Press.

Morton, N. E., and D. C. Rao
1978   Quantitative inheritance. *Yearbook of Physical Anthropology* **21**:12–41.

Morton, N. E., J. F. Crow, and H. J. Muller
1956   An estimate of the mutational damage in man from data on consanguineous marriages. *Proceedings of the National Academy of Sciences of the United States of America* **42**:855–863.

Motulsky, A. G.
1960   Metabolic polymorphism and the role of infectious diseases in human evolution. *Human Biology* **32**:28–62.
1975   G6PD and abnormal hemoglobin polymorphisms—evidence regarding malarial selection. In *The role of natural selection in human evolution,* edited by F. Salzano. New York: American Elsevier. Pp. 271–294.

Mourant, A. E., A. C. Kopeč, and K. Domaniewska-Sobczak
1978a   *The distribution of the human blood groups and other polymorphisms.* Oxford: Oxford University Press.
1978b   *Blood groups and disease.* Oxford: Oxford University Press.

Muller, H. J.
1927   Artificial transmutation of the gene. *Science* **66**:84–87.
1950   Our load of mutations. *American Journal of Human Genetics* **2**:111–176.

Murphy, E. A.
1978   Genetics of longevity in man. In *The genetics of aging,* edited by E. Schneider. New York: Plenum. Pp. 261–301.

Myrianthopoulos, N.
1972   Population genetics of Tay–Sachs disease. II. What confers the selective advantage upon the Jewish heterozygote? In *Sphingolipids, sphingolipidosis, and allied disorders,* edited by B. Volk and S. Aronson. New York: Plenum. Pp. 561–569.

Myrianthopoulos, N., and A. Aronson
1966   Population dynamics of Tay–Sachs disease. I. Reproductive fitness and selection. *American Journal of Human Genetics* **18**:313–327.

Neel, J. V.
1949a   The detection of genetic carriers of hereditary disease. *American Journal of Human Genetics* **1**:19–36.
1949b   The inheritance of sickle cell anemia. *Science* **110**:64–66.
1951   The population genetics of two inherited blood dyscrasias in man. *Cold Spring Harbor Symposia on Quantitative Biology* **15**:141–158.
1953   Data pertaining to the population dynamics of sickle cell disease. *American Journal of Human Genetics* **5**:154–167.
1958   The study of natural selection in primitive and civilized human populations. *Human Biology* **30**:43–72.
1962   Diabetes mellitus: a "thrifty" genotype rendered detrimental by "progress"? *American Journal of Human Genetics* **14**:353–362.
1963   *Changing perspectives on the genetic effects of radiation.* Springfield, Illinois: Thomas.
1968   The American Indian in the International Biological Program. *Scientific Publication—Pan American Health Organization* **165**:47–67.
1971a   Genetic aspects of the ecology of disease in the American Indian. In *The ongoing evolution of Latin American populations,* edited by F. Salzano. Springfield, Illinois: Thomas. Pp. 561–590.
1971b   Lessons from a primitive people. *Science* **170**:815–822.
1972   The detection of increased mutation rates in human populations. In *Mutagenic effects of*

environmental contaminants, edited by H. E. Sutton and M. I. Harris. New York: Academic Press. Pp. 99–119.

1973   "Private" genetic variants and the frequency of mutation among South American Indians. *Proceedings of the National Academy of Sciences of the United States of America* **70**:3311–3315.

1975   The study of "natural" selection in man: last chance. In *The role of natural selection in human evolution,* edited by F. Salzano. New York: American Elseview. Pp. 355–368.

1979   History and the Tay-Sachs allele. In *Genetic diseases among the Askhenazi Jews,* edited by R. M. Goodman and A. G. Motulsky. New York: Raven. Pp. 355–368.

Neel, J. V., and N. A. Chagnon

1968   The demography of two tribes of primitive, relatively unacculturated American Indians. *Proceedings of the National Academy of Sciences of the United States of America.* **59**:680–689.

Neel, J. V., and F. M. Salzano

1966   A prospectus for genetic studies on the American Indian. In *The biology of human adaptability,* edited by P. T. Baker and J. S. Weiner. Oxford: Oxford University Press (Clarendon). Pp. 245–274.

Neel, J. V., and W. J. Schull

1956   *The effect of exposure to the atomic bombs on pregnancy termination in Hiroshima and Nagasaki.* Washington, D. C.: National Academy of Sciences.

1968   On some trends in understanding the genetics of man. *Perspectives in Biology and Medicine* **11**:565–602.

Neel, J. V., and E. A. Thompson

1978   Founder effect and number of private polymorphisms observed in Amerindian tribes. *Proceedings of the National Academy of Sciences of the United States of America* **75**:1904–1908.

Neel, J. V., and K. M. Weiss

1975   The genetic structure of a tribal population, the Yanomama Indians. XII. Biodemographic studies. *American Journal of Physical Anthropology* **42**:25–51.

Neel, J. V., M. W. Shaw, and W. J. Schull

1965   *Genetics and the epidemiology of chronic diseases.* United States Public Health Service Publication **1163**.

Neel, J. V., W. R. Centerwall, N. A. Chagnon, and H. L. Casey

1970   Notes on the effect of measles and measles vaccine in a virgin-soil population of South American Indians. *American Journal of Epidemiology* **91**:418–429.

Nei, M.

1975   *Molecular population genetics and evolution.* Amsterdam: North-Holland.

Newcombe, H. B.

1964   Discussion. In *Second international conference on congenital malformations.* New York: International Medical Congress. Pp. 345–347.

1972   Effects of radiation on human populations. In *Human genetics,* edited by J. de Grouchy, F. Ebling, and I. Henderson. Amsterdam: Excerpta Medica. Pp. 45–57.

Otten, C.

1967   On pestilence, diet, natural selection, and the distribution of microbial and human blood group antigens and antibodies. *Current Anthropology* **8**:209–226.

Pauling, L. C., H. Itano, S. Singer, and I. Wells

1949   Sickle cell anemia, a molecular disease. *Science* **110**:543–548.

Pearl, R.

1924   Preliminary account of an investigation of factors influencing longevity. *Journal of the American Medical Association* (JAMA) **82**:259–264.

1931   Studies on human longevity. IV. The inheritance of longevity: preliminary report. *Human Biology* **3**:245–269.

Pearl, R., and R. D. Pearl

1934   *The ancestry of the long-lived.* Baltimore: Johns Hopkins University Press.

Penrose, L. S.
    1953   The genetical background of common diseases. *Acta Genetica et Statistica Medica* **4**:257–265.
    1955   Evidence of heterosis in man. *Proceedings of the Royal Society of London, Series B* **144**:203.
Peto, R., F. J. C. Roe, P. N. Lee, L. Levy, and J. Clack
    1975   Cancer and ageing in mice and men. *British Journal of Cancer* **32**:411–426.
Pettenkofer, H., B. Stoss, W. Helmbold, and F. Vogel
    1962   Alleged causes of the present-day world distribution of the human ABO blood groups. *Nature (London)* **193**:445–446.
Philippe, P.
    1976   Genetics of longevity. *International Congress Series—Excerpta Medica* **397**:192.
Post, R. H.
    1971   Possible causes of relaxed selection in civilized populations. *Human Genetics* **13**:253–284.
Provine, W. B.
    1971   *The origins of theoretical population genetics.* Chicago: University of Chicago Press.
Ramot, B. (Editor)
    1974   *Genetic polymorphisms and diseases in man.* New York: Academic Press.
Rao, D. C., and N. E. Morton
    1980   Path analysis of quantitative inheritance. In *Current developments in anthropological genetics. I. Theory and methods,* edited by J. Mielke and M. Crawford. New York: Plenum. Pp. 355–372.
Raper, A. B.
    1950   Sickle-cell disease in Africa and America—a comparison. *Journal of Tropical Medicine* **53**:49–53.
Reed, T. E.
    1961   Polymorphism and natural selection in blood groups. In *Genetic polymorphisms and geographic variations in diseases,* edited by B. Blumberg. New York: Grune and Stratton. Pp. 80–101.
    1969   Caucasian genes in American Negroes. *Science* **165**:762–768.
    1975   Selection and the blood group polymorphisms. In *The role of natural selection in human evolution,* edited by F. Salzano. New York: American Elsevier. Pp. 231–246.
Reed, T. E., and J. Chandler
    1958   Huntington's chorea in Michigan. I. Demography and genetics. *American Journal of Human Genetics* **10**:201–225.
Reed, T. E., and J. V. Neel
    1959   Huntington's chorea in Michigan. II. Selection and mutation. *American Journal of Human Genetics* **11**:107–136.
Reid, R. M.
    1973   Inbreeding in human populations. In *Methods and theories of anthropological genetics,* edited by M. Crawford and P. Workman. Albuquerque: University of New Mexico Press. Pp. 83–116.
Roberts, J. A. F.
    1957   Blood groups and susceptibility to disease: a review. *British Journal of Preventive and Social Medicine* **11**:107–125.
    1959   Some associations between blood groups and disease. *British Medical Bulletin* **15**:129.
Rossmann, D. L.
    1978   Increased fertility among amyotrophic lateral sclerosis and Parkinsonism-dementia complex cases on the island of Guam. Unpublished Ph. D. dissertation, Department of Anthropology, University of Michigan, Ann Arbor.
Sacher, G. A.
    1975   Maturation and longevity in relation to cranial capacity in hominid evolution. In *Antecedents of man and after* (Vol. I). *Primates.* The Hague: Mouton. Pp. 417–441.
    1976   Evaluation of the entrophy and information terms governing mammalian longevity. *Interdisciplinary Topics in Gerontology* **9**:69–82.

1978   Evolution of longevity and survival characteristics in mammals. In *The genetics of aging,* edited by E. Schneider. New York: Plenum. Pp. 151–168.

Schanfield, M.
1980   The anthropological usefulness of highly polymorphic systems: HLA and immunoglobulin allotypes. In *Current developments in anthropological genetics. I. Theory and methods,* edited by J. Mielke and M. Crawford. New York: Plenum. Pp. 65–85.

Schull, W. J.
1958   Radiation and human genetics. *Radiobiology and Cancer* pp. 423–439. Austin: University of Texas Press.
1959   Inbreeding effects in man. *Eugenics Quarterly* 6:102–109.
1965   Estimation of genetic parameters in population studies. *United States Public Health Service Publication* 1163:45–60.

Schull, W. J., and J. V. Neel
1958   Radiation and the sex ratio in man. *Science* 128:343–348.
1965   *The effect of inbreeding on Japanese children.* New York: Harper and Row.

Schull, W. J., and K. M. Weiss
1980   Genetic epidemiology: four strategies. *Epidemiological Review* 2:1–18.

Schull, W. J., J. V. Neel, and A. Hashizume
1968   Some further observations on the sex ratio among infants born to survivors of the atomic bombings of Hiroshima and Nagasaki. *American Journal of Human Genetics* 18:328–338.

Schull, W. J., T. Ishimaru, H. Kato, and T. Wakabayashi
1980   Radiation carcinogenesis: the Hiroshima and Nagasaki experiences. In *Genetic and environmental factors in experimental and human cancers,* edited by H. Gelboin *et al.* Japan Science Society Press. Pp. 313–326.

Sing, C. F., and M. H. Skolnick (editors)
1979   *Genetic analysis of common diseases: Applications to predictive factors in coronary disease.* New York: Alan R. Liss.

Smithies, O.
1955   Zone electrophoresis in starch gels: group variations in the serum proteins of normal human adults. *Biochemical Journal* 61:629–641.

Snyder, L. H.
1926   Human blood groups: their inheritance and racial significance. *American Journal of Physical Anthropology* 9:233–263.
1929   *Blood grouping in relation to clinical and legal medicine.* Baltimore: Williams and Wilkins.

Spuhler, J. N.
1963   The scope for natural selection in man. In: *Genetic selection in man,* edited by W. J. Schull. Ann Arbor, Michigan: University of Michigan Press. Pp. 1–111.
1977   The maximum opportunity for natural selection in some human populations. In *Demographic anthropology,* edited by E. Zubrow. Albuquerque: University of New Mexico Press. Pp. 185–226.

Steinberg, A. G., H. Bleibtreu, T. Kurczynski, A. Martin, and E. Kurczynski
1967   Genetic studies on an inbred human isolate. *Proceedings of the Third International Congress of Human Genetics* 1966:267–289.

Valentine, W. N., and J. V. Neel
1944   Hematologic and genetic study of the transmissions of thalassemia (Cooley's anemia; Mediterranean anemia). *Archives of Internal Medicine* 74: 185–196.

Van Ooyen, A., J. van den Berg, N. Mantei, and C. Weissman
1979   Comparison of total sequences of a cloned rabbit β-globin gene and its flanking regions with a homologous mouse sequence. *Science,* 206:337–344.

Vogel, F.
1975   ABO blood groups, the HL-A system and diseases. In *The role of natural selection in human evolution,* edited by F. Salzano. New York: American Elsevier. Pp. 247–269.

Vogel, F., and M. Chakravartti
    1966   ABO blood groups and smallpox in a rural population of West Bengal and Bihar (India).
             Humangenetik **3**:166–180.
Vogel, F., and A. G. Motulsky
    1979   *Human genetics.* Berlin and New York: Springer-Verlag.
Vogel, F., and R. Rathenburg
    1975   Spontaneous mutation in man. In. *Advances in Human Genetics* Vol. **5**. H. Harris and K.
             Hirschhorn. New York: Plenum. Pp. 223–318.
Wagener, D., L. Cavalli-Sforza, and R. Barakat
    1978   Ethnic variation of genetic disease: a role of drift for recessive lethal genes. *American Journal
             of Human Genetics* **30**:262–270.
Ward, R. H., A. Hooper, and J. Hurtzman
    1980   Pedigrees and blood pressure: genetic epidemiology in a migrant isolate, Tokelau. In
             Banbury Reports No. 4: Cancer incidence in defined populations, edited by J. Cairns, L. Lyon, and
             M. Skolnick. Cold Spring Harbor, New York: Cold Spring Harbor Lab. Pp. 351–361.
Weiss, K. M.
    1972   A general measure of human population growth regulation. *American Journal of Physical
             Anthropology* **37**:337–344.
    1976   Demographic theory and anthropological inference. *Annual Review of Anthropology* **5**:351–
             381.
    1981   Evolutionary perspectives on human aging. In. *Other ways of growing old,* edited by P.
             Amoss and S. Harrell. Stanford, California: Stanford University Press. Pp. 25–58.
Weiss, K. M., R. Chakraborty, P. P. Majumder, and P. E. Smouse
    1982   Problems in the assessment of relative risk of chronic disease among biological relatives of
             affected individuals. *Journal of Chronic Disease,* **35**:539–552.
Wiesenfeld, S. L.
    1967   Sickle-cell trait in human biological and cultural evolution. *Science* **157**:1134–1140.
Woolf, B.
    1955   On estimating the relation between blood group and disease. *Annals of Human Genetics*
             19:251–253.
Workman, P. L., B. Blumberg, and A. Cooper
    1963   Selection, gene migration and polymorphic stability in a U. S. White and Negro population.
             American Journal of Human Genetics **15**:429–437.
Wyman, L. C., and W. C. Boyd
    1935   Blood groups and anthropology. *American Anthropologist* **37**:181–200.
    1937   Blood group determinations of prehistoric American Indians. *American Anthropologist*
             39:583–592.

17

The Development of Ideas
on Human Ecology and Adaptation

Michael A. Little

Current Theory: Ecology, Evolution,
and Adaptation to the Environment

Physical anthropologists contribute to scientific explanation in two major areas. In the first, there is an attempt to understand human evolution according to its past and its ongoing processes. The second concerns the unique biocultural attributes of human populations, or how behavior and biology acting together contribute to the adaptability of human societies in a multitude of environments. These two areas of investigation and explanation are not mutually exclusive; evolutionary process requires continuing adaptation to changing environments, and human evolutionary history has been characterized by interrelated changes in cultural behavior and human biology. It is this latter area of investigation that serves as the subject matter under review in this chapter, that is, adaptation to the environment by living or recent human populations.

Adaptation as a Concept

The term adaptation is subject to a number of conceptual interpretations. It is often confused with fitness. Darwinian *fitness* refers to a genotypic or genetic-system state produced by natural selection that is relatively better than some other state within the context of a given environment (Dobzhansky 1968a). Hence, use of the term *fitness* is quite specific, whereas use of the term *adaptation* is not (Mazess

A HISTORY OF AMERICAN
PHYSICAL ANTHROPOLOGY, 1930–1980

1975a). Medawar (1951) identified three uses of adaptation: (*a*) adaptation as something possessed by an individual or a population, such as *an adaptation* to combat cold; (*b*) adaptation as a state of being, such as a population *is adapted* to a specific environment; and (*c*) adaptation as a process, such as in *incremental adjustments* to an environment conferring greater states of adaptation at each time level.

The first use of the term is usually more specific than the second; in the first use, an adaptation is identified as a given structure, function, or mechanism. Medawar's second use of the term is general, usually refers to the whole organism, and is often employed within an ecosystem context (Pianka 1974:187; Watt 1973:37). When adaptation as a state refers to a genetic or evolutionary state, then *adaptation* and *fitness* are similar in meaning (Stern 1970). Darwin (1859) used the term quite frequently in this way. For example, he stated (with reference to natural selection) "I can see no limit to this power, in slowly and beautifully adapting each form to the most complex relations of life [p. 469]."

As Dobzhansky (1968b) has noted "The statement that organisms are adapted to the environments in which they live and reproduce may seem to be trivial [p. 109]." This question of triviality or purported tautology concerning the concept of adaptation was reviewed by Alland (1975; Alland and McCay 1974). Alland (1975) cautioned that "to say that adaptive traits are those which are present in systems, or that those traits which are present in systems are adaptive, adds nothing to our understanding of process [p. 59]." Dobzhansky (1968b) addressed this question quite effectively by identifying the "engineering" component of selection, where organisms are designed to fit their environments, and by pointing out that the relative states of adaptation of some forms of life are superior to those of others. Dubos (1965) argued that "perhaps the only meaure of adaptive fitness to the environment is the extent to which the organisms of the species under consideration can occupy this environment, make effective use of its resources, and therefore multiply abundantly in it [p. 259]."

Some points of confusion (Alland and McCay 1974) seem to be associated with views of adaptation in an evolutionary or genetic sense versus those applied in a more general sense. It would appear that adaptation as a state in the individual can be measured according to both (*a*) survival and general well-being and (*b*) reproductive success. The two are certainly of concern in an evolutionary context, but the first can be studied alone within a nonevolutionary framework, if desired. Adaptations in this first category are more likely to be identified according to their physiological flexibility or genetic plasticity characteristics.

There are several other terms frequently found in conjunction with *adaptation*. When used with reference to human survival and well-being, a number of terms are employed to describe states of adjustment to the environment through the internal regulatory mechanisms of the body (Folk 1974; Prosser 1964). These terms, such as *acclimatization, acclimation, habituation* and *accommodation* refer to specific kinds of flexible responses to environmental stress (Baker 1966; Eagan 1963; Wohlwill 1974). Darwin (1859) recognized the plasticity of acclimatization responses in the following statement: "Hence I am inclined to look at adaptation to any special climate as a quality readily grafted on an innate wide flexibility of constitution, which is common to most animals [p. 141]." When prediction or evaluation of adaptation is attempted, the term *adaptability* is employed (Lasker 1969). Here, there is an interest in the range of or limits to adaptation, particularly among humans (Baker and Weiner 1966). As Dobzhansky (1968b) noted "Man is certainly superior in adaptability because he can create environments deliberately, according to plans devised by himself [p. 113]." It is of prime importance to know the extent of this adaptability in humans as well.

Human Ecology and the Environment

In order to understand fully the patterns of human adaptation to the environment, it is necessary to understand also the environmental or ecological systems of which humans are a part. *Ecology* is most commonly defined as the study of *organism-environment relations*. Marston Bates stated that "the problems of adaptation in structure and behavior are ecological problems, [1960:566]," and Pianka defined *adaptation* as "the conformity between organism and environment [1974:187]." Thus, we come full circle, particularly with the understanding that evolutionary process is really ecological change that has become fixed within the genetic systems of members of the biotic community.

The scientific philosophy that human populations should be studied within an ecological framework arose from the view that humans are subject to the same evolutionary and ecological laws as all other living forms. The presence of language, culture, and abstract reasoning in humans, however, does set them somewhat apart from other species by allowing, among other things, a more complex pattern of organism–environment interaction to take place. Culture, as a unique dimension of the human species, produces greater environmental complexity that feeds back on the human biological system as well as the cultural system. Because of this tight interrelationship between human cultural behavior, human biology, and an increasingly complex environment, a number of writers have argued for a combined biological and cultural approach to the study of human ecology (Baker 1962; Bates 1953; Bennett *et al.* 1975; Little and Morren 1976; Vayda and Rappaport 1968).

The material that follows deals with the development, over the last half century, of ideas about human ecology and adaptation by physical anthropologists. The science of physical or biological anthropology has been transformed dramatically during this period. An understanding of adaptation and ecology have contributed to that transformation.

History of the Concepts

Early History (1930–1950)

Fifty years ago, a collection of papers titled *Human Biology and Racial Welfare* (Cowdry 1930) was published. Its distinguished list of contributors from biology, geography, and anthropology included Walter Cannon, Charles B. Davenport, William Gregory, Aleš Hrdlička, Ellsworth Huntington, Raymond Pearl, Clark Wissler, Robert Yerkes, and Hans Zinsser. In addition to the founder and first president of the American Association of Physical Anthropologists (AAPA) from 1928–1932 (Hrdlička), three later AAPA presidents (Davenport, Gregory, and Pearl) were contributors to the volume. As a "state-of-the-art" report on human biology and race, the volume serves as a good indicator of current ideas on human population biology in 1930.

Hrdlička's chapter, "Human Races,"[1] and Davenport's chapter, "The Mingling of Races," reflect the hereditarian or extreme genetic determinism view. In these chapters races and their rigid genetic natures had fixed morphologies, physiologies, behaviors, and temperaments. Principal concerns were with taxonomy and origins. Any divergence from the three or four main races was explained by a racial admixture model based on highly subjective judgments. Moreover, observations were biased frankly in favor of European superiority, which was a prevailing view of the times. In contrast, the chapter by Huntington, "The Effect of Climate and Weather,' exemplified the environmental determinism view, equally biased in favor of European, or rather, temperate zone, superiority. Here, the climate was the dominant causal agent structuring much of human behavior and contributing to present racial characteristics.

Despite the scientific weakness of both the data and the polar views, the environmentalists, nevertheless, were attempting to deal with process and explanation, in contrast to the racial taxonomists' more static approach. Although Huntington did not elaborate, he referred several times to "forms of adaptation" in human populations responding to climatic parameters, such as temperature, humidity, and solar ultraviolet radiation. Some of his conclusions on morphological adaptation to climate would be acceptable today.

These extreme, nature–nurture positions tended to prevent any meaningful integration of theory or data. Synthesis of the environmental, hereditary, evolutionary, and population approaches remained for the future, despite some very sophisticated work in human population biology that was being conducted during this period by Pearl, as reported in the Cowdry (1930) volume.

As Baker (1962) observed, hereditary and environmental determinism go back to far earlier times than the 1930s. Baker argued that Franz Boas' strong views on

---

[1] Although Hrdlička's contribution to Cowdry's volume *appears* hereditarian in view, in fact, he was among the few anthropologists of the period who supported the notion of racial plasticity (Spencer 1981).

the separation of race and culture were in response to extreme attitudes of environmental and genetic determinism that were prevalent during the early part of the century. It is curious, however, that Boas did not take a more integrated viewpoint of environment, culture, and biology since he had conducted a classic study of environmental (biological) plasticity associated with a sociocultural phenomenon (migration) between 1908 and 1910 (Boas 1911). In this remarkable study, Boas found more advanced growth and development patterns among children born in the United States of immigrant parents than among those who were foreign-born. Moreover, he found that more advanced growth was associated with higher socioeconomic status and, hence, linked ethnic and socioeconomic factors to conditions of environmental change. In spite of this pioneering study by Boas (1911) and the later studies of migrants that it stimulated (Lasker 1946; Shapiro 1939), the static concept of race or population persisted well into the 1940s.

Kroeber (1948), with reference to these migration studies, grudgingly stated,

In short what these measurements and their statistical interpretation seem to establish is that hereditary racial types may possess a certain limited degree of plasticity, within the measure of which they can respond to alterations of environment. There is no indication that environment as such will alter a race progressively or cumulatively. If progressive adaptive alterations do not occur, it is presumably through natural selection, that is, survival value of certain traits [p. 168].

Although reference is made to "natural selection" and adaptation to the environment here, the greater part of the material on human biology in this second edition of *Anthropology* (Kroeber 1948) focused on race origins and classification and was basically unchanged from the first edition (Kroeber 1923). In brief, then, neither the giants of general anthropology nor the leaders in physical anthropology were inclined to view human culture and human biology as interacting and adaptive responses to environmental conditions.

Human ecology during the 1930s and 1940s was largely the "cultural ecology" of Forde (1934), Steward (1938, 1955) and other sociocultural anthropologists. Very little interest in adaptation, the environment, or ecology was expressed by physical anthropologists during this period. Even Hooton's (1946) comprehensive work in physical anthropology, *Up from the Ape*, was quite traditional and provided little information to indicate that the author was interested in human biological adaptation to the environment.

There were, however, numerous studied conducted on physiological adaptation to the climatic environment by biologists and physiologists who were not trained in anthropology. For example, Robinson and his colleagues (1941a, 1941b) studied responses to heat of Whites and Southern Black sharecroppers; Hicks and his co-workers (1931; Hicks and O'Connor 1938) explored the adaptation of Australian Aborigines to desert cold; Hurtado (1932) and Monge (1948) were involved in studies of adaptation to high-altitude hypoxia in Andean Indians. During and after World War II, several investigations were conducted to assess human adaptive limits to climatic parameters. The principal use for the information was military. A classic study by Adolph and associates (1947) dealt with human physiological adaptation to desert environments. In a review collection on temperature regulation edited by Newburgh (1949), the introductory chapter, which covered adaptation to climate was prepared by an anthropologist (Wulsin 1949).

The period between 1930 and 1950 was not an active one in physical anthropology with respect to ecology or environmental adaptation. However, the decade that followed proved to be a period of major growth in theory and methodology.

Later History (1950–1980)

At the midpoint of the century, three important works were published: (*a*) a book by Boyd (1950) on genetics and race; (*b*) the fifteenth volume of papers from the Cold Spring Harbor Symposia on Quantitative Biology (Warren 1950), which dealt with human evolution and origins; and (*c*) a book by Coon, Carn and Birdsell (1950) on race and race formation. In each of these works, race figured prominently in the theory and data presented. Yet, there was a marked difference in the perspectives represented when one contrasts them with works from the two previous decades. Perspectives were evolutionary, genetic, and centered on the population as the unit of scientific study. There remained, of course, some vestiges of interest in racial origins and classification, but, for the most part, natural selection through the environment was of prime concern.

This new atmosphere of scientific exploration of human biology and evolution was reflected in Washburn's (1951, 1953) writings on the "new physical anthropology." Washburn, who, along with Theodosius Dobzhansky, was a program organizer of the June, 1950, Cold Spring Harbor Symposium, suggested that there was a need to study and demonstrate "adaptive complexes . . . to gain an understanding of the human body [Washburn 1951:300]." Although the interest in adaptation and natural selection was rising, nevertheless, Bates, who attended the Cold Spring Harbor Symposium in June, 1950, expressed some concern that there was a "general lack of emphasis on the ecological aspects of the problem under review [1953:710]."

There *was* substantial coverage of the environment in the biogeographical treatment of human population variation in Coon *et al.*'s (1950) small volume. Although the book focuses on races, adaptation to the environment was its central theme, and human variations within climatic zones were treated in several chapters. Chapter 4, 5, and 6, for example, were subtitled "Adaptations to Excess Light and Heat under Different Degrees of Humidity," "Adaptations to Dry Cold," and "Adaptations to Cool, Damp Coudiness," respectively. This book was one of the first sophisticated works on human adaptation to the environment to be done by anthropologists. The environment was considered of prime importance also in Montague's introductory text, where he stated,

> Man lives in a physical environment which varies in different lands and often in neighboring localities of the same lands. The seasons, sunlight, temperature, humidity, barometric pressure,

rainfall, water, soil, foods and a thousand and one other factors, are all to be taken into consideration in the study of the mental and physical development of man. Man, in short, must always be studied in relation to his environment, past as well as present [1951:4].

Later research on human adaptation to the climatic environment was rich and varied and employed laboratory comparison and biogeographic field comparison methods of study (Baker 1960; Barnicot 1957, 1959; Coon 1955). Much of the early research consisted of testing the applicability of Bergmann's and Allen's rules of body size and shape (as postulated by Coon et al. [1950]) to human populations (Baker 1958a; Newman 1953, 1956; Roberts 1953; Schreider 1950, 1951). In additional studies, Newman and Munro (1955) found that the body size of United States soldiers from northern states was greater than that of soldiers from the warmer South, and thus demonstrated an acclimatizational response in body morphology; Weiner (1954) found a strong association between nose form and environmental vapor pressure; Roberts (1952) was able to show statistically that basal metabolic rates were lower in tropical than in temperate and arctic zone residents; and Roberts (1960) also suggested, from a study of Sudanese children, that climate will affect childhood growth through developmental acclimatization.

At the same time that anthropologists were concentrating on climatic adaptation through body morphology and body composition, environmental physiologists were continuing to define variations in climatic tolerance among native populations resident in stressful zones. Studies included physiological tests of Bantu mineworkers exposed to hot–wet conditions in South Africa (Wyndham et al. 1952) and tests of temperature responses to cold of Australian Aborigines (Schölander et al. 1958), Arctic Indians (Irving et al. 1960), Eskimos (Brown and Page 1952; Meehan 1955), Alakaluf Indians (Hammel 1960), and Laplanders (Schölander et al. 1957). A comprehensive review volume was published in 1964 that documented the physiological studies of human and other animal adaptation to the environment (Dill et al. 1964). These and other studies demonstrated, beyond a reasonable doubt, that human populations distributed throughout the world had adapted to the climatic conditions that characterized their environments.

By the late 1950s and during the 1960s, interests in morphological and body composition adaptations to climate had broadened to include physiological mechanisms of adaptation to climate (Baker 1958b; Baker and Daniels 1956) and also adaptation to other parameters of the environment, such as nutrition (Newman 1960) and disease (Livingstone 1960; May 1960; Motulsky 1960). Studies of body compositon in physical anthropology (Brožek 1963; Garn 1963) arose from skeletal biology pursuits and were linked closely to nutritional adaptation. Anthropometric (Garn 1962) and physique (Brožek 1956) surveys were conducted to assess nutritional status, and relationships between growth and nutrition in stressful environments were investigated (Mazess and Baker 1964; Newman 1962; Newman et al. 1963; Roberts 1960; Schraer and Newman 1958).

During the same period, research on human population and environment increased. Birdsell's (1953) earlier study of Australian tribal size and density relationships with rainfall and social variables seemed to signal a return of interest to a field pioneered by Pearl (1930) more than two decades earlier. Demographic work on physical anthropology was varied in scope (Spuhler 1959). Research dealt with evolutionary and genetic problems (Lasker 1960; Livingstone 1962; Salzano, 1962), and a variety of other sociocultural and genetic attributes of populations, including mating practices, gene flow, and consanguinity (Bonné 1963; Kunstadter *et al.* 1963; Roberts 1956; Salzano 1961). Demographic research provided a well-defined way to link human social behavior with human biology as well as serving to test for modes of human adaptation.

In 1964, the first edition of an important introductory textbook in physical anthropology was published by four British human biologists, Harrison, Weiner, Tanner, and Barnicot (1964). This was an important work because it was synthetic in nature, particularly its final section, "Human Ecology" (Weiner 1964). In the first paragraph of the introduction to this section, Weiner (1964) defined the scope of *human ecology* as

> The integrity, persistence, and, when it occurs, expansion of human groups rests on a continuous action on, and interaction with, the environment—a continuous exchange of materials and energy, out of which the group fashions the necessary materials and conditions for its existence. Ecology in its broadest sense, denotes the dynamic interrlations of the community with its total environment. The adjustments necessary for successful existence in a particular habitat are termed "adaptations" [p. 401].

In this slightly more than 100-page treatment of human ecology, Weiner (1964) first delineated this field of interest to human biologists; topics covered included (*a*) nutrition, (*b*) disease, (*c*) climate, and (*d*) population, and central emphasis of the work was on "ecological adaptive processes."

Another development of considerable significance occurred in 1964: the establishment of the International Biological Program (IBP), with its ecological orientation and its theme, "the Biological Basis of Productivity and Human Welfare."

Human Adaptability and the International Biological Program

The International Council of Scientific Unions established the IBP with a planning phase from 1964 to 1967 and an operational or research phase from 1967 to 1972. A number of sections to the program were identified according to research efforts. The Human Adaptability Section was to cover "the ecology of mankind" from a number of perspectives, including health and welfare, environmental physiology, population genetics, developmental biology, anthropology, and demography (Weiner 1965). As J. S. Weiner, (1977) who was International Convener for the human Adaptability Section, noted in retrospect,

> The IBP came just at the time when it could contribute significantly to the development of human population biology, a process which had begun after the Second World War with the supercession

and transformation of the old-fashioned and static subject of physical anthropology by an ecologically and genetically based discipline [p. 2].

Although preliminary planning for the Human Adaptability research began in 1962, a significant planning session was held in Austria at the Wenner-Gren Foundation Burg Wartenstein Conference Center in July, 1964. It was there that Weiner (1966) outlined the major categories of planned research, the other contributors provided statements on current knowledge over a wide range of topics for African, South American, Asian, Australian, and circumpolar populations (Baker and Weiner 1966).

This planning and subsequent research resulted in the participation of 40 nations and the completion of 230 projects under the Human Adaptability Section. Projects were classified under world-wide themes of (a) human growth and development, (b) physique and body composition, (c) physical fitness, (d) climatic tolerance, (e) genetic constitution, and (f) nutritional status; and regional–ecological themes of (a) high altitudes; (b) circumpolar and other cold climates; (c) tropical and desert climates; (d) islands and isolates; (e) migrant and hybrid populations; and (f) urban and rural groups in industrialized countries (Weiner 1977:13). These projects were compiled by Collins and Weiner (1977) with extensive bibliographies. A number of important international volumes have arisen from IBP-Human Adaptability (IBP-HA) work, including: standard methods in human biology (Weiner and Lourie 1969); a survey of world human growth (Eveleth and Tanner 1976); high altitude population biology (Baker 1978); circumpolar population biology (Milan 1980); population structure (Harrison 1977); exercise capacity (Shephard 1978); and physiological adaptation (Weiner, in press).

The Human Adaptability studies that were a part of the United States contribution to the IBP started from a single frame of reference that was environmentally oriented—that of studying *the adaptive mechanisms of populations living under some form of environmental stress* (National Academy of Sciences (NAS) 1974:69). There were three major integrated research programs: (a) the International Study of Circumpolar Peoples, with an Eskimo project under the direction of F. A. Milan (Jamison *et al.* 1978) and an Aleut project directed by W. S. Laughlin (Laughlin and Harper 1979); (b) the Population Gentics of the Native Americans, which focused on the Yanomama Indians of Brazil and Venezuela, under the direction of J. V. Neel (Neel *et al.* 1977); (c) the Biology of Human Populations at High Altitude, with research conducted in the southern Peruvian Andes, directed by P. T. Baker (Baker and Little 1976). These and other United States projects were discussed by Hanna and others (1972) in the context of Human Adaptability and by Lasker (1969) in a theoretical context.

The results of the Human Adaptability work in the United States and abroad contributed to our knowledge of human biology and ecology in many ways. World survey data of child growth, nutrition, and genetic polymorphisms provided baseline information of great value to international agencies, such as the World Health Organization (WHO) and the Food and Agriculture Organization (FAO).

This was also probably the last opportunity to study many technologically simple native societies living in close harmony with their environments before the incursion of Western society and advanced technology changed their lives forever through acculturation. The culture disappearance and biological assimilation in recent years of the populations studied during the IBP—the Hadze of Tanzania, the Pygmies of Zaïre and the Central African Republic, the Ainu of Japan, and some Eskimo and Australian Aboriginal groups—is testimony to the value of the Human Adaptability projects (Weiner 1977). Other studies were instrumental in developing new research designs and methods (Baker 1976; Neel 1970; Yoshimura and Weiner 1966). Also, the importance of international cooperation and active coordination was recognized, particularly in the case of circumpolar studies where four nations (France, Denmark, Canada, and the United States) participated in an integrated Eskimo Project in Alaska, Canada, and Greenland (Milan 1980).

Training in physical anthropology and human biology was influenced positively by the Human Adaptability projects in the United States. More than 40 students were trained for the Ph.D. degree through IBP–HA studies (NAS 1974:7). Moreover, the influx of these scientists into American institutions has contributed to the development and broadening of additional training programs in environmental science and human adapation research.

Approaches to the Study of Human Adaptation

Within the field of physical anthropology, there appear to be three major approaches that have been taken in investigations of human adaptation or adaptability. First, the *environmental physiology* approach studies the highly adaptable responses of human physiological mechanisms to conditions of environmental stress. Physiological responses are generally thought to be environmentally labile or flexible responses. Second is the *ontogenetic*, which studies human adaptation through research on the growth and development of children and adolescents and how human growth processes influence adult status. Third is an approach that has focused on *genetics and demography* with interests in microevolutionary process as well as adaptability. Brief discussions of the contributions of each of these approaches follow.

Environmental Physiology

Much of the method and theory applied by anthropologists in the study of human physiological adaptation has been drawn from the field of environmental physiology. Concepts such as *stress, homeostatis,* and *acclimatization* are derived from the physicological literature (Prosser 1964). Anthropologists have contributed to the understanding of environmental physiology in several ways: (*a*) the addition of the cultural and behavioral dimensions to conditions of and responses to environmental stress; (*b*) the emphasis on the population approach to human physiology in order to be able to explain not only average responses but also variations in patterns of physiological responses; (*c*) the incorporation of an evolutionary perspective to deal with human physiology as a genetic as well as a plastic response (Baker 1974, 1975; Damon 1975; Lasker 1969).

Most of the work conducted in human physiology to date includes (*a*) human responses to climatic stresses such as heat, cold, and terrestrial altitude and (*b*) physical work-capacity variations among populations around the world. This research is dealt with briefly in this section. (For a more complete review see Beall, in the present volume.)

Newman (1970, 1975) has outlined our present evolutionary and physiological state of knowledge on human adaptation to heat. It is agreed that much of early human evolution took place in the tropical zone of Africa; hence, humans have a long history of exposure to hot conditions and can be thought of as basically heat-adapted creatures. Throughout the world, there is a human dependence on thermal sweating to dissipate body heat. This provides for two major potential strains associated with heat stress: dehydration and hyperthemia. Standardized heat stress tests have been carried out on North and South American Indians (Hanna 1970; Hanna and Baker 1974), United States Blacks (Baker 1958b), Tanzanian urban dwellers (Doré *et al.* 1975), Nigerian workers (Ojikutu *et al.* 1972), and Congo Pygmies (Austin and Ghesquière 1976). Based on these studies by anthropologists and other studies by physiologists (Ladell 1964; Lee 1964), all human populations—arctic, temperate, and tropical zone dwellers—appear equally capable of physicological heat acclimatization, given comparable exposure conditions (Newman 1975). Principal differences in ultimate heat adaptability among human populations, then, lie in the realm of body size and composition variation, such as surface areas to weight ratios, stature, extremity proportions, and fat and muscle content of the body—morphological parameters.

Whereas humans might be thought of as "naturally" adapted to heat through their evolutionary heritage, their evolutionary experience with exposure to cold climates is much less. Important attributes of adaptation to cold are (*a*) prevention of body heat loss and hypothermia, (*b*) maintenance of surface termperatures at sufficient levels to avoid tissue damage, and (*c*) maintenance of relatively warm limb temperatures (especially hands and fingers) so that function is not impaired. Reviews of human responses to cold have reported that artic dwellers—such as Eskimos, Arctic Indians, and Laplanders—are more tolerant of low temperatures due to (*a*) morphological characteristics associated with body size, shape, and composition; (*b*) slightly elevated basal heat production when compared with temperate or tropical zone dwellers; and (*c*) high blood flow to the hands and feet when exposed to cold (Frisancho 1979;41–84; Hammel 1964; Little and Steegmann in press; Steegman 1975). The controls over these processes, whether genetic or not, are not completely known but are, nevertheless, complex. Culture, including technology and other manifestations, can modify (ameliorate or intensify) the affect of cold on individuals and, hence, influence the patterns of response.

Studies of high terrestrial altitudes and their resident and transient populations were given an impetus by the organization of the IBP. Integrated research projects were conducted in the Ethiopian highlands (Harrison *et al.* 1969), the Tien Shan mountains and Pamir plateau (Mirrakhimov 1978), the Andean altiplano (Baker 1969; Baker and Little 1976; Schull and Rothhammer 1977), and the Himalayan plateau (Weitz 1973). Reviews of this work in altitude physiology, morphology, growth, genetics, and demography are found in Baker (1978), Clegg and colleagues (1970), Frisancho (1975), Little (1981), and Mazess (1975b). The environmental stresses at high altitudes, above 3000 m, throughout the world are hypoxia (Buskirk 1978) and cold (Little and Hanna 1978), and these stresses can produce severe strain in the human organism. Although considerable research has been conducted on the adaptation of resident populations to the high-altitude habitat, much work still remains to define adequately the limits of human adaptability in this environment.

Studies of the physiology of work or exercise capacity in humans cut across habitats, environments, and ecosystems since they relate to the need of humans to subsist and produce food (Andersen 1966; Thomas 1975). A complete understanding of work-capacity variation and its role in human adaptability requires study of the relationships between work capacity and environmental stress, such as heat and high altitude. For example, physical work and warm environmental conditions are synergistic in producing thermal stress, such that work may be limited by high ambient temperatures and intense work requirements in heat will require maximal heat acclimatization (Weiner 1980). Activity, heat, and nutrition are also interdependent since high sweat rates lead to nitrogen losses (Weiner *et al.* 1972). At high altitude, the parameter of hypoxia will limit the work capacity of newcomers dramatically (Buskirk 1976), yet high-altitude natives show maximal work capacity abilities that are equivalent to those of sea-level dwellers at their home elevation (Buskirk 1978). In addition to ambient temperatures and high-altitude hypoxia, there are other factors that can affect work capacity: (*a*) poor nutritional status (protein or calorie deficiencies); (*b*) chronic or acute illness (parasites, infections); (*c*) body composition (low muscle mass); (*d*) age, sex, and size; and (*e*) physical fitness level from previous activity. Thus, we can see the complex interrelationships among many parameters encountered when one attempts to define states of adaptation and adaptability according to physiological systems.

Growth and Development

As Johnston (1980) observed with reference to human growth, "In viewing the various pathways along which individuals, and the population, become adapted to their environments, the developmental process emerges as paramount." What he referred to was the process of "developmental adaptation" during the growing period, which can influence, so profoundly, the structural and functional attributes of the adult organism. In the recent past, population differences in the adult and the growing child were attributed, generally, to racial or hereditary factors. As studies have become more sophisticated and data have accumulated, the plasticity and adapability of human growth processes to the environment have become more apparent (Tanner 1966, 1978). This holds for physiological as well as morphological and body composition development. The best documented influences of environmental paramaters are (a) nutrition (particularly calorie and protein intake), (b) disease, (c) environmental temperature, (d) terrestrial altitude, (e) activity, (f) urban or rural residence; (g) socioeconomic status, and others (Eveleth and Tanner 1976). To provide an example of the interaction of some of these parameters with growth, the case of high-altitude research will be discussed briefly.

Andean Indian growth in Peru, Bolivia, and Chile has been investigated in considerable depth (Frisancho 1976, 1979; Haas 1976; Hoff 1974; Mueller et al. 1978). Infant, child, and adolescent growth of high-altitude Aymara and Quechua Indians is slow and prolonged when contrasted with their sea-level counterparts. Birth weights at high altitude are low, and physical growth retardation of infants during the first 2 years of life is altitude-related (Haas 1976). On the other hand, Indian mothers, despite the low birth weights, are still able to gestate newborn infants that are slightly heavier than newborn infants of non-Indian mothers living at high altitude (Haas et al. 1980). The authors attribute the newborn weight advantage to a better state of adaptation in the Indian infants than in the non-Indian infants. Adolescent growth is also slow in highland Indians, and sexual dimorphism in size and body composition does not appear until about 16 years of age (Frisancho and Baker 1970). Growth among highlanders of both sexes continues until about 22 years of age, when full maturation in size is achieved. Thomas (1976) argued that this pattern of prolonged growth and late age of maturation is an adaptation to limited food calorie resources and that as a result, considerable savings in food production effort can be realized. This is a good example of a probable interaction of hypoxia and limited nutritional intake.

Another interaction pattern at high altitude occurs among the parameters of hypoxia, cold, and nutrition (Little 1981; Picón-Reátegui 1978). The ability to maintain warm limb temperatures in response to cold develops in childhood (Little et al. 1971) and leads to a high skin-surface heat loss. Associated with hypoxia, there is an increased ventilation, which leads to a high respiratory heat loss from the body. These modes of increased heat loss are probably what stimulate the elevated basal metabolism, which, in turn, increases the need for greater food calories.

Finally, what enables the highland Indian to perform work at sea-level-equivalent rates despite the limited amount of oxygen delivered to working muscle? Is this a genetic ability or the result of a developmental acclimation to high-altitude hypoxia? Frisancho and his co-workers (1973) demonstrated a clear developmental pattern from studies of migrants to high altitude. A relationship was found between age and high-altitude migration; the younger the age at migration to high altitude, the more closely the exercise capacity values approached those of the Indian residents. Duration of stay at high altitude after adulthood in those who migrated as adults only permitted a limited degree of improvement in exercise capacity over newcomers to altitude. Hence, a full period of childhood and adolescent exposure is necessary to adapt maximally to physical activity needs at high altitude.

These few examples of growth and environment interdependencies illustrate the importance of viewing growth as an adaptive process.

Genetics and Demography

Demography and genetics are natural partners within an evolutionary framework (Ward and Weiss 1976). The two, combined, constitute the field of population genetics (Baker and Sanders 1972; Spuhler 1959), which is central to an understanding of evolution. Weiss (1976), who identified anthropology as a biocultural evolutionary science, listed several demographic parameters of interest in an evolutionary as well as an anthropological context: fertility, mortality, population size and distribution, mating practices, and migration. Each of these parameters is an indicator of or is closely related to adaptation. Study of variation in human populations or demographic parameters within defined environments, then, is a highly productive approach to problems of human adaptation. Two examples can serve as illustrations: In the first, a migration model can be used to explore human plasticity responses to environmental variation. In the second, a postulated example of population control through fertility reduction is discussed.

Permanent migration of large numbers of individuals sets up a natural research design for comparative tests of environmental influences on human populations. In migrants, the process of adaptation to a novel environment can be studied (*a*) in adults during a short duration periods, (*b*) in the context of child development over one generation, or (*c*) over several generations to assess long-range patterns of adjustment. Comparisons can be made among nonmigrants or "sedentes" who remain in the "home" environment and members of the migration stream derived from the same population who settle in several new environments.

Boas (1911) was one of the first to exploit this phenomenon in his investigations of East Europeans who settled in American urban centers. Since that time, studies have been conducted of Japanese migrants to Hawaii (Shapiro 1939) and to California (Kondo and Eto 1975), and Chinese (Lasker 1946), Mexican (Goldstein 1943), Swiss (Hulse 1957), and Puerto Rican (Thieme 1957) migrants to the United States. Kaplan (1954) reviewed at length these early studies of migrants within the context of genetic plasticity. More recently, a migrant design has been used to explore problems of high-altitude adaptation in individuals who move from highland to sea-level zones (Abelson *et al.* 1974; Harrison 1966) and to investigate the relations among obesity, cardiovascular disease, and a Western life-style in Samoan migrants to Hawaii (Baker 1977).

Female fecundity (reproductive ability) and *fertility* (reproductive performance) are difficult parameters to study since variation in either is subject to so many influences. Of the two, fecundity is somewhat more manageable to study since most of its control is biological. About a decade ago, Frisch and Revelle (1970) provided evidence for a relationship between body weight and *menarche*, or the onset of reproductive ability in adolescent girls. Since that time, the hypothesis of a "critical weight that triggers menarche" has been refined to a critical body-fat content or fat–lean mass ratio that must exist before menarche will occur or menstrual cycles can be maintained (Fritsch *et al.* 1973; Frisch and McArthur 1974). This detailed work of Frisch and her colleagues has been severely criticized in the literature (Bongaarts 1980; Johnston *et al.* 1975; Trussell 1978). However, if the hypothesis of some relationship between fecundity and body composition (and, hence, nutrition) is supported, it will have interesting implications for the understanding of population control in nonwestern populations. For example, Frisch (1975, 1978) suggested that the low fertility of Bushmen and some New Guinea populations is due to low caloric input and inadequate fat reserves to carry some of these women through a full-term pregnancy. Howell (1976) feels that this hypothesis explains her data on San Bushman, in whom menarche is very late and the total fertility rate is not high by world standards. Limited caloric input during the very arid times of the year in nomadic pastoral populations of East Africa may contribute to low female fertility (Swift 1977), and the increases in fertility when pastoralists become settled farmers (Henin 1968) may be due to increased caloric input. All of these hypotheses require field, survey, and laboratory testing because of the complexity of reproduction, both biologically and behaviorally.

Current Trends in Human Ecology

Identifying and predicting trends in anything is often a risky business and may, in fact, be simply a reflection of an author's wishful thinking. With this caveat in mind, there are several lines and modes of research that are likely to contribute to our understanding of human populations in an environmental or ecological context, or at least within an ecological perspective. These are (*a*) approaches to modeling and simulation of demographic and ecological systems, including nutrient and energy flows through human systems; (*b*) a reintegration of ecological and evolutionary theory as an "evolutionary ecology" of human systems in the same way that Pianka (1974) has done for general biotic systems; (*c*) biocultural approaches to a "health ecology" dealing with problems of health, disease, nutrition, and the environment; and (*d*) a greater dependence on integrated, multidisciplinary research of complex systems with some support of international programs. I should hope that this work would embrace a biocultural approach in anthropological research and that conceptualizations of a "cultural ecology" or "biological ecology" could be avoided.

Modeling Approaches

Models, in the sense referred to here, are not theories or paradigms or verbal discriptions of integrated sets of relationships. Rather, a *model* is viewed as a representation of a system or process that assists in our understanding and allows for the testing and generation of hypotheses concerning the system or process. Ideally, then, such a model should have analytic power, be interactive and dynamic (rather than deterministic and static), and be capable of quantification. Some of the most complex ecosystem mathematical models developed to date arose from the biome research in the United States International Biological Program work (NAS 1974). The very sophisticated computer modeling generated in this work was ultimately used for the prediction of change in the ecosystem and for ecosystem management purposes. Humans were incorporated minimally in these models.

In human ecology, modeling is less sophisticated, but some models are quite good. Demographer–geneticists, perhaps, have done the most advanced computer work in dealing with the simulation of the effects of mating structure, inbreeding, migration, fertility, mortality, and other parameters on population structure through time (Dyke and MacCluer 1973; Leslie *et al.* 1981; Swedlund 1978). Energy flow modeling has been applied to a number of human populations, based on the modular framework developed by Odum (1971), to study how energy sources are tapped, transformed, and utilized in different environments. By use of these models, Thomas (1976) demonstrated the vital nature of trade in a highland Peruvian community, Morren (1977) illustrated how energetic effiiciency was "sacrificed" in order to gain protein among New Guinea Miyanmin, and Bedoian (1978) combined energy flow and economic models in synthetic modeling in southeastern Tunisia. Combined energy flow and population models have been developed for Andean populations (Baker 1979; Blakenship and Thomas 1977), and combined energy and nutrient flow population and ecosystem modeling of Kenyan pastoral nomads is underway (Dyson-Hudson 1980; Ellis *et al.* 1979; Little 1980).

Human Evolutionary Ecology

The field of *evolutionary ecology* as applied to humans was discussed at length by Thomas and his colleagues (1979), Durham (1976), Dyson-Hudson and Smith (1978), Smith (1979, 1982), and Winterhalder (1980). Much of the theory is drawn from MacArthur (1972; MacArthur and Pianka 1966) and Pianka (1974), in which the analytical approach is a mathematical modeling of ecological systems relationships, with an emphasis on the behavioral adaptations of animals (and humans) to the environment. Selection, Darwinian fitness, and adptations are central concepts to evolutionary ecology. Current writing on human systems has focused on resource exploitation and optimal foraging strategies of hunter–gatherer populations (Smith, 1982). In general, those who embrace this approach are not in favor of sociobiological approaches (Thomas *et al.* 1979). The major contributions of this latter approach are likely to be the greater attention directed toward long-term adaptations and adaptations to "temporal variability" (Winterhalder 1980), a close tracking of the most contemporary theory in ecology, and sophisticated analysis through modeling and simulation.

Health Ecology

The term *health ecology* refers to the grouping of basic science and applied studies in medical ecology, epidemology, medical anthropology, health, and nutrition. In an excellent overview of the scope of this field (which they refer to as "medical ecology"), McElroy and Townsend (1979) identify it as an approach "that views health and disease as reflections of ecological relationships within a population, between neighboring populations, and among the life forms and physical components of a habitat [p. 2]." Good health and functional ability is certainly an important component of human adapation (Boyden 1972; Mazess 1978); hence, the concerns of research in health ecology can be a part of human adaptability and its theory and can show considerable overlap with physiological, ontogenetic, and genetic adaptation studies. Some examples of these kinds of studies follow.

One problem centers around social trends in the bottle-feeding of infants and the subsequent effects on (*a*) material fertility, (*b*) child health, and (*c*) the nutritional status of the child. Within recent years, there has been a trend among lower-class urban and rural-peasant mothers in Latin America, Asia, and Africa to bottle-feed rather than breast-feed their infants (Jelliffe and Jelliffe 1972). This attempt to emulate socially the behaviors of middle- and upper-class Western mothers has had disastrous effects by contributing to population growth and infant disease and malnutrition. Since breast-feeding suppresses ovulation in the female, early cessation of breast-feeding increases the rate of new pregnancies and contributes to high rates of population growth. In addition, bottle-fed infants often are given diluted milk or substitutes of low nutrient value. This fact, when combined with the absence of maternal antibodies in breast milk, contributes to high rates of infant malnutrition and illness. Finally, any active immunity to disease that an infant might develop is likely to be limited by malnutrition (Frisancho 1979:182–184). The net result in a society with limited food resources is an insidious positive feedback system of population increase, infant morbility, and infant malnutrition, with the probable consequences of brain damage in some infants. Clearly, integrated studies of human values, environmental resources, and human health biology will assist in solving this serious problem of health ecology.

Another research area of prime importance in these times is health ecology in urban environments (Harrison and Gibson 1976; Harrison and Jeffries 1977). Ethnic and class diversity, environmental pollutants, noise, and crowding all contribute to a form of stress in urban environments that is qualitatively different from that in rural environments. Since rural-to-urban migration today is occurring at unprecedented rates, there is a need to understand these environment–health–behavior relationships soon.

Multidisciplinary and Integrated Research

A major difficulty in studying the ecology and adaptability of human populations has been and will continue to be the complexity of the systems investigated and the fact that no single investigator can hope to study a human system comprehensively. A solution to this problem is team research (Baker 1968), in which scientists from diverse fields collaborate to study a population or a problem that could not be managed by an investigator working along. This kind of multidisciplinary study was carried out successfully as a part of the HA projects of the IBP. Yet, there was minimal contact and virtually no collaboration between scientists trained to study human populations and animal and plant ecologists.

It is likely that with the creation of Unesco's Man and the Biosphere (MAB) Program in the early 1970s—due to the structure of the program—there will be more collaboration between these disciplines. (Jamison *et al.* 1976). The MAB program includes about 15 projects, many of which deal with ecosystems like tropical forests, grazing lands, arid zones, and mountains. Reciprocal human–environment impacts are the central focus of the overall MAB program. Also, one of the 15 projects is soley human in research orientation, and this project will be integrated in terms of individual research activities with the appropriate MAB ecosystem projects. The role of this "human population-oriented" project is to understand the human and environmental needs and consequences of the growth and redistribution of mankind. Problem areas that are recommended for investigation are (*a*) the effects of population movements, including urbanization, on human health and welfare; (*b*) the effects of environmental and human-imposed change on human health and welfare; (*c*) the study of human isolates; and (*d*) the promotion of new scientific approaches for the study of man–environment relationships. The focus is clearly ecological, and the potential for multidisciplinary integration and deeper understanding of humans in the biosphere is there.

Acknowledgments

I wish to offer my thanks to the following individuals for their assistance in preparing this paper: Linda Duffy, bibliographic work; Adrienne V. Little, editing; Jason P. Little, proofreading; and Sue McMahon, manuscript preparation.

References

Abelson, A. E., T. S. Baker, and P. T. Baker
    1974   Altitude, migration and fertility in the Andes. *Social Biology* **21**:12–27.
Adolph, E. F., and associates
    1947   *Physiology of man in the desert.* New York: Wiley (Interscience).

Alland, A., Jr.
    1975   Adaptation. *Annual Review of Anthropology* **4**:59–73.
Alland, A., Jr., and B. McCay
    1974   The concept of adaptation in biological and cultural evolution. In *Handbook of social and cultural anthropology,* edited by J. J. Honigmann. Chicago: Rand McNally. Pp. 143–178.
Andersen, K. L.
    1966   Work capacity of selected populations. In *The biology of human adaptability,* edited by P. T. Baker and J. S. Weiner. London and New York: Oxford University Press (Clarendon). Pp. 67–90.
Austin, D. M., and J. Ghesquière
    1976   Heat tolerance of Bantu and Pygmoid groups of the Zaïre River basin. *Human Biology* **48**:439–453.
Baker, P. T.
    1958a   The biological adaptation of man to hot deserts. *American Naturalist* **92**:337–357.
    1958b   Racial differences in heat tolerance. *American Journal of Physical Anthropology* **16**:287–305.
    1960   Climate, culture, and evolution. *Human Biology* **32**:3–16.
    1962   The application of ecological theory to anthropology. *American Anthropologist* **64**:15–22.
    1966   Human biological variation as an adaptive response to the environment. *Eugenics Quarterly* **13**:81–91.
    1968   Multidisciplinary studies of human adaptability: theoretical justification and method. *Materialy i Prace Anthropologiczne (Warsaw)* **75**:321–330.
    1969   Human adaption to high altitude. *Science* **163**:1149–1156.
    1974   An evolutionary perspective in environmental physiology. In *Environmental physiology,* edited by N. B. Slonim. St. Louis, Missouri: Mosby. Pp. 510–522.
    1975   The place of physiological studies in anthropology. In *Physiological anthropology,* edited by A. Damon. London and New York: Oxford University Press. Pp. 3–12.
    1976   Research stragegies in population biology and environmental stress. In *Measures of man: methodologies in biological anthropology,* edited by E. Giles and J. S. Friedlaender. Cambridge, Massachusetts: Peabody Museum Press. Pp. 230–259.
    1977   Environment and migration on the small islands of the South Pacific. In *Human population problems in the biosphere: some research strategies and designs,* edited by P. T. Baker. *MAB Technical Notes No.* **3**. Paris: UNESCO. Pp. 53–64.
    1978   (editor) *The biology of high altitude peoples.* London and New York: Cambridge University Press.
    1979   The use of human ecological models in biological anthropology: examples from the Andes. *Collegium Anthropologicum (Zagreb)* **2**:157–171.
Baker, P. T., and F. Daniels, Jr.
    1956   Relationship between skinfold thickness and body cooling for two hours at 15°C. *Journal of Applied Physiology* **8**:409–416.
Baker, P. T., and M. A. Little (editors)
    1976   *Man in the Andes: a multidisciplinary study of high altitude Quechua.* Stroudsburg, Pennsylvania: Dowden, Hutchinson, and Ross.
Baker, P. T., and W. T. Sanders
    1972   Demographic studies in anthropology. *Annual Review of Anthropology* **1**:151–178.
Baker, P. T., and J. S. Weiner (editors)
    1966   *The biology of human adaptability.* London and New York: Oxford University Press (Clarendon).
Barnicot, N. A.
    1957   Human pigmentation. *Man* **57**:114–120.
    1959   Climatic factors in the evolution of human populations. *Cold Spring Harbor Symposia on Quantitative Biology* **24**:115–129.
Bates, M.
    1953   Human ecology. In *Anthropology today: an encyclopedic inventory,* edited by A. L. Kroeber. Chicago: University of Chicago Press. Pp. 700–713.

1960   Ecology and evolution. In *Evolution after Darwin* (Vol. I), edited by S. Tax. Chicago: University of Chicago Press. Pp. 547–568.

Bedoian, W. H.
1978   Human use of the pre-Saharan ecosystem and its Impact on desertization. In *Social and technological management in dry lands*, edited by N. Gonzales. Washington, D.C.: American Association for the Advancement of Science. Pp. 61–109.

Bennett, K. A., R. H. Osborne, and R. J. Miller
1975   Biocultural ecology. *Annual Review of Anthropology* **4**:163–181.

Birdsell, J. B.
1953   Some environmental and cultural factors influencing the structuring of Australian aboriginal populations. *American Naturalist* **87**:171–207.

Blankenship, J. C., and R. B. Thomas
1977   Demographic impact of introducing modern medicine to a subsistence-level agrarian populations: a simulation. *Environmental Management* **1**:401–417.

Boas, F.
1911   *Changes in the bodily form of descendents of immigrants* (Senate Document 208, 61st Congress, second session.) Washington, D.C.: U.S. Government Printing Office.

Bongaarts, J.
1980   Does malnutrition affect fecundity? A summary of evidence. *Science* **208**:564–569.

Bonné, B.
1963   The Samaritans: A demographic study. *Human Biology* **35**:61–89.

Boyd, W. C.
1950   *Genetics and the races of man.* Boston: Little, Brown.

Boyden, S.
1972   Biological determinants of optimal health. In *Human biology of environmental change*, edited by D. J. M. Vorster. London: International Biological Programme. Pp. 3–11.

Brown, G. M., and J. Page
1952   The effect of chronic exposure to cold on temperature and blood flow to the hand. *Journal of Applied Physiology* **5**:221–227.

Brožek, J.
1956   Physique and nutritional status of adult men. *Human Biology* **28**:124–140.
1963   Quantitative description of body composition: physical anthropology's "fourth" dimension. *Current Anthropology* **4**:3–39.

Buskirk, E. R.
1976   Work performance of newcomers to the Peruvian highlands. In *Man in the Andes: a multidisciplinary study of high-altitude Quechua*, edited by P. T. Baker and M. A. Little. Stroudsburg, Pennsylvania: Dowden, Hutchinson and Ross. Pp. 283–299.
1978   Work capacity of high-altitude natives. In *The biology of high-altitude peoples*, edited by P. T. Baker. London and New York: Cambridge University Press. Pp. 173–187.

Clegg, E. J., G. A. Harrison, and P. T. Baker
1970   The impact of high altitudes on human populations. *Human Biology* **42**:486–518.

Collins, K. J., and J. S. Weiner
1977   *Human adaptability: a history and compendium of research.* London: Taylor and Francis.

Coon, C. S.
1955   Some problems of human variability and natural selection in climate and culture. *American Naturalist* **89**:257–280.

Coon, C. S., S. M. Garn, and J. B. Birdsell
1950   *Races: a study of the problems of race formation in man.* Springfield, Illinois: Thomas.

Cowdry, E. V. (editor)
1930   *Human biology and racial welfare.* New York: Harper (Hoeber).

Damon, A.
1975   *Physiological anthropology.* London and New York: Oxford University Press.

Darwin, C.

1859   *On the origin of species by means of natural selection, or the preservation of favoured races in the struggle for life.* London: John Murray.

Dill, D. B., E. F. Adolph, and C. G. Wilber (editors)
1964   *Adaptation to the environment,* Sect. 4, *handbook of physiology.* Washington, D.C.: American Physiological Society.

Dobzhansky, T.
1968a   On some fundamental concepts of Darwinian biology. *Evolutionary Biology,* Vol. 2, edited by T. Dobzhansky, M. K. Hecht, and W. C. Steere. New York: Appleton-Century-Crofts.

1968b   Adaptedness and fitness. In *Population biology and evolution,* edited by R. C. Lewontin. Syracuse, New York: Syracuse University Press. Pp. 109–121.

Doré, C., J. S. Weiner, E. F. Wheeler, and H. El-Neil
1975   Water balance and body weight: studies in a tropical climate. *Annals of Human Biology* 2:25–33.

Dubos, R.
1965   *Man adapting.* New Haven, Connecticut: Yale University Press.

Durham, W. H.
1976   The adaptive significance of cultural behavior. *Human Ecology* 4:89–121.

Dyke, B., and J. W. MacCluer (editors)
1973   *Computer simulation in human populations.* New York: Academic Press.

Dyson-Hudson, N.
1980   Strategies of resource exploitation among East African savanna pastoralists. In *Human ecology in savanna environments,* edited by D. R. Harris. New York: Academic Press.

Dyson-Hudson, R., and E. A. Smith
1978   Human territoriality: an ecological assessment. *American Anthropologist* 80:21–41.

Eagan, C. J.
1963   Introduction and terminology: habituation and peripheral tissue adaptations. *Federation Proceedings, Federation of American Societies for Experimental Biology* 22:930–933.

Ellis, J. E., C. H. Jennings, and D. M. Swift
1979   A comparison of energy flow among the grazing animals of different societies. *Human Ecology* 7:135–149.

Eveleth, P. B., and J. M. Tanner (editors)
1976   *Worldwide variation in human growth.* London and New York: Cambridge University Press.

Folk, G. E., Jr.
1974   *Textbook of environmental physiology.* Philadelphia: Lea and Febiger.

Forde, C. D.
1934   *Habitat, ecology and society: a geographical introduction to ethnology.* New York: Dutton.

Frisancho, A. R.
1975   Functional adaptation to high altitude hypoxia. *Science* 187:313–319.

1976   Growth and morphology at high altitude. In *Man in the Andes: a multidisciplinary study of high-altitude Quechua,* edited by P. T. Baker and M. A. Little. Stroudsburg, Pennsylvania: Dowden, Hutchinson, and Ross. Pp. 180–207.

1979   *Human adaptation: a functional interpretation.* St. Louis, Missouri: Mosby.

Frisancho, A. R., and P. T. Baker
1970   Altitude and growth: a study of the patterns of physical growth of a high altitude Peruvian Quechua population. *American Journal of Physical Anthropology* 32:279–292.

Frisancho, A. R., C. Martinez, T. Velásquez, J. Sanchez, and H. Montoye
1973   Influence of developmental adaptation on aerobic capacity at high altitude. *Journal of Applied Physiology* 34:176–180.

Frisch, R. E.
1975   Demographic implications of the biological determinants of female fecundity. *Social Biology* 22:17–22.

1978   Population, food intake, and fertility. *Science* 199:22–30.

Frisch, R. E., and J. W. McArthur

1974   Menstrual cycles: fatness as a minimum weight for height necessary for their maintenance or onset. *Science* **185**:949–951.

Frisch, R. E., and R. Revelle
1970   Height and weight at menarche and a hypothesis of critical weights and adolescent events. *Science* **169**:397–398.

Frisch, R. E., R. Revelle, and S. Cook
1973   Components of weight at menarche and the initiation of the adolescent growth spurt in girls: estimated total water, lean body weight and fat. *Human Biology* **45**:469–483.

Garn, S. M.
1962   Anthropometry in clinical appraisal of nutritional status. *American Journal of Clinical Nutrition* **11**:418–432.
1963   Human biology and research in body composition. *Annals of the New York Academy of Science* **110**:429–446.

Goldstein, M. S.
1943   *Demographic and bodily changes in descendants of Mexican immigrants.* Austin: Institute of Latin American Studies, University of Texas.

Haas, J. D.
1976   Prenatal and infant growth and development. In *Man in the Andes: a multidisciplinary study of high-altitude Quechua,* edited by P. T. Baker and M. A. Little. Stroudsburg, Pennsylvania: Dowden, Hutchinson, and Ross. Pp. 161–179.

Haas, J. D., E. A. Frongillo, C. D. Stepick, J. L. Beard, and L. Hurtado G.
1980   Altitude, ethnic and sex difference in birth weight and length in Bolivia. *Human Biology* **52**:459–477.

Hammel, H. T.
1960   Thermal and metabolic responses of the Alakaluf Indians to moderate cold exposure. *United States Air Force Systems Command, Research and Technology Division, Air Force Materials Laboratory, Technical Report,* **WADD-TR-60-633**. Wright-Patterson Air Force Base, Ohio.
1964   Terrestrial animals in cold: recent studies of primative man. In *Adaptation to the environment,* Sect. 4, *Handbook of physiology,* edited by D. B. Dill, E. F. Adolph, and C. G. Wilber. Washington, D.C.: American Physiological Society. Pp. 413–434.

Hanna, J. M.
1970   Responses of native and migrant desert residents to arid heat. *American Journal of Physical Anthropology* **32**:187–195.

Hanna, J. M., and P. T. Baker
1974   Comparative heat tolerance of Shipibo Indians and Pervian Mestizos. *Human Biology* **46**:69–80.

Hanna, J. M., S. M. Friedman, and P. T. Baker
1972   The status and future of U.S. Human adaptability research in the International Biological Program. *Human Biology* **44**:381–398.

Harrison, G. A.
1966   Human adaptation with reference to the IBP proposals for high altitude research. In *The biology of human adaptability,* edited by P. T. Baker and J. S. Weiner. London and New York: Oxford University Press (Clarendon). Pp. 509–519.

Harrison, G. A. (editor)
1977   *Population structure and human variation.* London and New York: Cambridge University Press.

Harrison, G. A., and J. B. Gibson (editors)
1976   *Man in urban environments.* London and New York: Oxford University Press.

Harrison, G. A., and D. J. Jeffries
1977   Human biology in urban environments: A review of research strategies. In *Human population problems in the biosphere: some research strategies and designs,* edited by P. T. Baker. *MAB Technical Notes,* **3**. Paris: UNESCO. Pp. 65–82.

Harrison, G. A., J. S. Weiner, J. M. Tanner, and N. A. Barnicot
    1964   *Human biology: an introduction to human evolution, variation, growth, and ecology.* London and New York: Oxford University Press.
Harrison, G. A., et al.
    1969   The effects of altitudinal variation on Ethiopian populations. *Philosophical Transactions of the Royal Society, Series B* **256**:147–182.
Henin, R. A.
    1968   Fertility differentials in the Sudan. *Population Studies* **22**:147–164.
Hicks, C. S., and W. J. O'Connor
    1938   Skin temperature of Australian aboriginals under varying atmospheric conditions. *Australian Journal of Experimental Biology and Medical Science* **16**:1–18.
Hicks, C. S., R. F. Matters, and M. L. Mitchell
    1931   The standard metabolism of Australian aboriginals. *Australian Journal of Experimental Biology and Medicine* **8**:69–82.
Hoff, C. J.
    1974   Altitudinal variations in the physical growth and development of Peruvian Quechua. *Homo* **24**:87–99.
Hooton, E. A.
    1946   *Up from the ape.* New York: Macmillan.
Howell, N.
    1976   Toward a theory of human paleodemography. In *The demographic evolution of human populations,* edited by R. H. Ward and K. M. Weiss. New York: Academic Press. Pp. 25–40.
Hulse, F. S.
    1957   Exogamie et hétérosis. *Archives Suisses d'Anthropologie General* **22**:103–125.
Hurtado, A.
    1932   Respiratory adaptation in the Indian natives of the Peruvian Andes. Studies at high altitude. *American Journal of Physical Anthropology* **17**:137–165.
Irving, L., et al.
    1960   Metabolism and temperature of Arctic Indian men during a cold night. *Journal of Applied Physiology* **15**:635–644.
Jamison, P. L., S. M. Friedman, and P. T. Baker
    1976   *Interactions of human populations and the environment: a prospectus on project 12 of the U.S. man and the biosphere program.* U.S. MAB **12**. University Park, Pennsylvania: Directorate Office.
Jamison, P. L., S. L. Zegura, and F. A. Milan (editors)
    1978   *Eskimos of northwestern Alaska: a biological perspective.* Strousburg, Pennsylvania: Dowden, Hutchinson, and Ross.
Jelliffe, D. B., and E. F. P. Jelliffe
    1972   Lactation, conception and nutrition of the nursing mother and child. *Journal of Pediatrics* **81**:829–833.
Johnston, F. E.
    1980   Some uses of current research on growth and development in the introductory course in physical anthropology. Paper presented at the Annual Meeting of the American Association of Physical Anthropologists, Niagara Falls, New York.
Johnston, F. E., A. F. Roche, L. M. Schell, and H. N. B. Wettenhall
    1975   Critical weight at menarche: critique of a hypothesis. *American Journal of Diseases of Children* **129**:19–23.
Kaplan, B. A.
    1954   Environment and human plasticity. *American Anthropologist* **56**:780–800.
Kondo, S., and M. Eto
    1975   Physical growth studies on Japanese–American children in comparison with native Japanese. In *Comparative studies on human adaptability of Japanese, Caucasians and Japanese–Americans,* Vol. 1, edited by S. M. Horvath, S. Kondo, H. Matsui, and H. Yoshimura.

Tokyo: Japanese Committee for the International Biological Program, University of Toyko Press. Pp. 13–45.

Kroeber, A. L.
    1923   *Anthropology*. New York: Harcourt.
    1948   *Anthropology*, second edition. New York: Harcourt, Brace.

Kunstadter, P., R. Buhler, F. F. Stephan, and C. F. Westoff
    1963   Demographic variability and preferential marriage patterns. *American Journal of Physical Anthropology* **21**:511–519.

Ladell, W. S. S.
    1964   Terrestrial animals in humid heat: man. In *Adaptation to the environment,* Sect. 4, *handbook of physiology,* edited by D. B. Dill, E. F. Adolph, and C. G. Wilber. Washington, D.C.: American Physiological Society. Pp. 625–659.

Lasker, G. W.
    1946   Migration and physical differentiation. A comparison of immigrant with American-born Chinese. *American Journal of Physical Anthropology* **4**:273–300.
    1960   Migration, isolation, and ongoing human evolution. *Human Biology* **32**:80–88.
    1969   Human biological adaptability. *Science* **166**:1480–1486.

Laughlin, W. S., and A. B. Harper (editors)
    1979   *The first Americans: origins, affinities, and adaptations.* New York: Fischer.

Lee, D. H. K.
    1964   Terrestrial animals in dry heat: man in the desert. In *Adaptation to the environment,* Sect. 4, edited by D. B. Dill, E. F. Adolph, and C. G. Wilber. Washington, D.C.: American Physiological Society. Pp. 551–582.

Leslie, P. W., W. T. Morrill, and B. Dyke
    1981   Genetic implications of mating structure in a Caribbean isolate. *American Journal of Human Genetics* **33**:90–104.

Little, M. A.
    1980   Designs for human–biological research among savanna pastoralists. In *Human ecology in savanna environments,* edited by D. R. Harris. New York: Academic Press. Pp. 479–503.

Little, M. A.
    1981   Human populations in the Andes: the human science basis for research planning. Mountain Research and Development **1**:145–170.

Little, M. A., and J. M. Hanna
    1978   The responses of high-altitude populations to cold and other stresses. In *The biology of high-altitude peoples,* edited by P. T. Baker. London and New York: Cambridge University Press. Pp. 251–298.

Little, M. A., and G. E. B. Morren, Jr.
    1976   *Ecology, energetics, and human variability.* Dubuque, Iowa: W. C. Brown.

Little, M. A., and A. T. Steegmann, Jr.
    n.d.   Acclimatization and adaptation: Responses to cold. In *Handbook of North American Indians,* Vol. 3, *Environment, Origins and Population,* edited by F. S. Hulse. Washington, D.C.: Smithsonian Institution, in press since 1972.

Little, M. A., R. B. Thomas, R. B. Mazess, and P. T. Baker
    1971   Population differences and developmental changes in extremity responses to cold among Andean Indians. *Human Biology* **43**:70–91.

Livingstone, F. B.
    1960   Natural selection, disease, and ongoing human evolution as illustrated by the ABO blood groups. *Human Biology* **32**:17–27.
    1962   Population genetics and population ecology. *American Anthropologists* **64**:45–52.

MacArthur, R. H.
    1972   *Geographical ecology.* New York: Harper and Row.

MacArthur, R. H., and E. R. Pianka
  1966   On optimal use of a patchy environment. *American Naturalist* **100**:603–609.
May, J. M.
  1960   The ecology of human disease. *Annals of the New York Academy of Science* **84**:789–794.
Mazess, R. B.
  1975a   Biological adaptation: aptitudes and acclimitization. In *Biosocial interrelations in population adaptation*, edited by E. S. Watts, F. E. Johnston, and G. W. Lasker. The Hague: Mouton Publishers. Pp. 9–18.
  1975b   Human adaptation to high altitude. In *Physiological anthropology*, edited by A. Damon. London and New York: Oxford University Press. Pp. 167–209.
  1978   Adaptation: A conceptual framework. In *Evolutionary models and studies in human diversity*, edited by R. J. Meier, C. M. Otten, and F. Abdel-Hameed. The Hague: Mouton Publishers. Pp. 9–15.
Mazess, R. B., and P. T. Baker
  1964   Diet of Quechua Indians at high altitude: Nuñoa, Peru. *American Journal of Clinical Nutrition* **15**:341–351.
McElroy, A., and P. K. Townsend
  1979   *Medical anthropology: an ecological perspective*. North Scituate, Massachusetts: Duxbury Press.
Medawar, P. B.
  1951   Problems of adaptation. *New Biology* **11**:10–26.
Meehan, J. P.
  1955   Individual and racial variations in vascular response to cold stimulus. *Military Medicine* **116**:330–334.
Milan, F. A. (editor)
  1980   *The human biology of circumpolar peoples*. London and New York: Cambridge University Press.
Mirrakhimov, M. M.
  1978   Biological and physiological characteristics of the high-altitude natives of Tien Shan and the Pamirs. In *The biology of high-altitude peoples*, edited by P. T. Baker. London and New York: Cambridge University Press. Pp. 299–315.
Monge, C.
  1948   *Acclimatization in the Andes*. Baltimore: Maryland: Johns Hopkins Press.
Montague, M. F. A.
  1951   *An introduction to physical anthropology*, second edition. Springfield, Illinois: Thomas.
Morren, G. E. B., Jr.
  1977   From hunting to herding: pigs and the control of energy in montane New Guinea. In *Subsistence and survival, rural ecology in the Pacific*, edited by T. P. Bayliss-Smith and R. G. Feachem. New York: Academic Press. Pp. 273–315.
Motulsky, A. G.
  1960   Metabolic polymorphisms and the role of infectious diseases in human evolution. *Human Biology* **32**:28–62.
Mueller, W. H., V. N. Schull, W. J. Schull, P. Soto, and F. Rothhammer
  1978   A multinational Andean genetic and health program: growth and development in an hypoxic environment. *Annals of Human Biology* **5**:329–352.
National Academy of Sciences (NAS)
  1974   *U.S. participation in the International Biological Program. U.S. National Committee for the International Biological Program. Report No. 6*. Washington, D.C.: National Academy of Sciences.
Neel, J. V.
  1970   Lessons from a "primitive" people. *Science* **170**:815–822.
Neel, J. V., M. Layrisse, and F. M. Salzano

1977   Man in the tropics: the Yanomama Indians. In *Population structure and human variation*, edited by G. A. Harrison. London and New York: Cambridge University Press. Pp. 109–142.

Newburgh, L. H. (editor)
1949   *Physiology of heat regulation and the science of clothing.* Philadelphia: Saunders.

Newman, M. T.
1953   The application of ecological rules to the racial anthropology of the aboriginal New World. *American Anthropologist* 55:311–327.
1956   Adaptation of man to cold climates. *Evolution* 10:101–105.
1960   Adaptations in the physique of American Aborigines to nutritional factors. *Human Biology* 32:288–313.
1962   Ecology and nutritional stress in man. *American Anthropologist* 64:22–33.

Newman, M. T., C. Collazos, and C. Fuentes
1963   Growth differences between Indians and Mestizos in the Callejón de Huaylas. *American Journal of Physical Anthropology* 6:21–38.

Newman, R. W.
1970   Why man is such a sweaty and thirsty naked animal: a speculative review. *Human Biology* 42:12–27.
1975   Human adaptation to heat. In *Physiological anthropology*, edited by A. Damon. London and New York: Oxford University Press. Pp. 80–92.

Newman, R. W., and E. H. Munro
1955   The relation of climate and body size in U.S. males. *American Journal of Physical Anthropology* 13:1–17.

Odum, H. T.
1971   *Environment, power and society.* New York: Wiley (Interscience).

Ojikutu, R. O., R. H. Fox, T. W. Davies, and C. T. M. Davies
1972   Heat and exercise tolerance of rural and urban groups in Nigeria. In *Human biology of environmental change*, edited by D. J. M. Vorster. London: International Biological Programme. Pp. 132–144.

Pearl, R.
1930   Some aspects of the biology of human populations. In *Human biology and racial welfare*, edited by E. V. Cowdry. New York: Harper (Hoeber). Pp. 515–552.

Pianka, E. R.
1974   *Evolutionary ecology.* New York: Harper and Row.

Picón-Reátegui, E.
1978   The food and nutrition of high-altitude populations. In *The biology of high-altitude peoples*, edited by P. T. Baker. London and New York: Cambridge University Press. Pp. 219–249.

Prosser, C. L.
1964   Perspectives of adaptation: theoretical aspects. In *Adaptation to the environment*, Sect. 4, *handbook of physiology*, edited by D. B. Dill, E. F. Adolph, and C. G. Wilber. Washington, D.C.: American Physiological Society. Pp. 11–25.

Roberts, D. F.
1952   Basal metabolism, race and climate. *Journal of the Royal Anthropological Institute* 82:169–183.
1953   Body weight, race and climate. *American Journal of Physical Anthropology* 11:533–558.
1956   A demographic study of a Dinka village. *Human Biology* 28:323–349.
1960   Effects of race and climate on human growth as exemplified by studies on African children. In *Human growth*, edited by J. M. Tanner. Oxford: Pergamon. Pp. 59–72.

Robinson, S., D. B. Dill, P. M. Harmon, F. G. Hall, and J. W. Wilson
1941a   Adaptation to exercise of Negro and White sharecroppers in comparison with northern Whites. *Human Biology* 13:139–158.

Robinson, S., D. B. Dill, J. W. Wilson, and M. Nielson
1941b   Adaptations of white men and Negroes to prolonged heat. *American Journal of Tropical Medicine* 21:261–287.

Salzano, F. M.
   1961   Studies on the Caingang Indians. I. Demography. *Human Biology* 33:110–130.
   1962   Some genetic aspects of the demography of American Indians. *Entretiens de Monaco en Science Humaines* 1:23–39.
Schölander, P. F., K. L. Andersen, J. Krog, F. V. Lorentzen, and J. Steen
   1957   Critical temperature in Lapps. *Journal of Applied Physiology* 10:231–234.
Schölander, P. F., H. T. Hammel, S. J. Hart, D. H. Le Messurier, and J. Steen
   1958   Cold adaptation in Australian aborigines. *Journal of Applied Physiology* 13:211–218.
Schraer, H., and M. T. Newman
   1958   Quantitative roentgenography of skeletal mineralization in malnourished Quechua Indian boys. *Science* 128:476–477.
Schreider, E.
   1950   Geographic distribution of the body weight/body surface ratio. *Nature (London)* 165:286.
   1951   Anatomical factors in body heat regulation. *Nature* 167:823–824.
Schull, W. J., and F. Rothhammer
   1977   A multinational Andean genetic and health programme: a study of adaptation to the hypoxia of altitude. In *Physiological variation and its genetic basis*, edited by J. S. Weiner. London: Taylor and Francis. Pp. 139–169.
Shapiro, H. L.
   1939   *Migration and environment: a study of the physical characteristics of the Japanese immigrants to Hawaii and the effects of environment on their descendants*. London and New York: Oxford University Press.
Shephard, R. J.
   1978   *Human physiological work capacity*. London and New York: Cambridge University Press.
Smith, E. A.
   1979   Human adaptation and energetic efficiency. *Human Ecology* 7:53–74.
   1982   Evolutionary ecology and the analysis of human social behavior. In *Rethinking adaptation: from deterministic to interactive models*, edited by R. Dyson-Hudson and M. A. Little. Bolder, Colorado: Westview Press.
Spencer, F.
   1981   The rise of academic physical anthropology in the United States (1880–1980): a historical overview. *American Journal of Physical Anthropology* 56:353–364.
Spuhler, J. N.
   1959   Physical anthropology and demography. In *The study of population*, edited by P. M. Hauser and O. D. Duncan. Chicago: University of Chicago Press. Pp. 728–758.
Steegmann, A. T., Jr.
   1975   Human adaptation to cold. In *Physiological anthropology*, edited by A. Damon. London and New York: Oxford University Press. Pp. 130–166.
Stern, J. T., Jr.
   1970   The meaning of "adaptation" and its relation to the phenomenon of natural selection. In *Evolutionary Biology*, Vol. 4, edited by T. Dozhansky, M. K. Hecht, and W. C. Steere, New York: Appleton-Century-Crofts. Pp. 39–66.
Steward, J.
   1938   *Basin-plateau aboriginal sociopolitical groups. Bureau of American Ethnology Bulletin* 137. Washington, D. C.: Smithsonian Institution.
   1955   *Theory of culture change*. Urbana: University of Illinois Press.
Swedlund, A. C.
   1978   Historical demography as population ecology. *Annual Review of Anthropology* 7:137–173.
Swift, J.
   1977   Sahelian pastoralists: underdevelopment, desertification and famine. *Annual Review of Anthropology* 6:457–478.
Tanner, J. M.
   1966   Growth and physique in different populations of mankind. In *The biology of human*

adaptability, edited by P. T. Baker and J. S. Weiner. London and New York: Oxford University Press (Clarendon). Pp. 45–66.

1978   *Foetus into man: physical growth from conception to maturity.* Cambridge, Massachusetts: Harvard University Press.

Thieme, F. P.

1957   A comparison of Puerto Rican migrants and sedents. *Papers of the Michigan Academy of Science, Arts and Letters* **4**2:249–256.

Thomas, R. B.

1975   The ecology of work. In *Physiological anthropology*, edited by A. Damon. London and New York: Oxford University Press. Pp. 59–79.

1976   Energy flow at high altitude. In *Man in the Andes: a multidisciplinary study of high-altitude Quechua*, edited by P. T. Baker and M. A. Little. Stroudsburg, Pennsylvania: Dowden, Hutchinson, and Ross. Pp. 379–404.

Thomas, R. B., B. Winterhalder, and S. D. McRae

1979   An anthropological approach to human ecology and adaptive dynamics. *Yearbook of Physical Anthropology* **22**:1–46.

Trussell, J.

1978   Menarche and fatness: reexamination of the critical body composition hypothesis. *Science* **200**:1506–1509.

Vayda, A. P., and R. A. Rappaport

1968   Ecology, cultural and noncultural. In *Introduction to cultural anthropology*, edited by J. A. Clifton. Boston: Houghton Mifflin. Pp. 477–497.

Ward, R. H., and K. M. Weiss

1976   The demographic evolution of human populations. In *The demographic evolution of human populations*, edited by R. H. Ward and K. M. Weiss. New York: Academic Press. Pp. 1–23.

Warren, K. B. (editor)

1950   *Origin and evolution of man.* Cold Spring Harbor Symposia on Quantitative Biology, Vol. 15. Cold Spring Harbor, New York: The Biological Laboratory.

Washburn, S. L.

1951   The new physical anthropology. *Transactions of the New York Academy of Sciences, Series 2* **13**:298–304.

1953   The strategy of physical anthropology. In *Anthropology today: an encyclopedic inventory*, edited by A. L. Kroeber. Chicago: University of Chicago Press. Pp. 714–727.

Watt, K. E. F.

1973   *Principles of environmental science.* New York: McGraw-Hill.

Weiner, J. S.

1954   Nose shape and climate. *American Journal of Physical Anthropology* **12**:1–4.

1964   Part V. Human ecology. In *Human biology: an introduction to human evolution, variation, growth and ecology*, edited by G. A. Harrison, J. S. Weiner, J. M. Tanner, and N. A. Barnicot. London and New York: Oxford University Press. Pp. 399–508.

1965   *International biological programme guide to the human adaptability proposals.* London: International Council of Scientific Unions, Special Committee for the IBP.

1966   Major problems in human population biology. In *The biology of human adaptability*, edited by P. T. Baker and J. S. Weiner. London and New York: Oxford University Press (Clarendon). Pp. 1–24.

1977   The history of the Human Adaptability Section. In *Human adaptability: a history and compendium of research*, edited by K. J. Collins and J. S. Weiner. London: Taylor and Francis. Pp. 1–23.

1980   Work and wellbeing in savanna environmments: physiological considerations. In *Human ecology in savanna environments*, edited by D. R. Harris. New York: Academic Press. Pp. 421–437.

Weiner, J. S.
    n.d.   *Components of human physiological function: thermal responses and respiratory function.* London and New York: Cambridge University Press (in press).

Weiner, J. S., and J. A. Lourie
    1969   *Human biology: a guide to field methods. IBP Handbook No.* **9**. Philadelphia: Davis.

Weiner, J. S., J. O. C. Willson, H. El-Neil, and E. F. Wheeler
    1972   The effect of work level and dietary intake on sweat nitrogen losses in a hot climate. *British Journal of Nutrition* **2** 7:543–552.

Weiss, K. M.
    1976   Demographic theory and anthropological inference. *Annual Review of Anthropology* **5**:351–381.

Weitz, C. A.
    1973   *The effects of aging and habitual activity on exercise performance among a high altitude Himalayan population.* Unpublished Ph. D. dissertation, Department of Anthropology, Pennsylvania State University, University Park.

Winterhalder, B.
    1980   Environmental analysis in human evolution and adaptation research. *Human Ecology* **8**:135–170.

Wohlwill, J. F.
    1974   Human adaptation to levels of environmental stimulation. *Human Ecology* **2**:127–147.

Wulsin, F. R.
    1949   Adaptations to climate among non-European peoples. In *Physiology of heat regulation and the science of clothing,* edited by L. H. Newburgh. Philadelphia: Saunders. Pp. 3–69.

Wyndham, C. H., W. M. Bouwer, M. G. Devine, and H. F. Paterson
    1952   Physiological responses of African laborers at various saturated air temperatures, wind velocities, and rates of energy expenditure. *Journal of Applied Physiology* **5**:290–298.

Yoshimura, H., and J. S. Weiner (editors)
    1966   *Human adaptability and its methodology.* Tokyo: Japan Society for the Promotion of Sciences.

18

The Development of Research Strategies for Studies of Biological Variation in Living Human Populations

Jere D. Haas

Introduction

As the discipline of physical anthropology grew and matured during the 50 years since the American Association of Physical Anthropology (AAPA) was established, it witnessed several major theoretical and methodological changes in the study of variation in living human populations. The purpose of this chapter is to trace the development of research designs employed by American physical anthropologists over the past 50 years. Of course, the methods and research designs of any scientific discipline are only tools applied by its membership to test various hypotheses that establish the theoretical basis of the discipline. It is, therefore, impossible to view the method without a careful regard for the theory. The preceding chapter by Little provides a comprehensive and insightful review of the development of human ecological theory. To avoid redundancy, this chapter will present some of the salient developments in research strategies while limiting reference to only those theoretical issues that are essential to this immediate task. I must point out that this is a personal interpretation of the discipline's history. It is not meant to be a comprhensive documentation and assessment of the intellectual development of American physical anthropology. For the sake of brevity, such a history must be focused and, as a result, will take on and perhaps accentuate the biases of the author.

This historical review will deal with the development of research strategies for studying phenotypic variation in living human populations. The major trends, by decade, from the 1920s to the present will be reviewed first, followed by a

A HISTORY OF AMERICAN
PHYSICAL ANTHROPOLOGY

discussion of several general gypes of research strategies that have been employed since 1930 in the major publications of the discipline, the *American Journal of Physical Anthropology (AJPA)* and *Human Biology*. Finally, the development of one particular research strategy, the study of migrating populations, will be presented in an effort to document the maturation of a scientific research methodology that might be considered unique to our discipline.

Brief Historical Summary

In order to appreciate the changes in physical anthropological research strategies during the past 50 years, we must recognize the tradition of American physical anthropological research that predated this period. From 1900 to 1930, the major research activity of physical anthropology was descriptive. There was an awareness that many of the heretofore isolated societies of mankind were being assimilated by western colonization. Physical anthropologists, therefore, were engaged in documenting the biological diversity that existed within and between populations in a "salvage" effort. Emphasis was placed on standardizing measurement techniques while anticipating that comparative and historical studies might be later carried out with a well-documented data base. Rarely were data collected to test hypotheses regarding human biological variation, although some classic analyses were done. The most important of these were Franz Boas's study of changing morphology and developmental plasticity in European migrants to the United States (Boas 1911) and Aleš Hrdlička's study of the environmental effects on morphology and physiological function of Native Americans in the American Southwest and Mexico (Hrdlička 1908).

A major concern one has about early descriptive studies is the representative nature of the subjects who were studied. On occasion, the entire community under study was measured, but more often only selected individuals were included in the sample. There is generally little information published with the data regarding the sampling procedure, either within or between communities, which obviously limits much of the application of these data for subsequent hypothesis testing. This is an important but often overlooked point for the evaluation of human biological studies that rely on secondary data sources, such as research on the secular trend in growth, menarche, and adult stature.

A great deal of the early data collection effort on living human populations was aimed at documenting existing theories of racial variation. Moreover, the need to catalog such a large quantity of descriptive data reinforced the concept of racial typologies as a means of facilitating classification and description. If one reads only the journals of the time, it is striking how few of the studies actually state a hypothesis to be tested, much less a research methodology or design to test the hypothesis. Apparently, the journals were repositories of descriptive material, and whatever hypotheses were formulated were presented and tested in monographs and symposia volumes that synthesized the descriptive data. Thus, if there was a research strategy that was common at the time, it was a comparative approach, examining intergroup variations of populations that had been previously described in considerable detail by several different anthropologists.

For the most part, this descriptive work on morphological variation continued to dominate the literature of the 1930s. However, at this time, two major changes in research methodology became apparent. The most important of these was the expansion of the descriptive studies to include the recently discovered blood-grouping techniques. The racial typologists of the day found this procedure particularly appealing because blood groups were seen as clearly inherited traits that were uninfluenced by ontogenic or environmental factors. Thus, they were perceived as "nonadaptive" traits that could further distinguish true racial (i.e., genetic) variation (Boyd 1940; Gates 1939).

The second important methodological shift can be seen in the attempts to link morphological variation with physical or functional variation. For example, the demonstration that large chest dimensions are related to greater lung capacity, and hence, might be adaptive under conditions of high altitude hypoxia, was reported by Hurtado in the AJPA in 1932. Also, studies of the relationship between body morphology and physical work capacity (Seltzer 1939) and between maternal malnutrition and reproductive performance (Price 1939) were reported in the latter part of the decade. It is important to remember that although the synthetic genetic theory of evolution was being developed by biologists at this time (Fisher 1930; Huxley 1942; Wright 1931), it had not yet made its impact on physical anthropology and human biology (see Weiss and Chakraborty, in the present volume).

During the 1940s, another area of biology and medicine was emerging that was to have significant influence on American physical anthropology. Laboratory and field studies in environmental physiology were beginning to quantify the extent to which individuals could function under conditions of environmental stress (Adolph and associates 1947; Robinson et al. 1941). These controlled experiments would prove to be the forerunner of the human adaptability studies of the 1950s, 1960s and 1970s. Not only did they provide new evidence for the physical anthropologists about the essential relationship between human morphological variation and environmental stress, but they provided the methodology to test the relationship. The links between morphological, physiological, and environmental variation were being uncovered. The experimental approach was also influencing other branches of physical anthropology, such as structural–functional research in anatomy (Washburn and Detwiler 1943).

At the close of this decade, W. E. Le Gros Clark presented the Earl Grey Memorial Lecture in London, in which he called attention to an emerging trend in physical anthropology. He referred to this new direction as racial physiology, which is the study "of growth, physique and physiological efficiency in relation to environment [Le Gros Clark, 1950:249]." He also noted that physical anthropology was late in entering the ecological phase of its natural development compared to other biological sciences. Le Gros Clark foresaw a trend that was to revolutionize the discipline as it was developing on both sides of the Atlantic Ocean.

It was during the decade of the 1950s that what could be seen as the the major transition in the discipline over the past 50 years occurred. The ecological approach to human variation was developed, and significant contributions in methodology were made by other disciplines in the biological sciences. Most notable were the methods and theories of population genetics, ecology, nutrition, environmental physiology, and epidemiology. In an effort to evaluate the statistical validity, and later, the biological bases, of Bergmann's and Allen's rules, comparative studies were conducted from previously published literature (Coon *et al.* 1950; Newman 1953, 1956; Roberts 1953; Schneider 1951) and then with original field- and laboratory-based research projects (Baker 1958, 1959). These studies were beginning to address the question of the adaptive significance of morphological variation.

The research designs that were employed tested single environmental stress models of physiological response and were rather limited in their direct application to human population biology. These designs were later to expand into multistress approaches that considered the complexity of the human environment and biological responses to it (see Beall, in the present volume). The extensive interpopulation analysis of body size and ambient temperature by Roberts (1953) employed simple correlation techniques that could not reveal causal relationships but stimulated considerable hypothesis formation and testing under experimentally controlled conditions. Baker's comparative studies of thermoregulation in American Caucasians and Blacks are examples of this latter approach (Baker 1958, 1959). From this decade on, it seems as if the methodologies of research in human variation began an exponential proliferation. The sorting of these early methodologies into the major subareas of genetics, demography, physiology, growth, ecology, and epidemiology helped structure our discipline as we know it today.

The 1960s were ushered in by significant field research on the relationship between disease and certain genetic traits (Livingstone 1960; Motulsky 1960) that were previously viewed as nonadaptive by the old racial typologists. These studies established a method of evaluating natural selection in human populations (see Weiss and Chakraborty, in the present volume). They revealed the need to consider further the methodologies and theories of other disciplines and pointed out that systematic field observations, coupled with laboratory research, should provide the empirical evidence for natural selection in man.

In an effort to coordinate some of this physical anthropological research with work from other disciplines that also studied man–environment interactions, the Human Adaptability Section of the International Biological Program (IBP–HA) was established in 1964. This interdisciplinary and international effort sought to obtain comparable data on population characteristics over a wide range of ecosystems. The studies that made up the IBP–HA Section were designed to be self-contained as well as comparative, in that specific questions of interpopulation and intrapopulation variation were to be addressed across and within specific ecological zones. Methodologies and techniques were standardized across projects, and many colleagues from disciplines like exercise physiology, nutrition, demography, population genetics, ecology, and medicine were brought together, often in the field. A common language was developed, and the research methodologies were shared (Weiner 1969, 1977; Weiner and Lourie 1969).

As the IBP activities drew to a close in the early 1970s, the newly formed Man in the Biosphere (MAB) Program started to follow up some of the important man–environment relationships that had developed under the IBP. Moreover, the research strategies that proved fruitful in the IBP projects were carried over and improved in the MAB projects (Baker 1977).

A major methodological development from the IBP–HA studies was the application of ecological models to explain complex biological, social, and environmental interrelationships. One significant consequence of this was the reunion of social and biological anthropologists, whose methods and theories had grown apart in the preceding decades as both subdisciplines grew more specialized. The opportunity to explore complex models was made possible by the development of, and easy access to, rapid-processing computer systems. The computer revolution also permitted the use of more sophisticaed statistical procedures, and this, expanded field research designs to gain control over many confounding variables. The strength of natural field experiments and epidemiological investigations into environmental health were greatly improved as a result of this computer sophistication, the outgrowth of which was the capability to test more complex hypotheses regarding human variation. This change is exemplified in the studies of population structure and quantitative genetics that developed in the 1970s in an effort to examine complex adaptive processes. On the negative side, this turning to sophisticated statistical analysis has lead to a tendency to overanalyze and overinterpret data that are often inappropriate for the testing of such complex hypotheses.

Methodological Development as Reflected by Content Analysis of Two Scientific Journals

This brief excursion through 50 years of human biology and physical anthropology research relies heavily on research reports that appeared in the two major journals of the discipline, the *AJPA* and *Human Biology*. The research strategies reported in these journals from 1930 to 1980 are summarized in Table 1 in an effort to identify obvious trends. The major subdivisions of physical anthropology are represented in the journals, but only those papers that deal with living human populations were included in the analysis. The research strategies employed in these papers could be categorized in many ways. The following are the general categories chosen for this review.

Table 1 Fifty Year trend in Research Methodologies of papers Published in the *American Journal of Physical Anthropology* and *Human Biology* (1930–1980).

	1930	1935	1940	1945	1950	1955	1960	1965	1970	1975	1980
American Journal of Physical Anthropology											
Total articles on living humans	20	9	18	7	16	24	24	25	57	50	48
Descriptive— no hypothesis	45.0[a]	44.4	16.7	28.6	18.7	29.2	54.2	28.0	21.1	20.0	22.9
Intragroup correlational analysis	5.0	0	11.1	14.3	35.5	12.5	29.2	12.0	28.1	34.0	27.1
Intergroup comparisons	30.0	22.2	44.4	57.1	12.5	33.3	12.5	28.0	17.5	26.0	39.6
Experimental laboratory testing	0	0	0	0	6.5	0	0	8.0	10.5	6.0	4.2
Methodology–techniques	20.0	33.3	11.1	0	18.7	16.7	4.2	20.0	12.3	6.0	6.3
Theoretical or review articles	0	0	16.7	0	6.5	8.3	0	4.0	10.5	6.0	0
Human Biology											
Total articles on living humans	19	25	19	14	19	21	19	27	39	38	54
Descriptive— no hypothesis	10.5	16.0	15.8	50.0	0	33.3	10.5	18.5	27.0	7.9	22.2
Intragroup correlational analysis	42.1	36.0	36.8	7.1	21.1	14.3	26.3	37.0	27.0	36.8	40.7
Intergroup analysis	10.5	32.0	36.8	26.6	21.1	23.8	15.8	22.2	23.1	39.5	25.9
Experimental laboratory testing	0	4.0	0	0	5.8	0	10.5	0	2.6	2.6	1.9
Methodology–techniques	15.8	8.0	5.3	7.1	47.4	9.5	5.3	14.8	5.1	7.9	5.6
Theoretical or review articles	21.1	4.0	5.3	7.1	5.3	19.0	31.6	7.4	17.4	5.3	3.7

[a]values presented are a percentage of the total papers dealing with living human populations published in a particular year.

1.   This category includes descriptive studies that had no stated hypothesis to be tested and generally employed descriptive statistical methods to provide information on new measures of human phenotypic variation or for new groups not previously described.

2.   Studies that could also be considered descriptive but that analyzed certain relationships between biological characteristics of a specific population or groups of individuals comprise the second category. The type of intragroup correlational analysis employed in these studies varies considerably over the 50 years. Usually a hypothesis is offered for testing, and the Pearson correlation is the statistical tool of preference. However, more sophisticated multivariate analytical methods were introduced in the 1940s and 1950s, and complex mathematical models started to be used in the 1960s.

3.   Within this category are intergroup comparisons that used distinct populations identified because they differed according to some nonbiological criteria, such as geography, social class, language, or ethnic background. Studies that identified individuals only according to sex, age, or phenotype (short versus tall, Rh positive versus Rh negative, etc.) are not included in this group but are considered in the second group for intrapopulation variation.

4.   This group includes studies that were conducted in laboratory settings and employed experimental manipulation of human subjects or testing conditions to test specific hypotheses.

5.   Included in this category are studies that dealt with the description, critique, or validation of a specific technique or methodology; that is new measuring techniques, statistical tools, laboratory procedures, and recording devices. The articles generally present no hypothesis to be tested but may provide descriptive data to demonstrate variation in the new measurement or comparative data for validation.

6.   Theoretical and review articles that do not present new research findings but review and integrate previous work comprise the final category. Review articles that test specific hypotheses by analyzing previously published data with additional statistical tests are not included here, but rather are assigned to the second or third group because they employ intragroup analysis.

Table 1 includes only articles published in the two journals every fifth year, starting with 1930. This sampling procedure provides a reasonably good estimate of the distribution of articles through time. Several issues of both journals were devoted to symposia presenting material in a format perhaps atypical for the volume. These deviations are generally reflected in the large number of review articles that appear in *AJPA* in 1940 and 1970 and in *Human Biology* in 1960. Abrupt changes between adjacent sampling years for certain categories of research design probably reflect a change in emphasis brought about by new editors as well as by new developments in the discipline. The overall impression one gets from this summary is of a predominance of purely descriptive studies throughout the 50 years. This is more apparent in *AJPA* than in *Human Biology*. Intragroup correlational studies predominate in *Human Biology*, whereas they only became popular in *AJPA* around 1950. This trend probably reflects the stronger emphasis on quantitative methods and the earlier use of newly developed statistical tools by the contributors to *Human Biology*. Intergroup comparison was employed as a research strategy in about equal proportions in both journals. This methodology generally relies on less sophisticated statistical techniques. It should be noted that although the vast majority of the contributors to the *AJPA* before 1950 were physical anthropologists, this discipline was clearly in the minority among contributors to *Human Biology*. It can be inferred that much of the analytical sophistication of the articles was provided by nonanthropologists, at least up to 1950.

In summary, for the period from 1930 to 1960, it appears that the physical anthropology of living peoples really had no unique research strategy to call its own. It borrowed freely from many related disciplines; that is not to say that physical anthropological applications of these borrowed methodologies has not been unique. The discipline clearly addressed specific theoretical questions that dealt with issues not covered by sister disciplines. As a result of efforts to answer some of these questions of physical anthropological importance, certain research strategies were borrowed and applied in interesting and innovative ways. As an example, we can follow the history of the application of one of these strategies that employs comparisons of migrant populations and observe how important specific anthropological questions have been examined through time, using this research approach.

Studies of Migrating Populations and Natural Experiments in Human Variability

Ever since Boas—in his classic 1911 paper, *Changes in the Bodily Form of Immigrants*—showed that developmental plasticity is an important characteristic of human variability, many physical anthropologists have examined migrating populations to test specific hypotheses regarding genetic and environmental interaction, variation in human growth, adaptability in changing environments, and developmental adaptation. The attractiveness of this approach, for the physical anthropologist, relates to several things. The most important is that as members of a discipline that studies evolution, and, hence, change over long periods of time, physical anthropologists are handicapped in not being able to observe these changes directly in living populations. We must make most of our inferences from the end result of change, generally with little knowledge of phenotypic variations at the start of an episode of selection, genetic drift, gene flow, or mutation. The recognition that evolution and adaptation occur as a result of changing environmental conditions suggests that one could observe the effects of changing environments with migrating populations in a kind of natural experiment. Of course, the limitations of this procedure should be recognized. One obvious problem is that evolutionary change requires many generations and the documentation of changing environments due to migration is limited to several generations at best. Also, migrants do tend to be different from those who stay home in ways that can bias the desired randomness of such an experimental design.

However, this first limitation can become an asset if one wishes to determine how much of the variation in a given biological characteristic is due to normal plasticity and how much is fixed by the genotype. Most notable of the early studies that employed this approach to examine plasticity are those by Shapiro (1939) on Japanese migrants to Hawaii; Lasker (1946), on Chinese–American migrants; and Greulich (1957), on Japanese migrants to the western coast of the United States. These studies revealed the tremendous variability in human growth responses to changing environments. The practical application of the results of this research became evident quite early when it was recognized that improvements in health and nutrition conditions played a significant role in accelerating the growth and development of migrants.

Another interesting application of these migration models was shown by Hulse (1957) in his study of endogamy, migration, and heterosis in Swiss populations in Switzerland and California. In this case, the migration process led to a breakdown in a breeding isolate, which had effects on the gene pool and, presumably, on the phenotypes of migrants to a new environment.

The human adaptability studies under the IBP further refined the use of migrating population to study biological variation. This approach not only served as a good research strategy for evaluating the adaptability of certain phenotypes in different environments (Baker 1975, 1977; Harrison 1966), but also served as a major focus of the IBP–HA in their studies entitled "Biosocial Adaptation of Migrant and Urban Populations."

Following from these human adaptability studies in the 1960s were a series of studies by Little *et al.* (1971), Frisancho *et al.* (1973), Haas (1980), and others that evaluated the role played by developmental acclimatization in the overall adaptive responses of adults living under environmental stress. The migration of children into and out of areas of environmental stress serves as a good test for the hypothesis that exposure to stress during sensitive periods of growth is important to the adaptive success of these children when they reach adulthood.

More recently the migration models of population genetics have been employed by physical anthropologists to evaluate the demographic, ethnohistorical, and genetic factors associated with variation in human population structure (Harrison and Boyce 1972). It may be that within this research area physical anthropology has been able to establish a research methodology that is unique to the discipline. It draws heavily from ethnohistorical research and social anthropology and thus provides a method for unifying some of the diverse subdivisions of the larger discipline.

The other recent methodological innovation that has been greatly influenced by the interdisciplinary studies of the IBP, and shows clearly the marks of an anthropological methodology, is the use of descriptive and simulation models to describe and test complex human ecological relationships (Jamison and Friedman 1974). Although this concept and many of the modeling techniques, such as energy flow, are borrowed from community ecology and demography, the refinement and application to humans has been very much the province of physical anthropologists.

Conclusion

I would like to reemphasize the general nature of this review of research methodologies in the physical anthropology of the living. It would be extremely difficult to catalog all research strategies employed by physical anthropologists and human biologists over the past half century. The approach used is defined by the problem, and the discipline has addressed an inordinate number of different research problems. Methods in the past were borrowed from other disciplines.. These methods evolved as physical anthropological theory evolved from a descriptive science to one interested in process. Much of our current research remains descriptive, but more is involved in testing hypotheses generated from the synthetic theory of evolution as applied to humans. The most encouragement I see from this is that the discipline has come of age and is starting to develop its own methodologies and research designs to examine questions that physical anthropologists are uniquely qualified to address.

References

Adolph, E. F., and Associates
   1947   *Physiology of man in the desert.* New York: Wiley (Interscience).
Baker, P. T.
   1958   Racial differences in heat tolerance. *American Journal of Physical Anthropology* 16:287–305.
   1959   American Negro–White difference in the thermal insulative aspects of body fat. *Human Biology* 31:316–324.
   1975   Research strategies in population biology and environmental stress. In *Measures of man: methodologies in biological anthropology,* edited by E. Giles and J. S. Friedlaender. Cambridge, Massachusetts: Schenkman Publishing. Pp. 230–259.
   1977   Problems and strategies. In *Human population problems in the biosphere: some research strategies and designs,* edited by P. T. Baker. *MAB Technical Notes, No. 3.* Paris: Unesco. Pp. 11–32.
Boas, F.
   1911   *Changes in the bodily form of descendants of immigrants.* Senate Document 208, 61st Congress, second session. Washington, D. C.: U. S. Government Printing Office.
Boyd, W. C.
   1940   Critique of methods of classifying mankind. *American Journal of Physical Anthropology* 27:333–364.
Coon, C. S., S. M. Garn, and J. B. Birdsell
   1950   *Races: a study of the problems of race formation in man.* Springfield, Illinois: Thomas.
Fisher, R. A.
   1930   *The genetical theory of natural selection.* London and New York: Oxford University Press (Clarendon).
Frisancho, A. R, C. Martinez, T. Velasquez, J. Sanchez, and H. Montoye
   1973   Influence of developmental adaptation on aerobic capacity at high altitude. *Journal of Applied Physiology* 34:176–180.
Gates, R. R.
   1939   Blood groupings and racial classification. *American Journal of Physical Anthropology* 24:385–389.
Greulich, W. W.
   1957   A comparison of the physical growth and development of American born and native Japanese children. *American Journal of Physical Anthropology* 15:489–516.
Haas, J. D.
   1980   Maternal adaptation and fetal growth at high altitude in Bolivia. In *Social and biological predictors of nutritional status, physical growth, and neurological development,* edited by L. S. Greene and F. E. Johnston. New York: Academic Press. Pp. 257–290.

Harrison, G. A.
    1966   Human adaptation with reference to the IBP proposals for high altitude research. In *The biology of human adaptability*, edited by P. T. Baker and J. S. Weiner. London and New York: Oxford University Press. Pp. 509–519.
Harrison, G. A., and A. J. Boyce
    1972   The framework of population studies. In *The structure of human populations*, edited by G. A. Harrison and A. J. Boyce. London and New York: Oxford University Press (Clarendon). Pp. 1–16.
Hrdlička, A.
    1908   *Physiological and medical observations among the Indians of south western United States and northern Mexico. Bulletin of the Bureau of American Ethnology* **34**. Washington, D. C.: Bureau of American Ethnology.
Hulse, F. S.
    1957   Exogamie et heterosis. *Archives Suisses d'Anthropologie Generale* **22**:103–125.
Hurtado, A.
    1932   Respiratory adaptation in the Indian natives of the Peruvian Andes. Studies at high altitude. *American Journal of Physical Anthropology* **17**:137–165.
Huxley, J. S.
    1942   *Evolution, the modern synthesis*. London: Allen and Unwin.
Jamison, P. L., and S. M. Friedman (editors)
    1974   *Energy flow in human communities*. University Park, Pennsylvania: United States International Biology Program and Social Science Research Council.
Lasker, G. W.
    1946   Migration and physical differentiation. A comparison of immigrant and American born Chinese. *American Journal of Physical Anthropology* **4**:273–300.
Le Gros Clark, W. E.
    1950   Man and environment. *American Journal of Physical Anthropology* **8**:248–250.
Little, M. A., R. B. Thomas, R. B. Mazess, and P. T. Baker
    1971   Population differences and developmental change in extremity responses to cold among Andean Indians. *Human Biology* **43**:70–91.
Livingstone, F. B.
    1960   Natural selection, disease, and ongoing human evolution as illustrated by the ABO blood groups. *Human Biology* **32**:17–27.
Motulsky, A. G.
    1960   Metabolic polymorphisms and the role of infectious disease in human evolution. *Human Biology* **32**:28–62.
Newman, M. T.
    1953   The application of ecological rules to the racial anthropology of the aboriginal New World. *American Anthropologist* **55**:311–327.
    1956   Adaptation of man to cold climates. *Evolution* **10**:101–105.
Price, W. A.
    1939   Decline in reproductive efficiency of primatives with change of nutrition. *American Journal of Physical Anthropology* **25**:9 (abstract).
Roberts, D. F.
    1953   Body weight, race and climate. *American Journal of Physical Anthropology* **11**:533–558.
Robinson, S., D. B. Dill, J. W. Wilson, and M. Nielson
    1941   Adaptations of white men and negroes to prolonged heat. *American Journal of Tropical Medicine* **21**:261–287.
Schneider, E.
    1951   Anatomical factors in body heat regulation. *Nature (London)* **167**:823–824.
Seltzer, C.
    1939   The relationship of body build to oxygen metabolism in rest and during exercise. *American Journal of Physical Anthropology* **25**:14–15 (abstract).

Shapiro, H. L.
   1939   *Migration and environment: a study of the physical characteristics of the Japanese immigrants to Hawaii and the effects of environment on their descendants.* London and New York: Oxford University Press.
Washburn, S. L., and S. R. Detwiler
   1943   An experiment bearing on the problems of physical anthropology. *American Journal of Physical Anthropology* 1:171–190.
Weiner, J. S.
   1969   *A guide to the human adaptability proposals. IBP Handbook No.* 1. (second edition). Oxford: Blackwell.
   1977   The history of the human adaptability section. In *Human adaptability: history and compendium of research,* edited by K. J. Collins and J. S. Weiner. London: Taylor and Francis. Pp. 1–23.
Weiner, J. S., and J. A. Lourie
   1969   *Human biology: a guide to field methods. IBP Handbook No.* 3. Philadelphia: Davis.
Wright, S.
   1931   Evolution in Mendelian populations. *Genetics* 16:97–159.

19

An Historical Perspective on Studies of Human Growth and Development in Extreme Environments

Cynthia M. Beall

Physical anthropology in America has long been associated with growth studies (Garn 1980). Indeed, Aleš Hrdlička, the founder of the American Association of Physical Anthropologists (AAPA), once defined physical anthropology by saying: "It is essentially the study of human variation, of the human life cycle in all its phases [Hrdlička 1927:2]." Hrdlička also noted, in the first issue of the *American Journal of Physical Anthropology* (*AJPA*) that the scientific aims of physical anthropology include

> Studies concerning the numerous environmental groups of humanity—groups developed and continuing under extremes of elevations, climate and nourishment; or under the greatest specialization in clothing, food, occupation or habitats, that are liable to permanently affect the body or its functions. All such conditions are followed by functional or structural reactions and accommodations of the system and it is to be determined how these ultimately affect the progeny [Hrdlička 1918:21].

This is a concise statement of the goals of growth studies: to learn in what ways human groups differ (Tanner 1951), why they do so, and how size and form are attained and modified (Garn 1957; Tanner 1966). Since it is difficult and often unethical to perform experiments with human populations, the scientist interested in the modification of size and form usually must rely on natural experimental settings in order to reach conclusions regarding how and why groups differ. Environmental contrasts like those noted by Hrdlička provide such opportunities to study the "effect on the progeny."

Contemporary physical anthropologists continue to maintain interest in this issue today since growth and development are viewed in an environmental context as processes potentially subject to evolutionary and adaptive modification (Baker

1967; Frisancho 1980; Gould 1977, 1980; Mazess 1975). One of the commonly utilized models for examining these processes is the study of populations living under physiologically stressful conditions or "extreme environments" (e.g., Frisancho 1980; Hiernaux 1964, 1968; Lasker 1969; Tanner 1966). Thus, from its inception, physical anthropology in the United States has been concerned both with the human life cycle and with physical and social environmental extremes. The longevity and persistence of these themes are my reasons for adopting the particular organizing principle used in the present chapter on environmental influences on growth and development. It is, of course, recognized that many studies of human growth and development undertaken by physical anthropologists do not utilize this approach (see Little, present volume); however, it is an approach that offers a certain perspective on the subfield of human growth within the field of physical anthropology.

In this chapter, the history, present status, and future trends of the study of environmental influences on human growth and development, emphasizing the "environmental extremes" noted by Hrdlička are selectively summarized. The discussion focuses primarily on the 50 years since the first AAPA meetings in 1930, although, necessarily, some attention is paid to previous scientific endeavors comprising the state of knowledge at that time. First, two general approaches to studying environmental influences on human growth that have been especially important throughout this time period are reviewed—secular trend and migration models (see Haas, in the present volume). Next, climate, altitude, and nutrition—the principal environmental influences studied by physical anthropologists—are selected and discussed from the standpoint of history, interest, and the continuity or discontinuity in studies over the past five decades. Throughout the review, special attention is given to research strategy, which in some instances has not changed substantially since an early outstanding study and in others has changed fundamentally as the result of new data opening major new perspectives.

This review relies principally on the primary literature in American physical anthropology and, following the lead of an earlier reviewer, Marcus S. Goldstein (1940), draws especially on papers published in the *AJPA* and in *Human Biology* to indicate the variety of work being done. It is recognized that, for the field of growth, this is quite a limitation since a great deal of information is contributed to journals outside the field in areas such as public health or pediatrics and these are not emphasized here. However, since the purpose of this chapter is to review growth as a subfield of physical anthropology and to evaluate it from the standpoint of its contribution to our understanding of the issues of evolution and adaptation, which are central to physical anthropology, this limitation is justified.

Reviewing trends in physical anthropology prior to World War II, Goldstein (1940:191) explained that his "temerity" in attempting such an undertaking was prompted by several factors, including: (*a*) that as one of the younger scholars in the field, he was personally concerned about its future and (*b*) that the inadequacies of the presentation would certainly provoke further discussion on the subject. These statements apply to the present review as well.

Early Studies

Before reviewing the various environmental influences, it is useful to have a perspective on the state of knowledge about environmental influences on growth 50 years ago on the occasion of the first meeting of the AAPA. Physical anthropologists, of course, did not begin work in a vaccum. A tremendous amount of information on growth and development existed at that time, as Scammon (1927) and Tanner (1979) have noted. With respect to our particular interest here, an outstanding summary of the knowledge of environmental influences on growth can be found in Sanders's *Environment and Growth* (1934), for which Aleš Hrdlička wrote an introduction. Presented by Sanders as an analysis of the relative contributions of heredity and environment to growth, it is a well-written critical synthesis of literally hundreds of studies, accumulated between roughly 1880 and 1930, that demonstrate the plasticity of human growth. The book deals especially with variation in the social environment, including socioeconomic status and war (what Sanders termed the "improbable" aspects of environment), although climatic, seasonal, and nutritional factors are also considered and often with samples numbering in the thousands and tens of thousands—impressive numbers for those days of pencil and paper calculations. Thus, sophisticated knowledge about environmental and biological variation at all stages of the life cycle prior to maturity was available early in the history of the discipline.

Major Research Strategies of Historical Importance

When tracing the history of the physical anthropologist's interest in various environmental factors influencing growth, it is useful to first consider two research strategies that have historically been important. A very early example of one type is a study of secular trend in the body size of children and adults and age at menarche. This was studied by Boas among Toronto school children (Boas 1898) and by Mills in his worldwide survey of age at menarche (Mills 1937). Since then, scientists have described secular trends in numerous populations as diversive as Italian–Americans (Damon 1965), Harvard athletes (Polednak 1975), and Mexican–Americans in Texas (Malina and Zavaleta 1980) as well as examples of reverse secular trends during World War II (e.g., Markowitz 1955; Takahshi 1966; Vlatovsky 1966).

These studies share a research design in common—the size of individuals of the same age in the same population (variously defined) or the age of occurrence of a particular event is compared at two or more points in historical time. The earlier studies often compared only two generations or decades, whereas the later ones span multiple generations or centuries. Also, the earlier studies focused on European and American populations, whereas more recent studies have turned to currently developing countries (e.g., Himes and Malina 1975; Himes and Mueller 1977; Malina and Zavaleta 1980) and found secular trends of smaller magnitude, if at all. Still, the design has not changed since Boas's time. These findings have been reviewed by Meredith (1976).

Another research strategy initiated by early students of the subject is the migration model. Franz Boas pioneered its use with a study of some 18,000 children in New York City whose parents were immigrants from Europe, In an elegant design, he controlled for selective migration, secular trend, and the length of time in the new environment and was able to demonstrate environmental plasticity of head shape (Boas 1912)—a variable widely used at that time as an invariant classificatory feature.[1]

The basic migration model has since become a continuously popular approach, having many versions. These include the early studies of Japanese in Japan and in the United States and Hawaii (Spier 1929; Shapiro 1939; Ito, 1942; Gruelich, 1957), of Chinese in China and Hawaii (Appleton 1927, 1928), and of Mexicans in Mexico and the United States (Lasker 1952; Lasker and Gaynor-Evans 1961), in which the two fundamental issues were selective migration and environmental modifications of phenotype. Later studies focused on certain aspects of the different environments, such as studies of Americans and Japanese in tropical, urban Brazil (Eveleth 1966; Eveleth and DeSouza-Freitas 1969), Italian-Swiss colony in California (Hulse 1957), Europeans in Guatemala (Johnston et al. 1976), high-altitude natives at low altitude (Beall et al. 1977), low-altitude natives at high altitude (Frisancho et al. 1973b; Haas et al. 1980), and Italians in Belgium (Susanne 1979), to name just a few.

Individual research designs using the migration model are diverse and range from a simple, one-population–two-environments design to various permutations involving multiple populations and environments that incoporate the added twists of varying age at migration and length of exposure to the new environment. The principal issue under investigation was sometimes selective migration, as in the case of two early studies of Japanese migrants (Shapiro 1939; Spier 1929), at other times, environmental plasticity of form (e.g., Boas 1912; Shapiro 1939). In some cases, researchers selected populations in order to "control" for as many aspects of the environment as possible while varying an "experimental treatment" of interest in testing an hypothesis, for example, Eveleth's (1966) comparative study of upper-class American children living in tropical Brazil and temperate United States. There appears to be no major trend in the application of this model, and its use continues unabated, limited only by our ingenuity in discovering appropriate populations and interest in constructing strong research designs. Again, there have been no major developments since Boas.

---

[1]For further discussion of the theoretical implications of Boas's seminal study, see Armelagos et al. in the present volume.

It is a weakness of both the secular trend and the migration models that the environmental contrasts between decades and generations, between origin and destination, or between migrants and nonmigrants, are multiple and unmeasured. Appleton (1927, 1928) contrasted the growth of Chinese children in Hawaii and China and noted that the environmental contrast included differences in hygiene, sanitation, climate, disease, and poverty. The term *environmental growth factor* was coined to easily refer to the variety of factors producing differential growth (Lasker 1946, 1952). Shapiro provided a thoughtful discussion on this subject:

> There is no doubt that the relationship of physical man to his environment is a problem of the greatest complexity and that in statistical studies precise weighting for environmental influences is hardly possible at this stage of investigation. Yet the fundamental import of the problem demands continued effort to understand it and to express it in quantitative terms [Shapiro 1939:185].

However, in the application of the secular trend and migration models, the specific environmental influence has not been a major concern until recently, and the majority of studies "test for the effects of" a given environmental contrast without specifying and measuring precisely what the contrast entails. The quantitative characterization of environment and the determination of its relevant factors have been difficult to achieve, and this may be one reason for the variety of results reported in the literature from studies that superficially appear to be replicates. Elucidating, specifying, and measuring the environmental contrasts utilized in these models is one area in which contemporary and future studies may make important contributions and advances. The major environmental factors studied by physical anthropologists—climate, altitude, and nutrition—are considered separately in the following sections.

Climate

Climate is an environmental variable that, when reduced to mean monthly temperature (MMT) or mean annual temperature (MAT), is measurable and quantifiable. Not surprisingly, therefore, the study of the effect of climate on growth was an early interest of physical anthropologists. Early studies are exemplified by the work of Brenton (1921) on seasonal variation in prenatal growth and, particularly, Mills's studies (1937, 1942) of the effect of tropical residence on growth. Mills tested in various ways the hypothesis of an earlier age at menarche and growth depression in the tropics. He hypothesized that thermoregulatory considerations underlie the climatic variation in growth—a hypothesis still tendered even though the biology of these modifications remains unknown (Eveleth and Tanner 1976).

Two research designs employed by Mills (1937) continue to be used. One is that of assembling published data on many populations in different climates in order to test a hypothesis about the relationship between a biological characteristic and a climate—in this case, to demonstrate the fallacy of the belief in earlier maturation in the tropics (Mills 1937). Roberts's (1953, 1960, 1973) mathematical correlational analyses of MAT and worldwide variation in size and form during growth and adulthood represent an elegant refinement and thorough application of this approach. From such work it has been possible to demonstrate worldwide clines of growth in shape or form that correlate with MAT variations in ways consistent with the hypothesis that thermoregulatory considerations are involved.

Second, Mills (1942) applied a migration model to the same problem by comparing the growth of native Panamanians and North Americans born in Panama with North America-born recent migrants to the Panama Canal Zone and found some evidence for a depression of growth in the tropics. Two later refinements of this migration model are Eveleth's (1966) use of a semilongitudinal sample of upper-class American children in Brazil and Johnston and coworkers' (1976) use of longitudinal samples comparing European and Guatemalan children living in Guatemala with European children living in the United States. These studies offer evidence that boys are more affected than girls and that growth is more affected by climate during childhood than during adolescence. Earlier work by Gruelich (1957) and Boas (1923) had produced similar observations regarding the differential environmental sensitivity of males and females, of children and adolescents.

Research designs in climate studies have become more complex, and the experimental models more complete, although they have not substantially changed from the landmark studies of Mills. Now there is greater interest in considering variables other than temperature under the rubric of "climate," for example, seasonal variation in ultraviolet light (Bogin 1978). Sanders (1934) also noted seasonal variation in activity and nutrition.

In order to understand more about the mechanisms of these relationships, future studies may actually assess, for example, thermoregulation during growth under extreme temperatures or vitamin D metabolism under variable ultraviolet light isolation in an effort to understand the dynamics of underlying growth patterns. From an evolutionary and adaptive standpoint, the functional outcome in terms of morbidity and mortality are important, but they are infrequently considered (e.g., Little and Hochner 1973; Malina and Himes 1978; So 1975). Furthermore, future studies may continue to explore the different influences on males and females and on different stages of the life span.

Altitude

Another readily quantifiable environmental influence on growth is altitude. A high-altitude effect was mentioned by Hrdlička in 1918; however, it was not until 1932 that Hurtado published the first report on altitude and growth in the primary literature in physical anthropology and thereby initiated some long-standing traditions. One was his insistence that the study of *true adaptation* (presumably, genetic, although he did not define the term) deal with the investigation of populations who have inhabited an environment for centuries and that it include a comparison of such populations with others who have not inhabited that environment for a similar period of time. Another was comparison of such populations on the basis of growth, not only in size but also in morphology and physiological function.

After Hurtado's classic study, there was a hiatus of nearly 40 years before the publication of Frisancho and Baker's (1970) report on physical growth and Frisancho's studies (1969, 1970) of functional growth at high altitudes in Peru. These studies reported prolonged slow growth in height and weight, a poorly defined adolescent spurt, and slow skeletal maturation, but a rapid and accelerated development of the chest and of pulmonary function among high-altitude Andean natives. Since then, research into the influence of altitude has continued along the lines introduced by Hurtado. For example, there is continued emphasis on body shape measurements, such as the relative proportions of the chest (e.g., Palomino *et al.* 1979)—in a field often relying heavily on simple body size measurements, such as height and weight. Similarly, there is continued emphasis on functional growth measures (Mueller *et al.* 1978). The integration of these measures has been unique to studies of this particular environmental influence. Moreover, just as Hurtado's sampled ranged in age from 4 through 75 years, subsequent research efforts have been directed toward all stages of the life span from prenatal (e.g., Haas 1976; Haas *et al.* 1980) through childhood and adolescence (e.g., Beall *et al.* 1977; Stinson 1980) and adulthood (e.g., Frisancho 1976; Mueller *et al.* 1978).

With the replication of Hurtado's model in numerous populations, several interesting new perspectives on the question of the influence of altitude on growth have arisen. For example, the many studies carried out in the Andes have been paralleled by a few in other high-altitude areas of the world, such as the Simien Plateau (Ethiopia) and the Himalayas, and it appears that the influence of altitude on growth is not uniform in all populations—a finding that has important microevolutionary implications (Pawson 1976). Also, there has been appreciation of growth variation within a single high-altitude zone and population (Mueller *et al.* 1980; Stinson 1980). In addition, there is increasingly awareness of the complexity of high-altitude environments and of the fact that the reduction of environmental contrasts to just a single variable, such as the number of meters above sea level, when in fact many factors vary with altitude (e.g., Frisancho 1976; Thomas 1976), is a conceptual oversimplification.

Research designs employed by students of high-altitude adaptation and growth have ranged from the two-populations—two-environments design, first used by Hurtado (1932), to various multiple combinations of populations and environments providing increasingly powerful natural experimental designs (e.g., Haas *et al.* 1980; see also, Haas in the present volume). Future studies must correct the uncertainties in some of our current understandings of growth at high altitude, much of which is still based on the relatively weak research design (as distinct from the methodology) pioneered by Hurtado, and must expand our understanding of population differences in growth at high altitude. The current realization of the complex configuration of factors, apart from hypoxia, that may distinguish high and low altitude will undoubtedly orient future studies in this area.

Nutrition

Although nutritional variation is potentially quantifiable, doing so is a tedious and complicated task, and few studies have attempted it. Hence, it is often difficult to precisely characterize nutritional stress in a population. Aside from Sander's convincing demonstration of the influence of nutritional factors on growth and development in 1934, only a few pre-World War II investigations focused on this particular facet of environmental contrast (e.g., Cogwill 1936; Hunt 1937; Jackson 1939; Mitchell 1933). However, the inclusion of a section on diet and growth in Krogman's (1945) bibliography of physical anthropology indicates some interest in the topic. The first edition of Tanner's (1952) classic work on growth at adolescence described findings from wars and famines as the principal evidence for nutritional influence on growth and development. Although work by nutritionists and public health workers (e.g., Jelliffe 1966) began to describe the growth effects of certain nutritional conditions, an anthropological approach to these data did not appear until later.

The interest in nutrition burgeoned during the 1960s, when numerous papers on the effects of nutritional variation and its influence on growth and development appeared (e.g., Frisch and Revelle 1969; Garn et al. 1969; Sabharwal et al. 1966). The availability of data on large samples of large populations, such as the Interdepartmental Committee on Nutrition for National Defense (ICNND) surveys in Asia and Latin American and the Institute of of Nutrition of Central America and Panama (INCAP) surveys in Central America, provided a tremendous impetus to further study of nutrition by physical anthropologists. Studies of body size and composition, tempo of growth, and skeletal and biochemical maturation flourished. Similarly, the founding of the Guatemalan multidisciplinary prospective longitudinal study and its successor, a prospective experimental study, have also had great impact (e.g., Himes et al. 1975; Malina et al. 1974; Martorell et al. 1975; Yarbrough et al. 1975).

A debate has emerged from these and similar studies over the meaning and interpretation of such general findings as the small body size and delayed maturation of undernourished children and of the significance of the apparent age and sex differences in response to the stress (e.g., Stini 1969, 1972a, 1972b) as well as of the relative importance of nutrition compared with other factors influencing growth. Of special significance to the physical anthropologist is the issue of a multiple versus a single universal reference curve of growth (e.g., Garn and Clark 1976; Habicht et al. 1974). Other important issues include determining the role of nutritional status in the production of morphological variation and its resultant effect on a variety of functions, such as work capacity, intellect, and reproduction (e.g., Bleichrodt et al. 1980; Frisancho et al. 1973a, 1973b; Green 1974; Mueller

1979). Because of the great variation in the duration, severity, and timing of different types of malnutrition, only tentative conclusions can be made at this time.

This detailed study of populations experiencing nutritional stress has also enhanced our appreciation of other interacting environmental influences on growth including disease, sanitation, and socioeconomic status. Some of these findings, such as those focusing on the synergy of disease, nutrition, and growth (e.g., Martorell *et al.* 1975), have been made possible by the special circumstances and design of a major prospective multidisciplinary study. The accurate quantification of such patterns has further amplified our capability to conceptualize growth in a more realistic manner as an adaptive response to multiple influences in both the physical and sociocultural environment.

The research models used by physical anthropologists studying nutrition and growth have run the gamut from the quasi-experimental designs used to study the other stresses to a few truly experimental designs involving nutritional intervention in prospective studies.

The repeated demonstration of nutritional influences on growth and development, plus the possibility of nutritional variation between any two populations, has prompted a reconsideration and reevaluation of studies of other environmental factors that influence growth. The necessity of considering the possible role of nutrition as an intervening variable between environmental input and a growth outcome is now recognized. In order to evaluate nutrition's influence, we must understand what nutritional variation can and cannot produce in terms of effect on human growth. Thus, apart from its own vital contribution to our understanding of human variation and adaptation, the study of nutrition is integral to contemporary studies of all other environmental factors (Haas and Harrison 1977). This realization has produced a major discontinuity in the study of environment and growth.

Current and Future Trends

There is an interesting pattern of contrasts among the three principal environmental variables: climate, altitude, and nutrition. For climate and altitude, there are several impressive investigations, conducted in the 1930s, that set a task for subsequent studies utilizing the same basic research models: to replicate the earlier studies in additional populations. In both cases, this has been amply done with stronger research designs and greater analytical detail. The study of climate and growth appears likely to move toward a consideration of the functional outcomes of and underlying mechanics producing growth variation. The study of altitude and growth began with such questions and has now moved on to explore, more thoroughly, certain portions of the basic model—especially the possibility of multiple environmental factors and population variation in response to them. In each case, greater attention is paid to theoretical implications, and greater sophistication is applied to the focusing of research designs so that they can address more precise questions. However, there have been few breakthroughs in methods, measurement, or approach deriving from these studies. In contrast, nutritional studies in physical anthropology apparently did not go through an initial early phase of development before reappearing and modelling themselves along the lines of an earlier study. Instead, they took their models from other fields.

Turning ahead, a number of future trends are discernible in contemporary work dealing with human growth in environmental extremes. One is the identification of two new environmental extremes—the fifth and the ninety-fifth percentiles—discovered and elaborated by Garn and his associates (e.g., Garn 1980). The use of the concept of statistical extremes within a population and the concurrent use of very large samples has permitted quite precise quantification of some environmental influences and responses—thus, meeting Shapiro's (1939) challenge to do so. Related to this development is the application of new analytical techniques to the identification and ranking among many measured characteristics, of causes of growth variation within a population (e.g., Johnston et al. 1980). Habitual physical activity as an influence on nutritional requirements and growth and development may receive greater attention in the future, especially in view of its potential importance for adult growth (e.g., Borkan and Norris 1980; Higman 1979; Mack and Johnston 1974; Parizkova and Carter 1976).

Another trend is to expand the tradition of the recent past, which narrowly focused on child growth, to include adult growth or *biological aging*. It has often been the practice to lump everyone over 17 years of age and under senility together in the "adult" category. The pitfalls of doing so have been recognized since the studies of Boas (1940), Lasker (1953), and Lasker and Gaynor-Evans (1961) presented data on adult age changes and demonstrated that these could confound population comparison. Studies during the 1930s and 1940s sometimes included both children and adults (e.g., Goldstein 1939; Hellebrandt and Braun 1939; Hurtado 1932), and the bibliographies of physical anthropology and reviews published by Cobb (1944), Krogman (1945), and Garn (1952) each contain a section on adult age changes. More recently, studies have become increasingly age parochial, focusing on ever-shorter segments of the life span (e.g., Fergusson et al. 1980). Currently, the growth and development of adults is becoming a focus of attention, not just as a confounding artifact in adult population comparisons, but also as the subject of investigation into the nature and magnitude, as well as sources of variation of growth and development (e.g., Borkan and Norris 1980; Garn et al. 1967, 1968; Himes and Mueller 1977a, 1977b; Plato and Norris 1980; Susanne 1980; Trotter et al. 1961, 1968).

Related to this expansion of research interest to encompass adult growth is a trend toward reintegrating the earlier stages of the life cycle into the larger picture of the entire life span and paying more attention to the relationships between various stages of the life span (e.g., Abel 1980; Falkner 1980; Garn et al. 1977; Roche et al. 1981). For example, the mechanisms underlying small adult stature in populations suffering from mild to chronic malnutrition during growth were explained by the discovery of the different effects of malnutrition during childhood and adolescence on two different biological systems (Frisancho *et al.* 1970a, 1970b).

This example also demonstrates the importance of using more than one physiological system in order to understand the biological mechanisms underlying different growth patterns and outcomes. It is a long-standing complaint that growth standards are rather limited to height and weight (Howells 1948; Krogman 1955). In their massive compilation of growth studies done between 1960 and 1974, Eveleth and Tanner (1976) found far more data on height and weight than on any other variable, although body composition data and skeletal development data were often available for more recent studies. Since it is sometimes held that shape is more subject to natural selection by environmental forces than is size, the ontogeny of this aspect of human populations is important for studies of evolution and adaptation. Thus, another trend may be a renewed interest in growth in the human form stimulated by new techniques (e.g., Eveleth 1975, 1978; Goldstein and Johnston 1978; Meredith 1979), perhaps drawing on successful developments in evolutionary theory in other fields (Gould 1977, 1980).

Still another trend is that of making a greater contribution to the theoretical issues in physical anthropology. This has proceeded slowly, possibly due, in part, to the fact that many physical anthropologists who are interested in growth research tend to contribute to other fields, such as public health and epidemiology. This concern for theory began in the mid-1960s when the International Biological Program (IBP) explicitly integrated studies of growth and physique into the larger issues being addressed by physical anthropologists (e.g., Baker 1967; Lasker 1969; Tanner 1966; Weiner 1966). The data base and the theoretical developments proceeding from these studies have stimulated increasingly sophisticated and complex models of the relationship between human populations and their respective environments that have incorporated many of the findings from the investigations of growth in extreme environments. These include the interaction and simultaneous occurrence of multiple environmental influences, including the energy costs of adaptation, and life-stage and population variability and sex differences in response to the environment (e.g., Frisancho 1980; Thomas *et al.* 1979). These in turn have renewed attention in the theoretical significance of the study of growth and its outcomes, which will be important for the fuller contribution of growth studies to the understanding of the fundamental processes of evolution and adaptation studied by all physical anthropologists.

References

Abel, E. L.
  1980   Smoking during pregnancy: a review of effects on growth and development of offspring.
           Human Biology 52:593–626.
Acheson, R. M.
  1960   Effects of nutrition and disease on human growth. In *Human Growth*, edited by J. M. Tanner.
           Oxford: Pergamon. Pp. 73–92.

Appleton, V. B.
    1927   Growth of Chinese children in Hawaii and China. *American Journal of Physical Anthropology*
            10:237–251.
    1928   Growth of Kwangtung Chinese in Hawaii. *American Journal of Physical Anthropology* **11**:473–
            500.
Ashcroft, M. T., P. Heneage, and H. G. Lovell
    1966   Heights and weights of Jamaican children of various ethnic groups. *American Journal of
            Physical Anthropology* **24**:35–44.
Baker, P. T.
    1967   Current status of U. S. participation in the international biological programme. *American
            Journal of Physical Anthropology* **26**:361–365.
    1977   Problems and strategies. In *Human population problems in the biosphere: some research strategies
            and designs. MAB Technical Notes*, **3**, edited by P. T. Baker. Paris: UNESCO.
Beall, C. M., P. T. Baker, T. S. Baker, and J. D. Haas
    1977   The effects of high altitude on adolescent growth in southern Peruvian Amerindians.
            Human Biology **49**:109–124.
Berkson, J.
    1930   Evidence of a seasonal cycle in human growth. *Human Biology* **2**:523–538.
Bleichrodt, N., P. J. D. Drenth, and A. Querido
    1980   Effects of iodine deficiency on mental and psychomotor abilities. *American Journal of
            Physical Anthropology* **53**:55–67.
Boas, F.
    1898   *The growth of Toronto children. Report of U. S. Commissioner of Education for 1896–7.* Pp. 1541–
            1599.
    1912   *Changes in bodily form of the descendents of immigrants.* New York: Columbia University Press.
    1923   The growth of children as influenced by environmental and hereditary conditions. *School
            and Society* **17**:305–308.
    1940   Age changes in and secular changes in anthropometric measurements. *American Journal of
            Physical Anthropology* **26**:63–68.
Bogin, B.
    1978   Seasonal pattern in the rate of growth in height of children living in Guatemala. *American
            Journal of Physical Anthropology* **48**:205–210.
Borkan, G. A., and A. H. Norris
    1980   Biological age in adulthood: comparison of active and inactive U. S. males. *Human Biology*
            52:787–802.
Brenton, H.
    1921   Climate and race as factors influencing the weight of the newborn. *American Journal of
            Physical Anthropology* **4**:237–249.
Chang, K. S. F., M. M. C. Lee, W. D. Low, and K. Evan
    1963   Height and weight of southern Chinese children. *American Journal of Physical Anthropology*
            21:497–509.
Cobb, W. M.
    1944   Bibliography in physical anthropology. July 1, 1943 through June 3, 1944. *American Journal
            of Physical Anthropology* **2**:381–413.
Cowgill, G. R.
    1936   *Diets in relation to growth: considerations of importance to physical anthropologists. American
            Journal of Physical Anthropology* **21**(Suppl. 11).
Damon, A.
    1965   Stature increase among Italian–Americans: environmental, genetic or both? *American
            Journal of Physical Anthropology* **23**:401–408.
Eveleth, P. B.
    1966   The effect of climate on growth. *Annals of the New York Academy of Sciences* **134**:750–759.

1975   Differences between ethnic groups in sex dimorphism of adult height. *Annals of Human Biology* **2**:35–39.

1978   Differences between populations in body shape of children and adolescents. *American Journal of Physical Anthropology* **49**:373–382.

Eveleth, P. B., and J. A. DeSouza Freitas

1969   Tooth eruption and menarche of Brazilian-born children of Japanese ancestry. *Human Biology* **41**:176–184.

Eveleth, P. B., and J. M. Tanner

1976   *Worldwide variation in human growth.* International Biological Programme **8**. London and New York: Cambridge University Press.

Falkner, F. (editor)

1980   *Prevention in childhood of health problems in adult life.* Geneva: World Health Organization.

Fergusson, D. M., L. J. Horwood, R. T. Shannon

1980   Length and weight gain in the first three months of life. *Human Biology* **52**:169–180.

Frisancho, A. R.

1969   Human growth and pulmonary function of a high altitude Peruvian Quechua population. *Human Biology* **41**:365–379.

1970   Developmental response to high altitude hypoxia. *American Journal of Physical Anthropology* **32**:401–408.

1976   Growth and morphology at high altitude. In *Man in the Andes: a multidisciplinary study of high-altitude Quechua. US/IBP Synthesis Series No.* **1**, edited by P. T. Baker and M. A. Little. Stroudsburg, Pennsylvania: Dowden, Hutchinson and Ross. Pp. 180–207.

1980   *Human adaptation. A functional interpretation.* St. Louis, Missouri: Mosby.

Frisancho, A. R., and P. T. Baker

1970   Altitude and growth: a study of the patterns of physical growth of a high altitude Peruvian Quechua population. *American Journal of Physical Anthropology* **32**:279–292.

Frisancho, A. R., S. M. Garn, and W. Ascoli

1970   Childhood retardation resulting in reduction on adult body size due to lesser adolescent skeletal delay. *American Journal of Physical Anthropology* **33**:325–336.

1970b   Unequal influence of low dietary intakes on skeletal maturation during childhood and adolescence. *American Journal of Clinical Nutrition* **23**:1220–1227.

Frisancho, A. R., K. Guire, W. Babler, G. Borkan, and A. Way

1980   Nutritional influences on childhood development and genetic control of adolescent growth of Quechuas and Mestizos from the Peruvian lowlands. *American Journal of Physical Anthropology* **52**:367–376.

Frisancho, A. R., J. E. Kalayman, and J. Matos

1977   Influence of maternal nutritional status on prenatal growth in a Peruvian urban population. *American Journal of Physical Anthropology* **46**:65–74.

Frisancho, A. R., J. Sanchez, D. Pallardel, and L. Yanez

1973   Adaptative significance of small body size under poor socio-economic conditions in southern Peru. *American Journal of Physical Anthropology* **39**:255–262.

Frisancho, A. R., R. B. Thomas, and P. T. Baker

1969   Growth patterns of a highland Peruvian population: a preliminary analysis. *American Journal of Physical Anthropology* **23**:331–332.

Frisancho, A. R., T. Velasquez, and J. Sanchez

1973b   Influences of developmental adaptation on lung function at high altitude. *Human Biology* **45**:583–594.

Frisch, R., and R. Revelle

1969   Variation in body weights and the age of the adolescent growth spurt among Latin American and Asian populations, in relation to calorie supplies. *Human Biology* **41**:185–212.

Fry, E. I., K. S. F. Chang, M. M. C. Lee, and C. K. Ng

1965   The amount and distribution of subcutaneous tissue in southern Chinese children from Hong Kong. *American Journal of Physical Anthropology* **23**:69–79.

Fry, E. I., and J. Zarins
    1967   Measures of bone density responses of Hong Kong children to rice and rice–wheat diets. *American Journal of Physical Anthropology* **27**:238 (Abstract).

Garn, S. M.
    1952   Physical growth and development. *American Journal of Physical Anthropology* **10**:169–192.
    1957   Research in human growth. *Human Biology* **29**:1–11.
    1963   Letter to the Editor. Physical Anthropology. *American Journal of Physical Anthropology* **21**:255–256.
    1980   Human growth. *Annual Review of Anthropology* **9**:275–292.

Garn, S. M., and D. C. Clark
    1976   Problems in the nutritional assessment of black individuals. *American Journal of Public Health* **66**:262–267.

Garn, S. M., M. A. Guzman, and B. Wagner
    1969   Subperiosteal gain and endosteal loss in protein-calorie malnutrition. *American Journal of Physical Anthropology* **30**:153–156.

Garn, S. M., C. G. Rohmann, B. Wagner, and W. Ascoli
    1967   Continuing bone growth through life: a general phenomenon. *American Journal of Physical Anthropology* **26**:313–318.

Garn, S. M., H. A. Shaw, and K. D. McCabe
    1977   Birth size and growth appraisal. *Journal of Pediatrics* **90**:1049–1051.

Garn, S. M., B. Wagner, C. G. Rohmann, and W. Ascoli
    1968   Further evidence for continuing bone expansion. *American Journal of Physical Anthropology* **28**:219–222.

Goldstein, H., and F. E. Johnston
    1978   A note on studying shape change in children. *Annals of Human Biology* **5**:33–39.

Goldstein, M. S.
    1939   Development of the bridge of the nose. *American Journal of Physical Anthropology* **25**:101–118.
    1940   Recent trends in physical anthropology. *American Journal of Physical Anthropology* **26**:191–209.

Gould, S. J.
    1977   *Ever since Darwin. Reflections in natural history.* New York: Norton.
    1980   *The panda's thumb. More reflections in natural history.* New York: Norton.

Greene, L. S.
    1974   Physical growth and development, neurological maturation, and behavior functioning in two Ecuadorian Andean communities in which goiter is endemic. II. PTC taste sensitivity and neurological maturation. *American Journal of Physical Anthropology* **41**:139–152.

Gruelich, W. W.
    1957   A comparison of the physical growth and development of American born and native Japanese children. *American Journal of Physical Anthropology* **15**:489–515.

Haas, J. D.
    1976   Prenatal and infant growth and development. In *Man in the Andes. A multidisciplinary study of high altitude Quechua,* edited by P. T. Baker and M. A. Little. Stroudsburg, Pennsylvania: Dowden, Hutchinson and Ross. Pp. 161–179.

Haas, J. D., and G. A. Harrison
    1977   Nutritional anthropology and biological adaptation. *Annual Review of Anthropology* **6**:69–101.

Haas, J. D., E. A. Frongillo, Jr., C. D. Stepwick, J. L. Beard, and L. Hurtado
    1980   Altitude, ethnic and sex difference in birth weight and length in Bolivia. *Human Biology* **52**:459–477.

Habicht, J. P., R. Martorell, C. Yarbrough, R. M. Malina, and R. E. Klein
    1974   Height and weight standards for preschool children. How relevant are ethnic differences in growth potential? *Lancet* **1**:611–615.

Hardy, M. C.
    1938   Frequent illness in childhood, physical growth and final size. *American Journal of Physical Anthropology* **23**:241–260.

Hellebrandt, F. A., and G. L. Braun
    1939   The influence of sex and age on the postural sway of man. *American Journal of Physical Anthropology* **19**:347–360.

Hiernaux, J.
    1964   Weight/height relationship during growth in Africans and Europeans. *Human Biology* **36**:273–293.
    1968   Bodily shape differentiation of ethnic groups and of the sexes through growth. *Human Biology* **40**:44–62.

Higman, B. W.
    1979   Growth in Afro-Caribbean slave populations. *American Journal of Physical Anthropology* **50**:373–386.

Himes, J. H., and R. M. Malina
    1975   Age and secular factors in the stature of adult Zapotec males. *American Journal of Physical Anthropology* **43**:367–370.

Himes, J. H., R. Martorell, J. P. Habicht, C. Yarbrough, R. M. Malina, and R. E. Klein
    1975   Patterns of cortical bone growth in moderately malnourished preschool children. *Human Biology* **47**:337–350.

Himes, J. H., and W. H. Mueller
    1977   Age-associated stature loss and socioeconomic status. *Journal of the American Geriatrics Society* **25**:171–174.
    1977   Aging and secular change in adult stature in rural Colombia. *American Journal of Physical Anthropology* **46**:275–280.

Howells, W. W.
    1948   Birth order and body size. *American Journal of Physical Anthropology* **6**:449–460.

Hrdlička, A.
    1918   Physical anthropology: its scope and aims: its history and present status in America. *American Journal of Physical Anthropology* **1**:3–23.
    1927   Anthropology and medicine. *American Journal of Physical Anthropology* **10**:1–10.

Hurtado, A.
    1932   Respiratory adaptations in the Indian natives of the Peruvian Andes. Studies at high altitude. *American Journal of Physical Anthropology* **17**:137–161.

Hunt, E.
    1937   *The dietary and nutritional effects of increased milk solids in low cost diets of pre-school Negro boys.* *American Journal of Physical Anthropology* **22**(Suppl. 8).

Ito, P. K.
    1942   Comparative biometrical study of physique of Japanese women born and reared under different environments. *Human Biology* **14**:279–351.

Jackson, C. M.
    1938   The effects of underfeeding on growth. *American Journal of Physical Anthropology* **23**:497.

Jelliffe, D. B.
    1966   *The assessment of the nutritional status of the community with special reference to field surveys in developing regions of the world.* Monograph Series, No. **53**. Geneva: World Health Organization.

Johnston, F. E.
    1974   Control of age at menarche. *Human biology* **46**:159–191.

Johnston, F. E., T. O. Scholl, B. C. Newman, J. Cravioto,, and E. R. DeLicardie
    1980   An analysis of environmental variables and factors associated with growth failure in a Mexican village. *Human Biology* **52**:627–636.

Johnston, F. E., H. Winer, D. Thissen, and R. B. McVean
    1976   Hereditary and environmental determinants of growth in height in a longitudinal sample

of children and youth of Guatemalan and European ancestry. *American Journal of Physical Anthropology* **44**:469–475.

Kano, K., and C. S. Chunt
   1975   Do American born Japanese children still grow faster than native Japanese? *American Journal of Physical Anthropology* **43**:187–194.

Kaplan, B. A.
   1954   Environment and human plasticity. *American Anthropologist* **56**:780–800.

Kimura, K.
   1967   A consideration of the secular trend in Japanese for height and weight by a graphic method. *American Journal of Physical Anthropology* **27**:89–94.
   1976   On the skeletal maturation of Japanese–American white hybrids. *American Journal of Physical Anthropology* **44**:83–90.

Krogman, W. M.
   1945   Bibliography in physical anthropology. July 1, 1944 through June 30, 1945. *American Journal of Physical Anthropology* **3**:367–407.
   1955   The physical growth of children. An appraisal of studies 1950–55. *Monograph of the Society for Research in Child Development* **20**:1–91.

Lasker, G. W.
   1946   Migration and physical differentiation. A comparison with American-born Chinese. *American Journal of Physical Anthropology* **4**:272–300.
   1952   Environmental growth factors and selective migration. *Human Biology* **24**:262–289.
   1953   The age factor in bodily measurements of adult male and female Mexicans. *Human Biology* **25**:50–63.
   1969   Human biological adaptability. *Science* **166**:1480–1486.

Lasker, G. W., and F. Gaynor-Evans
   1961   Age, environment and migration: further anthropometric findings on migrant and non-migrant Mexicans. *American Journal of Physical Anthropology* **19**:203–211.

Little, M. A., and D. H. Hochner
   1973   *Human thermoregulation, growth and mortality. Addison Wesley Module in Anthropology, No.* **36**. Reading, Massachusetts: Addison-Wesley.

Mack, R. W., and F. E. Johnston
   1974   Growth, calorie intake, and activity levels in early infancy: a preliminary report. *Human Biology* **46**:345–354.

Malick, S. L., and I. P. Singh
   1978   Growth trends among male body of Ladakh—a high altitude population. *American Journal of Physical Anthropology* **48**:171–176.

Malina, R. M., J. P. Habicht, C. Yarbrough, R. Martorell, and R. E. Klein
   1974   Skinfold thicknesses at seven sites in rural Guatemalan Ladino children. Birth through seven years of age. *Human Biology* **46**:453–469.

Malina, R. M., and J. H. Himes
   1978   Patterns of childhood mortality and growth status in a rural Zapotec community. *Annals of Human Biology* **5**:517–531.

Malina, R. M., and A. N. Zavaleta
   1980   Secular trend in the stature and weight of Mexican–American children in Texas between 1930 and 1970. *American Journal of Physical Anthropology* **52**:453–461.

Markowitz, S. D.
   1955   Retardation in growth on children in Europe and Asia during World War II. *Human Biology* **27**:258–273.

Martorell, R., C. Yarbrough, A. Lechtig, J. P. Habicht, and R. E. Klein
   1975   Diarrheal disease and growth retardation in preschool Guatemalan children. *American Journal of Physical Anthropology* **43**:341–346.

Mazess, R. B.
    1975   Human adaptation to high altitude. In *Physiological Anthropology*, edited by A. Damon.
            London and New York: Oxford University Press. Pp. 167–209.
Meredith, H. V.
    1976   Findings from Asia, Australia, Europe and North America on secular change in mean
            height of children, youths, and young adults. *American Journal of Physical Anthropology*
            44:315–326.
    1979   Relationship of lower limb height to sitting height in black populations of Africa and the U.
            S. *American Journal of Physical Anthropology* **51**:63–66.
Meredith, H. W.
    1941   Stature and weight of private school children in two successive decades. *American Journal of
            Physical Anthropology* **28**:1–40.
Meredith, H. W., and E. M. Meredith
    1944   The stature of Toronto children half a century ago and today. *Human Biology* **16**:126–131.
Mills, C. A.
    1937   Geographic and time variations in body growth and age at menarche. *Human Biology* **9**:43–
            56.
    1942   Climatic effects on growth and development. *American Anthropologist* **44**:1–13.
Mitchell, H. H.
    1933   A study of factors associated with the growth and nutrition of Puerto Rican children.
            Human Biology **4**:469–508.
Mueller, W. H.
    1979   Fertility and physique in a malnourished population. *Human Biology* **51**:153–166.
Mueller, W. H., F. Yen, F. Rothhammer, and W. J. Schull
    1978   A multinational Andean genetic and health program: VI physiological measurements of
            lung function in an hypoxic environment. *Human Biology* **50**:489–514.
Mueller, W. H., et al.
    1979   A multinational Andean genetic and health program. VIII. Lung function changes with
            migration between altitude. *American Journal of Physical Anthropology* **51**:183–196.
Mueller, W. H., et al.
    1980   The Aymara of Western Bolivia. V. Growth and development in an hypoxic environment.
            Human Biology **52**:529–546.
Newman, M. T.
    1960   Adaptation in the physique of American Aborigines to nutritional factors. *Human Biology*
            32:288–313.
    1975   Nutritional adaptation in man. In *Physiological Anthropology*, edited by A. Damon. London
            and New York: Oxford University Press.
Newman, M. T., and E. Munro
    1955   The relation of climate and body size in U. S. males. *American Journal of Physical
            Anthropology* **13**:1–18.
Palomino, H., W. H. Mueller, and W. J. Schull
    1979   Altitude, Heredity, and body proportions in northern Chile. *American Journal of Physical
            Anthropology* **50**:39–50.
Parizkova, J., and J. E. L. Carter
    1976   Influence of physical activity on stability of somatotypes in boys. *American Journal of Physical
            Anthropology* **44**:327–349.
Pawson, I. G.
    1976   Growth and development in high altitude populations: a review of Ethiopian, Peruvian
            and Nepalese studies. *Proceedings of the Royal Society of London, Series B* **194**:83–98.
    1977   Growth characteristics of populations of Tibetan origin in Nepal. *American Journal of
            Physical Anthropology* **47**:473–482.

Plato, C. C., and A. H. Norris
    1980   Bone measurements of the second metacarpal and grip strength. *Human Biology* **52**:131–150.
Polednak, A. B.
    1975   Secular trend in body size among college athletes. *American Journal of Physical Anthropology* **42**:501–506.
Roberts, D. F.
    1953   Body weight, race and climate. *American Journal of Physical Anthropology* **11**:533–558.
    1960   Effects of race and climate on human growth as exemplified by studies on African children. In *Human Growth*, edited by J. M. Tanner. Oxford: Pergamon. Pp. 59–72.
    1973   *Climate and human variability*. Reading, Massachusetts: Addison–Wesley.
Roche, A. F., S. M. Garn, E. K. Reynolds, M. Robinow, and L. W. Sontag
    1981   The first seriatim study of human growth and middle aging. *American Journal of Physical Anthropology* **54**:23–24.
Sabharwal, K. P., S. Morales, and J. Mendez
    1966   Body measurements and creatinine excretion among upper and lower socio-economic groups of girls in Guatemala. *Human Biology* **38**:131–139.
Sanders, B.
    1934   *Environment and growth*. Baltimore, Maryland: Warwick and York.
Scammon, R. E.
    1927   The literature on the growth and physical development of the fetus, infant, and child: a quantitative summary. *Anatomical Record* **35**:241–267.
Schutte, J. E.
    1980   Growth differences between lower and middle income black male adolescents. *Human Biology* **52**:193–204.
Shapiro, H. L.
    1939   *Migration and environment. A study of the physical characteristics of the Japanese immigrants to Hawaii and the effects of environment on their descendants*. London and New York: Oxford University Press.
So, J. K.
    1975   Genetic, acclimatizational and anthropometric factors in hand cooling among northern and southern Chinese. *American Journal of Physical Anthropology* **43**:31–38.
Stini, W. A.
    1969   Nutritional stress and growth: sex differences in adaptive response. *American Journal of Physical Anthropology* **31**:417–426.
    1972   Reduced sexual dimorphism in upper arm muscle circumference associated with protein-deficient diet in a South American population. *American Journal of Physical Anthropology* **36**:341–352.
    1972   Malnutrition, body size and proportion. *Ecology of Food and Nutrition* **1**:121–130.
    1975   Adaptive strategies of human populations under nutritional stress. In *Biosocial Adaptations*, edited by E. Watts, F. Johnston, and G. Lasker. The Hague: Mouton Publishers.
Stinson, S.
    1980   The physical growth of high altitude Bolivian Aymara children. *American Journal of Physical Anthropology* **52**:377–386.
Susanne, C.
    1979   Comparative biometrical study of stature and weight of Italian migrants in Belgium. *American Journal of Physical Anthropology* **50**:349–366.
    1980   Aging, continuous changes of adulthood. In *Human physical growth and maturation. Methodologies and factors*, edited by F. E. Johnston, A. F. Roche, and C. Susanne. *Nato Advanced Study Institutes Series*. New York: Plenum. Pp. 203–218.
Takahaski, E.
    1966   Growth and environmental factors in Japan. *Human Biology* **38**:112–130.

Tanner, J. .M.
1951   Growth and constitution. In *Anthropology today*, edited by A. L. Kroeber. Chicago: University of Chicago Press. Pp. 750–770.
1952   *Growth at adolescence*. Oxford: Blackwell.
1955   *Growth at adolescence*. Springfield, Illinois: Thomas.
1962   *Growth at adolescence* (second edition). Oxford: Blackwell.
1966   Growth and physique in different populations of mankind. In *The biology of human adaptability*, edited by P. T. Baker and J. S. Weiner. London and New York: Oxford University Press (Clarendon). Pp. 45–66.
1979   A concise history of growth studies from Buffon to Boas. In *Human growth* (Vol. 3), edited by J. M. Tanner and F. Falkner. New York: Plenum. Pp. 515–593.
Thomas, R. B.
1976   Energy flow at high altitude. In *Man in the Andes. A multidisciplinary study of the high altitude Quechua*, edited by P. T. Baker and M. A. Little. *US/IBP Synthesis Series No.* 1. Stroudsburg, Pennsylvania: Dowden, Hutchinson and Ross. Pp. 379–464.
Thomas, R. B., B. Winterhalder, and S. D. McRae
1979   An anthropological approach to human ecology and adaptive dynamics. *Yearbook of Physical Anthropology* **22**:1–46.
Trotter, M., and R. R. Peterson
1967   Relation of transverse diameter of adult femur to age in American Whites and Negroes. *American Journal of Physical Anthropology* **27**:246.
Trotter, M., R. R. Peterson, and R. Wette
1968   The secular trend in the diameter of the femur of American Whites and Negroes. *American Journal of Physical Anthropology* **28**:65–74.
Vlatovsky, V. G.
1966   The secular trend in the growth and development of children and young persons in the Soviet Union. *Human Biology* **38**:219–230.
Weiner, J. S.
1966   Major problems in human population biology. In *The biology of human adaptability*, edited by P. T. Baker and J. S. Weiner. London and New York: Oxford University Press (Clarendon). Pp. 1–24.
Williams, B. J.
1969   Light intensity and sexual maturity. *American Journal of Physical Anthropology* **30**:151–162.
Yarbrough, C. J., P. Habicht, R. M. Malina, A. Lechtig, and R. E. Klein
1975   Length and weight in rural Guatemalan Ladino children: birth to seven years of age. *American Journal of Physical Anthropology* **42**:439–448.

20

The Past Fifty Years
of Human Population Biology in North America:
An Outsider's View[1]

G. Ainsworth Harrison

During a visit to friends in Europe while his security clearance was being challenged, Robert Oppenheimer was asked why he did not come to live in Europe. He replied that in the early part of this century, Europe was the place where the scientific action was, "but now the Europeans have to come to us!" This is as true in physical anthropology as it is in nuclear physics, though the actual movement of people may not (unfortunately) be quite so necessary. Most developments in our subject can well be communicated through the written word because, unlike most sciences, we do not have complicated machinery and practical techniques.

Why is it that North America occupies this quite central position in physical anthropology? It is true that both the number of North American researchers involved in this field and the financial resources available here are great, but these are only partial explanations. Just as important to my mind is the structure of North American academia. Young researchers are given much more opportunity to show their quality and originality here than in Europe, especially continental Europe, where traditionally, the young follow their elders for so long that by the time they have the opportunity to be creative they have lost the capacity to do so. Here in America, young people are given their heads, but they are also put under great pressure to work and succeed; the effect, however uncomfortable for the individual, has been quite dramatic.

[1]This chapter is based on a luncheon address originally delivered to the American Association of Physical Anthropologists, Friday, April 24, 1981, in Detroit Michigan.

Conceptual Reorientations

Fifty years ago, the physical anthropology of recent populations was preoccupied, in North America as elsewhere in the world, with race and the reconstruction of racial phylogenetic affinities. Anthropometry was the main technique used and, probably because of this, researchers were primarily interested in growth studies. Much of this work was barren, mainly because it adopted a typological perspective toward human variety.

A few people did, however, begin to challenge the traditional view, and one of the first and most original of these was F. S. Hulse, who has always seemed to me to be able to point his finger at critically important questions. This is well evidenced in his early collaborative research with H. L. Shapiro on Japanese migration to Hawaii (Shapiro and Hulse 1939). This study was a natural extension of the type of work undertaken by Franz Boas and others on migrants, but it raised quite dramatically the critical issue of migrant selectivity in the use of migrants for unraveling nature–nurture issues, and it is set within the clear realization of all the potential opportunities provided by migration for analyzing components of human adaptability: opportunities we are only now beginning to exploit fully.

Other approaches to partitioning the components of variation, particularly twin studies and, more recently, path analysis (Rao and Morton 1980), have also allowed more subtle and meaningful interpretation of anthropometric and other quantitative variation. To my mind, one of the most seminal works in this area was a study of morphological variation in twins undertaken by R. H. Osborne and F. V. de George (1959). It was subsequently the basis of an extremely penetrative study by Hiernaux (1963) of ecology and affinity in central Africa. Ironically, whereas most research in this field has probably been aimed at understanding heritable components of variation, it is the environmental components that have turned out so far to be the more biologically interesting ones.

This brings me naturally to the developments in genetics, especially population genetics and microevolution. Fifty years ago, genetics was practically unheard of; today, it permeates all physical anthropological thinking. Of inestimable significance in this metamorphosis was the publication of three books outside anthropology: Dobzhansky's *Genetics and the Origin of Species* (1937), Mayr's *Systematics and the Origin of Species* (1942) and Simpson's *Tempo and Mode in Evolution* (1944)—all published by Columbia University Press, and all ignored by anthropologists to their peril.

These three works, more than anything else, transformed typological anthropology into population anthropology. Since, then a whole range of human genetic polymorphic markers have been discovered, many of them in North America; we now know an enormous amount about the genetic composition of many human populations. Most important of all, the models of population genetic structure formulated by Sewall Wright, R. A. Fisher, and J.B.S. Haldane have been developed and refined, and, to some extent, tested in man, and these have profoundly influenced general thinking in physical anthropology.

For reasons not completely clear to me, much of anthropological genetics in North America has been undertaken outside physical anthropology departments and by researchers who do not regard themselves primarily as anthropologists. Thus, one can cite the outstanding contributions of J. V. Neel, W. J. Schull, N. E. Morton, and their colleagues. This contrasts somewhat with the European situation. There are, of course, notable exceptions—so many as to question the validity of the generalization—but I think it is fair to say that anthropologists in anthropological departments in North America, although giving full recognition to the implications of population genetics to our subjects, have tended to get on with other things.

Perhaps they were wise, for whereas the general achievements in human population genetics have been profound, the specific achievements have, I think, been disappointing. We still know next to nothing about human polygenic inheritance or how quantitative variation evolves. The drift-versus-selection controversy goes endlessly on with little definitive evidence either way—and because of the very nature of the problem, little is likely to be forthcoming. And most disappointing of all to us as anthropologists is the fact that knowledge of the relationships between human populations is as tentative as ever and with few further insights than those gleaned by the old anthropometrists and craniometrists; at least they had the remains of former populations to study. Despite our knowledge of the general roles of drift and selection, we still have to assume, in attempting to detect relationships, that similarity indicates phylogenetic affinity. The main problem, of course, is that the history of all human populations has been extremely complicated, and it was never likely that one would get much knowledge of this history from patterns of gene frequency differences between populations at any one time, except in the most general of ways.

However, whereas genes tell us little in detail about history, history can help us greatly in explaining genes. One of the most important developments in physical anthropology has been the incorporation of historical demography into our discipline. Since practically all genetic processes require time to effect their results and typically operate through demographic phenomena, we are fortunate to be studying a species that provides written records of its previous behavior. It has long been recognized in North America, and especially by Gabriel Lasker, that demography and historical demography have important contributions to make to our discipline, and it is gratifying to see work of this kind continuing, such as that being currently carried out at the University of Massachusetts. The availability of high-speed computers has also made possible the analysis and simulation of demographic processes that were previously totally intractable (Dyke and MacCluer 1974).

However, the main development in recent years in the physical anthropology of modern human populations has, I think, been the in-depth, integrated investigations of whole populations: studies such as those directed by J. V. Neel on the

Yanomamö (Neel *et al.* 1977), W. S. Laughlin on the Aleuts (1980), and P. T. Baker on the Quechua Indians at high altitude in Peru (Baker and Little 1976). These represent a truly outstanding change of direction in goals as well as in the very conception of what our subject is all about. Some of them have been conceived as means of understanding evolutionary processes, such as the Neel and Laughlin researches. For if one really wishes to understand the nature of between-population differences—the old concern of physical anthropology—one needs to analyze what is happening, and has happened, within populations; that is where the differences arise.

But others of these studies have not been primarily concerned with evolution but, rather, with ecology. This has been the main focus of the remarkable achievements of Paul Baker and his brilliant team. In the Quechua studies, attention was given to the entire structure and functioning of the population, social as well as biological; to every aspect of adaptation, behavioral, physiological, developmental, and genetic; and to the measurement of the fitness of the population in all its conceivable forms, individual and group as represented in biological and demographic as well as social and economic terms. It is through such studies that we are beginning to understand how whole populations as populations work. They have also provided opportunities for developing integrating ecological concepts and methods such as, for example, the analysis of energy flow systems as pioneered by Thomas (1973) and demographic–economic modelling.

Outside Relations

How far have these remarkable achievements in North America influenced the situation in Europe and, especially, in the United Kingdom? The answer, of course, is "a great deal," though it is not easy to distinguish between the effects of "meme" flow and independent evolution! On a smaller scale, most of the developments I have mentioned have occurred in Britain, Holland, Belgium, France, and Italy (and, incidentally, to a very considerable degree in Australia), though other parts of continental Europe have tended to remain more traditional.

In Britain, the discipline was greatly influenced in the postwar years by two men, J. S. Weiner at Oxford and N. A. Barnicot at University College, London. They revolutionized physical anthropology primarily by developing the subject as a natural science, and it is no doubt not a coincidence that one was first trained as a human physiologist and the other as a zoologist. The strength of its attachment to biology has, I think, distinguished the British contribution from many others, and this played an important part in reestablishing in Britain the respectability of the discipline as human population biology or biological anthropology. This has not occurred however, without some penalty. As I have already indicated, the ecological approach to whole population analysis, which is turning out to be so fruitful, demands that equal attention be devoted to cultural processes as to biological ones. The same is true in behavioral studies. It is much easier to achieve this in North America where the unity of anthropology has been better preserved.

Anglo–American relations in physical anthropology have long been good and I do not think there are any fundamental disagreements. In evolutionary genetics, the driftist position is stronger in the United States than it is in the United Kingdom, where selectionists predominate. This difference probably reflects the comparative influence of Sewall Wright and R. A. Fisher, but in both countries, there are many workers to be found in each camp and even more who take a middle-of-the-road view. Resources more than anything else have influenced the comparative commitment to ecology, for its is costly in both money and manpower.

There also seems to be a considerable flow of researches between North America and the United Kingdom. At times, and particularly during the summer months, the composition of the senior staff in my department makes it indistinguishable from an American one. And there is an even greater flow of research students; during the past few years, nearly half our students have been from North America. However, there appear to be few occasions where North American and British researchers, excepting students, have worked together in the field. Much mutual advantage could probably be gained through a more formal exchange of teaching staff. In departments with small staffs, such as prevail in physical anthropology, the movement of teachers with different ranges of competence and philosophies is highly desirable and, to my mind, needs to be strongly promoted.

Overall, I think we can conclude that notwithstanding many organizational problems and particularly that of finding positions for the up-and-coming generation of researchers and teachers, physical anthropology today is in good stead worldwide. And, in human population biology at least, we have at last overcome, I believe, that damning criticism of the "tarnish of amateurism" (Zuckerman 1958). Here, if not elsewhere in the subject, controversy no longer prospers on itself and castles can be built with bricks rather than air. Surely we can now claim to be an academic discipline

As for the future, we shall no doubt learn ever more about the nature of human variety at the cellular and biochemical level, and this may eventually lead to a precise and detailed understanding of what we currently see as quantitative variation, including quantitative variation of behavioral traits and abilities. But in the foreseeable future, I would be very surprised if ecological studies did not occupy center stage. With certain sections of cultural anthropology moving in a similar direction, the prospects look most exciting. It is also within the ecological context that I think most future population genetics research will be carried out, for we are already witnessing the important of developments of genetic epidemiology (Reich et al. 1980).

Within this ecological framework, I hope that biological anthropology does not restrict itself to traditional societies and equilibrium situations. There is much we can offer, both in academic understanding and in practical help by giving attention to acculturating societies and populations in modern industrialized and urban situations. And, whether we like it or not, that is where most people in the future will be. Clearly, the contribution that American physical anthropology can make here is enormous, and I wish it well for the formidable task ahead. May the next 50 years be as productive as the last.

References

Baker, P. T., and M. A. Little (editors)
    1976   *Man in the Andes.* Stroudsburg, Pennsylvania: Dowden, Hutchinson and Ross.
Dobzhansky, T.
    1937   *Genetics and the origin of species.* New York: Columbia University Press.
Dyke, B., and J. W. MacCluer (editors)
    1974   *Computer simulation in human population studies.* New York: Academic Press.
Hiernaux, J.
    1963   Heredity and environment: their influence on human morphology. *American Journal of Physical Anthropology* **21**:575–590.
Laughlin, W. S.
    1980   *Aleuts. Survivors of the Bering Land Bridge.* New York: Holt, Rinehart and Winston.
Mayr, E.
    1942   *Systematics and the origin of species.* New York: Columbia University Press.
Neel, J. V., M. Layrisse, and F. M. Salzano
    1977   Man in the tropics: the Yanomama Indians. In *Population structure and human variation,* edited by G. A. Harrison. London and New York: Cambridge University Press. Pp. 109–142.
Osborne, R. H., and F. V. de George
    1959   *Genetic basis of morphological variation.* Cambridge, Massachusetts: Harvard University Press.
Rao, D. C., and N. E. Morton
    1980   Path analysis of quantitative inheritance. In *Current developments in anthropological genetics,* edited by J. H. Mielke and M. H. Crawford. New York: Plenum.
Reich, T., B. Suarez, J. Rice, and C. R. Cloninger
    1980   Current directions in genetic epidemiology. In *Current developments in anthropological genetics,* edited by J. H. Mielke and M. H. Crawford. New York: Plenum. Pp. 000–000.
Shapiro, H. L., and F. S. Hulse
    1939   *Migration and environment.* London and New York: Oxford University Press.
Simpson, G. G.
    1944   *Tempo and mode in evolution.* New York: Columbia University Press.
Thomas, R. B.
    1973   *Human adaptation to a high Andean energy flow system.* Occasional Papers in Anthropology No. **7.** University Park: Pennsylvania State University Press.
Zuckerman, S.
    1958   Summing up. In *The scope of physical anthropology and its place in academic studies,* edited by D. F. Roberts and J. S. Weiner. Wenner-Gren Foundation for Anthropological Research, Church Army Press.

Author Index

A

Abbott, M., 392, 394
Abel, E. L., 456, 457
Abelson, A. E., 418, 422
Abler, W. L., 87, 90
Acheson, R. M., 457
Ackernecht, E. H., 343, 349
Adams, J., 390, 394
Adams, W. E., 171, 172
Adloff, P., 241, 253
Adolph, E. F., 409, 411, 422, 423, 437, 444
Ahlqvist, A. R., 364, 366
Aird, L., 387, 394
Alexander, F., 286, 301
Alexander, W., 381, 394
Alland, A., 406, 423
Allen, H., 339, 349
Allison, A. C., 383, 384, 385, 395
Allison, M. J., 343, 344, 350
Allman, J. M., 167, 172
Altmann, S., 57, 61, 62, 66
Andersen, K. L., 416, 423
Anderson, D. D., 288, 301
Andrew, R. J., 84, 90, 156, 173
Andrews, P., 212, 217, 221
Andrews, R. C., 239, 240, 252, 254
Anfinsen, C. B., 107, 140
Angel, J. L., 321, 342, 350
Anthony, R., 263, 270
Appel, F. W., 80, 90
Appleton, V. B., 450, 451, 458
Arambourg, C., 81, 90, 264, 267, 270

Ariëns Kappers, C. U., 77, 78, 83, 90
Armelagos, G. J., 319, 321, 322, 323, 324, 337, 343, 347, 350, 351, 353
Armstrong, E., 89, 90
Arnheim, N., 117, 140
Aronson, A., 386, 400
Ashton, E. H., 81, 82, 90, 219, 221, 319, 322
Austin, D. M., 415, 423
Ayala, F. A., 113, 135, 140
Azuma, S., 66

B

Baba, M., 122, 140, 161, 173, 212, 222
Bachman, J., 20, 24
Bailey, P., 83, 91
Baker, P. T., 34, 41, 43, 45, 407, 408, 411, 413, 414, 415, 416, 417, 418, 420, 422, 423, 424, 425, 426, 427, 428, 438, 439, 443, 444, 445, 453, 457, 458, 470, 472
Baltzell, E. D., 24
Barbour, G. B., 242, 254
Bard, P., 76, 91
Barnicot, N. A., 411, 412, 423, 427
Barth, F., 152, 173
Bartholomew, G. A., 249, 254
Barzun, J., 12, 14, 16, 23, 25
Basmajian, J. V., 214, 229
Bass, W. M., 311, 312, 322, 343, 347, 349, 353, 354, 356
Bates, M., 407, 410, 423, 424
Bateson, W., 372, 395
Bauchot, R., 85, 91, 101

473

Beall, C. M., 450, 453, 458
Beaumont, P. B., 269, 270
Beeton, M., 392, 395
Behrensmeyer, A. K., 134, 140, 248, 249, 250, 254
Bell, J., 316, 318, 326
Bender, M. A., 156, 173
Bendyshe, T., 15, 25, 282, 301
Benedict, R., 12, 25
Bennett, K. A., 407, 424
Benviste, R. E., 113, 117, 140
Berckhemer, F., 265, 270
Bergsland, K., 298, 301
Bergson, H., 14, 21, 25
Bernhard, G., 81, 91
Bernstein, L. S., 63, 66
Berry, A. C., 313, 322
Bert, J., 63, 66
Bielicki, T., 316, 322
Bingham, H. C., 32, 45, 50, 66
Birdsell, J. B., 245, 249, 254, 410, 411, 424, 438, 444
Birkby, W. H., 313, 322
Bishop, A., 156, 173
Bishop, W. W., 248, 254
Bitterman, M. E., 84, 91
Black, D., 76, 91, 263, 265, 270
Black, F. L., 385, 395
Black, R. F., 288, 301
Blackith, R. E., 313, 322
Blakeley, R. L., 345, 350
Blakenship, J. C., 420, 424
Blanc, A. C., 265, 271
Bleichrodt, N., 454, 458
Blumberg, B. S., 293, 302, 387, 395
Boas, F., 282, 301, 409, 418, 424, 436, 442, 449, 450, 452, 456, 458
Boaz, D., 250, 254
Boaz, N. T., 247, 248, 249, 250, 252, 254
Bodmer, W. F., 126, 140, 378, 379, 386, 388, 395, 396
Bogin, B., 452, 458
Bolk, L., 373, 395
Bongaarts, J., 419, 424
Bonne, B., 412, 424
Bonner, T. I., 113, 117, 140
Bordes, F., 264, 270
Borkan, G. A., 456, 458
Bory de Saint-Vincent, J., 18, 20, 22, 25
Botstein, D., 389, 395
Boule, M., 262, 263, 264, 265, 267, 270
Bouyssonie, A., 263, 271
Bowers, P. M., 289, 301
Bown, T. M., 169, 173
Bowsher, D., 83, 91

Boyce, A. J., 443, 445
Boyd, W. C., 267, 271, 310, 322, 373, 374, 379, 386, 395, 404, 410, 424, 437, 444
Boyden, S., 421, 424
Brace, C. L., 12, 13, 14, 15, 16, 17, 20, 24, 25, 249, 254, 264, 268, 271
Brain, C. K., 249, 254
Braun, G. L., 456, 461
Breitinger, E., 267, 271
Brenton, H., 451, 458
Breuil, H., 265, 271
Brew, J. O., 1, 9, 31, 33, 34, 45, 46, 49, 54, 66
Broca, P., 19, 20, 21, 22, 25, 263, 271
Brooks, S. T., 363, 366
Broom, R., 78, 79, 81, 91, 240, 241, 242, 251, 254
Brose, D. S., 268, 271
Brothwell, D. R., 343, 346, 350, 351
Brown, A. B., 346, 351
Brown, G. M., 411, 424
Brozek, J., 39, 46, 411, 424
Bruce, E., 113, 135, 140
Brues, A. M., 382, 395
Buchanan, J. A., 381, 395
Bucy, P. C., 81, 91
Buettner-Janusch, J., 62, 66, 156, 158, 173, 206, 222
Bugge, J., 171, 173
Buikstra, J. E., 321, 322, 343, 344, 345, 347, 351
Bunak, W., 81, 91
Burleigh, R., 346, 351
Burnet, M .E., 393, 395
Burns, K. R., 366
Bushmakin, N., 76, 91
Buskirk, E. R., 416, 424
Butler, H., 171, 173
Butler, P. M., 174
Butzer, K. W., 247, 249, 250, 254, 255
Buxton, A. P., 53, 54, 66

C

Cachel, S. M., 163, 170, 174
Cadien, J., 390, 399
Camp, C. L., 242, 243, 255
Campbell, B. G., 87, 91, 174, 206, 222, 231, 237, 268, 271
Campbell, H. R., 366, 368
Campos, G. B., 83, 102
Candela, P. B., 373, 395
Cannings, C., 390, 396
Capitan, L., 263, 271
Carlson, D. S., 320, 322, 347, 351
Carlsoö, S., 320, 322
Carlyle, T., 13, 25

Carpenter, R., 32, 46, 50, 52, 55, 57, 66, 67
Carter, C. O., 391, 396
Carter, J. E. L., 456, 463
Cartmill, M., 154, 155, 156, 157, 159, 160, 161, 162, 165, 166, 167, 168, 169, 170, 174, 249, 255
Cavalli-Sforza, L. L., 114, 126, 140, 141, 378, 379, 386, 388, 396
Cave, A. J. E., 264, 267, 277
Chagnon, N. A., 379, 401
Chakraborty, R., 302, 303, 386, 391, 396
Chakravartti, A., 385, 386, 396, 404
Chalmers, N. R., 63, 67
Chandler, J., 388, 402
Chang, C., 79, 91
Charles, R. H., 264, 271
Charles-Dominique, P., 157, 158, 159, 160, 161, 174
Charteris, J., 248, 255
Chase, A., 12, 23, 25, 377, 396
Chi, T. K., 79, 91
Chiarelli, A. B., 214, 222
Chu, E. H. Y., 156, 174
Chung, C. S., 392, 400
Ciochon, R. L., 131, 140, 169, 175, 214, 222
Clark, D. L., 454, 460
Clark, D. W., 290, 296, 299, 301, 302
Clarke, C. A., 387, 396
Clarke, E., 85, 91
Clarke, S. K., 347, 351
Clauser, C. E., 40, 46
Clegg, E. J., 416, 424
Cobb, W. M., 359, 366, 456, 458
Cockburn, A., 351
Cogwill, G. R., 454, 458
Cohen, B. H., 392, 396
Cohn, H. A., 76, 91
Coimbra-Filho, A. F., 168, 175
Collett, M. A., 315, 322
Collias, N., 57, 67
Collins, E. T., 166, 175
Collins, K. J., 413, 424
Compère, J., 83, 86, 91
Connolly, C. J., 76, 79, 81, 92
Conroy, G. C., 169, 175
Cook, D. C., 343, 344, 345, 347, 351
Cook, P., 393, 396
Cooley, T. B., 382, 396
Coolidge, H. J., 52, 58, 67
Coon, C. S., 21, 22, 25, 26, 36, 46, 266, 267, 271, 374, 396, 410, 411, 424, 438, 444
Cope, E. D., 188, 222
Coppens, Y., 235, 237, 246, 255, 257
Corrucini, R. S., 131, 132, 133, 140, 212, 214, 222, 319, 322

Cotard, H., 21, 26
Count, E. W., 80, 92
Covert, H. H., 250, 255
Cowdry, E. V., 408, 424
Cowey, A., 83, 92
Coxe, W. S., 81, 92
Cracraft, J., 111, 141
Cragg, B. G., 83, 92
Craig, D., 240, 255
Crawford, M., 392, 399
Crawford, M. H., 375, 396
Crichton, J. M., 313, 322
Crick, F. H., 107, 140
Crile, G., 80, 92
Cronin, J. E., 106, 107, 111, 112, 113, 117, 119, 128, 129, 131, 132, 133, 134, 135, 141, 145, 154, 160, 161, 162, 213, 222, 230, 248, 252, 255
Crook, J. H., 63, 67
Crosby, E. C., 83, 92
Crow, J. F., 376, 378, 379, 396
Curtis, G. H., 246, 255
Cutler, R. G., 392, 396
Cybulski, J. S., 345, 351

D

Damon, A., 34, 35, 42, 46, 415, 424, 449, 458
Damsten, O., 364, 366
Danforth, C. H., 375, 397
Daniel, P. M., 83, 92
Daniels, F., 411, 423
Darga, L. L., 117, 141
Darnell, R., 1, 9, 32, 33, 46
Dart, R. A., 54, 67, 77, 78, 81, 82, 92, 240, 247, 255
Darwin, C., 18, 26, 111, 141, 239, 255, 406, 407, 424
Davies, D. A., 360, 366
Davin, A., 314, 326
Davis, D. D., 150, 175
Davis, P. R., 226
Day, M. H., 319, 323
de George, F. V., 468, 472
Delson, E., 134, 135, 141, 146, 159, 164, 165, 166, 167, 168, 175, 185, 212, 214, 217, 222, 229
de Mortillet, G., 262, 272
Dene, H., 154, 161, 175
Denham, R. A., 320, 323
Deniker, J., 22, 26
Denniston, C., 378, 396
Desmoulins, A., 20, 26
De Souza-Freitas, J. A., 450, 459
Deterra, H., 78, 92
Detwiler, S. R., 245, 260, 437, 446
DeVore, I., 59, 61, 62, 63, 67, 68, 69, 73, 249, 255

Dewey, J. R., 321, 323, 347, 351
Dewhurst, K., 85, 91
DeWitt, H., 386, 399
Dewson, J. H., 87, 92
Diamond, I. T., 83, 92
Dill, D. B., 411, 423
Dixon, W. J., 386, 302
Dobzhansky, T., 54, 67, 244, 255, 266, 267, 272, 405, 406, 407, 425, 468, 472
Dolhinow, P., 64, 69
Donisthorpe, J., 58, 67
Doolittle, R. F., 114, 141
Doré, C., 415, 425
Dozy, A. M., 383, 398
Drennan, M. R., 81, 92
Dubois, E., 77, 93, 265, 272
Dumond, D. E., 289, 290, 304
Durant, A., 13, 26
Durant, W., 13, 26
Durham, W. H., 420, 425
Dusser de Barenne, J. G., 76, 80, 93, 94
Dutrillaux, B., 115, 141
Dwight, T., 316, 323
Dyke, B., 420, 425, 428, 469, 472
Dyson-Hudson, R., 420, 425

E

Eagen, C. J., 407, 425
Eaglen, R. H., 162, 175
Eck, F. F., 134, 141
Eckhardt, R. B., 214, 222
Edinger, T., 83, 93
Edwards, A. W. F., 114, 141
Edwards, J. H., 391, 397
Efstratiadis, A., 137, 141
Eiseley, L., 307, 323
Eldredge, N., 111, 135, 141, 217, 222, 252, 256, 273
Elderton, E. M., 314, 323
Elftman, H., 320, 323
Elias, N., 85, 93
Ellefson, J. O., 51, 63, 67
Elliot, O., 364, 367
Elliot Smith, G., 77, 100, 149, 150, 167, 175, 189, 223, 264, 272, 315, 323
Ellis, J. E., 420, 425
Elmendorf, J., 347, 351
El-Najjar, M. Y., 347, 351, 365, 367
Elston, R. C., 390, 397
Emlen, J. T., 67
Epstein, H. T., 87, 93
Ericksen, M. F., 343, 351
Erickson, P. A., 1, 9, 12, 26

Erickson, T., 79, 98
Esper, J. E., 337, 338, 351
Eto, M., 418, 427
Evans, G. F., 450, 456, 462
Eveleth, P. B., 43, 44, 45, 46, 413, 417, 425, 450, 452, 457, 458, 459
Evernden, J. F., 246, 255
Ewens, W., 386, 397

F

Falconer, D. S., 391, 397
Falk, D., 78, 79, 82, 83, 86, 87, 89, 93, 169, 175, 251, 255
Falkner, F., 456, 459
Fanning, E. A., 368
Faul, H., 262, 267, 272
Faust, M. A., 313, 323
Fawcett, C. O., 314, 315, 323
Ferrell, R. D., 293, 294, 302
Ferris, S. D., 107, 113, 114, 117, 124, 141
Finnegan, M., 313, 323
Fisher, R. A., 314, 323, 372, 374, 376, 377, 397, 437, 444
Fitch, W. M., 114, 129, 142
Fleagle, J. G., 165, 166, 182, 212, 219, 220, 223, 228
Flecker, H., 360, 367
Foerster, O., 76, 93
Fogden, M. P. L., 158, 176
Folk, G. E., 406, 425
Ford, E. B., 382, 397
Ford, S. M., 170, 176, 214
Forde, C. D., 409, 425
Fossey, D., 63, 67
Fraipont, J., 263, 264, 272
Francis, C. C., 360, 367
Frayer, D. W., 214, 223, 268, 272
Friedman, S. M., 443, 445
Frisancho, A. R., 415, 417, 421, 425, 443, 444, 448, 453, 454, 457, 459
Frisch, J. E., 55, 56, 68
Frøhlich, B., 292, 302
Fry, E. I., 459
Fulton, J. F., 76, 94

G

Gajdusek, D. C., 379, 387, 397
Galaburda, A. M., 80, 90
Galambos, L., 31, 46
Galvin, C., 366, 369
Gamble, D. P., 79, 94

Garber, P. A., 167, 168, 176
Garn, S. M., 21, 26, 287, 302, 347, 351, 352, 410, 411, 424, 426, 438, 444, 447, 454, 456, 460, 464
Garrod, A. E., 372, 393
Gartlan, J. S., 61, 63, 68
Gasman, D., 14, 26
Gates, R. R., 244, 255, 374, 379, 397, 437, 444
Gaudry, A., 21, 26
Gautier-Hion, A., 68
Gazin, C. L., 152, 153, 159, 176
Geidel, R. A., 346, 347, 352
Gerszten, E., 343, 350
Geschwind, N., 84, 87, 94
Ghesquière, J., 415, 423
Gibbes, R. W., 18, 26
Gibson, J. B., 421, 426
Giddings, J. L., 296, 302
Gidley, J. W., 151, 176
Gilbert, B. M., 366, 367
Gilbert, R. I., 347, 352
Gilbert, W., 137, 142
Giles, E., 364, 367
Gingerich, P. D., 87, 94, 119, 142, 160, 162, 163, 165, 166, 168, 169, 176, 216, 217, 223
Girgis, M., 83, 94
Glass, B., 379, 389, 397
Gleser, G. C., 361, 363, 364, 369
Gliddon, G. R., 18, 20, 28
Goldfuss, A., 338, 352
Goldstein, M. S., 34, 46, 342, 352, 418, 426, 448, 456, 457, 460
Gomberg, N., 319, 320, 323
Goodall, J., 63, 64, 68
Goodman, A. H., 347, 352
Goodman, M., 105, 106, 107, 108, 114, 115, 117, 118, 119, 120, 122, 142, 143, 161, 176, 211, 223, 233, 237
Gorjanovic-Kramberger, D., 263, 272
Gossett, T. F., 12, 26
Gould, S. J., 85, 86, 87, 88, 94, 99, 135, 141, 235, 237, 243, 252, 255, 256, 262, 264, 265, 273, 448, 457, 460
Grand, T. T., 320, 323
Greene, J. C., 307, 323
Greene, L. S., 454, 460
Greenfield, L. O., 212, 214, 215, 223, 234, 237
Gregory, W. K., 51, 68, 149, 151, 152, 153, 159, 165, 176, 177, 189, 195, 198, 202, 204, 209, 223, 224, 239, 241, 242, 243, 244, 256, 265, 273
Gruelich, W. W., 442, 444, 450, 452, 460
Gunness-Hay, M. E., 343, 352
Gunther, M., 376, 397
Gustafson, G., 365, 367

H

Haach, D. L., 87, 94
Haas, J. D., 417, 426, 443, 444, 453, 455, 458, 460, 461
Habicht, J. P., 454, 460
Haddow, A. J., 53, 54, 68
Haeckel, E., 21, 26, 239, 256
Haines, D. E., 89, 96
Haldane, J. B. S., 374, 376, 382, 388, 397, 398
Hall, K. R. L., 61, 62, 63, 67, 68, 69
Hall, W. C., 83, 92
Haller, J. S., 1, 9, 12, 26
Halstead, L. B., 243, 256, 265, 273
Hamill, P. V. V., 40, 46
Hammel, H. T., 411, 415, 426, 431
Hammond, M., 262, 264, 265, 273
Hanna, J. M., 413, 415, 416, 426, 428
Hanihara, K., 364, 367
Haraway, D., 51, 69
Hardy, V., 312, 323
Harpending, H., 379, 389, 398
Harper, A. B., 288, 289, 292, 298, 300, 302, 413, 428
Harrington, J. E., 158, 177
Harris, H., 375, 398
Harrison, G. A., 412, 413, 416, 418, 421, 423, 424, 426, 427, 443, 445, 455, 460
Hassler, R., 83, 94
Hauser, O., 263, 273
Hay, J. G., 320, 323
Hay, R. L., 246, 248, 249, 256
Heberer, G., 202, 204, 205, 224
Heim, J. L., 263, 273
Heinbecker, P., 283, 299, 302
Hellebrandt, F. A., 456, 461
Hellman, M., 224, 242, 243, 256
Henneberg, M., 379, 398
Hennig, W., 114, 143, 155, 177, 213, 224
Henin, R. A., 419, 427
Hershkovitz, P., 86, 94, 119, 143, 157, 164, 167, 169, 177, 214, 224
Herrick, J. B., 382, 398
Hicks, C. S., 409, 427
Hieple, K. G., 320, 323
Hiernaux, J., 448, 461, 468, 472
Higley, E., 381, 395
Higman, B. W., 456, 461
Hill, A. H., 360, 367
Hill, W. C. O., 152, 177
Himes, J. H., 425, 450, 454, 456, 461
Hinsley, C. M., 1, 10
Hirschfeld, L., 381, 398
Hirschler, P., 80, 94

Hladik, C. M., 158, 177
Hockner, D. H., 452, 462
Hodes, W., 87, 91
Hodge, F. W., 19, 26
Hodges, P. C., 360, 367
Hofer, H., 81, 83, 88, 95
Hoff, C. J., 417, 423
Hoffstetter, R., 166, 168, 177
Holder, P., 342, 352
Holloway, R. L., 79, 83, 84, 85, 86, 87, 95, 251, 256
Holtby, B., 316, 323
Holtzman, S. F., 262, 264, 273
Hook, A., 13, 26
Hooton, E. A., 15, 26, 52, 53, 69, 151, 156, 177, 191,
    195, 198, 199, 224, 242, 256, 264, 265, 266, 273,
    283, 286, 302, 309, 323, 342, 349, 352, 357, 358,
    367, 373, 374, 398, 409, 427
Hopkins, D. M., 295, 302
Horr, D., 63, 69
Hoskins, C. R., 267, 276
Howe, W. L., 313, 323
Howell, F. C., 232, 237, 247, 250, 252, 256, 259, 267,
    269, 273
Howell, N., 419, 427
Howells, W. W., 12, 27, 149, 177, 202, 204, 206, 224,
    264, 266, 267, 268, 269, 274, 276, 278, 315, 317,
    324, 364, 367, 457, 461
Hoyer, B. H., 113, 117, 119, 143, 160, 178
Hrdlička, A., 1, 6, 8, 10, 12, 15, 17, 19, 23, 27, 188,
    224, 239, 240, 241, 244, 256, 261, 262, 263, 265,
    268, 274, 282, 283, 284, 286, 302, 340, 352, 358,
    367, 436, 447, 452, 461
Hubel, O. H., 83, 86, 95
Hublin, J. J., 268, 274
Hughes, A. R., 247, 259
Huizinga, J., 315, 327
Hulse, F. S., 418, 427, 443, 445, 450, 468, 472
Humphrey, C. T., 83, 92
Hunt, E. E., 245, 256, 311, 312, 315, 324, 368, 454,
    461
Hurtado, A., 409, 426, 427, 452, 453, 456, 461
Hürzeler, J., 204, 224
Hutt, C., 57, 69
Hutt, S. J., 57, 69
Huxley, J. S., 12, 27, 54, 69, 118, 143, 266, 274, 437,
    445
Huxley, T. H., 148, 178, 196, 224, 305, 324
Hylander, W. C., 178, 321, 324

I

Imanishi, K., 55, 69
Ingalls, W. N., 318, 324

Ingram, V. M., 107, 143
Itani, J., 55, 56, 63, 69
Ito, P. K., 450, 461
Iwai, E., 83, 95

J

Jaeger, J. J., 249, 256
Jackson, C. M., 454, 461
Jakimov, V. P., 81, 95
Jamison, P. L., 422, 427, 443, 445
Jantz, R. L., 316, 324
Jarcho, S., 343, 353
Jay, P. C., 64, 69
Jeffries, D. J., 421, 426
Jelliffe, D. B., 421, 427, 454, 461
Jelliffe, E. F. P., 421, 427
Jenkins, F. A., 251, 257, 320, 324
Jepsen, G. L., 266, 274
Jerison, H. J., 82, 86, 88, 96
Jochelson, W., 286, 302
Johanson, D. C., 117, 135, 143, 235, 237, 246, 247,
    250, 252, 257, 260
Johnson, L. C., 345, 353
Johnston, F. E., 321, 324, 416, 419, 427, 450, 452,
    456, 460, 461, 462
Jordan, W. D., 17, 27
Jordann, H. V. F., 87, 96
Jorgensen, J. B., 82, 85, 96, 288, 291, 303
Jolly, C., 134, 143, 158, 171, 178
Jones, E. C., 86, 96
Jones, J., 339, 353
Jukes, T. H., 138, 143, 378, 398
Jungers, W. L., 171, 178

K

Kaas, J. H., 86, 96
Kalin, J., 204, 224
Kan, Y. W., 383, 398
Kanagasuntheram, R., 171, 178
Kaplan, B. A., 418, 427
Kavanagh, M., 63, 70
Kawabe, M., 63, 70
Kawai, M., 55, 56, 70
Kay, R. F., 159, 160, 161, 164, 165, 166, 168, 170,
    174, 178, 213, 223, 225, 250, 251, 255, 257
Keane, A. H., 282, 302
Keith, A., 13, 14, 15, 27, 77, 80, 96, 189, 192, 197,
    225, 240, 257, 262, 263, 264, 265, 266, 269, 274,
    276
Kelso, J., 40, 47
Kennedy, K. A. R., 62, 70, 239, 258

Kerley, F. R., 47, 343, 349, 353, 364, 368
Kidd, C. V., 31, 47
Kimura, K., 364, 367
Kimura, M., 120, 125, 143, 376, 378, 398, 396
King, J., 120, 125, 143
King, J. L., 378, 398
King, M. C., 114, 135, 143
Kinzey, W. G., 167, 168, 179
Klaatsch, H., 263, 274
Klein, D., 51, 70
Klein, L., 51, 70
Klinger, H. P., 106, 108, 143
Knudson, A. G., 391, 398
Kochetkova, V., 80, 81, 82, 85, 86, 96
Kohl-Larsen, L., 245, 257
Kohne, D., 113, 144
Kondo, S., 418, 427
Krantz, G. S., 84, 85, 96
Kreiner, J., 83, 96
Krishnamurti, A., 83, 96, 171, 178
Kroeber, A. L., 52, 53, 70, 409, 428
Krogman, W. M., 265, 274, 357, 358, 360, 361, 362, 363, 365, 368, 454, 456, 462
Kuhn, T. S., 59, 70
Kummer, H., 64, 72
Kunstadter, P., 412, 428
Kuypers, H. G., 83, 96

L

Ladell, W. S. S., 415, 428
Lallo, J., 321, 324, 346, 353
Lampl, M., 293, 302
Lancaster, J. B., 51, 63, 70
Landauer, C. A., 317, 324
Landsteiner, K., 372, 398
Langdon, F. W., 339, 353
Laporte, L., 248, 255
Larsen, C. S., 345, 353
Lashley, K. S., 79, 80, 97
Lasker, G. W., 11, 27, 37, 47, 306, 324, 379, 398, 409, 412, 413, 415, 418, 428, 442, 445, 448, 450, 451, 456, 457, 462
Laughlin, W. S., 285, 288, 290, 291, 295, 296, 299, 303, 413, 428, 470, 472
Leakey, L. S. B., 54, 70, 77, 97, 202, 225, 241, 245, 246, 247, 257, 267, 275
Leakey, M.D., 246, 247, 248, 257
Leakey, R. E. F., 250, 252, 257
Lee, A., 314, 324
Lee, D. H. K., 415, 428
Lee, P., 382, 396

Le Gros Clark, W. E., 54, 70, 76, 77, 78, 80, 97, 148, 149, 150, 153, 166, 167, 179, 196, 197, 198, 202, 203, 204, 205, 206, 207, 209, 225, 243, 252, 253, 260, 262, 267, 275, 279, 437, 445
LeMay, M., 87, 97, 268, 278
Leslie, P. N., 420, 428
Lestrel, P. E., 86, 97
Leutenegger, W., 87, 97
Levin, G., 77, 97
Levine, P., 388, 389, 398
Levit, S. G., 376, 377, 398
Levitsky, W., 84, 94
Lewis, G. E., 224, 225
Lewis, O. J., 214, 225, 235, 237
Lewontin, R. C., 125, 144, 375, 399
Levêque, F., 269, 275
Li, W. H., 389, 399
Libby, W. F., 288, 303
Liebhaber, S. A., 132, 144
Lindburg, D., 63, 70, 71
Lisowski, F. P., 319, 325
Little, M. A., 407, 415, 416, 417, 420, 423, 428, 443, 445, 452, 470, 472
Livingstone, F. B., 12, 27, 375, 383, 384, 385, 386, 387, 389, 399, 411, 412, 428, 438, 445
Lohest, M., 263, 272
Long, J. K., 311, 312, 324
Lowenstein, J. M., 112, 144
Lourie, J. A., 413, 433, 439, 446
Lovejoy, A. O., 23, 27
Lovejoy, C.O., 212, 225, 251, 257, 268, 275, 320, 321, 323, 324, 325, 347, 356
Lowther, G. R., 249, 259
Luckett, W. P., 119, 144, 154, 160, 168, 170, 179, 214, 217, 226
Lumsden, W. H. R., 53, 54, 70
Lurie, E., 22, 27
Lyell, C., 18, 27
Lyon, D. W., 359, 363, 369

M

MacArthur, R. H., 420, 429
McArthur, J. W., 419, 424
McCay, B., 406, 423
McCluer, J. W., 420, 425, 469, 472
McCown, T. D., 62, 70, 80, 96, 239, 258, 263, 266, 269, 276
MacCurdy, G. G., 264, 275
MacDonnell, W. R., 314, 325
McElroy, A., 421, 429
McGeorge, L. W., 158, 180
McGrew, W. C., 249, 258

McHenry, H. M., 86, 97, 144, 212, 222, 319, 325, 347, 353
McKenna, M. C., 153, 154, 169, 180
McKern, T. W., 362, 366, 367, 368
McKusick, V. M., 379, 399
MacMichael, A., 386, 399
MacPhee, R. D. E., 154, 168, 179
MacRoberts, M. H., 63, 71
Mack, R. W., 456, 462
Mackinnon, J., 158, 179
Mackinnon, K., 158, 179
Macklin, M. T., 391, 399
McWilliams, K. R., 365, 367
Major, C. I. F., 148, 180
Malina, R. M., 450, 452, 454, 461, 462
Mandarino, L., 390, 399
Mann, A. E., 250, 257, 268, 275
Mano, T., 63, 70
Maples, W. R., 366
Manouvrier, L., 262, 264, 265, 275
Manter, J. T., 320, 325
Markowitz, S. D., 449, 462
Marett, R. R., 13, 27
Marsh, G. H., 288, 303
Marshall, W. H., 80, 97
Marston, A. T., 265, 275
Martin, A. O., 379, 399
Martin, D. L., 347, 353
Martin, H., 263, 275
Martin, R. D., 88, 97, 155, 157, 159, 161, 164, 167, 169, 180, 182
Martin, S. L., 132, 144
Martin, W. E., 35, 47
Martorell, R., 454, 455, 460, 462
Maruyama, T., 310, 327
Massey, F. J., 286, 302
Matthew, W. D., 149, 151, 180
Maxam, A. M., 136, 144
Maxwell, M. S., 296, 303
May, J. M., 411, 429
Mayer, D., 338, 353
Mayr, E., 12, 28, 54, 71, 231, 232, 237, 245, 250, 258, 262, 266, 267, 275, 468, 472
Mazess, R. B., 406, 411, 416, 421, 428, 429, 448, 463
Means, J. H., 343, 353
Medawar, P. B., 406, 429
Meigs, C. D., 18, 27
Meigs, J. A., 338, 353
Meihoff, E. C., 87, 94
Meikle, W. E., 111, 131, 134, 140, 141, 217, 222, 252, 255
Meindl, R. S., 212, 225
Mensforth, R. P., 353

Merchant, V., 321, 325
Meredith, H. V., 457, 463
Messing, J., 136, 144
Mettler, F. A., 82, 97
Metress, J. F., 345, 356
Michevich, M. F., 134, 144
Miekle, J., 392, 399
Milan, F. A., 413, 414, 422, 427, 429
Millar, R., 243, 258, 265, 276
Miller, G. S., 188, 189, 226, 239, 248, 258, 265, 276
Miller, H. W., 31, 47
Mills, C. A., 449, 451, 452, 463
Mirrakhimov, M. M., 416, 429
Mishkin, M., 83, 95
Mitchell, H. H., 454, 463
Mivart, St. G., 149, 180
Mizuhara, H., 56, 70
Molnar, S., 347, 353
Monge, A. P., 378, 396
Monge, C., 409, 429
Montagna, W., 85, 98, 156, 180, 181
Montagu, M. F. A., 12, 15, 27
Moodie, R. L., 338, 341, 354
Moorrees, C. F. A., 286, 287, 302, 303, 365, 368
Morant, G. M., 315, 325
Morbeck, M. E., 214, 226, 320, 325
Mørch, E. T., 376, 399
Morgan, T. H., 372, 399
Morren, G. E. B., 407, 420, 428, 429
Morrison, J. A., 52, 71
Morse, D., 343, 354, 366, 368
Morton, D. J., 189, 194, 226
Morton, N. E., 378, 390, 391, 392, 399, 400
Morton, S. G., 17, 18, 22, 27, 338, 354
Moskowitz, N., 83, 98
Moss, M. O., 317, 318, 325
Motulsky, A. G., 378, 379, 380, 383, 384, 385, 386, 388, 400, 404, 411, 429, 438, 445
Mourant, A. E., 386, 387, 388, 389, 400
Mueller, W. H., 417, 429, 450, 453, 454, 456, 461, 463
Muller, H. J., 376, 377, 400
Murrill, R. I., 87, 97
Musgrave, J. H., 268, 276
Murphy, E. A., 392, 394, 400
Myers, C. S., 311, 325
Myrianthopoulos, N., 386, 400

N

Napier, J. R., 62, 71, 158, 167, 181, 202, 219, 226
Napier, P. H., 167, 168, 181, 219, 226
Neel, J. V., 289, 303, 377, 378, 379, 380, 381, 382,

385, 386, 388, 400, 401, 403, 413, 429, 430, 470, 472
Nei, M., 135, 145, 293, 303, 375, 389, 399, 401
Nelson, G., 111, 145
Neumann, G. K., 311, 312, 325, 326
Newburgh, L. H., 430
Newcombe, H. B., 380, 391, 401
Newman, M. T., 411, 415, 430, 431, 438, 445
Newman, R. W., 415, 430
Niemitz, C., 158, 181
Nishida, T., 56, 71
Nishimura, A., 67, 55
Nissen, H. W., 32, 47, 50, 71
Noback, C. R., 83, 85, 98
Nolte, A., 57, 71
Norris, A. H., 456, 458, 464
Nott, J. C., 18, 20, 28
Novacek, M. J., 154, 181
Nuttall, G. H. F., 107, 145

O

Oakleaf, M., 34, 40, 47
Oakley, K. P., 231, 237, 242, 243, 244, 258, 260, 267, 276, 279
O'Brien, E. M., 250, 258
O'Brien, R., 35, 47
O'Connor, B. L., 214, 226
O'Connor, W. J., 409, 427
Odum, H. T., 420, 430
Ojikutu, R. O., 415, 430
Olivier, G., 87, 98
Olson, E. C., 12, 28
Olson, R., 13, 28
Oppenoorth, W. F. F., 265, 276
Ortner, D. J., 42, 47, 344, 347, 354
Osborn, H. F., 191, 192, 226, 241, 244, 258, 262, 264, 265, 276
Osborn, R., 58, 71
Osborne, R. H., 468, 472
Ossenberg, N. S., 292, 304
Otten, C., 385, 388, 401
Owsley, D. W., 347, 354
Oxnard, C. E., 157, 184, 219, 221, 226, 258, 319, 320, 322, 325, 327

P

Packer, A. D., 79, 98
Page, J., 411, 424
Pakkenberg, H., 84, 98
Pales, L., 337, 354
Palkovich, A. M., 347, 354

Palomino, H., 292, 303, 453, 463
Parizkova, J., 456, 463
Parsons, F. G., 318, 325
Parsons, P. A., 313, 323
Parsons, P. G., 360, 366
Partridge, T. C., 247, 258
Peters, C. R., 250, 258
Passingham, R. E., 86, 98
Pasteur, G., 22, 28
Patterson, B., 152, 159, 181, 203, 204, 206, 221, 226
Patterson, H. S., 18, 28
Pauli, R. H., 283, 299, 302
Pauling, L., 120, 146, 233, 237, 382, 401
Pawson, I. G., 453, 463
Pearl, R., 392, 401, 412, 430
Pearl, R. D., 392, 401
Pearson, K., 314, 316, 318, 326, 361, 368, 392, 395
Pedersen, P. O., 281, 303
Penfield, W., 76, 79, 81, 98
Penniman, T. K., 1, 10, 31, 42, 49, 71
Penrose, L. S., 315, 326, 376, 385, 391, 397, 402
Peterson, R. R., 465
Peto, R., 393, 402
Pettenkofer, H., 385, 402
Petter, J-J., 157, 181
Petter-Rousseaux, A., 157, 181
Peyrony, D., 263, 271
Philippe, P., 392, 402
Pianka, E. R., 406, 407, 419, 420, 429, 430
Pickering, S. P., 99
Picon-Reategui, E., 417, 430
Pilbeam, D., 84, 85, 86, 87, 99, 135, 145, 208, 209, 212, 214, 215, 227, 235, 237
Piveteau, J., 158, 181, 204, 227
Plagenhoef, S., 320, 326
Plato, C. C., 456, 464
Platt, J. R., 329, 336
Pocock, R. I., 150, 159, 181
Poirier, F. E., 71
Polednak, A. B., 449, 464
Polling, D., 392, 394
Pollock, J. I., 158, 181
Post, R. H., 377, 402
Powell, T. P. S., 86, 96
Preusschoft, H., 320, 326
Price, W. A., 437, 445
Prosser, C. L., 406, 414, 430
Prost, J. H., 251, 258, 320, 326
Provine, W. B., 12, 28, 266, 276, 376, 402
Pruner-Bey, F., 19, 28
Pryor, J. W., 360, 368
Pubols, B. H., 86, 99
Pubols, L. M., 86, 99

Putnam, F. W., 339, 354
Putschar, W. G. J., 344, 345, 354

Q

Quiring, D. P., 80, 92

R

Radinsky, L. B., 83, 85, 86, 87, 99, 145, 169, 182, 212, 227
Radl, E., 15, 28
Radosavljevich, P. R., 309, 326
Rak, Y., 252, 259
Ramot, B., 388, 402
Randall, F. E., 35, 47
Rao, D. C., 391, 400
Raper, A. B., 382, 402
Rappaport, R. A., 407, 432
Rasmussen, T., 79, 81, 98
Rathenburg, R., 380, 404
Read, D. W., 86, 97
Reed, T.   , 381, 386, 388, 389, 390, 402
Reich, T., 470, 472
Reid, R. M., 379, 402
Reingold, N., 31, 48
Remane, A., 204, 227
Rensch, B., 82, 84, 99, 118, 145, 266, 276
Retzius, A. A., 18, 28
Revelle, R., 419, 424, 454, 459
Reyment, R. A., 313, 322
Rhine, J. J., 366, 368
Richard, A., 158, 182
Richman, E. A., 347, 354
Rightmire, G. P., 313, 326
Ripley, S., 63, 71, 320, 326
Ripley, W. Z., 22, 28
Robbins, L., 312, 326
Roberts, D. F., 315, 327, 411, 412, 430, 438, 445, 452, 464
Roberts, J. A. F., 381, 387, 388, 402
Roberts, R. B., 119, 143
Robinson, J. T., 78, 91, 204, 227, 249, 252, 259
Robinson, S., 409, 430, 437, 445
Roche, A. F., 416, 427, 456, 464
Romer, A. S., 159, 182, 241, 259
Romero-Herrera, A. E., 114, 145
Roney, J. G., 337, 342, 354
Rose, J. C., 347, 354
Rose, K. D., 165, 166, 182
Rosenberg, P., 13, 28
Rosenberger, A. L., 159, 168, 175, 182, 214, 227
Ross, D., 33, 48

Rothhammer, F., 416, 417, 429, 431
Ruffer, M. A., 341, 344, 355
Ruschenberger, W. S. W., 339, 355
Ruse, M., 20, 28
Russell, D. E., 153, 158, 182
Russell, R. J., 165, 171, 182
Ryan, A. S., 250, 259, 268, 276

S

Saayman, G. S., 63, 72
Sabharwal, K. P., 454, 464
Sacher, G. A., 82, 87, 88, 99, 100, 393, 402
Sade, D., 41, 63, 71
Salzano, F. M., 380, 388, 401, 412, 431
Sander, M. T., 418, 423
Sanders, B., 449, 452, 454, 464
Sandison, A. T., 343, 350
Sanger, F., 136, 145
Sanides, F., 83, 97, 100
Santa Luca, A. P., 268, 276
Sapir, E., 282, 299, 303
Sarich, V. M., 107, 112, 113, 117, 119, 128, 129, 133, 135, 141, 145, 154, 160, 161, 162, 169, 211, 227, 230, 233, 237, 252, 259, 260
Saul, F. P., 345, 355
Savage, D. E., 204, 229
Scammon, R. E., 449, 464
Schaller, G., 58, 72, 249, 259
Schanfield, M., 386, 403
Schepers, G. W. H., 77, 78, 79, 91, 100, 240, 251, 254
Schiller, F., 16, 18, 19, 28
Schlosser, M., 204, 227
Schmerling, P. C., 338, 355
Schneider, E., 438, 445
Schoeninger, M., 160, 162, 163, 176, 216, 217, 223, 346, 355
Schölander, P. F., 411, 431
Schraer, H., 411, 431
Schreider, E., 84, 100, 411, 431
Schull, W. J., 318, 327, 364, 369, 378, 380, 386, 392, 401, 403, 416, 417, 429, 431
Schultz, A. H., 52, 72, 80, 100, 189, 196, 197, 202, 204, 227, 267, 276
Schulz, P. D., 347, 353
Schwager, P. M., 347, 351
Schwalbe, G., 204, 228, 263, 264, 265, 276
Schwartz, D., 85, 93
Schwartz, J. H., 160, 161, 183, 186, 217, 228
Schwidetsky, I., 86, 100
Sciulli, P. W., 347, 355
Scott, B. M., 298, 303
Seligsohn, D., 164, 183

Seltzer, C., 437, 445
Sera, G. L., 263, 277
Sergi, S., 78, 100, 265, 266, 277
Severtsov, A. N., 118, 145
Shapiro, H. L., 309, 327, 409, 418, 431, 442, 446, 450, 451, 464, 468, 472
Shariff, G. A., 82, 100
Sheine, W. S., 165, 183
Shellshear, J. L., 76, 77, 100
Shelton, W. C., 35, 47
Shephard, R. J., 413, 431
Shibata, I., 76, 100
Shipman, P., 250, 259
Shirek-Ellefson, J., 63, 72
Shuey, R. T., 248, 259
Sillen, A., 346, 355
Simmons, D. J., 347, 356
Simonds, P. E., 56, 63, 72
Simonin, C., 361, 368
Simons, E. L., 118, 135, 145, 153, 159, 165, 168, 170, 183, 184, 204, 208, 210, 211, 219, 223, 228
Simpson, G. G., 54, 72, 108, 145, 150, 151, 152, 153, 158, 159, 184, 205, 229, 266, 277, 468, 472
Sing, C. F., 392, 403
Singer, R., 363, 368
Skolnick, M., 389, 392, 395, 403
Slightom, J. L., 132, 137, 145
Singer, R., 81, 100
Smith, E. A., 420, 425, 431
Smith, F. H., 268, 277, 279
Smithies, O., 375, 403
Smith Woodward, A., 243, 259, 264, 279
Snow, C. C., 365, 368
Snow, C. P., 13, 28
Snyder, L. H., 373, 403
So, J. K., 464
Sokal, R. R., 111, 145
Sollas, W. J., 240, 241, 259, 263, 277
Solow, B., 314, 327
Sontag, L. W., 31, 48
Southwick, C. H., 57, 67, 72
Spencer, F., 1, 7, 10, 16, 28, 262, 263, 265, 277, 283, 303, 408, 431
Sperry, R. W., 80, 84, 101
Spoehr, A., 342, 355
Spuhler, J. N., 287, 291, 292, 293, 303, 379, 403, 412, 418, 431
Stanton, W., 12, 17, 29
Stehlin, H. G., 152, 184
Steinberg, A. G., 379, 403
Steinbock, R. T., 343, 355
Stephan, H. R., 87, 101
Stephen, H., 83, 85, 101

Stern, J. T., 157, 184, 214, 216, 229, 251, 259, 320, 327, 406, 431
Stevenson, P. H., 360, 368
Steward, J., 409, 431
Stewart, J., 390, 397
Stewart, T. D., 33, 48, 78, 101, 266, 277, 283, 304, 308, 327, 342, 348, 349, 352, 355, 356, 357, 362, 363, 364, 365, 368, 369
Stini, W. A., 454, 464
Stinson, S., 453, 464
Stirton, R. A., 204, 229
Stocking, G. W., 1, 10, 12, 18, 23, 29, 31, 48
Stoessiger, B. N., 315, 327
Stoltz, L. P., 63, 72
Stothers, D. M., 345, 356
Stoudt, H. W., 40, 46, 48
Stout, S., 347, 356
Straus, W. L., 54, 72, 196, 203, 229, 239, 259, 264, 267, 277
Stringer, C. B., 268, 277, 278
Strouhal, E., 320, 323
Struhsaker, T. T., 63, 72
Suchey, J. M., 366, 369
Sucklin, J. A., 171, 184
Sugiyama, Y., 55, 56, 72
Susanne, C., 450, 456, 464
Susman, R. L., 251, 259
Sussman, R. W., 64, 72, 158, 184
Suzuki, A., 55, 56, 69, 72
Suzuki, H., 316, 327
Swedlund, A. C., 420, 431
Swift, J., 419, 431
Szalay, F. S., 119, 146, 154, 155, 157, 159, 160, 164, 165, 166, 167, 168, 170, 184, 185, 214, 217, 219, 229
Szathmary, E. J. E., 292, 304

T

Takahashi, E., 449, 464
Tandler, J., 148, 171, 185
Tanner, J. M., 43, 46, 412, 413, 417, 425, 427, 431, 432, 447, 448, 449, 454, 457, 465
Tarling, D. H., 169, 185
Tashian, R. E., 233, 237
Tattersall, I., 158, 161, 183, 186, 217, 229, 316, 327
Tebbets, G., 320, 328
Teilhard de Chardin, P., 165, 186
Tekkaya, I., 252, 253
Temerin, L. A., 86, 97
Templeton, A., 117, 124, 146
Thieme, F. P., 318, 327, 364, 369, 418, 432

Thomas, R. B., 416, 417, 420, 421, 424, 428, 432, 443, 445, 453, 457, 465, 470, 472
Thomas, T. P., 202, 225
Thompson, D. D., 316, 317, 327, 347, 356, 365, 366, 369
Thorington, R. W., 167, 186
Thorndike, E. L., 51, 72
Tildesley, M. L., 80, 101
Tobias, P. V., 77, 84, 101, 247, 252, 259, 262, 278
Todaro, G. J., 113, 117, 140
Todd, T. W., 359, 360, 363, 369
Topinard, P., 19, 21, 29
Tower, D. B., 82, 101
Townsend, P. K., 421, 429
Trinkaus, E., 264, 268, 269, 275, 278
Trotter, M., 361, 362, 363, 364, 369, 380, 401, 456, 465
Trussell, J., 419, 432
Tugby, D. J., 82, 101
Turner, C. G., 288, 291, 304
Turner, W., 19, 29, 265, 278
Tutin, C. E. G., 249, 258
Tuttle, R. H., 212, 213, 214, 229, 251, 259, 317, 327

U

Ubelaker, D. H., 321, 325, 343, 345, 356, 364, 368
Upenskii, S. I., 85, 101
Uzell, T., 212, 229

V

Valentine, W. N., 382, 403
Vallois, H. V., 16, 21, 23, 29, 262, 263, 264, 267, 269, 278, 270
Vandenberg, J. G., 52, 72
Van der Klaauw, C. J., 318, 327
Vandermeersch, B., 269, 275, 278
Vander Merwe, N. J., 346, 356
Van Gerven, D. P., 312, 319, 320, 321, 322, 323, 327, 347, 351
Van Ooyen, A., 389, 403
Van Valen, L., 86, 101, 154, 155, 156, 159, 165, 166, 186
Vayda, A. P., 403, 432
Virchow, R., 21, 29, 308, 327
Virey, J. J., 20, 22, 29
Vlatovsky, V. G., 449, 465
Voegelin, E. W., 31, 48
Vogel, F., 378, 379, 380, 385, 386, 388, 402, 403, 404
Vogel, J. C., 346, 356
Vogel, P., 398
Voight, J., 84, 98

Von Bonin, G., 76, 78, 79, 80, 81, 83, 84, 102
Von Koenigswald, G. H. R., 204, 265, 280
Vrba, E. S., 247, 249, 260

W

Walker, A. C., 157, 171, 184, 186, 209, 212, 214, 229, 250, 257, 260
Walker, E., 76, 102
Wallace, A. R., 239, 260
Wallace, D. T., 87, 97
Ward, R. H., 390, 391, 404, 418, 432
Ward, S. C., 347, 353
Warren, J. C., 338, 356
Warren, K. B., 267, 278, 410, 432
Washburn, S. L., 59, 60, 62, 63, 67, 72, 73, 204, 206, 208, 219, 230, 245, 251, 260, 267, 279, 410, 432, 437, 446
Watt, K. E. F., 406, 432
Weidenreich, F., 77, 80, 102, 245, 260, 262, 263, 265, 266, 279
Weiner, J. S., 43, 45, 243, 260, 265, 267, 279, 315, 327, 407, 412, 413, 414, 415, 416, 423, 424, 425, 427, 432, 433, 439, 446, 457, 465
Weinert, H., 195, 230, 266, 279
Weinstein, R. S., 347, 356
Weiss, K. M., 249, 260, 310, 327, 379, 386, 388, 392, 393, 396, 401, 403, 404, 418, 432, 433
Welker, W. I., 76, 83, 102
Wells, C., 343, 356
Wells, J. P., 320, 327, 328
Werle, P. P., 360, 367
Werner, G., 83, 102
Wesselman, H. B., 249, 256
West, F. H., 289, 304
Weton, Z., 316, 322
White, T. D., 117, 135, 143, 235, 237, 245, 246, 250, 252, 257, 260
Whitney, W. F., 339, 356
Whitsel, B., 83, 102
Whitteridge, D., 83, 92
Wicken, J. S., 118, 146
Wiercinski, A., 316, 328
Wiesel, T. N., 83, 95
Wiesenfeld, S. L., 386, 404
Wilder, H. H., 193, 230
Wilkinson, R. G., 312, 328
Williams, C. A., 186
Williams, H. U., 341, 356
Wilson, A. C., 106, 129, 132, 135, 143, 145, 146, 211, 227, 233, 237
Wilson, A. P., 62, 73
Wilson, J. A., 83, 95

Winge, H., 148, 186
Winslow, J. B., 281, 304
Winterhalder, B., 421, 432, 433
Wolpoff, M. H., 12, 29, 84, 86, 102, 103, 249, 268, 269, 279
Woo, J., 79, 103
Woo, T. L., 314, 323, 328
Wood Jones, F., 149, 150, 186, 189, 230, 315, 323
Woodward, A. S., 243, 259, 264, 279
Woolf, B., 386, 404
Woolsey, C. N., 76, 80, 83, 103
Workman, P. L., 390, 404
Wright, S., 437, 446
Wulsin, F. R., 34, 48, 410, 433
Wyman, J., 338, 356
Wyman, L. C., 373, 374, 404
Wyndham, C. H., 411, 433

Y

Yarbrough, C. J., 454, 462, 465
Yerkes, A. W., 32, 48, 50, 73, 193, 230

Yerkes, R. M., 32, 48, 50, 73, 193, 230
Yoshiba, K., 63, 73
Yoshimura, H., 413, 433
Young, R. W., 317, 318, 325
Yunis, J. J., 115, 146

Z

Zapfe, H., 202, 230
Zborowski, H., 381, 398
Zdansky, O., 265, 280
Zegura, S. L., 291, 304, 422, 427
Zihlman, A., 215, 230, 251, 260
Zilles, K., 79, 103
Zimmerman, M. R., 344, 356
Zuckerkandl, E., 106, 108, 114, 118, 120, 146, 233, 237
Zuckerman, S., 50, 51, 55, 73

Subject Index

A

ABO blood groups
  distribution, 310, 373, 374, 375, 381–382
  relation to infectious diseases, 385
  relation to noninfectious diseases, 387–389
Acclimatization, 406–407, 414–416
Adapid hypothesis, 168
Adapis, 202
Adaptation, *see also* Human variation
  to altitude, 417–418, 437, 452–454
  to climate, 451–452
  as a concept, 405–407
  developmental, 416–417
  genetic, in human biological variability, 418–
    419, 442–444
  to nutritional stress, 454–455
  to sunlight, 452
  to temperature, 452
Aeolopithecus, 153, 208
Afar, Ethiopia, 235
African hominid fossils, cost of recovery, 253
Age determination, 359
Aging, study of, 392–393, 456
Alaskan, early archeological sites, 288–289, 291
Albinism, 379
Aleutian Islands, 286
Aleut, 281, 283, 470
  craniometry, 290, 291, 296–297
  origin and divergence, 297–300
Allometry in primates, 80, 85, 87–88
Altitude, influence on growth and development,
    417–418, 437

American Academy of Forensic Sciences
  founding, 365
American Association for the Advancement of
  Science, 7, 54
American Board of Forensic Anthropologists, 365
American Indians, *see* Native Americans
American Journal of Physical Anthropology
  founding, 6, 9, 15
  contents, 244, 330–334, 439–442
American Museum of Natural History, New York,
    34, 36, 188, 195, 239, 240, 241
"American School" of Anthropology, 20
Amino acid sequence studies of primate proteins,
    114–119
Amniogenesis, 169
Anagale, 150
Anagenesis, 118, 123
Anangula blade industry, 288, 290
Anangula Island, 286, 288, 290
Anthropoidea
  anatomy, 170
  evolution, 168–170
  monophyletic origin, 204
  phylogenetic relation, with the early Eutheria,
    126
  retina, 169
  tarsioid origin
    morphological evidence, 149–150
    molecular evidence, 118–119
Anthropometry, 306, 308, 313–316, *see also*
  craniometry
Aotus, 169
Apidium, 153, 208

Archaeolemur, 171
Artificial deformation of skull, 340, 341, 348
Asiatic Expedition, 1937, 51–52
Ateles geoffroyi, 50
Athabascan tribes, 298
Auditory exostoses, 340
Australia antigen, 387
Australopithecus
    anatomy, 209
    dating, 133–136
    dental wear patterns, 250
    dietary hypothesis, 249, 252
    East African, 232, 233, 245–247
    endocranial studies, 78–79, 81
    exclusion from human lineage, 262
    single species hypothesis, 249–250
    South African, 232, 233, 241–243
    species,
        A. afarensis, 78–79, 234, 235, 236, 252
        A. africanus, 247, 249
        A. boisei, 235, 247, 250, 252
        "*A.prometheus,*" 242, 243
        A. robustus, 235, 249, 252
Autoimmune disease, 386

B

Baboon, *see Papio*
Baringo, 247
Barnicot, N. A., 470
Barro Colorado Island, Panama, 57
Bergmann and Allen's rule, 411, 438
Bering landbridge, 283, 290, 294, 295
Bering Strait, 283, 285
Beringia, 283, 294, 295
Biocoenoses, 250
Biomechanical analysis, 320–321
Biometry, Galton School of, 291, 371, 372
Biostatistics, application, 313–316
Bipedalism, 246
Bishop (Bernice P.) Museum, 36
Blending inheritance, 371
Blumenbach, J. F., attitude toward race, 15, 22, 308
Boas, F.
    on origin of the Eskimos, 282
    on racial plasticity, 408–409
    role in the development of discipline, 4–5
    on secular trends in body size (Toronto study),
        449
    study of immigrants, 309, 436, 442, 468
Bone, trace element analysis in, 346
Boule, M.

    multilineal view of human phylogeny, 264
    views on Neandertal fossils, 263–264
Boyd, W. C.
    contribution to population genetics, 373–375
    criticism of, typological analysis, 310
Brachiation, 189, 193, 198, 203, 209
Brain, *see* Primate neuroanatomy
Brain-body scaling, *see* Allometry
British contribution to development of human
        population biology, 412, 470–471
Broca's "Institute" of Anthropology, 5–6
Brown University, 156
Buffon, G. L. L., Comte de,
    on orangutans, 50
Burg-Wartenstein Conferences, 39, 42, 43, 62, 105,
        106, 413, *see also* Wenner-Gren Foundation
Burkitt's lymphoma, 387

C

Camper, Petrus, 305
Case Western Reserve University, 358
Carcinogenesis, 387, 391, 393
Cayo Santiago primate colony, 52, 58
Central Asiatic Expedition (1921), 239–240, 253
Cercopithecus aethiops, 61, 63
Cercopithecus ascanius, 53
Chimpanzee, *see Pan*
Choukoutien, China, 263, 265
Circeo, Italy, 266
Cladistics, 112, 113–114
Climate, influence of, 410–412, 415–416, 451–452
Clovis culture, 292
"Coefficient of Racial Likeness" (CRL), application,
        314–315
Cold Spring Harbor Symposium in Quantitative
        Biology, 1950, 12, 204, 231, 245, 267, 410
Columbia University, 3, 4, 9, 23, 37, 38, 52, 251
Commander Islands, 283, 285
Comparative neuroanatomy, 82–83
Complement fixation tests, application of, 111
Cortical mapping
    of human brain, 76
    of nonhuman brain, 80–81
Cranial index, 308–309
Craniometry
    development, 17–20, 305–306, 308, 309
Crow's "Index of total selection," 379
Cultural ecology of J. Steward, 409
Cuvier, G., 22, 202
Cystic fibrosis, 386

D

Darwinism, opposition to, 14–15, 20–21
Dating techniques
  fission track, 248
  paleomagnetism, 248
  potassium-argon (K/Ar), 248
  radiocarbon (^{14}C): conventional method, 248, 267, 288
Daubentonia, 150, 167, 171
Davenport, C. B., 408
Demography, 418–419, 469
Dendropithecus, 212
DNA hybridization techniques, 112–113, 117
Developmental adaptation, 416–417
Diabetes mellitus, 389
Dickson Mounds, 321
Dietary
  adaptation, among primates, 165, 166–168
  analysis
    using ^{12}C/^{13}C ratio, 346
    trace elements, 347
  indicators, in nutritional status, 454–455
  Robinson's, hypothesis, 249
Disease, population genetics, 337–349, 381–384, 385–392
Drift, genetic, 375, 379, 381
Duke University, 157
Dryopithecines, 193, 198, 202, 208, 234

E

East Lake Turkana, 246, 247
Ecole d'Anthropologie (Paris), 5–6, 262
Ecological models, 420, 439, 442–444
Ecology
  human
    development, 405–422, 436–442
    current theory and trends, 405–408, 419–422, 442–444
    protohominids, 249–250
Electromyography, 251
Electrophoresis, 113–114
Elliot Smith, G.
  endocranial studies, 77, 189, 264
  on primate phylogeny, 189, 190
  rejection of Wood Jones's hypothesis, 150
  tarsioid hypothesis, 149
Endocasts, fossil hominids, 77, 78–79, 82, 84, 89, 189, 251
Environmental growth factor, 451

"*Eoanthropus dawsoni*," *see* Piltdown hoax
Eocene primates, 157, 191
Eohippus, 203
Epidemiology, 321, 342–344, 471
Epiphyses
  age of union, 360
  estimation of age from, 360
Erythroblastosis fetalis, differential fertility in, 388
Erythrocebus patas, 61
Eskimo
  Asiatic, 293
  Asiatic affinities, 283–285, 287–288, 293
  dental patterns, 286–287
  of Greenland, 286, 296–297
  linguistic differentiation, 282
  morphological variation, 283
  origin and divergence, 285, 297–299, 300
  racial classification, 281, 282
  St. Lawrence Island, 293
Eugenic movement, 376–377
Eutherian, evolution, 121, 154
Evolutionary rates, determination, 121–122

F

Fayum, Egypt, 160, 169, 208, 233
FBI Law Enforcement Bulletin, 357, 361, 366
Fels Research Institute, 41
Fels, S., philanthropy, 32
Footprints, human, Laetoli, Tanzania, 246–247
Forbes Quarry, 263
Forensic anthropology, development, 357–366
Functional morphology, applied to
  early fossil hominids, 250–251
  human skeleton, 316–321
  nonhuman primates, 157, 163–166, 193–194, 214, 216, 219
Funding organizations, *see* National Geographic Society; National Institutes of Health; National Science Foundation; Wenner-Gren Foundation

G

Galago demidovii, locomotion studies of, 157
Galton, F., 291, 371, 372
Garusi, Tanzania, 245
Gaudry, A., 21
Genetic
  code, 105–107, 112–113, 136–138

Genetic *(cont.)*
  drift, 375–381
  load, 375–378, 378–379
  polymorphisms, maintenance of, 384–392
  study of populations, development of, 309–313,
    373–375, 418–419
  variability, 381–384
Gorilla
  early field studies of, 50, 52
  genealogical relationship of, 119, 235
  recent field studies of, 56, 58, 63
  species of
    Gorilla gorilla beringii, 58
    Gorilla gorilla, 63
Gregory, W. K.
  on primate phylogeny, 149, 150, 160, 241
  support of *A. africanus*, 241, 242
Growth and development, 316–321, 416–419,
  455–456
  study of, in extreme environments, 448–457
G-6-PD deficiency, thalassemia and, 384

H

Hadar, Ethiopia, 246, 247, 250
Hadropithecus, 171
Hamadryas baboons (*Papio hamadryas*), early study
  of, by S. Zuckerman, 51
Haplorhine-Strepsirhine dichotomy, 159–160
Haplorhini, 150
Hardy-Weinberg equilibrium, 378
Harvard University, 1, 2–4, 23, 35–36, 43, 266, 357
Haeckel, E., 14, 239
Hemiacodon, 151
Hemoglobinopathies, 382–384
Hepatitis, 387
Herpes virus, 387
Heterosis, 378
Histochemistry, 347
HLA system, 386
Hominid
  evolutionary schemes
    multilineal scheme, 261–266
    "trellis" model, 262
    unilineal scheme, 261–266
  phylogenetic schemes, according to
    Delson, E., 212, 213, 214
    Elliot Smith, G., 189, 190
    Gregory, W. K., 189, 190, 191, 193, 195, 204,
      209
    Greenfield, L., 214, 215
    Gingerich, P. D., 216

Heberer, G., 204, 205
Hooton, E. A., 198, 199
Keith, A., 189, 190
Le Gros Clark, W. E., 197, 198, 203, 204, 206,
  207
Mayr, E., 236
Morton, D. J., 189, 194
Pilbeam, D., 206, 208, 209, 212
Sarich, V., 211
Schultz, A. H., 196, 197
Simons, E. L., 203, 204, 210, 211
Straus, W. L., 196, 203
Szalay, F. S., 217
Tuttle, R. H., 214, 216
Washburn, S. L., 204, 208, 211, 212
Wood Jones, F., 189, 191, 194
Hominoidea, molecular phylogeny of, 136
Homo erectus, 77–78, 81, 89, 243, 245, 265, 267–268
Homo habilis, 82, 89, 235, 250, 251
Homo sapiens neandertalensis, 77, 81, 232, 236, 237,
  261–262, *see also* Neandertal
Homo sapiens sapiens, anatomically modern, first
  appearance, 232, 236, 237, 268, 269
Homo transvaalensis, 245
Homunculus patagonicus, 195
Hooton, E. A.
  intellectual background, 12–13, 14, 15
  interest in primate studies, 53–54
  on human phylogeny, 198, 199
  on lemurs, 156
  on Pecos Pueblo, 342
  opposition to Le Gros Clark's arboreal hypoth-
    esis, 157
  role in the development of discipline, 6–7, 9
  students, 21, 373
  typological analyses, criticism of, 311, 373
  views on "population", 231
Howler monkey *Alouatta palliata)*,
  early field study of, 50
Hrdlička, A.
  "double-thumb" hypothesis, 285
  Francophilia, 15
  ideas on the origin of the Eskimos, 283–286
  intellectual background, 15–17
  Neandertal hypothesis, 261–262, 266, 268, 269
  role in the development of discipline, 5–8
  study of environmental impact on human
    organism, 436, 447, 452
  survey of Alaska, 33, 282–283
  views on *A. africanus*, 240–241
  views on Piltdown remains, 244, 265
  work in the Aleutian and Commander Islands,
    283

Human Biology, contents of, 439–442
Human variation, studies of
   conducted by the International Biological
      Program (IBP), 413, 414
   in extreme environments, 449–455
   current trends in, 455–457
Hypertension, 390–391

I

ICNND, *see* Interdepartmental Committee on
   Nutrition and National Defense
Immunological,
   studies of primate proteins, 111–112
   techniques, 111–119
Inbreeding experiments, 378–380
Inca bones, 244
INCAP, *see* Institute of Nutrition of Central
   America and Panama
Incisor shoveling in Native Americans, 291
Index of progression, 85
Index of Total Selection of Crow, 379
Institute of Nutrition of Central America and
   Panama (INCAP), 40, 454
Interdepartmental Committee on Nutrition and
   National Defense (ICNND), 40, 454
International Biological Program (IBP), 43, 412,
   413–414, 416, 420, 438–439, 443, 457
Inupiaq Eskimos, 291, 298

J

Japan Monkey Centre, 58
Japanese primate research, scope of, 56
Johns Hopkins University, 32, 51, 250

K

Kamchatka, 281, 283
Kalahari desert, 249
Kay Behrensmeyer's Site, *see* KBS
KBS (Kay Behrensmeyer's Site) tuff, 248
Keith, A.
   intellectual background, 13–15, 22
   theory of "cerebral rubicon," 80–81
   views on human phylogeny, 189, 190, 263, 264
Kenyapithecus, 208
Kerley, E. R.
   role in development of forensic anthropology,
      364–365

Kodiak Island, 283, 290
Koobi Fora, 248, 250
Koshima Island, macaques of, 56
Krapina, Yugoslavia, 263
Kroeber, A. L., interest in primate studies, 54
Krogman, W. M., role in development of forensic
   anthropology, 36, 362, 363
Kuriles, 285
Kuru, 387

L

Laboratoire d'Anthropologie (Paris), 5, 6, 16, 262
La Chapelle-aux-Saints, France, 263
Laetoli, Tanzania, 233, 245, 246, 248, 252
La Ferrassie, France, 263
Lake Turkana, Kenya, 233, 246, 247
Language, origins of, 87
La Quina, France, 263
Lamarck, J. B., 20, 21, 371
Leakey, L. S. B.
   sponsorship of primate field studies, 58
   East African Expeditions of, 245
   Foundation, 253
Le Gros Clark, W. E.
   Earl Grey Memorial Lecture (1956), 437
   hominoid endocranial studies, 77, 80
   influence on G. G. Simpson, 151
   on mammalian evolution, 151
   on primate phylogeny, 149, 151–152
   reassessment of *Tupaia*, 149–150
   role in development of modern primatology,
      148–151, 152, 162, 166
Le Moustier, France, 263
Lemur
   field studies of, 157
   locomotion studies of, 158
Lemuriformes, 150, 151, 160
Lepilemur, 157
Leprosy, 385
Limnopithecus, 202, 204
Linnaean system of classification, 307
Longevity, 392–393
Lothagam, Kenya, 135, 233, 247
Lukeino, Kenya, 247

M

MAB, see *Man and the Biosphere* Program
Macaca, 76
   M. fuscata, 55, 63

M. mulatta, 57, 63
M. nemestrina, 63
M. radiata, 57
Madagascan lemurs, 157–158, 166
Mahalanobis D^2, 291, 315
Makapansgat, South Africa, 242, 247
Malaria, 384–385
Mammals, evolution, 151, 152
Man and the Biosphere Program (MAB), studies of, 43, 422, 439
Mandrillus leucophaeus, 63
Manouvrier, L., 16, 262
Marsupials, 158
Mead, M., 43
Megaladapis, 83, 171
Mendel, G., 372
Metopic suture, loss, 170
Microcebus, locomotion studies, 153
Migration
    models, 443, 451
    studies, employment of, 418, 442–443, 450, 451, 468
Miocene apes, 198, 202, 204, 208, 209, 212, 214, 233
Mitochondrial DNA maps, 117, 233
Modjokerto, Java, 265
Molars, primate, 165
Molecular clock, *see also* Zuckerkandl
    controversy, 120–121, 128–133, 138
    dates and fossil record, 120–126, 133–136, 233
Mongolia Expedition (1921), 191, 239
Morton, S. G.
    craniometric techniques developed by, 17–20, 22
    influence on P. Broca, 18–19
Mosaic evolution, 252
Mousterian culture, 269
Multilineal evolution, 261–262, 263, 264, 265, 266
Multivariate analysis, 314–315, 334
Mutation, 372, 375–378
    hypothesis of neutral, 127–128
    radiation as a source of, 380–381
    rate studies, 380–381

N

Native Americans
    dental morphology, 291–292
    evolutionary history, 294–299, 300
    genetic distance, 291–292
    linguistic variation, 293
    Neumann's classification of, 311–312
National Academy of Sciences, 38, 413

National Geographic Society, funding of research by, 42, 246, 253
National Institute of Health, funding of research by, 8, 34–35, 37, 38, 39–40, 42, 43–45
National Research Council, 7, 33
National Science Foundation, funding of research by, 8, 38, 39, 41–42, 43–44, 253
Natural selection, 122–128, 374–375, 376–378, 379, 381–382, 384–389, 409, 454–455
    at molecular level, 122–125
Neandertal
    endocranial studies of, 81
    hypothesis, 261–262, 263–266, 268, 269
    relation to modern *H. sapiens*, 77, 81, 232, 236, 237, 261–262, 268–269
    specimens
        Circeo, 266
        Florisbad, 77
        Krapina, 263
        La Chapelle-aux-Saints, 263, 264
        La Ferrassie, 263
        Le Moustier, 263
        Neandertal, 262
        Saccopastore, 265
        Saint-Césaire, 269
        Skhul, 77, 265, 269
        Steinheim, 266
        Swanscombe, 77, 266
        Tabun, 265
        Teshik-Tash, 263
Necrolemur, 152, 153, 157, 160
New Physical Anthropology, The, 245
Neutral theory of evolution, 375
Ngandong Beds, Java, 265
Ngorora, Kenya, 247
Non-Darwinian evolution, 125–128
Notharctus, 149, 151
Nucleic acids, comparative study, in primates, 112–113
Nutrition, deficiency in, 421, 454–455
    effect on fecundity, 419
    effect on fertility, 419
    effect on menarche, 418–419

O

Oldowan tools, 245
Olduvai Gorge, 245, 246, 247, 248
Oligocene anthropoids, 169, 212
Omo River Basin, Ethiopia, 246, 247, 248, 253
Omomyidae, 166, 168
Onion Portage, 288, 290, 295

Oregon Regional Primate Research Center,
    establishment of, 157
Oreopithecus, 153, 204, 214
Orthogenesis, 205
Osborn, H. F.
    Dawn Man Theory, 191, 241, 244
    views on primate phylogeny, 191, 192–193, 195
Osteodontokeratic tools, 247

P

Paleoasiatics, 285
Paleoecology, human, 249, 250, 253
Paleogene, 169
Paleopathology
    Association (United States), 349
    early development of, 338–339
    epidemiological approach in, 321, 334, 342–344
    current trends in, 344–349
Paleopropithecus, 171
Paley, W. 14
Pan
    early observations of, 50, 52
    genealogical relationship of, 105, 107–111, 121,
        215, 235, 236
    modern field studies of, 63, 64
Papio
    field studies of, 51, 59, 61, 63, 64
    genealogical relationship of, 134–136
    P. anubis, 61, 63
    P. cynocephalus, 63
    P. hamadryas, 51, 60, 63, *see also* Hamadryas
        baboons
    P. ursinus, 51, 61, 63
Parapithecus, 191
Peabody Museum (Harvard), 26, 33
Pecos Pueblo, Hooton's study of, 309–310, 342
Peking Man (*Sinanthropus pekinensis*), *see* Homo
    erectus
Peopling of the New World, 281–301
Phenacolemuridae, 152
Piltdown hoax, 188, 243–244, 262, 265, 267
Pithecanthropus, *see Homo erectus*
Plesiadapis, 151, 153, 155, 154, 159, 160, 165
Plesianthropus transvaalensis, 242
Pliopithecus, 193, 202, 204, 208, 212
Polygenism in France, 15, 18–19, 20–21
Polymorphism, balanced, 373, 375, 378, 390,
    maintenance of, 381
Pongo pygmaeus, 63
Population genetics, 378–384, *see also Genetics*
Pre-Neandertal theory, 267

Pre-Sapiens theory, 241, 252, 262, 265, 267
Presbytis entellus, 57, 61, 63
Primates
    classification, 147–173
    definition, 149–156
    dental anatomy, 157, 159, 164–166
    evolution, 163–170
    field studies of, 52, 53, 55–57, 58, 61, 63–64, 157–
        158
    functional morphology studies of, 157, 163–166,
        193–194, 214, 216, 219
    neuroanatomy, 75–89, 189
    phylogenetic schemes
    according to
        Elliot Smith, G., 195–196, 212
        Gregory, W. K., 189, 195, 209, 212
        Hooton, E. A., 198
        Le Gros Clark, W. E., 196, 203, 206, 209
        Leakey, L. S. B., 206, 209
        Osborn, H. F., 189, 191, 193
        Pilbeam, D., 206, 209, 214, 221
        Sarich, V. M., 210, 211
        Schultz, A. H., 196, 197, 198
        Simons, E. L., 202, 206, 207, 214
        Simpson, G. G., 206
        Straus, W. L., 196, 203
        Szalay, F. S., 214, 219
        Washburn, S. L., 202, 209, 212, 214, 219
        Wood Jones, F., 189, 191, 193
    visual cortex of, 83
Primatological conferences, post-1960, 62–63
Proconsul, 202, 203
Pronycticebus, 153
Propithecus, 158
Propliopithecus, 153, 191
Prosimians
    classification of, 149–150, 151–152, 153, 154–
        156
    field studies of, and evolutionary implications,
        156–158
Prudential Insurance Company of America, 283
Pseudoloris, 153
Ptilocercus, 149
Punctuated equilibrium, 134–135, 136, 252, 264
Putnam, F. W., role in development of discipline,
    2–4

R

Race
    classification of, 21–23, 307–313, 373–375, 408–
        409

Race *(cont.)*
  concept, development of, 11–23, 306–313
Radiation, genetic effect, 376–377, 380–381
Radiocarbon dating, 248, 267, 288
Radiography, use, 360
Ramapithecus, 112, 153, 208, 214, 233, 234, 237, 252
Recessive alleles, 374, 382, 383, 385
Red King hypothesis, 114–115, 119
Rh factor, 379, 385, 388, 389
Rhesus monkeys, *see Macaca*
Rift Valley, 243
Robinson's dietary hypothesis, 249
Romanticism, 14–15, 21–23

Sterkfontein, South Africa, 241, 242
Stewart, T. D., 33, 79
  editorship of *AJPA*, 244
  role in development of forensic anthropology,
    361–364
Straus, W. L., contributions to physical anthro-
    pology, 54, 196, 203, 219, 239, 264, 267
Strepsirhini, 157, 160, 162
Strepsirhini-Haplorhini dichotomy, 112
Strontium, 346
Sulcal patterns in Old and New World primates, 87
Swanscombe, England, 266
Syphilis, 337, 338, 345, 385

S

T

Saccopastore, Italy, 78, 265
Sahabi, Libya, 247
St. Lawrence Island, 293
Sangiran, Java, 465
Scala naturae, 171
Schistosomiasis, 344
Schultz, A. H., role in development of physical
    anthropology, 32, 33, 51, 52, 80, 196, 197, 203
Secular trends, study of, in body size, 449–451, 456
Segregation analysis, 390
Seward Peninsula, 296
Sexing of skeleton, 360
Shapiro, H. L., 361
Sickle cell disease, 382–384
Simons, E. L., role in the development of modern
    primatology, 152–153, 164–165, 208–209,
    212, 214, 218
Simpson, G. G.
  role in the development of modern primatology,
    54, 151–152, 159, 163
  views on primate phylogeny, 151–152, 205, 206
  study of *Plesiadapis*, 151
  reassessment of *Tarsius*, 151
Sinanthropus pekinensis, *see Homo erectus*
Siwalik Hills, 252
Skeletal biology, trends in, 313–321, 331–334
Skhul, Israel, 77, 265
Smallpox, 385
Smithsonian Institution, *see* United States National
    Museum of Natural History
Société d'Anthropologie de Paris, 5, 6, 20–21
South African early hominids, *see Australopithecus*
Spider monkey (*Ateles geoffroyi*), early study of, 50
Spy, Belgium, 263
Statistics, use, 313–316, 439
Stature, estimation, 361

Taphonomy, 244, 248, 250
Tarsier, genealogical relationship of, 119
Tarsius, 118–119, 149, 160–161, 168, 171
Tarsioid hypothesis, 149, 150, 189, 191, 193
Taung, South Africa, 77–78, 79, 240, 241, 242, 249,
    251
Taxonomy, cladistic approach to, 112, 113–114
Tay-Sachs disease, 386, 389
Tepexpan fossil, 78
Terry Collection, 358, 359, 360
Teshik-Tash, 263
Tetonius, 151
Thalassemia, 382, 284
Thanatocoenoses, 250
Theropithecus
  behavioral studies of, 63
  divergence from *Papio*, 133–136
  genealogical relationship of, 134–136
Thule culture, 296
Tilney, F., 78
Todd collection, 358, 359, 360
Todd, T. W.
  role in development of stature estimates, 360
Trace element analysis of bone, 346, 348
Transvaal, 241
Tree shrew, *see Tupaia*
Trephination, 340, 348
Trinil, Java, 265
Trotter, M., role in development of stature
    estimates, 361
Tuberculosis, 344, 385, 386
Tupaia
  anatomical features, 149
  classification, 147
  evolution, 155
  exclusion from Primates, 152, 154

reassessment of, 154, 155
Typological models, 306

U

Umnak Island, 286
Unilineal evolution, 263, 265, 266, 267
United States National Museum of Natural History (USNM), 5–6, 33, 348, 359, 366
United States Public Health Service, 40
University College, London, 470
University of Arizona, 9
University of California
    at Berkeley, 3, 9, 211, 246, 247, 249
    at Los Angleles, 9, 249
University of Chicago, 9, 202, 251
University of Kentucky, 361
University of Massachusetts, 469
University of Michigan, 9, 35, 249
University of Paris, 157
University of Pennsylvania, 3, 9, 34
University of Wisconsin (Madison), 9, 12, 251

V

Variation, *see also Adaptation, Genetic variability, Nutrition, Race*
    environmental, 437, 451–454
    genetic, 381–384, 418–419
    morphological, 417–418, 437, 438
    racial, 306–313, 418–419, 442–444
    research strategies for study of, 373–375, 435–443
Viking Fund, 34
Virchow, R., 21
Vitalism, 21

W

War dead, identification of, 361–363
Warren, J. C., 338
Washburn, S. L.
    ideas on classification and human evolution, according to, 105, 204, 208, 209, 211, 231, 245, 251, 267, 410, 437
    role in the development of primate behavioral studies, 38, 39, 41, 51, 52, 58–61
Washington University, St. Louis, Missouri, 358
Weidenreich, F., 15, 77, 78, 79, 80, 266, 267
Weiner, J. S., role in the development of discipline, 43, 243, 265, 267, 470, 412–413, 449, 457, 470
Wenner-Gren, A., philanthropy of, 32
Wenner-Gren Foundation, funding of research, 8, 32–33, 34–39, 41–45, 62–63, 232, 413, *see also* Burg-Wartenstein Conferences
Wood Jones, F., 149, 150, 189, 191, 193
Wright, S., 391, 468, 471

Y

Yale University, 32, 34, 50, 206
Yanomama, 381, 470
Yearbook of Physical Anthropology, 36, 41
Yerkes, R., 50, 408

Z

Zuckerman, S., 51, 57, 59, 60, 471
Zinsser, H., 408
Zuckerkandl, E., coining of term: "molecular anthropology" by, 233
Zinjanthropus, 232